D1365040

THE FIGHTING AMERICAN

The FIGHTING AMERICAN

*

A war-chest of stories
of American soldiers
from the French and
Indian Wars through
the First World War

*

Edited, with an Introduction by
F. van WYCK MASON

*

REYNAL & HITCHCOCK — NEW YORK

To

THE OFFICERS AND MEN
of
AMERICA'S NEWEST AND GREATEST ARMY

ACKNOWLEDGMENT

To Mr. J. G. E. Hopkins, Instructor of
English at the College of Notre Dame, Staten
Island, New York, the anthologist is greatly
indebted for valuable and painstaking assistance.

CONTENTS

THE WAR OF 1812 (1812-1814)

THE MEXICAN WAR (1846-1848)

INDIAN WARS

THE CIVIL WAR (1861-1865)

WAR WITH SPAIN (1898)

WORLD WAR I (1917-1918)

INTRODUCTION

by F. VAN WYCK MASON

THE UNITED STATES is now engaged in the greatest of all her wars. In it Americans are doing some of the most bitter fighting in our entire history as a nation. On the home front American women and men too old to fight are playing an important part in furthering the victory of the United Nations and are in closer contact with war than ever before. Because of these facts it is only natural that the public should be curious about how a man acts and feels when under fire.

These stories have to do with Americans in battle; they deal not only with soldiers but with women, noncombatants, even children. The campaigns of any war inevitably involve the civilian population of a country as well as its fighting men. Without going too deeply into the grimmer aspect of war, the editor has attempted to select certain characteristic situations, some softened by a romantic interest and others enlivened by humorous incident. In every case, however, the stories have been picked for their basic authenticity of action and feeling. American women will read about their forbears and, in their example, may find a strength of deed and mind that will stand them in good stead during these times. And every American civilian will not only learn how a soldier feels in battle but will take pride in his splendid heritage.

This volume on the fighting American proposes to introduce representative types of our soldiers. Herein are depicted colonial skirmishers, militia, regulars, National Guards, and leathery Indian fighters from the frontiers. There are tales about the infantry, cavalry, artillery, engineers, and nearly all the arms and services. You will encounter good soldiers, bad soldiers, heroes, cowards, and that variable mixture of which the majority of any army consists.

By no means all of the fighting Americans described were troops in the formal sense of the word. Many were soldiers in name only—armed civilians fighting for their principles, their lives, or their homes—such as Herkimer's men at Oriskany, the defenders of the Alamo, and the men who did battle at Lexington and Breed's Hill.

It is probably a fact that no major army in history has undergone as many violent and complete transformations within such brief periods of time as that of the United States. In order to account for the peculiarities, weaknesses, and abilities of the various armies raised by this country, we must try to fathom the national character. It is indeed a paradox that so naturally aggressive and often pugnacious a people should abominate the idea of peacetime military service and a large standing army. It is nevertheless true that throughout our history the American people have always maintained a deep-seated reluctance to have anything to do with things military until absolutely compelled.

For the origin of this unfortunate aversion, we must go far back in the history of the mother continent. From the Middle Ages on down to the French Revolution, wars in Europe were fought by relatively small armies in the pay of sovereigns which fought primarily for their wages and the plunder they were able to obtain from the countryside. These mercenary troops were tough, professional soldiers who had little or no consideration for the civilians with whom they came in contact.

To the average humble person dwelling in Europe between the fifteenth and eighteenth centuries, the sight of a uniform seldom meant anything but hardship and grief. He quite naturally looked upon the soldier as the instrument of an oppressor and very often the latter's executioner. For it was the man in uniform who, at the point of a sword or bayonet, enforced the collection of taxes, seized conscripts, and requisitioned painfully earned crops, herds, and other property.

Furthermore these professional fighters brought home hideous diseases contracted in far lands, which they proceeded to spread among the innocent civilians. The King's soldier could arbitrarily be billeted in a man's home, where more often than not he tyrannized over the household and made free of its womenfolk. And all too frequently he would repay hospitality by persuading the brawny young sons of the family to enlist in the military service—a career which almost invariably ended in physical and moral decay, crippling wounds, or death.

At the time our founding fathers fled from Europe, the common soldier was a far cry from his successor of this and the last century. He had become dulled and brutalized through suffering under a disciplinary code that was harsh beyond belief. He was ignorant, vicious, and usually riddled by venereal disease. A sizeable proportion of the rank and file were ex-convicts, ne'er-do-wells, and psychopathic cases—a tough, hard-bitten lot, distrusted, feared, and hated by all.

It was not until the French Revolution that this type of soldier began to disappear from the scene. When the security of the new French Republic was threatened by the professional armies of Europe's reigning monarchs, the revolutionary leaders, in the urgency of the hour, conceived an entirely new and radical principle—the citizen army, composed of civilians inducted into military service and adequately trained. The reason such an army was able to take the field and conquer was because it was fighting for a common ideal that held it together and not merely for pay and plunder.

But it was the old professional armies and not the later citizen armies that were remembered by the original settlers of this country and those that followed them for the next two hundred years. And it was not only to escape oppression by such troops but also to avoid service in their ranks that vast numbers sought the New World. Once established in America, these emigrants did their best to prevent foraging and conscription parties, tax collectors and punitive expeditions, from becoming a part of the American tradition.

There is another reason for the native American's ingrained objection to military organization. This lies in the fact that in our colonial wars regiments of European regulars and their gallant but hidebound officers usually came to grief because they knew nothing and were unwilling to learn anything about the type of warfare waged on this continent. Fort William Henry, Abercrombie's failure at Ticonderoga, and of course Braddock's historic defeat all contributed to the colonial American's distrust of the professional soldier. To this day in many parts of our country the pomp and circumstance of war remain synonymous with incompetence and defeat. Except for the inhabitants of certain sections of our Southern states, our people do not take to soldiering readily. The American instinctively dislikes regimentation, discipline, and, more recently, personal discomfort.

Unfortunately for our founding fathers the European nations continued along the path of conscription and aggression. Taxes continued to be collected and the poor man to be robbed of his crops, while larger and larger armies were raised and trained. Therefore, from time to time America became constrained to defend herself—whether she wished to or not. Her suspicion of all things military has now and again come within an ace of depriving her people of those freedoms which constitute their credo.

On the following pages, the attentive reader will time and again become conscious of the dreadful price that was paid by different generations of Americans who were forced to fight in fearful ignorance of the science and art of war. Many of the tales in this collection are replete with deeds of heroism, self-sacrifice, and unselfishness, but far too many of these gallant feats were necessitated by the incapacity of some leader.

Had our ancestors but agreed that required military service was to be one of the cornerstones of this Republic, what dark, despairing years, what tragic defeats might have been avoided! Had a reasonable proportion of our healthy, intelligent young men been encouraged to adopt a military instead of a business or professional career, how much shorter many of our wars might have been! Had this country possessed adequate forts, depots, and arsenals in 1774, 1810, 1846, 1896, 1913, and 1938, what a tremendous saving they would have brought about in the financial expenses of those conflicts! Had all this been done how many of our finest men might have survived to be more useful to the nation than as carven names on memorial stones!

Thus, this book on the Fighting American is primarily intended for an American audience, but it is hoped that readers of other nationalities, by considering these tales, may come to understand why we Americans have fought in such an ungainly, disorganized, and expensive fashion. At the same time it is not an apology, for I do not feel that as a people we have any need to apologize for our fighting qualities, despite the handicaps that have been mentioned.

Inevitably, then, the question arises—why have these hastily improvised American armies eventually won all our past wars? Sometimes we have gained our victory through luck; occasionally it has been won through the incapacity of our enemies; at times—as in 1812—peace has come to us because our enemy became sickened of fighting or was too involved elsewhere; or else, as in 1782, and 1918, we have triumphed due to a dogged conviction in the justice of our stand. To my mind, however, the chief explanation for our victories lies in the fact that most of our people enter battle with the hope that in the end they can dispense with warfare for the rest of their lives.

The United States, like the British Empire, is slow to wrath, for we have seldom deliberately gone out of our way to seek trouble. Yet, when necessity has spurred us on, we have been able to concentrate an abundant peacetime energy and ingenuity on instruments and means of destruction. The result of this diversion has been unhappy for the enemy.

This volume makes no attempt to analyze our national military philosophy. Its purpose is to describe, in the words of our own fiction writers, how the American acts in battle; how he wins and loses, lives and dies in war.

Some readers doubtless will detect, and wonder over, the omission of certain celebrated battle stories. A very few omissions were due to the fact that permission for the stories' inclusion in this collection could not be obtained. Beyond that, however, like any anthology, this book is an expression of the editor's own personal taste. If the reader misses a particular favorite, the editor can only tender his regret and hope that the diversity of the fare will in other respects compensate him for his disappointment.

The editor admits to a measure of impatience with those self-conscious and precious writers of belles-lettres who attempt with psychiatric tremolos, to describe in detail the reactions of soldiers on a battlefield. As a veteran of the last war and as a member of the sixth generation of his family to wear the uniform of the United States Army, this editor must retain toward such efforts a certain degree of ironic skepticism, whatever their literary merit.

The collection includes selections from some novels which may not constitute great literature but are reprinted because, in the editor's opinion, they best portray the voices, faces, and emotions of Americans fighting for their lives. Also, for the reason that they are true expressions of the humor, the quiet fortitude, and the rugged courage of our soldiers, a number of famous short stories have been included—as well as some yarns scarcely known to the average reader.

In those frequent cases where a battle sequence has been selected from a longer book, the editor, without dwelling too much on the actual shock of conflict, has deleted paragraphs and pages not directly pertinent to the engagement in question. In every instance he has attempted to present a description as nearly dramatically complete as possible.

Some selections from older writers may appear quaint and stilted by comparison with the more fluent and realistic works of modern writers, yet it is well to remember that in many cases the flowery speech and nonsensical gallantries described are accurate representations of how soldiers thought and acted in those days.

The editor trusts that when the reader puts aside this book he will feel a quiet pride in these men who have fought and in these women who have suffered for our country.

II

These chroniclers of THE FIGHTING AMERICAN themselves make up an interesting study. Our historical novelists boast a rich and varied ancestry which goes back to the minstrels and gleemen of the age of chivalry, back to Scheherazade and the Arabian Nights, back to the Greek fabulists and historians, even back to Homer himself. Just as these ancient tellers of tales immortalized their ages in vivid and colorful outline, so have our own novelists given us an undying picture of our nation's childhood and youth.

In this hurried age few Americans, save for a few specialists, make a practice of reading history. Yet there has always been a tremendous vogue for historical fiction. For this there are sound reasons. The historical novelist places his characters and their stories within a broad framework of factual history wherein they work out their several destinies. At the same time he builds up a unified dramatic structure and adds the ingredients of realism, sex, and romantic appeal. If the tale is a good one the reader soon loses himself in it, identifying himself with the characters and so vicariously reliving history. A skillful portrayal of war, for instance, will inspire within a reader the emotion and perilous thrills of conflict.

Yet there is more to it than that. The writer of historical fiction has the power to create myths, to form legends about great men that will supersede and obscure in the mind of the reader the historian's evaluation of his subjects. How much more vivid than the actual rank and file of the British army are Mulvaney, Ortheris, and Learoyd! How many of us know any more about the siege of La Rochelle than what we learned from D'Artagnan's exploits? Just how many of us can distinguish the Julius Caesar of *De Bello Gallico* and Suetonius from the myth created by Shakespeare?

Thackeray, in one of his *Roundabout Papers,* describes his boyhood infatuation with Natty Bumppo, with Longue Carabine. He admits that his whole conception of the United States was colored by the epic figure of Cooper's woodsman. For generations Europeans have thought of this country in terms of *Uncle Tom's Cabin,* literary chromo if ever there was one.

If we were to analyze the various methods and techniques employed down through the years by historical novelists of American wars, we should find that they veer between the extremes of stark realism and mawkish romance; their characters vary from the sublime to the downright silly. Yet the central theme remains constant throughout: an honest glorification of their countrymen's deeds in the field, the projection of the American soldier as a fundamentally honorable fellow in battle.

Earliest examples of historical fiction in the United States are almost ridiculously poor. Yet a few readable pieces do exist. One of these is Herman Mann's rearrangement of the personal narrative of a woman soldier in the Revolution. It has been included in this collection as representative of our early work. Even in this somewhat better than average bit of writing there are obvious faults and crudities. The treatment of facts is scarcely imaginative, while little attempt at contrast in characters has been made. The development of plot is practically nonexistent, and there is no personal approach to the subject.

This formula was all too common, and obtained over several such novels before James Fenimore Cooper began to handle American themes in the true technique of the novel. Today, Cooper's novels are properly criticized for their verbosity, their artificial dialogue, the insipidity of the women, and the exclusively masculine character of the action. Nonetheless, Cooper remains the sturdy doyen of historical fiction.

William Gilmore Simms rarely departed from the literal facts of history; accordingly, his tales of the Revolutionary War in the Carolinas betray a wooden quality distasteful to modern readers. Though his novels are accurate and grandly conceived, his main characters remain shadowy, while that poetic sense which often strives to break through Cooper's stolid sentences is wholly lacking. Simms paints his people in the high romantic tradition, making them speak with a certain magniloquence which their creator sadly mistook for epic grandeur. His partisan heroes are inevitably black of hair and stormy of expression—just so many reflections of the author's admiration for Byron. The Indian story I have chosen to represent Simms nicely reveals both his faults and his virtues.

Whereas in Cooper's writings, rivers, lakes, and forests—the immensity of a natural setting—become almost living characters—indeed the most honest characters in his novels—this magic is lost among his imitators.

Kennedy, writing in the eighteen-thirties, reveals considerably more polish and a stylistic skill approaching that of his master. A friend of Thackeray's and an author only by avocation, his use of history is true, valid, and well documented. He is clever enough to conceal himself as author and never come to the fore. He does not make his tale topheavy with historical framework, nor does he sink it with an overabundance of characters, as in the case of Simms or Cooper.

Kennedy's characters are imbued with a large part of that grace and worldly charm characteristic of their creator. For the first time in American historical fiction, females are lifelike and play major parts in the plots. Even so, the reader is left somewhat in doubt, for the author's heroes and heroines are nineteenth-century ladies and gentlemen sketched against a seventeenth-century or Revolutionary background. So skillfully, however, were Kennedy's historical details and the plot dovetailed in his *Horseshoe Robinson* that it was impossible to extract a selection which would stand by itself.

Richard Montgomery Bird, on the other hand, was quite as sketchy at drawing character as was Simms. Yet he developed real skill in mak- a plot move with speed and pace. This talent guaranteed until very late in the nineteenth century the popularity of his best book, *Nick of the Woods*. Bird's pictures of Indians were in sharp contrast with the idealized portraitures of Cooper; his redskins were "bad Injuns," deceitful, primitive, and savage. In this at least he was an innovator. His bloodthirsty, half-crazed Quaker scout in the piece I have included possesses a genuine eeriness and originality.

Among the other pre-Civil War historical novelists, James Kirke Paulding had a contemporary popularity, but this versatile author never took sufficient trouble with his work. His novels are all written *currente calamo,* as, for instance, the early *Salmagundi,* written with Washington Irving. *Westward Ho* had the makings of a fine frontier novel, but the modern reader will detect in it only a hint of great possibilities.

Literary art after the Civil War was marked by a growing sophistication and a spirit of expansion. That cynical reaction which appears in the wake of all wars in this instance took the form of humorous self-scrutiny. It was an era of ruthless, devil-take-the-hindmost struggle for wealth, in which the idealized novel with its Rousseauesque Indians completely vanished. The new potentates, the oil men and copper kings and coal barons, ignored the strugglings of a native art and turned their eyes eastward toward Europe. By the hundred these financial wizards and aesthetic ignoramuses bought old masters of more or less dubious origin and set their sons and daughters to dreaming of "furrin" elegancies at violent odds with traditional republican virtues.

Thanks to this neglect, the softer conservatism of our early historical fiction writers survived only in the dime novels. When a few good historical novels were finally written in the eighties, they took the form of outraged satires on existing political evils, such as Henry Adams' *Democracy*.

The few contemporary novels on the Civil War were almost uniformly bad. John Esten Cooke, who wrote of Lee and his paladins, was merely a lesser Simms. Joseph Kirkland was not much better, although his *Captain of Company K* does show a certain crude power in its battle scenes of Grant's campaign in the West. On other side of the picture

J. W. DeForest did extremely well in his *Miss Ravenel's Conversion* and richly deserved Howells' tribute of "the first American realist."

In choosing representative Civil War scenes for this book, I have been forced to draw largely upon writers of our own time. In my opinion their superior craftsmanship and realistic methods more than counterbalance the "personal experience" element that limited so many of the older writers.

Of course not all the writers of the seventies and eighties suffered from technical incompetence or allowed themselves to be warped by the intolerable Nice-Nancyness of the times. Unfortunately their interest did not lie in American themes. Lew Wallace and Edward Bellamy wrote well, but the subject of *Ben Hur* was far afield from the author's native Indiana, while the *Duke of Stockbridge* urged a social thesis in which Bellamy was interested to the exclusion of narrative art and character development.

A new formula for historical fiction was badly required, and S. Weir Mitchell first supplied it in his *Hugh Wynne: Free Quaker,* published in 1897. This novel maintained the nicest possible balance between its protagonists and the historical atmosphere; its interest lay primarily in the characters, and the great events wherein they moved occupied a secondary place. In other words, this was the first successful subordination of framework to picture.

The Red Badge of Courage, Stephen Crane's great tour de force, appeared in 1895. The works of Mitchell and Crane led to a series of more or less historical novels that enjoyed a popularity between 1897 and 1905. They were patterned more on Mitchell's writing than on the impressionism of Crane. The latter called himself a realist and forever preached the artist's necessity to get close to life; yet he himself wrote with the eye and mind of a poet, which explained his lack of imitators. Mitchell's prose was uninspired but easy; he wrote a dialogue halfway between the contemporary and the antique, which lent an agreeable eighteenth-century illusion without puttting an undue strain on the receptive faculties of the ordinary reader.

Paul Leicester Ford possessed an unusually profound knowledge of Revolutionary history but ruined his *Janice Meredith* for modern tastes by the priggish airs of his characters and the patent unreality of his plot.

Winston Churchill, despite his popularity, remains little more than an echo of Mitchell, as do George Cable, Thomas Nelson Page, and James Allen—all of whom suffered from an excess of the romantic in their interpretation of life. In the rosy-hued novels of these hard-working authors all the brothers were brave and all the sisters were virtuous. Though this pretty conceit suited that decade, it does not amuse a more realistic generation.

It may thus be perceived that during the first decade of the twentieth century writing in the field of historical fiction was cloyed by romantic excesses and obvious unrealities.

The historical novel's present-day popularity seems to have been anticipated by the early work of Zane Grey, James Boyd, and Emerson Hough. Then, too, the best of the World War novels found a notable success and demonstrated that historical tales will always have a public— provided that they are told with honesty and artistic competence. Flag waving is far from enough, as was proved by three books that had a phenomenal success: *All Quiet on the Western Front* (1927), *The Case of Sergeant Grischa* (1928), and *A Farewell to Arms* (1930).

James and Thomas Boyd and Walter D. Edmonds were all writing with subtle skill and a genuine dignity before 1928. Kenneth Roberts scored a belated but sensational success with *Rabble in Arms* in 1928.

From that time to the present, many excellent novels have been dedicated to an earnest and thoughtful presentation of the spirit and growth of our country. Today, in order to receive attention an historical novel must be strictly documented and written with realism. Most important of all, it must stand on its own as a fascinating story with interesting characters, intrinsically independent of its value to history.

THE FRENCH AND INDIAN WARS

1754-1763

THE FRENCH AND INDIAN WARS

1754-1763

During that part of the Seven Years War which we Americans are accustomed to call the French and Indian War, there became evident the first sure signs of a burgeoning national spirit. This conflict marked the decline of old sectional jealousies in the face of a common danger, it initiated an inclination toward union and aroused a general feeling that colonial status in Britain's empire did not offer sufficiently fair rewards.

Also, there became deeper rooted among the colonials a conviction that British arms and formal military organizations, although showy on parade, were not efficient in action. This they felt was amply demonstrated by Abercrombie's failure before Ticonderoga and again in the capture of Fort William Henry. In this war the inadaptability of Britain's officers when confronted by conditions of war alien to those of Europe's orderly battlefields aroused the contempt and the anger of the militia who knew, at least, the utility of a tree for purposes of defence. Braddock, laying about him with his sword in a vain attempt to make his men stand up to the invisible enemy, is a tragic and a portentous figure.

The colonial militiaman, therefore, came to regard order and discipline in armies as allied, somehow, to stupidity and arrogance. The brilliant raid of Major Robert Rogers against the Indian town of St. Francis pleased the colonial soldier as a classic example of turning against the foe his own tactics of craft and surprise. Unfortunately he did not pause to reflect upon the long months of training which rendered Rogers' Rangers an effective and disciplined striking force. Nor would he have given due credit to the soldierly efficiency that brought the Highlanders to the relief of Fort Pitt.

BRADDOCK'S EXPEDITION AGAINST
FORT DUQUESNE

by JOHN JENNINGS

OUR MARCH from Fort Cumberland thus far had demonstrated that the order in which we moved was not well chosen. In consequence, it had been decided to adopt a different plan. The army was to march as a unit, led by a corporal and four light-horse, as scouts and advance party. After these came a sergeant and a detachment of carpenters, charged with making such quick repairs to the road—cutting trees, moving rocks, strengthening bridges—as the advance work parties had overlooked. Their rear was brought up by an officer and ten light-horse. A brief interval followed, after which came a company of carpenters and fifteen seamen and a tumbrel with tools, to assist in such repairs as could not be accomplished before their arrival by the first party of carpenters. These were followed by the vanguard, composed of the first grenadiers of the Forty-fourth, under the command of Major Chapman, and two pieces of field artillery.

The main body closely followed the vanguard and was headed by Sir Peter Halkett and the Forty-fourth. The long train of wagons, artillery and pack horses next occupied the center of the road, broken into divisions, each division laden as follows: powder, provisions, regimental baggage, artillery stores, General's baggage, provisions, artillery, artillery stores, hospital stores, regimental baggage, provisions, powder. The men of the main body itself marched at intervals on either flank of the wagon train. Thus the Colonel's company of the Forty-fourth, led upon the left flank. This was followed, after a short interval, by the Major's company upon the right, by an interval and the second captain's company on the left, another interval and the fourth captain's company on the right, and so on down the line until the Forty-fourth was closed in the rear by the second grenadiers on the left.

The provincial troops took the center in much the same sort of order, being led by a field officer on the left and Captain Waggoner's Virginian

From: *Gentleman Ranker*. Copyright 1942 by the author. Reynal & Hitchcock.

Rangers on the right, an interval and Captain Dagworthy's Maryland company on the left, an interval and Captain Gates' Independent New York Company on the right, and so on. The Forty-eighth, in the reverse order of the Forty-fourth completed the line of the main body, and was brought up by Colonel Dunbar. After Dunbar came the Provost Guard and the women, followed by the second grenadier company of the Forty-eighth, two fieldpieces and the first grenadiers of the Forty-eighth forming the rear guard, and the whole was brought up by another corporal and four light-horse. Thus the line of the train was calculated to present no weak spots for possible ambush.

Such a surprise was further guarded against by flanking parties. The first grenadiers of the Forty-fourth were to provide forward point flankers on either hand, while the first grenadiers of the Forty-eighth were to throw them out in the rear. In addition, each company was to throw out two parties to march through the woods upon the side of the train which it covered. The first, a detachment of twenty men under the command of a subaltern, was to keep constant touch with the company from which it was detached, marching always parallel with it. The second, a squad of ten men and a sergeant, was to march still further out upon the flank through the woods, and keep constant touch with the subaltern's detachment, marching always parallel with them. Thus a great cloud of covering flankers was to be always out on either hand to form, in theory, an almost continuous ring about the entire army through which no hostile force could possibly approach unseen.

On paper the plan must have been impressive. How it worked in practice is another story. We in the ranks, of course, were given no hint of what was expected of us. It was enough for us to obey orders as they were given to us.

I felt better than I had for some time when, the morning after Anne's departure, I was awakened by the tap of the drums. If my back was yet tender, it was at least well enough knit by now to be beyond danger of the sores being reopened by the chafing of my pack, and the flux with which I had been threatened on leaving the fort had passed off with my three days' rest. Consequently it was almost with eagerness that I tumbled from my blankets and went about my prescribed duties for breaking camp.

Rest had refreshed the others as well, it seemed, for a spirit of enthusiasm and that determination which accompanies a second start was everywhere. Tents were quickly knocked down and lashed in bundles and stowed away, rations hastily gulped. The sky was clear and the day promised to be fair, only one small, wispy cloud floating directly overhead, pink in the rays of the sun that had not yet risen from behind the mountain.

As the day before had been devoted to rearranging the plan of camp according to the plan of march, we fell in, at the assembly positions assigned to us, forming a line, with all the intervals properly spaced save those of advance and rear guard, about half a mile in length. Colonel Halkett, accompanied by Major Chapman and Lieutenant-Colonel Gage, a tall, heavily-built man with sandy reddish hair, a rather sharp face and a weak mouth, made a careful inspection of our dispositions. As they came to Caruthers I heard Halkett's orders:

"Select your flankers, Captain, but do not throw them out until you have the command to march. See that they maintain proper contact at all times."

Caruthers saluted, and they passed on, down the right flank. Sergeant O'Hara, with the first two squads was designated to duty at right point, while Sergeant Bell with the last was assigned to the left. After that we received the order to stand at rest.

But there was little attempt at conversation among us. Each was occupied with his own thoughts and with watching the scene taking place behind us. As the entire line sloped down from our position it was possible to look far back to where it became lost amid the trees. It was a stirring sight. The other companies were forming. Teams were being hitched to the wagons. Drivers' whips were cracking, and their shouts echoing through the forest. Messengers from the staff were galloping along the line. Those wagons that were already harnessed were being moved into position. O'Hara grinned.

"Sure this is somethin' like," he remarked.

Presently everything was in readiness. The General and his staff made a loping circuit of the entire force, checking this position here, reposting that command there. As they rode forward upon our left and back upon our right I had good opportunity to observe the various reactions with which they viewed the day's prospects. Orme looked eager, almost gay, as did Morris. Shirley looked bored and impatient, as though he disapproved. Mr. Washington, whom I now saw for the first time close to, looked ill, physically unhappy but determinedly interested. The General himself looked grimly satisfied, as though now at last matters were going as he desired. They fell into position a little behind and to the right of that occupied by Colonel Halkett, and the General appeared to consult with Washington and Orme.

After a moment a messenger whirled away and rode down the line. There was a little delay, while the men waited, standing stiff at attention and the sun appeared over the mountain behind us, warming our backs and bringing out the forest shadows hard and clear. Presently the detachment of Indians, under the lead of Christopher Gist, the grizzled old woodsman and trader who had been commissioned to command them as scouts, slipped silently past and disappeared up the road forward. Once again the command to stand at ease went down the line, and a mutter of protest from the men, anxious for any activity, also went down the line.

"What's th' idea?"

"What're we waitin' for?"

"We goin' ter stand 'ere orl dye?"

"Quiet! Quiet there!" barked the officers.

I caught O'Hara's eye and saw it flutter in a wink.

For half an hour we waited, evidently giving the scouts time to lose themselves in the forest ahead. Then we were called again to attention. Unable to look behind us we could only speculate as to what was happening, though we could hear the mutter of voices as the General's commands passed to his aides and from them to his messengers. An orderly from the light-horse rode past us and spoke to the officer commanding the advanced party, and he in turn turned to give a command to the corporal in charge of the light-horse screen. A moment later the advance party moved out a unit at a time. We watched until they disappeared; watched until the connecting file they had left posted at the bend, where the leafy tunnel turned off to the right, raised his arm above his head and whistled in signal to those behind that the party was in position. At once we could hear the commands ring out behind us, beginning at the staff, "Forward!" to be caught up by the brigade commanders, "Forward!", and taken, in turn by the various lesser commanders, "Company—detachment—detachment—company—company—company—Forward—," diminishing in ratio to the distance they were behind. "March!—March—ho—harrh—hip—harrh!", each captain or officer using his own way of pronouncing the command and his own concept of the proper tone.

The effect was instantaneous and uniform. The drums banged, fifes squealed. First one company, then the next and the next moved forward on the road. Behind the wagons rumbled and lurched. Whips cracked. A messenger galloped up to Caruthers, who turned an ear to his command, then spun, and marching backwards bellowed the relay to the company.

"Flankers to point—at the double—"

"Detachment—right oblique—at the double!" bellowed O'Hara.

"Detachment left oblique at the double!" I could hear Bell echo.

"Hup!" shouted Caruthers.

"Harch!" echoed O'Hara.

"Ho!" yelled Bell.

We plunged off at a tangent, running, muskets at the trail, packs bouncing upon their backs, leafy branches slapping at our faces, brush catching at our heels. At intervals O'Hara would designate one to fall out and serve as connecting file.

"Powers! fall out an' keep contact. Don't be losin' sight av th' company or th' man on yer right!"

"Cudlin! fall out an' keep contact. Don't lose sight av Powers on yer left or th' squad on yer right!"

Presently he halted us and checked with the connecting files while we gratefully seized the opportunity for a blow. Already there were indications that the clarity of the weather was not to prove an unmitigated blessing. It was oppressively hot. A third man was dropped behind to make contact with an advance file thrown forward from the Major's company behind us, and when these dispositions had all been correctly made, O'Hara turned to us with a grin.

"All right, boys!" he commanded. "Let's be movin'. Keep closed up. There'll be no haltin' or fallin' out without orders from th' comp'ny, so take a tuck in yer belts. Ye can march at route order!"

Anyone who has hunted with a group through thick brush, trying to keep contact with the man on either side, knows how difficult it is. For us the difficulty was increased by the fact that we could not choose our cover, but must keep directly through the woods at a stated interval, from our main body, regardless of the terrain, and by the fact, as well, that what we did was not done for pleasure but at command.

At the outset the going was not difficult, for the way lay across the little valley in which the camp had been located, through fairly open woods and occasionally through small natural meadows. But presently the road turned off into a narrow gully, gouged by a small runlet from the flank of Little Allegheny Mountain, and began to climb toward the summit of the ridge. Here our difficulties really began, for we were forced to climb abruptly up the deep flanks of the ravine, and then, half-way up, to strike a parallel course with that of the road, through dense brush and tangled woods, through tumbled windfalls and laurel thickets, through masses of thorny bush and acres of intertwining wild grapevines.

At the start the men of the party had looked upon the separation from the main body, and the feeling of freedom and independence which it brought, as a privilege; a decided advantage to marching directly under the sharp eyes of the commissioned officers. But as the going became more and more difficult they began to grumble and curse and look upon the assignment as something like punishment.

"Sye!" growled one, "wot t' 'ell've we done. 'Ow abaht givin' someb'dy else a try at it?"

"Wot's th' idea, anywyes?" muttered another. "Wot's th' use of orl this? No savage in 'is proper mind'd be aht in this stuff, an' 'ow'd we see 'im if 'e was?"

"Bloody bugger's got a pick on us, that's wot!" said another.

"Hush yer lip!" O'Hara commanded, "an' keep movin'."

I might have been inclined to agree with the others had I not had that one view of Indians slipping upward through the forest toward the gap in the mountain on the day of our hunt, as well as the experience of the bobwhites.

"'Twould surprise you," I said, "to know the places they will go. It makes good sense that someone should guard the flanks."

"Brother roundmouth speaks!" sneered Nypper Smart.

"Hold your tongue, Smart," I told him.

"Quit fartin' through yer teeth!" he growled.

It was perhaps fortunate for us that as the road progressed, it, too, became more difficult. The wagons had the same rough going as had been encountered on the way over the mountain to Spendlowe's Camp, and it became necessary for the vanguard to make frequent halts to allow them to catch up. The further we went the more frequent—and welcome —became these halts, and the shorter became the intervals of marching, for obviously we could not continue while the main body stood. Despite this, however, we had scarce proceeded above two hours when we came within sound of the ringing axes of the work party sent out the day before. Thereafter our forward progress was slowed not only by the difficulties of the wagons with the roads, but also by the creeping progress of those before us.

Toward midday we were recalled to the main body and relieved by another squad. Thenceforward our progress was even more slow, and we spent hours, it seemed, resting upon our muskets, not even daring to drop our packs, awaiting the command to move again, a few steps forward. In the woods, at least there had been a measure of shade, if the going had been hard. But here in the broad gash cut through the forest there was not even protection from the sun, and each hour of the day seemed to bring its own variety of biting, burning, stinging, gnawing insect pests. All the while the steady clop-chop-ch-clop-chop of the axes of the work party rang through the woods before us, while the querulous curses, the crack of whips and the ring of iron-shod wheels upon the rocks of the roadway came drifting up to us from behind upon the still, hot, sultry air.

Once we heard a shot, far up ahead, and then a whole series of shots, and we all tensed and waited, wondering what might be toward. But it was an hour before a group came trudging back along the roadway, carrying between them the limp form of one of the work party who had temporarily laid aside his axe for a moment and gone a few steps into the woods to relieve himself. Fortunately for him a nearby guard had caught sight of one of the three Indians who had fallen upon him, so that they had had no more than time to strike him down and half rip the scalp from his skull. He had fired, and so started a flurry of shots that had frightened the marauders away. It was a sobering sight to see the way the man's head lolled upon his shoulders and how the blood streamed down the side of his face and colored his shirt, but it had a sanguine effect upon the men, for it was evidence of the enemy's boldness and skill in the forest. Thereafter there was less grumbling about the need for flank duty.

One would imagine that at our slow rate of progress it would have been a simple matter to keep the line closed up, and the entire army moving as a unit. Such, however, was not the case. So rough was the road, so great the boulders, so many the stumps, so deep the potholes, so terrible the grades; and so poor were the nags that had to draw the wagons and so rickety the wagons themselves, that the train was able to move forward with only the most excruciating slowness. Each wagon and each gun had to be carefully eased over each obstacle. Pack horses had to have their loads lightened and bring them up the mountain in relays. Often the men themselves had to take a hand with the horses in drawing the heavily-laden vehicles up the steep inclines.

Consequently, though the head of the column thrust forward but slowly, the rear fell further and further back, like the end of a long and ever-lengthening tail. By five in the afternoon, when the vanguard marched into the previously prepared clearing called Martin's Plantation, in which we were to camp for the night, a distance of some five miles from our starting point of the morning, Colonel Dunbar and the rear had come no more than two miles from Spendlowe's Camp. It was eleven the next morning before the last of the column could come in, and as a result we spent that day at Martin's.

This was apparently too much for the General's patience, for when we marched the following day we lost no time waiting for slow wagons to catch up, but left them under guard to make the best of their way forward, while a number of those most broken-down were left at Martin's Meadow in care of a detachment from the Forty-eighth, to be brought forward later on. By this means we managed a fair day's march, crossing the main ridge of Allegheny Mountain and descending upon the other side through the steep, wild tangle of forest, over a road worse than any we had yet encountered, to Savage River. This we crossed without difficulty, and camped two miles beyond at the foot of another mountain, which appeared to bear no name. On this day it was rumored that because of the extreme roughness of the road our line was sometimes stretched out to a length of four or five miles.

On the following day we marched again, regardless of those behind us, and soon gained the summit of the mountain before us though the road climbed steadily for two miles at one point without a level stretch or a down grade throughout. Beyond the mountain we came into a region of upland bog densely forested with tall pines and thick, dark hemlock. Much work had been done here by Sir John and his woodchoppers, and the boggy stretches were well traversed by a road of logs, cut and laid one beside another, like a vast endless bridge. On this account the going was not so bad as it had been. Nevertheless, we were all glad when we came to the end of it and dropped into the more open forest beyond, for it was gloomy and forbidding country, for all it was cool and shady, and not one living thing, not even a rabbit or a squirrel or a sparrow did we see in all our way across it. On this day the flanking parties had their worst going, for they were often forced to wade through black muck up to their waists, and the sunken roots and knobs of stumps and rotted, stinking timbers laid traps for unwary legs and ankles, tore buttons from gaiters and made shreds of breeches.

That night we dropped down to the Little Meadows on the banks of the upper waters of the unpronounceable Youghiogheny river—the first water we came to that flowed westward toward the Ohio instead of east and south to the Potomac—and there we camped for two days, awaiting the arrival of the rest of the army.

It would be tedious, not to say unnecessary, to detail each step of our journey to the Monongahela. Even if I were to describe fully, as it happened, each adventure that befell us in our march it would still be overlong. There are certain things, however, that must be told, for they bore upon events that followed, and these I will touch upon as briefly as may be.

It was evident, by the time we reached the Little Meadows, that unless we increased our pace measurably we would never reach Fort Duquesne before the French could reenforce it. Even the dullest private could see that. As for the General, it was obvious from a distance that he was beside himself with rage and worry. A council of war was consequently called at this place, in which important decisions were arrived at.

As a private it was not for me to know what those decisions might be. But as one assigned that day to duty with the General's guard and placed on post outside the tent in which the council was held, I can testify that high words passed, that voices were raised for and against various points that came up. And when the various members of the council came out of the tent it was easy to see who was pleased and who was disgruntled by the decisions reached. Sir Peter Halkett looked like the cat that had swallowed the canary. Lieutenant Colonel Gage seemed elated, as did Major Sparks. Lieutenant Colonel Burton seemed mildly pleased. But Major Chapman looked grim and angry, while Colonel Dunbar seemed positively incensed. Sir John St. Clair, as usual, seemed rather stupidly bored.

Some of the reasons for this were apparent when the orders of the day were read to the troops that evening. According to these the army was to be divided. Two light detachments, composed of the pick of the troops, were to march as rapidly as possible from the Little Meadows toward Fort Duquesne, while the rest, with the women and the bulk of the supplies and provisions was to follow at the best possible pace.

The first detachment was to number some four hundred men, under the command of Lieutenant Colonel Gage and Sir John St. Clair. One company of the Forty-fourth and one of the Forty-eighth were to accompany this detachment, whose duty it was to open the road, upon which no work had been done beyond this point. The balance of the force was to be composed of men from the provincial companies, and was to march the following morning at four o'clock. The second detachment, and main body, was to be composed of the two senior companies of grenadiers, and the pick of the men from the two regular regiments, numbering in all some eight hundred men, and was to be commanded by Colonel Halkett, assisted by Lieutenant Colonel Burton and Major Sparks. Colonel Dunbar and Major Chapman were to command the

second division, which, it was felt, would doubtless arrive before Duquesne too late to take part in any action that might take place there.
The General himself was to accompany Halkett's brigade, as were the
light-horse, which by now stood once again complete, Harry Owen and
his detachment having caught up with us once more.

In addition to all this there was further evidence of the General's haste
in the orders given to officers and men. Officers were requested to take
with them only such baggage as was absolutely essential, while the men
were told that they might take with them no more than one spare shirt.
Four howitzers, four twelve-pounders and twelve cohorns were all the
artillery that was to be taken, and the detachment of seamen was to accompany these. The only wagons to go would be those which served the
artillery and carried necessary ammunition for the troops. All other
supplies were to be carried by pack horses.

These orders were received variously in the camp, but among those
who had been designated to accompany the first brigade a general spirit
of optimism prevailed. At last, it was felt, the fighting portion of the
army could move rapidly and strike effectively. Individual reactions were
also interesting. It was rumored that the General had not consulted his
officers in council to decide which should be designated to go, but had
arbitrarily made his own selection. This gave great offense to those named
to stay behind, and added to the bad blood already engendered by the
jealousies and rivalries among them. Among the men there was more
resignation, for many of them were already too listless from the effects of
the flux to care one way or another.

My own newly acquired views had tended to throw me as much
among my friends among the provincials as among my own comrades in
the regiment and consequently, as I was frequently a visitor beside their
campfires, I was perhaps better able to observe the reactions of the entire
army than were most other regulars. Boone, who was to remain behind
with the North Carolinians, was utterly cast down at the thought. On the
other hand, Morgan, whose wagon was designated to carry ammunition,
but who was still bitterly resentful of his treatment at Fort Cumberland,
regarded it simply as a part of his contract and therefore all in the day's
work. Harry Owen was elated.

"By God!" he boomed at me across the campfire that night, "we're
gettin' somewhere now. I tell ye, Steve, I see Colonel Washington's hand
in this, for more than once I have o'erheard him urge th' General to
forget his wagons and baggage an' push on with th' men, carryin' no
more than a blanket an' what provisions they might carry on their backs."

"He hasn't gone that far," I said.

"No, but he'll come to it, mark my words," Owen replied.

Neither of us noticed the tall figure that paused on the outer edge of the ring of light cast by our fire until he spoke.

"You are a greater optimist than I, if you believe that, Owen," he said.

The big Virginian looked up startled, and then leaped to his feet with a surprised oath.

"By God, Colonel" he exclaimed. "I didn't see ye come up."

I rose more slowly, recognizing the spare figure and rocklike features of Colonel Washington.

"I did not mean to intrude," he said. "I was looking for Captain Stewart."

He looked somewhat curiously at me, as he said it, for it was unusual to encounter a regular before a provincial campfire. Owen caught the look and smiled.

" 'Tis no intrusion, God love ye, Colonel," he said. "This here's Steve Trent, o' th' Forty-fourth."

The Colonel held out his hand to me simply and without affectation.

"It is a pleasure, indeed, Mr. Trent," said he in his low, rich voice, "to see that it is not all bad blood between regulars and provincials!"

I took his hand and was surprised to see that he was not above a year or two older than I. From a distance I had judged him to be older, but this might have been due to worry and his evident ill health. He was obviously a man who took matters seriously.

"Your humble servant, Colonel Washington," I said formally. "Perhaps I have more reason than my comrades to feel fellowship with the Americans, for you see, sir, I have been married since I came here."

He looked at me with a certain curiosity that I felt was not entirely inspired by what I had said.

"Indeed?" said he. "I am glad to hear it. I wish there could be more such matches. It might save a deal of misunderstanding. In fact, I almost think it would have been a wise move had the authorities in England seen fit to send out a few women who might marry among our men. But I suppose that is too much to expect."

He smiled as he said it, and I saw that he was only half in earnest. It was Owen who answered him, though, quite unexpectedly.

"I wouldn't be too sure o' that, Colonel," he remarked dryly.

The Colonel's eyebrows rose in amused interrogation, but Owen looked suddenly confused.

"If ye're seekin' Captain Stewart, sir," he said, "ye might find him in his tent, three fires down th' line."

Colonel Washington smiled, and it was remarkable how his severe features lighted with it.

"I see," he said. "Thank you, Owen. Good night to you, and to you, Mr. Trent."

"Good night, sir," I replied.

"Good night to ye, Colonel," said Owen.

The tall figure turned and stalked away in the darkness. I turned to the Sergeant.

"Now what did you mean by that?" I demanded curiously.

"Oh, nothing, nothing," he grinned. " 'Twas naught but gibble-gabble."

I saw that he had no intention of enlightening me further, and so let the matter drop.

The two detachments marched as ordered, Sir John and Colonel Gage leaving with the dawn of the seventeenth, and our own brigade under Sir Peter Halkett following upon their heels the next daybreak. We rounded the slopes of a short ridge, angling down through broken meadows and patches of scattered oak and beech and maple to the ford of the first branch of the Youghiogheny, called the Little Crossings. The stream was wide, about eighty yards across, and shallow, but it was yet some time before we got all our wagons and artillery and pack horses over. Once across we marched again, four miles up a steep hill and to the foot of the greatest mountain we had yet come upon, stretching in a long, blank ridge across our path. Here we came upon the rear of the party sent out the day before who were, as Colonel Washington later put it, stopping "to level every molehill and bridge every brook." As we could not pass beyond, the road up the mountainside not yet being considered fit, we halted there for the night.

Some excitements happened here, which had they been heeded as carefully as they should by all of us, might have saved us much. Our Indian scouts had all been sent out with the first detachment, and it happened that while the second division was marching forward from the Little Meadows, the chief Monacatuca and his son were being taken prisoners by a band of French and Indians lurking in the neighborhood of Gage's camp.

Fortunately for them, several of the Indians in the attacking party were former friends of the old chief, and these, when the French proposed putting them to death, balked and threatened to come over to the English. In the end it was decided to compromise by tying them to trees and leaving them. Monacatuca's son, however, managed to free himself and went for aid, whereupon the old chief was rescued by the other Indians of our command.

The story of this adventure was still being bruited about the camp on our arrival, and scarcely had we come to a halt when further excitement was aroused by the arrival of a runner from the mountain-top, where Colonel Gage was holding the high pass of the road with a strong advance detachment, bringing word that a great body of the enemy were marching in our direction.

Instantly the camp was in an uproar, and it was thought by some that we should all march at once to meet them. General Braddock, however, was not one to be easily rushed into unnecessary action. Instead he at once sent back a messenger to discover the truth of the report.

It was nightfall before this man returned, and then, it was proved, the cause of all the furore had been the discovery of several Indians very near the outposts of the advanced party. No such large force as had been reported appeared, however, and as a result, as so often happens when men have been unduly alarmed, our vigilance relaxed beyond what we had right to allow.

This is not to say that the customary pickets were not all properly placed about the camp, or that the officers in charge were negligent in their rounds. But the attitude of the men themselves became careless, and even I, who by my own experience should have known better, was at fault in this.

It happened that the squad to which I was attached was one of those designated that night to guard duty, and with the others, I was assigned a post upon the outskirts of the camp. It was my duty here to walk a beat some hundred feet in length between two trees. On either side of me were other pickets, whose duty was to do the same, and so it went in a complete circle about the encampment. This outer ring of guards was supplemented at intervals by parties posted within the circle, each under the command of a sergeant, whose duty it was to visit the sentries on his post at least once every half hour. Once an hour the round of both sentries and pickets was made by the officer of the day. At Spendlowe Camp it had been customary for the sentries to build themselves huts or bowers, in which to shelter themselves against the weather and the clouds of mosquitoes that infested the woods after dark, and to make fires, by which it was thought that they would be better able to see.

As the men had a tendency to go to sleep in their huts, however, and as the fires only tended to make the outer ring of the night about their post the blacker and to throw the sentry's form into silhouette, both of these practices had been forbidden at Martin's Meadow, so that now it was necessary to walk one's post in total darkness.

The night at Little Crossings Camp was dark and moonless. On the one hand my post joined that of Dick Powers, while an unknown soldier of the Forty-eighth walked upon the other. It was a little after midnight, and the officer of the day had just completed his rounds when Powers called me to his end of the beat.

"Hist, Trent!" he called in a low voice.

"What's up?" I asked, coming under the great oak that marked the common end of our posts.

"Is all clear your end?" he asked. "Is the O.D. gone his rounds?"

"Aye," I replied. "Why?"

"'Tis the damned flux," he replied. "I must relieve my bowels or bewray myself."

"Have a care," I warned him. "If the O.D. comes back and finds you not on post he'll have the hide off your back."

"I can't help it," he replied. "I'm that griped in my belly I can't straighten my back! Here, keep an eye on my weapon the whiles I step off here in the woods. If any come, give me warning."

He thrust his musket into my hand and disappeared in the dark of the forest.

I knew that I must approach the other end of my post and give the word to the guard there, or else I would have the sergeant of the guard upon me. Accordingly I leaned Powers' musket against the rough bark of the oak and walked leisurely back along my beat. At the far end I spoke to the other guard, turned about and started slowly back. Halfway to the oak a small sound ahead and slightly to my left caught my ear and arrested me in midstride. It had sounded like a dull thud and a grunt, followed by a tearing sound and a slight crackling of the bushes. But though I waited a long moment listening, no other sound came. Then, just as I was starting forward again, I heard a twig snap lightly near the oak. 'Twas only Powers returning for his musket, I thought, and so continued my beat without giving the matter further consideration.

When I came to the oak, however, Powers was not there. I put out my hand to touch his musket, and found it gone. Thinking that he had perhaps returned and taken it and resumed his post, I stood still, listening for the sound of his footsteps, until, all at once, it struck me that he had not known that I had left the gun there.

At the same instant I heard the sound of a body moving in the thickets on my left. I whirled and threw up my musket to the ready.

"Powers!" I called. "Powers!"

There was no answer.

I called again, and moved a step in the direction whence the sound had come.

It was this movement, doubtless, that saved my life, for even as I moved something whirred past my ear, thucked against the heavy bark of the oak and dropped to the ground.

I needed no further warning, but threw up my musket and fired in the direction whence I thought the thing had come. In the silence that followed the flash and roar of my weapon I heard the sound of heavy bodies crashing away from me through the underbrush.

"Sergeant of the guard!" I bellowed. "Guard! Guard!"

It could not have been above half a minute before the sergeant and the entire picket were upon my post, armed with muskets ready and a half a score of lanterns, but to me lying there upon my belly in the blackness of the night it seemed half an age. When they came I was far too agitated to conceal anything but rose, trembling and told my story. When I had finished a few men plunged into the brush, while others covered them with their muskets. Within a dozen paces of where I stood they came to an abrupt halt.

"Christ!" I heard one of them exclaim.

"Here he is, Sergeant," another called.

We all plunged forward then and ran to the spot, and the sight that met our eyes in the yellow circle of lantern light was one that made me turn aside into the brush and vomit.

The savages had come upon Powers, literally, with his breeches down, and had buried a tomahawk in the back of his neck, half-severing his head from his shoulders. He had never had a chance to cry out, and I think it likely that he never knew what struck him. His scalp was gone, and the top of his skull was a horrible, grisly mass that gleamed redly in the lantern light.

We carried his body back into camp, being met on the way by the officer of the day and another picket. There we laid him out as decently as we could for burial in the morning and returned to our posts.

The tomahawk that had been flung at me I found, and kept as a grisly souvenir, but for the rest of my tour of duty, although the guards were immediately doubled, allowing two men to a post instead of one, I could not help starting at the slightest rustle of a leaf in the underbrush or flutter of a twig in the trees overhead. The slightest sound, then and for a long time afterwards, set my stomach to jumping nervously and my scalp to prickling. Nor could I rid myself, however much I sought to reassure my conscience, of the depressing feeling that I had, in some way, been responsible for Powers' death.

☆

☆   ☆

THIS WAS THE FIRST of a series of such occurrences. Thereafter, scarcely a day passed but what one, sometimes two, sometimes three or more men straggled or went into the bushes to relieve themselves, in spite of strict orders and the horrible warnings, and paid for their carelessness with their lives. Day after day we pushed deeper into the dark forests, over the long, steep ridges which draw this country into long, irregular folds, crossing great swamps, fording rushing rivers, struggling through tangled thickets; and each day there was increased evidence that, though not more than three or four times did we catch sight of them, the eyes of the enemy were constantly upon us.

We marched on the nineteenth, the work party having completed their road construction, over the great mountain, and beyond through wild and tangled, tumbled country—so rocky that there was scarce earth enough upon it to drive a tent peg and no water whatever—nine miles to the ground called Bear Camp, for the reason that when the work party was preparing the ground they had surprised a family of bears feasting upon the berries which grew there in abundance. This was our longest day's march thus far, and it was seven in the evening before we reached our ground.

We rested here two days, while the work parties labored on the road ahead. Another scalping, that of a man in the Forty-eighth, occurred here which might have been prevented, for it was carried on in daylight within plain sight of one of the outer sentries. But he had neglected to draw his charge for some time. His powder was damp and his musket missed fire, so that he could only stand and watch the horrible butchery take place before his eyes.

The result of this was an order that all pickets were always to load afresh when they went on duty, taking particular care to save the ball thus drawn, which the commanding officers of the companies were to see returned to the train for melting and recasting.

At the same time the Articles of War were read over to the men, the regulations calling for the frequent repeating of them, and particular emphasis was placed upon that article relating to the alarming of camps, the recent murders having roused in the sentries a tendency to fire wildly at the least disturbance in the brush, thus keeping the camp in a state of constant nervous tension.

Further orders were that the subalterns' detachments on the flanks during the march were in future to maintain a distance from the main body of one hundred yards, while the sergeants' outlying flank detachments were to keep always within sight of the subalterns' parties. Upon every halt, though ever so small, the men were to form two deep, face outwards and stand shouldered.

Officers and sergeants were to be very attentive to the beat of the drum, some straggling having taken place through carelessness in this respect, and care was to be taken always to halt when the long roll was heard to be beat in a part of the line from which they were detached, and to march upon the beating of the long march. Further, all field officers, and officers commanding any part of the line were to be particularly careful to beat the long roll and the long march upon their halting and marching.

This last was taken as a rebuke to Sir Peter Halkett, he, as brigadier, having on several occasions during the march from the Little Crossings to Bear Camp halted the main body without beating the long roll. It was the first outward and visible sign of a coolness between Sir Peter and the General which was to end ultimately in the breaking off of speaking relations between them.

On the twenty-third we pressed on from Bear Camp over six miles of very rough road to camp at Squaws' Fort, on the hill flank overlooking the Great Crossing of the Youghiogheny, a pleasant prospect, for all its wildness, looking out over the narrow valley with the bright, shallow little river swinging in broad curves down it.

I had opportunity to observe here that Washington looked more ill and miserable than ever. As he rode into the camp his face was flushed with fever, his eyes were heavy and his mouth drawn with misery, and the pains of the flux had him bent near double in the saddle. Yet he sat his horse with dogged determination, bound not to give in to his illness until he was ordered to do so. I wondered that the General did not command him back to the second division, for it was obvious that he was unfit, for the moment, for active duty.

Three Mohocks, lean, hungry-looking savages, came into our camp here, and said that they were just come from Duquesne, and indicated that they were deserters. They brought word that some reenforcements were arrived there from Montreal, and that more were expected, but that they had been delayed by the low state of the rivers beyond the mountains, the season being very early and exceedingly dry. They said further that there were very few provisions in the fort, and that the French had been disappointed of their supplies by the dryness of the season having stopped the navigation of Buffler River.

These men the General treated with every mark of respect and made lavish presents to them, but offered no rum, which was the thing they desired most. Consequently they went off again in the night, and took with them one lazy Indian of our own scouts, who had been long suspected of disaffection. Doubtless they had been set to spy upon us, and took this means of doing so.

On the twenty-fourth we broke camp at five in the morning and at once descended through the open woods to the ford at the Great Crossings. The river here was about a hundred yards across and some three feet deep, flowing swiftly over a stony bottom, and it took some time to get the army and all the wagons over. In the course of the business it was necessary for some of the men to lay aside their arms and help, and this kept a number of us circulating back and forth between the low banks. Some of this duty fell to me, and I was not ungrateful for it, for the day was hot and the water cool upon my legs.

It was while I was thus engaged that I observed a number of provincials, among whom were several light-horse, setting up a small camp at the east side of the ford. I would have thought little of it had not Harry Owen come up to supervise certain details, looking very glum and downcast. Seeing this, I paused in my work and shouted to him.

"Ho, Harry! What goes on?"

He looked up and saw me standing by the riverbank at the edge of the stream of activity, and came over to stand beside me.

" 'Tis th' Colonel," he said, "Colonel Washington. General's orders— he's too ill to go on. He's being left here with Doctor Craik and a guard till such time as he's fitten to move again."

"And high time," I said. "I thought last night he looked too ill to be kept at duty."

"Aye," he growled, and spat into the swirling water by his side. "That's right enough. But 'tis th' devil's own luck for me."

"Why?" I asked.

"Why?" he mimicked. "Because I'm picked to command his guard, that's why!—an' like as not 'twill mean I'll miss th' fightin', though th' Colonel assures me that th' General has promised to have him fetched forward in time for any action!"

"Nonsense!" I scoffed. "I doubt there'll be a fight. The French are but weakly garrisoned. When they see the force we've brought against them, they'll give up without a struggle."

He looked at me curiously.

"Ye still believe that, d'ye?" he demanded. "After all ye've seen of Injun ways ye think 'twill be a mere matter o' marchin' up to th' fort and havin' th' Frog-eaters run away?"

I thought of Powers and frowned.

"I see what you mean," I said, "and I think I have as good cause as any to realize the dangers of the march. But we must remember that however hard they seem, these losses we suffer now are no more than mere harassments, and can have no real effect on our progress. A few must fall because of them. But the bulk of the army will come safe before the French fort, and then there can be no question of the outcome."

He shrugged.

"Aye," he said, "there lies th' rub. Ye're all o' ye so damned sure ye'll reach th' fort. What ye say is true enough—if ye reach Duquesne. But what if ye don't reach th' Ohio, eh? What then?"

"What's to prevent?" I demanded. "Ambush? You've seen how the flanks are guarded!"

"Aye," he agreed grudgingly. "I'll grant ye yer rumbelly gundiguts takes proper care on th' march, but I'll warrant ye th' savages have tricks they ain't uncorked yet, an' unless I miss my guess ye'll not find th' march straight to th' fort so easy as ye anticipate."

A hail from the opposite bank reminded me that I had duties to perform. I jumped.

"I must be going," I said, "if I'm not to be staked out for Caruthers to dance on my belly. Take care of yourself and the Colonel."

He threw me a wry grin.

"Don't let 'em do no fightin' till I ketch up with ye," he said.

"I won't," I assured him, and fell to work.

That day's march took us up again into the mountains to within a short distance of the Great Meadows. On the way we came upon the remains of an Indian camp, which our scouts told us had just been abandoned, and indeed it was easy to see that whoever had been there had but just left, for the fires were still smoking. According to our Indians about a hundred and seventy French and their red allies had lain there. That they had been there for some time was evident from the rude huts they had built and the foul condition of the camp. As a mark of defiance to us they had stripped a number of trees, which they had painted various colors, and on which they had written all kinds of threats and bravadoes and scurrilities in French.

After a march of about six miles we camped, after joining forces with the advanced party, and from this point onward we were not again separated.

Before we marched the next morning, before dawn, two men who went without the pickets were killed and scalped. But though we scoured the neighboring woods for their assailants, we could find no trace of them. During the day we marched down into the thickety hollow called the Great Meadows, past the pitiful, rotting remnants of the log stockade in which Colonel Washington had made his stand the year before. Looking upon it as we passed, I wondered not so much that he had been driven from it, but rather that he had managed to hold out for so long as he had, for the spot being commanded on almost every side by higher ground, it was possible for an enemy to shoot down into the little fort from almost every angle. A worse spot could scarcely have been found, and the only thing that I could see that might recommend it as a "charming field for an encounter" was that it was comparatively open. In my ignorance of Indian fighting I considered this an advantage, as, I daresay, did practically all of my companions in the Forty-fourth and Forty-eighth, not to mention the bulk of the regular officers and the General himself.

In this day's march we of the advanced parties had the luck to see several Indians skulking in the woods. But by our orders we were restrained from attacking them at sight and were required to halt and send back word of our discovery. By the time a detachment of light-horse, our own Indians and some volunteers had come forward to scour the woods for them they had utterly disappeared. However, their appearance had a good effect, for it placed each one of us upon his mettle to such an extent that a party of hostile Indians endeavoring to reconnoiter our camp that night with dogged persistence, was discovered and fired upon and driven off each time by the ring of outer sentinels.

At this camp a further precaution against surprise was inaugurated by sending out two captain's detachments of fifty men each, to lie the night at a distance of a half mile from camp. At daybreak the pickets advanced, while the two detachments, spread in line of skirmishers, came in. By this measure, it was believed that any Indians who had concealed themselves near the camp must be trapped between, but the parties returned without having seen any of them.

In addition to this, a reward of five pounds was offered to each soldier or Indian who would bring into camp a hostile Indian's scalp; a move calculated to offset somewhat the increasing nervousness of the men in the woods, to encourage them to greater watchfulness, and to set them to do a little scalping on their own account.

Our march the next day, June twenty-sixth, was over extremely rough roads, up through a dark forested hollow, a scant four miles, to a rocky camp site called the Rockfort, in the neighborhood of the spot where Colonel Washington had fallen upon the luckless de Jumonville the year· before; a dark prospect, overlooking a rugged mountain slope and a dark, deep cleft valley winding away to the north and west. We were told by the provincials who had been here before us and by our Indians, that we were now approaching the western side of the mountains, and that henceforth our way would be down, rather than up. Yet the ridges seemed to run as high and the valleys as deep as ever. The hills ran rounded, in snakelike curves, and ended abruptly in points, where the rivers that wound about their feet forked. Their flanks fell off abruptly, and dropped at breathless pitch into the deep, narrow valleys to climb again as sharply on the other side.

In the day's march, indeed at our very halting place, we came upon the remains of another Indian encampment in which the fires were still burning cheerfully. Here again they had marked up in triumph the number of scalps they had taken from us. Some had written their names, while others had paused to inscribe the scurrilous and indecent taunts of which they appeared so fond. We found evidence of their haste in a commission to one, the Sieur de Normanville, which we chanced to pick up beside the road.

From this camp a trail led to the mouth of Redstone Creek at the Monongahela River by a pass in the mountain flank, and as it was evident that the enemy had fled this way a detachment was sent out in pursuit. They discovered that the enemy had divided soon after leaving the Rockfort, and half had gone toward Duquesne while the others had gone toward Redstone. But they continued on the track of those that had gone toward the creek. On arrival there they found their quarry flown, though they had left behind them a small quantity of provisions of poor quality and a very large batteau, which they destroyed. Later this party joined us at the camp known as Gist's Plantation, from the fact of Christopher Gist—the trader, who had been Washington's guide on his journey to warn the French out of the territory in '53, and who was the present commander of our regiment of eight Indian scouts—having there a cabin from which he had, in former times, traded with the Indians of the region.

On the twenty-seventh we marched down over a series of rough hogbacks, six miles to Gist's, and on the following day we proceeded to the main crossing of the Youghiogheny, where we arrived in the midst of as violent a downpour of rain as I have ever experienced.

We camped that night in the wet, and our rest was made the more miserable by a series of alarms, none of which appeared, upon investigation, to have any occasion for being given, but which, nevertheless, did nothing to set our jangled nerves at rest.

As this point was one which might easily be chosen by the enemy for attack upon our lines, every care was taken in crossing the Youghiogheny the next morning. The river was about two hundred yards across and some three feet deep, with wooded banks that might well conceal an ambuscade. I will confess that as I waded across with my fellows of the advanced guard, my musket at the ready, I was conscious of a queasy feeling at the pit of my stomach, for I half expected the bushes along the farther bank to blossom out in puffs of smoke and to hear the whine of bullets about my ears.

No such thing occurred, however, and we found the far bank deserted when we climbed out upon it. Having made safe landing, then a signal was made to the main force upon the other bank, when the rest of the army began to cross.

The rain continued throughout this day, and the handling of the artillery and wagons, not to mention the pack horses, was a difficult matter. I wondered what would happen if the French should seize the opportunity to attack, for despite the canvas covers with which our firelocks were protected from the wet it was next to impossible to keep our primings dry, and often as not the wet leaked down the nipples of our guns and damped the charge itself, making it necessary to draw the piece. Either the French had the same difficulty, however, or they were unaware that we were troubled with it, for neither they nor their red friends put in an appearance. Our march did not exceed two miles this day. Because of the quantity of flour destroyed by the wet, a despatch was sent back to Colonel Dunbar for one hundred pack-horse loads of provisions, a number of beeves, and fresh flour to be sent up under the escort of one hundred men and a captain.

It was three days' march beyond this—a march that carried us over a small mountain and across a great swamp to the headwaters of Turtle Creek—when there occurred an affair that might well have brought disaster upon us but for our commander's tact and diplomacy—qualities for which he was by no means famous—and which demonstrated the difficulties with which we were faced with regard to the Indians, both our own and those hostile.

It was in the afternoon, and we were approaching the point at which we were to camp, when a ragged scattering of shots came from our rear. At once the long roll was sounded, and the army stood upon its arms for a matter of two hours, while a detachment from the rear guard went back to investigate. At the end of that time we were rewarded by the sound of a second, and more regular volley, and a few moments later a runner appeared in search of the General, every line of his face set in an expression of the gravest concern.

As a part of the advance guard it was impossible that I or my fellows could know what this was all about. We heard only the shooting, endured the long wait and heard the last volley which was fired. But the story of the event was quick to pass around the camp and bore witness to the soldiers' nervousness.

It appeared that a group of stragglers following behind our line of march, had been set upon by a party of hostile Indians. This was the first firing which we had heard. As was customary we were halted and our own Indians were sent to scour the woods in the rear, assisted by a detachment from the grenadiers of the Forty-eighth, who formed the rear guard. The grenadiers combed the woods all during the long period of waiting, and had at last seen some Indians, upon whom they opened fire, despite that fact that these Indians held up a branch and grounded their arms, which was the signal agreed upon with our own scouts to indicate friendship. That they were our own friends proved indeed to be so, and most tragic of all, the son of Monacatuca, that same son who had escaped once before to save his father's life, was slain by the volley.

By this the few Indians we had, and the only scouts upon whom we could depend in any degree—though heaven knows they were unreliable enough!—might well have been lost to us, had not the General sent for Monacatuca and the other Indians and condoled with them, making lavish presents to atone for the loss and ordering a full military funeral for the slain lad, with all the ceremony and pomp usually accorded dignitaries of the highest rank. This so impressed the Indians that rather than resenting the occurrence they were more attached to us than ever.

That same evening returned to camp three Indians and Mr. Gist, who had been persuaded with much difficulty to go forward and reconnoiter the enemy's position. These reported that, as far as could be ascertained, none of the passes between us and the fort was yet occupied, and one of the Indians brought back the scalp of a French officer who had been out hunting, and which he had taken within a half a mile of the fort. Gist, however, had had a narrow escape, having been near cut off hard by the fort by two of their Indians who had discovered his hiding place.

On the next day, which was the seventh of July, we marched by the Indian path and endeavored to cross Turtle Creek and mount the ridges beyond, which were said to lead directly to Duquesne. It was discovered, however, that the Creek flowed here between precipitous banks, over which it was impossible to drag the artillery. Consequently Sir John St. Clair was detached and sent to look for a means to cross, though why his judgment, after the errors of the past, should have been relied upon, is more than I can say. While this was about, the army camped, waiting.

The report which Sir John brought back must have been unfavorable, for in the morning we bore off to the left, at what was almost a right angle to our former course; following the line of an Indian trail, down into the valley of Long Run, and camped for the night upon an open swale between this and the winding reach of Crooked Run, within two miles of the Monongahela.

Here, toward evening, we were heartened by the arrival of Colonel Washington, sent forward at his own insistence by Colonel Dunbar with the supplies we had sent for. I chanced to be on guard duty that night where the road entered the camp, so that I was among the first to see him, and I could not but notice how haggard and worn he looked. He had wasted shockingly beneath his illness, and seemed little better than skin and bones. Indeed, so emaciated was he that it was necessary for him to ride upon a pillow to keep his bones from chafing the skin from his frame upon the saddle. Nevertheless, his eyes had lost their lackluster look and were bright with excitement as he came in, and he recognized me with a nod as he passed, a circumstance that I found somehow flattering. Owen, who rode a little distance behind him, leaned down to clap me on the shoulder in passing.

"I see ye've saved th' fightin' for them as can do it," he taunted, grinning.

"We've done what fighting's to be done," I retorted. "There's naught left for you but to ride in at the front while 'Monseer' flies out at the back."

"Aye?" he laughed, and winked. "Well, tomorrow will tell th' story. But maybe ye're right, lad, maybe ye're right."

When he spoke of tomorrow Owen voiced the thought that was in everyone's mind. That camp near the Monongahela was different from all the other camps we had made; different in a subtle, intangible sort of way. To be sure it looked the same. There was the long row of wagons down the center, their loose wheels leaning crazily this way and that, their tongues propped high in the air, with harnesses hung upon them, the wheels blocked so that they could not roll, the lights of the fires glowing redly on their boat-shaped bodies and white, weather-streaked tops. There were the small tents of the men, and the larger tents of the officers, with the lanterns gleaming yellow within and the laughter drifting out through opened flaps, into the night. There were the groups of slouching men, off-duty, about the fires; the heavy taunting laugh of some provincial as he finished telling some tale of Indian horror to set a regular's teeth on edge. There were the Indians gathered in an exclusive little knot about their own fires, with the tall buckskinned figure of George Croghan striding among them. There were the guards and pickets on duty, and the officers and non-commissioned officers of the day making their appointed rounds.

There was all this, that made it the same. And there was something else, too, that made it different, and as nearly as anyone might say this was the thought of tomorrow.

Tomorrow! A day to look forward to! Behind us lay our march; all the sweat and agony, all the horror and misery and failure, all the scorching days and bitter nights, the tortuous climbs, the precipitous descents, the weary roads, the ticks, the rattlesnakes, the vermin, the hunger, the gripings in the belly, all the pain and despondency and anxiety and bitterness and discord and disappointment and discontent. The nightmare was all but over; and like a sleeper who tosses in his sleep, dreaming yet knowing that he dreams, we were anxious for its ending.

Ahead, scarce fifteen miles, at most two short days' march, lay Duquesne. In forty-eight hours we would be before it, pinching it into its narrow triangle between the rivers, cutting it off from outside reach, tying the Frenchman's hands, battering down his wooden ramparts with our heavy guns. If he was to do anything about it, it would have to be tomorrow, else it would be too late for him to act. But whatever he might do it would be too late anyway. There was nothing we would not face rather than go back over that dreadful road. And so we thought of to-

morrow, anticipating it, looking forward to it, as a man looks forward to
the accomplishment of a last step in any given task.

There was little apparent on the surface to indicate that this was so. A
council of war was called at the General's tent, but this had been done
before. All the men were ordered to draw and fresh load their pieces, but
this was frequently done to avoid any man's letting a damp charge remain
in his musket. Nevertheless, everyone was conscious of the difference in
this and other camps we had made. At retreat, before the mounting of
the evening guard, it was read in orders that Lieutenant Colonel Gage
would march at three in the morning, accompanied by the two companies
of grenadiers, one hundred and sixty rank and file of the Forty-fourth
and Forty-eighth, Captain Gates' Independent Company, and two six-
pounders with proper guides—in all some four hundred men—to pass the
fords of the Monongahela and take post at the second to secure passage
of the river. Further instructions were passed down after supper to the
men to see to their arms and equipment, and have everything in readiness
for dress parade and inspection in the morning.

It was this last that brought the only expression of resentment that I
heard in that place.

"For Godsake!" growled Jacob Helm, "what's th' idear o' that?"

"Carn't we tyke th' bloody fort an' clean our bleedin' pieces afterwards?" Nypper Smart demanded petulantly. "Wot's th' use o' orl this
'ere spit 'n' polish orf 'ere in th' bloody woods?"

O'Hara cocked a belligerent eye at them both.

" 'Tain't for ye to be questionin'," he remarked. "But ye may learn if
ye be not told. 'Tis to make a proper impression on th' enemy—to be
showin' 'em that an army's come before 'em that does things in true
military fashion, an' that there's no use their poppin' an' spittin' at us
from behint trees, for we mean to be overrunnin' av them anyways."

His answer puzzled me, but I was to see presently what he meant.

The drums that routed us out of our blankets at two in the morning
were muffled, it seemed to me, by the darkness and the encroaching forest.
The men came grumbling to the fires, which were stirred up in order that
we might have hot rations in our bellies before we marched. By their
orange glow we fell into our places, and while our shadows danced black
and huge against the forest trees, Colonel Gage and the General made
their inspection of our ranks, stopping here or there to adjust this strap
or examine that piece or to see to a man's bayonet in his scabbard. Presently the General was satisfied, and the two officers came stalking back
up the line.

"Well, Colonel," I heard the General remark, "you understand your orders."

"Yes, sir," said Gage. "I'm to take the fords, and hold on at the second until the rest of the army comes up."

"That's right," Braddock nodded. "You'll find them at the second ford if you find them anywhere. That's the one they'll try to hold against us, for they'll have the advantage of high ground there. If you find them too strong, hold on on this side and wait for the rest of us. We can afford to take our time now. No use wasting men that we may need later on taking a ford, though I don't mind telling you I look on the fort as good as ours."

"And so do I, sir," agreed Gage.

"Well then, you'd better be off," said Braddock. "Mind you, no heroics at the ford! If they're too strong, wait."

"Right, sir," Gage replied, and an instant later we swung from the camp with the drums tap-tapping us on our way.

The first faint, gray light of dawn was creeping through the forest when, about an hour later, we stumbled down the long hill and found ourselves on the banks of the Monongahela. Straight tree trunks, that had before been like great black pillars all around us, now were gray and ghostly. Behind us the forested slope rose abruptly toward the lightening sky. Before us there was a short, steep, wooded bank, clothed in hardwood and tangled with pea vine and wild grape, and beyond that the river swept, in a great curve, in toward our feet and out again and down and away out of sight.

It was a broad stream, much wider than I had expected, for it dwarfed the Youghiogheny and was even wider than the Potomac above tidewater. In the early light of dawn its water looked cold and steely, and though it did not appear to be deep its current moved along, slow and relentless and swirling. The opposite bank was lower than that on which we stood, sloping up from a sandy shingle to a level plain, dotted with open walnut woods and broken meadowland and fringed with bushes along the river's edge. This plain was about a quarter of a mile wide, and beyond it the hills shot up again, steep and dark and wooded, toward the sky.

We halted here upon the high bank, while scouts were sent forward to reconnoiter the ford. Presently, one returned to report that there was no sign of the enemy. Colonel Gage received the report near the head of the line and as I was in the first squad, I could hear his comments plainly, as well as his orders to the company commanders who had gathered round him.

"So?" he said. "Well, we'll take no chances. Caruthers, you move your men up by skirmishers through the woods. The rest of you follow along the road, but be ready to deploy at once if the alarm is given. I doubt not they'll try to trick us into showing our strength here if they can."

The officers scattered and ran back along the line, while the first company spread out in line of skirmishers in the woods on either side of the trail and began a slow, cautious advance in the direction of the ford. It was an eerie business, this creeping through the underbrush in the half-light of the morning, and I was conscious of a tightening of my whole being, a tensing of all my muscles at the realization that now, in a few moments, I might be exchanging shots with an enemy intent on killing me as I must be intent upon killing him. The thought of what might happen to me if I missed, the memory of those twisted bodies about the burning wreckage of the cabin by the Potomac, the thought of Powers' crumpled shape, made my mouth dry and brought a hard knot to my belly.

But, for the moment, at least, as it proved, I was in no such danger, for we found the scouts' report correct. There was not a soul to be found upon our side of the ford.

On arrival at the ford two companies were promptly posted so as to cover the crossing, and a detachment was sent to pick their way across. Nothing happened, and presently the subaltern in command of the advance party signaled that the far bank was clear. Fifty men of the Forty-eighth and Forty-fourth, under Ensign Primrose Kennedy, were left upon the near bank, while the rest were ordered to fix canvas upon our pieces and prepare to cross. Those who wished were permitted to remove their breeches and gaiters, but most refused the privilege. I think O'Hara expressed the general feeling.

"Sure, wouldn't I feel foolish now," he said, "to go to fightin' in me shirttails?"

Sir John St. Clair's work party came down behind us to begin work upon the steep banks and make them passable for the wagons and heavy artillery, and as we plunged downward and stepped out into the cool water we could hear already the sound of their axes dinging on the wood.

The water, despite its turgidness, proved not deep, being in one place no more than up to our waists, and the rest, where it riffled across a stony bar, being only up to our knees. On the far bank we were given opportunity to fall out and dry ourselves as best we might, and it was about an hour before we moved on again, leaving behind us a small guard to secure this side of the ford from any threatened attack.

Our way now lay along the narrow plain between the river and the mountain, through the open walnut wood and meadow dotted with thickets of willow, hawthorn, greenbrier and elder, and here and there shaded by a towering elm. It was easy marching, and presently the sun came up from behind the hills and warmed our backs and dried our damp breeches and gaiters upon our legs. I saw now why we were to cross the river twice, for all along the eastern bank, from the point where we had come down to ford, on down to the mouth of Turtle Creek, the mountainside rose sheer and tangled at a breathless angle to a height of some six hundred feet. To build a road over the top of this ridge would have taken weeks, and to follow the riverbank upon that side would have been an impossibility.

By eight o'clock we had approached within a mile of the second ford, and here Colonel Gage dispensed with the scouts and sent the two companies of grenadiers forward, through the scattered brush toward the river's edge, in line of skirmishers. Once again, as I pressed forward through the brush, my musket held at the ready before me and one eye bent to the men on either side, I felt that dry tightening of the throat, the gathering knot in my belly. But we saw nothing of the enemy until, just as we reached the brushy riverbank, a score of naked savages flung themselves from the bushes and fled for the water.

A scattering of shots ran along our line, and I could see the white splashes where the balls struck. I was scarcely conscious of firing myself until I felt the musket kick against my shoulder, and the white puff of smoke floated across my vision. As I looked it drifted clear and I saw the Indians scrambling in the water, dropping their arms and hatchets in their haste to gain the farther bank. One man I saw had fallen, and his body was floating off peacefully on the current, turning over and over as it bumped against the stones. But the others as far as I could see, all gained the other shore in safety and disappeared in the underbrush.

We were called in then and sent back to our places in the line, while Colonel Gage called a conference of the officers. Again they were near enough for me to overhear.

"That's where we'll find them," Gage said, glancing off across the river. "Like as not those were scouts placed to warn them of our approach, and we caught 'em napping. What do you suggest, gentlemen?"

"What is there to suggest?" demanded Gates, a blocky, square-built New Yorker in his late twenties. "What we've got to do is go over there and kick 'em out, if we're to get to the Forks. I don't mind telling ye I've no stomach for the road back!"

Gage smiled thinly.

"Quite so, Captain," he agreed. "But have you no suggestions as to how it shall be done?"

Gates shrugged his heavy shoulders and shook his head.

"I'll follow your orders, Colonel."

I saw Caruthers pass his hand nervously across his mouth and glance across the river. I felt that I hardly blamed him at the moment, for it was not an inviting prospect, especially when one considered that the woods and bushes that lined the farther bank might well be filled with French and savages awaiting only the appearance of a mass of troops to open fire. A little to our right, upon the opposite side, was the mouth of Turtle Creek, between its high, steep banks. Below that, and directly opposite us, the steep hills fell back somewhat from the river's edge. Nevertheless, the bank upon the other side of the ford was high; higher than that upon which we now stood. It was thickly wooded, moreover, and afforded pretty cover for an ambuscade. Back of the first abrupt rise this bank leveled off and stretched back, rising slightly, a distance of some two hundred or more yards. Behind this the ground rose abruptly once more, under dense woods, to a second and broader shelf, beyond which the steep wooded mountainsides once more rose abruptly toward the sky. At the edge of the second rise we could make out what appeared to be a clearing and the roof of a small cabin—a cabin which I was later to discover had formerly belonged to John Frazier, and for that matter still did, though the French for the moment prevented his occupying it.

The same thought seemed to be in the minds of all the officers, for none spoke. Gage smiled his thin smile once again.

"Very well then, gentlemen," he said. "This is what I propose."

He went on to outline his plan, and this plan we presently proceeded to carry out. The detachment was divided into three small columns, while the two six-pounders, with a small supporting force were so posted as to be able to rake the brush upon the far bank at the first sign of hostile fire. Two of the three columns were detached and sent, one to cross as far upstream toward the mouth of Turtle Creek as was possible, the other to cross at a point some two hundred yards below. The third column was to wait until the heads of the first two had gained the far bank, or had drawn the enemy's fire, and was then to strike out directly across the ford under cover of the artillery. Thus it was hoped that the enemy might be induced to spread his fire sufficiently to enable us to take his position in the front. Or, if he refused to accept the bait offered by the two flanking columns, to gain the far bank with them and catch him in a vise.

It might have worked out so—I do not know—had any enemy been there to receive us. But there was none. As I waded out into the stream with the center column, despite the fact that no fire from the opposite shore had greeted either of the other two, I felt as naked and alone as the day I was born. Though there were other men in bright red coats all about me I felt as prominent as a statue, and felt sure that every rifle in the brush was aimed straight at me. But nothing happened, and with the others I stepped unharmed upon the other bank.

If I was surprised to come thus across unhindered, my surprise was nothing compared to the amazement of Colonel Gage. So astounded was he that for a moment he forgot he was an officer and addressed those of us who were around him almost as equals.

"Well!" he exclaimed. "Well, by God, now, he's missed his chance! I believe we've got them on the run. I believe we have. Mark my words, we'll be in Fort Duquesne this night, or I'm not Tom Gage!"

"Aye, sir! Aye, that we will," agreed three or four of the men.

The sound of their voices seemed to remind him of his position, for he gave them a baleful look and cleared his throat severely, after which he gave orders that we be posted advantageously to hold the ford. At the same time a ring of outposts was thrown out to guard against any possibility of surprise from the direction of the fort, a messenger was despatched to the General to inform him that we held the crossing, and we settled down to wait.

I braced myself for a long period of idleness, for if I knew aught of the army's methods of procedure it would be some time before the rest came up. In this, as it proved, I was not far wrong. Sir John St. Clair and his work party appeared within an hour, and fell to work with axe and shovel to prepare a roadway up the bank for the wagons and artillery. But the main body did not appear until eleven, and then, because the road was not yet complete it was one o'clock before they were all across. Yet, when it came, I would not have missed that moment, for I saw a sight then such as I think I shall not have the fortune to behold again in my lifetime.

It was my fortune to be posted on the bank where the road came up from the ford, and with the rest of my platoon enjoyed an unrivaled view across the plain upon the far side. Just below us the senior officers of our command took up their position, the outlying parties being left to the command of lieutenants and ensigns. There was Gage himself and Gates and Caruthers. There was Captain Dobson of the Forty-eighth and Captain Cholmondeley of the same and Captains Tatton and Hobson of the Forty-fourth and Captain-Lieutenant Smith of the artillery, who commanded our two six-pounders. So close were they that I could overhear their conversation plainly, and I will not blush to admit that I listened, though I heard little of interest until the rest of the troops appeared.

They came at a few moments before the hour of eleven, a party of light-horse in the lead, appearing suddenly out of the thickets on the far side of a broad meadow, followed by the advance guard, which was followed in its turn by the lengthening red ribbon of the main body itself, broken here and there by the white tops of the lumbering wagons.

They marched bravely and with precision, the drums rattling and banging, the fifes squealing out the *Grenadier's March,* their thin, reedy piping coming clearly to us across the intervening distance. Arms swung in unison. Each whiteclad thigh and brown-gaitered leg moved with the rest as though drawn by the same invisible string. Flags fluttered gaily in the wind, and the sun shone bright upon the rows of slanted muskets, and gleamed upon the men's buckles and the officers' gorgets. The officers' horses danced and capered to the music, and even the wagons for once seemed to catch the spirit of the thing and moved in a regular, orderly line. I saw then what O'Hara had meant by his comment of the night before. It was as though they were on parade: precise, military, powerful, a relentless, irresistible force moving determinedly against its objective; a sight that could not fail to be impressive.

"Ah, now," I heard Gage say below me, "there's something to feast your eyes upon. I hope the frog-eaters are watching from the hills!"

"Aye," agreed Gates. " 'Twill give 'em something to think about, that's certain!"

The whole long line wound out into the meadow and fell precisely aside, in long-drawn ranks to let the endless stream of wagons and the artillery pass by. Behind came the General and his staff, riding stiffly, as if in review of the troops; splendid, every one in his best and brightest uniform except Washington. I noticed with something like surprise that he was dressed in buckskins, like any common teamster, and I noted, too, that Bishop, the General's own body servant rode by his side. Below me I heard someone laugh.

"See where our buckskin General rides!" I heard one of the officers exclaim.

A general laugh greeted the sally.

"Would you believe it, gentlemen?" I heard Gage ask sneeringly, "Mr. Washington had the effrontery to suggest that all the officers discard their uniforms and dress like the men. He'd have us all dismount, too, by God!

Said we'd be less conspicuous, and less apt to be picked off in case of an action!"

"Good God!" I heard Cholmondeley gasp.

"Is the man a coward?" one of the others demanded.

"Your guess is as good as mine," Gage replied, "Though I think I should hardly go as far as that. He did offer to lead his Virginians and the Indians in advance to clear the woods of skulking Indians."

This brought another laugh.

"Much good that would do!" Caruthers remarked. "They'd run at the first fire, and leave the work for the regulars to do!"

I wondered if Gates would take exception to this, but being a New Yorker he remained silent. I imagine he felt that what was said about a Virginian could scarcely apply to him.

"I understand Colonel Halkett had some such similar proposal," someone said.

Gage chuckled.

"Aye," he said, "our gloomy Scot would have all the Highlanders drafted to beat the woods before us. The General would have none of it."

"And quite right, too!" said Caruthers sycophantically. "Where's the need to weaken our force for such nonsense. The flank parties and advance guards will be enough for the purpose, and we'll make a better showing *en masse!*"

"Well, gentlemen," said Gage, "we'd best be going over to make our report and pay our respects. Caruthers, Cholmondeley, Tatton, Smith, you stay here and keep matters in hand. Caruthers take charge. You other gentlemen, come with me."

I could hear the creak of leather and the stamp of their horses' feet below me as they mounted, and presently I saw them ride out into the ford and splash across. As I watched them go I thought of the conversation I had overheard, and wondered if there was anything to the recommendations that Washington and Halkett had made.

I was to discover the answer to that for myself presently.

☆
☆   ☆

IT HAS BECOME the fashion to cast the blame for the disaster on the banks of the Monongahela upon the shoulders of a single man. Nothing could be more unfair. The blame lies not with any one man but with all those petty politicians who, both at home and in the colonies, were so engrossed in their own squabblings that they could not recognize the larger issue of the public good; with those dishonest traders who sought to line their own pockets at the expense of the expedition, who sought to, and who did, foist off upon us rotten provisions, broken-down wagons and poor sickly, wind-broken, spavined nags to draw them, with those members of the expedition itself, officers and men alike, who could not discard their little interprovince and home-and-colony hatreds for the sake of the good of all.

I have heard it said that Braddock was a stupid man; that he was rash; that he was self-important; that he was pig-headed. It is a tendency among people, longing anxiously for a given end, to forget that public servants appointed to attain those ends are as human as themselves. They look for the qualities of angels, and when, perhaps, failure shows the man in question to be short of perfection, they are apt to seize upon and complain bitterly of faults which, in another less highly placed, they would pass off with a shrug.

As a matter of fact Edward Braddock was not stupid. Nor could it be said that he was brilliant—but then, how many among us are? He was not rash, for he took every precaution against disaster, and it was only by an odd chance, by a freak of luck, that disaster fell upon him. Neither was he self-important, as I myself can testify, who saw him both informally as a fellow guest at a London table and as a common private in the ranks. He had been given a task to accomplish, and authority far insufficient with which to accomplish it. If he was sometimes peremptory; if he made the fullest use of his authority in the conduct of his mission, it would be strange if in some eyes, particularly in those clouded with jealousy, he did not appear self-important.

But the greatest libel of all is that he was pig-headed, for had he succeeded in his mission that same characteristic, now condemned as pig-headedness, would be hailed as proper British pluck and determination! In face of obstacles which would have turned back many a less dogged man at the outset, Braddock persevered and won through almost to within sight of his goal. The wonder is not that he failed. That was a part of the bitter irony of fate. Rather is it amazing that he won as far as he did.

Braddock has been further criticized for not having followed the suggestions of Washington and Halkett. For this he has been labeled a poor soldier. He has been censured for parading his men upon the meadows at the second crossing of the Monongahela. Yet there was reason for both.

During our long march—a march impossible to accomplish in precise military order—much of the military discipline essential to the precise and unified movements of an army in action, much of the habit of obedience to officers had been relaxed. The parade upon the meadows was calculated to reawaken that habit of obedience and to remind the men that unified action was essential to success. It was also intended to impress any French or hostile savages that might be watching, with our strength.

The criticism that he ignored the suggestions of Washington and Sir Peter requires more complex refutation, yet it was precisely because he was so thoroughly a soldier that he rejected them. It must be remembered that Braddock had been forty years an officer in the army. Strategy and tactics, the art and science of war as it was fought on European battle-fields—the only battlefields on which British generals had experience—the Articles of War, the manual and the book of regulations had been his daily diet throughout those years. He had proven himself proficient in them, and it was for this that he had been chosen. In the light of war, as it was known in England, he was an able soldier.

Now, armies are made up of able soldiers; of men who have made a lifetime study of war as it has been fought in the past; of men who have demonstrated their ability to apply their knowledge to ordinary conditions of battle. They are the men who carry on wars, and who win or lose them. Occasionally an innovator appears upon the scene who introduces a new tactic or takes advantage of an extraordinary condition to win a brilliant victory, and these men, according to their success are the geniuses of military science, for it is they who keep the art of war alive and growing.

But innovators are not welcome in an army, for their theories are new and untried, and there is too great a risk of failure, and failure in a war is irreparable. For every innovator who succeeds, and gains fame, there are a dozen who fail, and gain oblivion. Consequently military men look with suspicion upon their suggestions, and reject them when it seems apparent that the orthodox will do as well. Washington and Halkett were innovators. Their suggestions were sound, but there was no reason for Braddock to believe that in his case the ordinary means would not suffice. His front was properly protected and his flanks were screened by the requisite out-parties, and there was every reason to believe that the French would attempt no resistance anyway, for he was superior in numbers, his artillery was heavier, and once he arrived before the fort he could cut them off from reenforcement at his leisure. To detach men as Washington and Halkett had suggested, and send them forward through the woods, would only be to weaken his main force by that many and to expose the individuals among them to ambush and surprise, and since there seemed no need for it, why do it?

It should be borne in mind that Contrecoeur, the French commander, also had his innovators in the persons of de Beaujeu, Dumas and de Ligneris. Contrecoeur was a veteran and had learned his tactics and military science in the same school as Braddock. We know now that he was preparing to evacuate the fort as Braddock approached. Looking upon the situation with the eyes of a military man, he recognized its hopelessness, and was prepared to withdraw with the least possible loss of life. But for innovators the game would have been played out as Braddock anticipated.

But de Beaujeu begged permission to lead out a party of volunteers and Indians to harass and check the advancing British. Observe that even the innovator, de Beaujeu, had no notion that they would be stopped completely! All he hoped to accomplish was their delay. Contrecoeur had need of a straw at which to grasp. Braddock could let his straws go floating. But Contrecoeur was desperate. So he grasped at this straw, and it turned out to be a veritable raft. But Braddock should not be blamed for what neither he nor Contrecoeur, nor anyone else, had been able to foresee.

I have said that it was one o'clock in the afternoon before the entire army was across the river. It was nearly two before we were formed for the march. The General's elation at having been allowed to cross unmolested knew no bounds, nor did he endeavor to conceal it.

"By God!" I heard him say to Sir John St. Clair, as he spurred his mount up the bank upon which I was posted, "We've got 'em now! Since they have made no attempt to oppose us here, it is unlikely that they will try to stop us between here and the fort. Mark my words, Sir John, we'll dine tomorrow in Duquesne!"

Sir John nodded dourly.

"Aye," was all he replied.

The line of our march differed little from that in which we had come thus far. The guides and six light-horse led, followed at the distance of a musket-shot by Mr. Gordon with a party of engineers, whose task it was to mark out the road as they went. Immediately behind these came the van of the advance party, composed of the two companies of grenadiers and some of the detachment from the Forty-fourth and Forty-eighth. These were followed by the balance of the advance party, comprising Captain Gates' company and the rest of the detachment of regulars. The work party under Sir John St. Clair came next, closed in the rear by the two fieldpieces, six-pounders, the rear guard, and two tumbrels full of tools. The usual flank parties filed through the woods on either hand, my own post being in the first rank of the first company of grenadiers in the lead of van, with O'Hara, as number one man in the file closers at my elbow.

There was a little interval between the advance party and the main body, which was again led by a detachment of light-horse. Behind these marched the sailors sent from the fleet to assist with the handling of the guns, followed by the vanguard, a section of the artillery, the wagons, flanked on either hand by the main body of infantry, the rest of the artillery, the second portion of the vanguard and the rear guard. Because of the quantity of cattle and pack horses that were forced to march through the woods on either flank, extra heavy flank guards were thrown out on either hand.

Thus drawn up, our line extended nearly a mile from the riverbank in the rear to the six light-horsemen at the head. But even though we had taken our positions we were not yet to march. The advance party had long since eaten its noonday rations, but the main body, and the staff had not yet dined. Accordingly, we must needs stand and wait while this was done. The men of the main body stood to arms, or lolled about at their positions and munched cold rations, while a table was laid with cloth and silver, just off the line of march, near the center of which the General and his staff were fed in correct style.

This was all nearly enough as it should be. No one was impatient. The fort was now within our reach, and we had only to put out our hands and take it when we were ready. A few moments, an hour or two, more or less, could make no difference. Consequently the men of the advance party rested upon their muskets idly, chaffing one another good-naturedly, the while they waited for the others to eat. As one of these, I bore my share in it, thinking no more and no less than the rest about what the day might have in store for us beyond that point. A little ahead of us I could see Mr. Gordon, the engineer, puttering about upon the trail, marking those trees with blazes that must be taken out by Sir John and his party before the wagons could be dragged by. Behind us I could not see so far, for the van of the advance party and Sir John's detachment stretched back along the twelve-foot cut of the road to where they disappeared in a little gully. Beyond the gully, I knew the main body stood similarly drawn up. On either side of the gash sliced through the forest by Sir John's axemen the woods were thick and matted.

Dusty green leaves overhung the roadway and presented a shadowy wall to either side. By stooping and peering a little under them, one could look back into the shadowy forest a short distance. The men who made up the flanking parties, as far as visibility went, were better off than those in the road, for their vision was not distracted by the sunlit slash of the roadway. Forward, the woods seemed somewhat more open, for there no pathway, other than the footworn Indian trail, had been cut to open a contrast between the open sunlight and the shadow of the woods. Somewhere ahead, and not very far distant, if one could judge from the contour of the land as seen from the far side of the second crossing of the river, there was another gully. But from the head of the line it was impossible to see it.

This, then, was how we stood at a little after two, when the order came forward for the advance party to move forward, to march until three and then to halt once more to await the approach of the main body. Movement rippled along the line. The van came to attention, and ahead of us the detachment of engineers that had been lounging along the bank, began to fall into line. The light-horsemen in the lead prepared to swing up into the saddle. Gist and Croghan, who had been squatting among the Indians, rose and stepped into the roadway. The drummers set themselves to beat the long march. Signals went out to the flankers to prepare to move. Away up forward, beyond the light-horse, the engineer, Gordon, still puttered about with his instruments, fussing over the lie of the road like a precise old maid.

Looking ahead in the interval, waiting for the order to march, I thought I made out a movement in the forest beyond where Gordon stood. Others must have seen it, too, for I was conscious of a stiffening all around me; a sudden sharpening of attention. Then Gordon himself saw it, and his shout of warning rang as he turned and scurried toward us. At the same instant the movement I beheld beyond him became no longer nebulous and indistinct, but took form and direction. I could see the shadowy shapes of Indians, hundreds of them, it seemed, flitting through the trees toward us. And I could make out, too, a more compact body of whiteclad men, and a tall Frenchman, dressed like an Indian in white buckskin leggings, at their head. I could see the sun glint for an instant upon the silver gorget at his breast, marking him as an officer, as he turned and waved, left and right with his hat.

I have heard the strategy of that day described; how the French, coming unexpectedly upon the British whom they hoped to catch at the ford, were first to recover from their surprise; how they split and thrust their lines down either side of the British line, like the two tines of a fork; how they trapped the British in the long, tunneled tomb of their own making. I know nothing of that. I know only what my eyes saw and my ears heard and my senses felt on that day of horror. At the one moment I was looking back a little sheepishly to the dread and queasiness with which I had approached the two fords, and hoping, now that I was again secure and all prospect of action was past, that none of my companions had observed my nervousness. In the next I was in the midst of battle; in the crash and horror, in the fighting and the dying, in the shooting and the running and the desperate fear and the turning to stand and fight again for one's life, and I had no time to think about it.

When the French officer waved his hat it was as though he had waved a wand; as though the earth opened. Instantly the disorderly band of flitting savage-shadows disappeared as if the woods had swallowed them. It was uncanny, almost ghostly. At one moment they were there, coming toward us, a horde of weaving, leaping, silent figures, paint-daubed and streaked like the figures in a nightmare. In the next they were gone, and the woods seemed empty, save for the compact mass of French regulars and militia who continued to run toward us, close grouped but without semblance of military order.

That was the last most of us saw of the Indians, though we were given ample reason to know that they were there. The signal that sent them skulking into the underbrush was also the signal for them to break their silence, and at once the forest rang with their wild, blood-chilling yells. If we could not see them we could hear them as they went whooping through the cover left and right. And we were presently to feel them.

For the moment, however, the advantage was with us. It would be difficult to say whether we or the French were the more surprised at the abruptness of the meeting, but we, at least, were first to open fire. The light-horse and our Indians flung themselves to either side, and sought to weave their way back through the underbrush on either hand, out of the line of fire. The party of engineers went down upon one knee and fired in unison along the cut of the road.

In the confines of the wood the crash was deafening, and through the rifts in the smoke that eddied up among the leaves I could see the French recoil. Some fell, almost soundlessly it seemed, their knees buckling slowly beneath them, their bodies pitching forward into the soft leaf mold. Others turned to flee. The rest, urged by the officer in the white leggings, began to deploy in the woods, but unlike the Indians they remained visible to us. I could feel someone tugging at my sleeve, and looked to find O'Hara urging me back, and all at once realized that the company, indeed, the entire advance party and the work party behind were endeavoring to form platoon front in the road and in the wood on either hand, at the same time falling back upon the two fieldpieces in the rear.

"Fall in! Fall in there!" O'Hara was bellowing.

He gave me a push that sent me on my way and moved on to the next man and the next and the next, punching, shoving, urging action. Caruthers, too, was among the men, as were Tatton and Hobson and Cholmondeley and the other officers. There was no time to think; only to act, and here the habit of obedience, the military discipline, told. The stumps, the brush, the trees that had been cut and laid beside the road, hampered our movements. But we fell back in fairly good order, and in a moment the guns were clear. I saw the gunners ram home their charges; saw the match applied.

Almost in unison the guns thundered—"Baam—blaam!", and I could feel the shock against my eardrums. The bushes by the roadside dipped and bent as in a sudden, gusty wind, and dust stirred up from the roadway to mingle with the smoke. Leaves and twigs fluttered down, and over the ringing in my ears I could hear the whine of the grapeshot as it thwacked and ricocheted from the trees ahead.

For an instant even the whoops of the Indians seemed stilled. In the silence we could hear the voices of the French officers raised in a note of urgency, haranguing their men, trying to rally them. A rising spatter of shots was beginning to sound on the left. I could see no sign of the tall officer in the white buckskin leggings. But two others appeared to have taken his place.

I am not conscious to this day of having heard the command to fire. I remember only the thud of the musket against my shoulder, and the crash as the whole of our front erupted smoke and flame. Simultaneously the two fieldpieces blasted again down the roadway, and again the bushes swayed, and the air was filled with acrid, eye-smarting gun smoke. I remember dropping to one knee, while I automatically loaded my piece, and the rear rank fired above our heads. Again the six-pounders spoke, and again in the silence we could hear the voices of the French officers raised, frantically urging their men to the front.

There was a note in their voices that brought the cheers to our throats. But even as we shouted the woods before us and to the left belched smoke and flame. I heard the angry snarl of bullets in the air above me, for I was fortunately yet crouched, awaiting the fire of the third rank. Nevertheless, something jerked at my tall grenadier's cap, lifting it from my head with violence and flinging it, I don't know where, behind me. I saw Corporal Flanagan jerk erect, his head back, his hands clenched over his face, to turn and fall slowly on his side. Behind me a man pitched forward across the butt of my musket, twisting as he fell, so that I could see the dazed look upon his face and the bright blood bubbling from his mouth. The third rank, which had been preparing to fire, seemed suddenly seized with belly cramps, for all along the line men doubled up and slid forward, encumbering those in front with their bodies.

My recollection of the rest of that day is a confused blur of crashing gunfire, of an acrid, stinging fog of smoke, of running and shouting, of savage yells, of screams of fear and panic, of loading and firing, and firing and loading again, all jumbled together to form the back-ground for a few brief, flashing pictures that stand out amid the pandemonium as lightning flickers from among the thunderheads.

That fire from the woods, beginning first upon the left and then continuing upon the right, was not, like ours, a volley followed by a pause and another volley. Rather it was continuous, and it was this, I think, that did the most damage, for we knew not how to meet it.

Long enough to return two crashing volleys, we stood it; volleys that went smashing through the leaves and scarred the tree trunks, but had no other visible effect. Not a single enemy was in sight now, and yet that terrible fire continued to pour upon us from either flank. Half—no, more than half—of the first two companies were down, and others were falling all around us like flies. Every man about the guns was gone. We could not step without setting foot upon a comrade. Above the crash of gunfire the air was filled with the cries of the wounded and the whoops of the Indians in the brush upon our flanks. Those of us that were left milled helplessly in the road for an instant, and then, as if by common consent began to move back, loading and firing now aimlessly into the bushes.

Officers and noncommissioned officers were among us, using fists and swords to try and whip us into line, but how could we form line, when we knew not which way to face? I remember O'Hara seizing me by the shoulder and whirling me about, his mouth close against my ear.

"Form up! Form up!" he yelled.

"In God's name, how?" I remember demanding, but he was already turned away from me and was snatching at others, trying to yank them together into some semblance of a line.

The officers on their horses made conspicuous targets, and I saw Captain Tatton bend in his saddle and pitch forward, while his mount bolted. Captain Caruthers was still up, however, and I could see his sword rising and falling as he beat the flanks in an effort to make the men form ranks.

All at once the road seemed to become even more congested, and I saw Colonel Burton's lean form towering above the heads of the panicked mob. Behind him a little was Braddock, his face purple, his mouth open and yelling unheard curses as he whipped at the dense packed mass with the flat of his sword, his napkin still tucked under his chin. Even as I caught sight of him I saw his horse plunge and go down; saw Burton turn and dismount and help him extricate himself from the tangle of his saddle; saw him mount again on Burton's horse and ride down a group of men who were attempting to take cover behind the trees that lined the side of the road and fire from their shelter. I saw the bright blade flash in the air and the General's face twist in anger; saw the men throw up their arms to protect themselves; saw them scurry back into the road, while others, farther along, ran to the trees. All at once I realized vaguely that the advance party had, without realizing it, fallen back upon the main body which was coming up to help, and that we were all tangled hopelessly in the roadway.

I have heard it said since the battle, by fireside strategists that had we been allowed to fight behind trees as did a few of the Virginians who broke from the roadway and scattered in the woods upon the flanks, there would have been a different story to tell of that day. But I doubt it. We were trapped, the bulk of us, in the open cut in the forest, and the enemy was all around. What shelter is a tree whose every side is exposed to fire from an invisible enemy?

What became of our flanking parties I do not know. Doubtless most were killed. Some were driven in upon the rest of us, for I saw faces in the roadway that had been detached to flank duty. Probably some fell before our own fire in those first devastating volleys that we had poured out into the forest. In the smoke and in the shadow it was impossible to tell friend from foe, if, indeed, we saw any foe at all. I could not swear to it. Beyond a few painted savages who leapt defiantly into the road behind us to snatch a bloody scalp and disappear as quickly again into the thickets, I saw none that I could positively identify as enemies after that first glimpse of them before us in the forest.

Once a volley rang out above the scattered firing on our left, and we could see vague figures flitting through the smoke from tree to tree. Instantly we poured a volley upon them, but they turned out to be our own men, Virginians under Colonel Washington who had attempted to adopt the enemy's own tactics. In the smoke of our own volley I recognized the tall thin form of the Colonel as he bounded back toward us through the thickets, and withheld the shot that might have cut him down.

Oddly enough the various units and companies were not yet all broken and mixed together. What was left of the first company was still huddled in a single group, with a few strange faces, frightened and powder-blackened, to be sure, among us. Perhaps there is something about a familiar face in disaster that makes it a sort of landmark to rally upon. At any rate it was so, and we were close bunched near the head, now become the tail, of the army. I could not see Caruthers anywhere, nor could I see his horse, but I doubted not, if I thought of it at all, that he was there for, whatever he was, he was no coward.

Thus far I had come untouched through the worst, and I was no longer aware of the singing death about me. Almost, I think, I was beginning to recover from the first access of panic, when something caught me behind the left shoulder and sent me spinning to the ground.

I was conscious of no immediate pain; only the sudden numbing blow that was impossible to stand against. And as I fell I remember thinking, with a sense of surprise, that that shot had not come from either side of the roadway, but rather had been fired behind me. I turned as I went down, looking back, and saw Nypper Smart staring at me with a smirk of evil satisfaction upon his features, and the smoking musket dropping from his shoulder.

Yet even as I looked I saw O'Hara come beside him and place the muzzle of his musket beneath his armpit. I saw O'Hara's grim face twist as he pulled the trigger; saw the white smoke blossom underneath the Nypper's arm, as though a bag of flour had there been abruptly bursted; saw the look of surprise and horror as it spread upon the cockney's face and his knees gave way beneath him; saw the movement of O'Hara's lips, cursing him as he fell. Then abruptly a mass of men swirled in between us and I lost sight of the big Irishman.

I did not stay down. I was conscious and the memory of the horrors I had seen in the road behind us spurred me up. At once, as I did so I could feel the wound; the agonizing tearing of the flesh, the warm, sticky blood as it flowed down back and side beneath my sweat-soaked coat.

I got to my feet, my left arm hanging useless, and stumbled a few paces after my companions, who had already drawn a little distance away. As I did so a hand reached up from the ground before me and clutched my thigh.

"Trent!" a weak voice gasped. "Trent, in God's name!"

I looked down and saw Gerald Caruthers there beside me, his once immaculate breeches now smeared red and soaked with blood. It was impossible to tell where he was shot, but it appeared to be in the groin, and quite unconsciously I stooped to help him up.

Even as I did so a naked, paint-daubed figure sprang from the edge of the wood and bounded toward us. Caruthers screamed and tried to stand, but slipped and fell so that I was standing astride his body. The Indian's tomahawk was whirled high for the stroke, as he leaped toward us. I had no weapon for defense, for I had dropped my own musket when I fell. Instinctively I crouched across Caruthers body and flung up my good arm to protect my head as best I could. At the same instant a bright bayonet drove in past me and impaled the painted body, just in the belly, where the ribs converge to form a V inverted.

The blade seemed to shorten before my eyes in the dark skin. The wild whoop of triumph choked off to become a grunt of mingled pain and astonishment. The arm that wielded the tomahawk went slack and the weapon flipped harmlessly into the bushes. At the same time I felt rather than saw O'Hara's bulk drive on over us, thrusting the sagging savage back upon the end of his musket. The dark legs collapsed and the Indian went over on his back. O'Hara calmly set foot upon his chest and wrenched his weapon free. Fascinated, I watched the red blood well up from the hole it left in little, sparkling ruby bubbles. In the next moment O'Hara was at my elbow, tugging at my good arm.

"Come out av this!" he was saying. "Come out av it, before another comes."

"Wait, Jack!" I cried, hanging back.

"Wait?" he demanded astonished. "What—"

" 'Tis the Captain," I said in desperate haste. "See! He cannot walk!"

O'Hara turned back and dropped my arm.

"Why, so it is!" he remarked.

Apparently he no more thought twice about it than had I, for he shifted his musket to his right hand and bent down with his left extended.

"Easy does it, sir," he said. "Put yer arm across me shoulder, so! Gintleman, get ye around t'other side an' support him with yer good arrum!"

I did as he bade and between us we raised Caruthers and carried him, for his legs would not support him, back to where the rest were still milling in the smoke and flash of battle.

I was not conscious that we had come so far back, yet we must have done so, for suddenly there was a wagon, and then another and another, standing abandoned in the middle of the road, its traces cut, its harness dangling, its horses gone. Here and there, above the *mêlée* I could see a drover trying to turn his team about and save his wagon as well as himself. But it was only here and there. Most of them had already fled and left their wagons where they stood.

As we came among them I stumbled, and O'Hara cursed.

"Damn!" I heard him mutter. "It needs a whole man. Trint, ye're in no case to be carryin' wounded. Get ye to th' rear. Here, I'll find a helper with th' Captain."

Before I could reply, for I was dizzy now, and my reactions were not so prompt as they might be, he raised his voice and shouted.

"Helm, there! Hey, Helm, lend a hand here!"

I looked up and for an instant caught sight of the great, taffy-headed Marylander, his little eyes wild with fright, his face white as death. But it was only for an instant. Before O'Hara could call to him again he had turned, back toward the river and taken to his heels, plunging away among his hurrying fellows, to be swallowed up in a moment in the throng.

"Why th' damned bastard!" O'Hara swore. "What th'—"

"Wait, Jack!" I cried, "here's the very thing!"

It was Dan Morgan I had caught sight of, whipping his team about in the narrow roadway, laying right and left of him with his long black-snake whip in the effort to clear the road sufficiently to allow him to bring his high-topped wagon about. He was just succeeding as I caught sight of him.

"Fetch him to the wagon, Jack!" I shouted, and left to him the burden of helping the wounded officer to the tailboard, the while I ran forward and grasped at the horses' bridles. Morgan's arm swung back with the whip and the team reared, but he did not strike when he saw who it was. I saw that there was blood on his neck and blood streaming from his mouth, and it was only later that I discovered that a ball had pierced the fleshy part of his neck from behind, passing out through his mouth, most miraculously leaving his tongue all but untouched, missing the jugular and taking with it only a few teeth. He shouted something unintelligible at me, and I replied pointing to the back of the wagon, that we wished to put in a wounded man. He looked back, and saw O'Hara helping Caruthers up over the end, and turned back with a nod. In a moment I stepped back and released the bridle, and his whip cracked once more. The horses plunged and jumped, and in an instant the wagon was careening away toward the ford.

I turned back then to look for O'Hara, but he had already been swallowed up in the mob. We were near the center of the line now, and things were growing hot. I could see the standards of the Forty-fourth planted off to one side of the stalled train, and Colonel Halkett and a number of other officers trying to rally the men upon it. But the men streamed past in panic-stricken flight now, not heeding them. I started toward them, but even as I did so I saw Sir Peter go down abruptly. His son leaned down to lift him, as he did so he, too, was hit and crumpled, falling face down across his father's body.

A few men were kneeling in the road, firing doggedly into the bushes. A few of the Virginians and Marylanders and South Carolinians were out on the flanks trying to hold off the onslaught. Many of the regulars were trying to imitate their way of fighting behind trees, and Braddock, a little way down the road was still trying to dislodge them and send them back into the middle of the road. From where I stood, uncertain what to do next, I could see him. He was in a frenzy now, and I could hear his bawled curses as he slashed at the men, above the sound of crackling gunfire from the woods.

"God damn you, form and fight!" he bellowed. "Form on the standards and fall back on the ford! God damn you, form!"

He was no longer whipping them with the flat of his sword. Instead he was cutting and slashing and stabbing in the effort to get them out in the open where the officers might have some measure of concerted control, and the blade of his sword, as it rose and fell, was red with the blood of his own men. The horse he rode was not the same I had seen him take from Burton, and I learned later that it was the fifth he had ridden, four others having already been shot out from under him. As he rode down upon them the men would turn and protest.

"How can we fight bushes?"

"How can we fight what we cannot see?"

But I doubted if he heard them. I saw him ride down upon a tall recruit from the Forty-eighth. As he came up the man half turned and cowered against his sheltering tree trunk, raising his musket before him in self-defense. I don't know if the General thought he was going to shoot, but his blade flicked in and I saw it pass through the man's throat. At the same instant his horse reared and pawed out savagely at the air. The General's body went straight in the saddle, and then plunged forward and down.

I saw Orme make his way toward where Braddock had fallen, and at the same time found myself carried back in that direction, for the General's collapse had been the signal for a sudden break toward the rear. As we came abreast of the spot I saw Orme standing astride the fat legs, while Bishop, the general's servant, who had been detailed to stay by Washington, supported his master's body behind him. As each man passed Orme clutched at his sleeve and shouted.

"Here! lend a hand here with the General!"

But they tore themselves free of his grip and fled stumbling, with time for none but their own skins. Orme's tone changed from command to entreaty and even to bribery.

"Here, ten guineas, twenty, forty, sixty, to the man that will help here!"

But money would be no good to a dead man. The angry bullets whacking at the trees about them, snipping the leaves from the branches, dropping a man here and a man there as they went, served to remind them all that this was an unhealthy place.

As I came to him Orme snatched at my sleeve.

"Here, Trent!" he exclaimed, "at least you'll lend a hand!"

Then his eye fell upon my left arm and followed in to my shoulder and his face fell.

"You'll be no good to us with that arm," he said heavily. "You'd best get along with the rest."

"I'll stay," I said simply.

He made no reply, but gave me a quick look and then returned to the task of trying to find other volunteers. Presently we were joined by Colonel Washington, and then by George Croghan, in his buckskins, and Captain Stewart of the Light Horse.

The General was moaning where he lay, and his breath was coming in quick gasps, and he was muttering to himself. As Croghan knelt beside him he tried to raise himself.

"Go—on," he gasped. "Rally—Washington—. Who— —?"

A spasm of pain seemed to stab him in the chest, for he coughed, and the bright blood flecked his lips. All at once his eyes grew crafty and he looked around at the little knot about him. Then all at once he made an attempt to seize one of the pistols in Croghan's belt. But the big Pennsylvanian forestalled him and snatched the weapon away. He looked up at Washington.

"We'll have to find means to carry him between us," he said.

"Yes," agreed Stewart. "What about his sash?"

It was a happy thought. Between them they unwound the scarlet sash from about the General's middle. It was fully seven feet long and as wide as a blanket once folded. This they spread upon the ground and gently they laid the dying officer upon it.

"Now then!" said Croghan, straightening. "Me and Orme can take one end."

His glance fell on me.

"Can ye help Stewart an' th' Colonel on t'other?" he demanded.

"I—I'll try," I replied weakly, for I was by now beginning to feel faint.

"Take hold then," he commanded.

I bent and caught a corner, as did Washington and Stewart beside me, while Croghan and Orme stooped to catch at their end. Before Orme could straighten, however, he stumbled, coughed and fell forward on hands and knees.

"He's hit!" Washington exclaimed.

"Aye!" Croghan agreed. "A mean 'un, too."

His eye fell upon me again.

"Here you, soldier," he commanded. "You help him. We'll handle this!"

Between them they managed to raise the sash and move with it along the road, bumping it on rocks and stumps as they went, while I took a grip upon my failing senses and managed to get a shoulder under Orme's arm and stumbled on behind. It was a full moment before I became aware that Bishop was helping me upon the other side.

Three times I almost stumbled and fell under my burden, and then all at once I came up blindly against Colonel Washington's back in the road, where he had halted, near oversetting him and his burden.

"Easy you—" he began, and I was aware of his eyes upon me, though I could not well bring my own gaze into focus. It was a moment before I realized that Harry Owen was there, dismounted, in the roadway, and between them they were engaged in boosting the sagging General into his saddle.

Bishop left me at this point, and went to lead the horse, while Washington and Croghan steadied the General one on each side and Owen came back to help me with the captain.

I am a little hazy about when it was that we came to the wagon. My shoulder was throbbing by then, sending great waves of pain stabbing through my back and shoulder and down into my side and belly. Nausea seemed to affect my eyesight, and figures moved about me as if they had no legs or heads. Everything seemed a long way off and voices seemed to come from a great distance. Vaguely I remembered helping rather aimlessly to lift first Braddock and then Orme into the wagon. I could hear the General's voice mumbling monotonously. Then they were all gone, all of a sudden, Washington and Croghan and Owen and Bishop, and I was alone by the end of the wagon. I remember wondering where O'Hara was. Then the wagon lurched. I reached out my good arm and caught a dangling rope at the tail and clung to it, moving my feet mechanically as the wagon dragged me forward.

Presently I felt the ground going down under me, and in a moment I was in the water. It was good and cool around me, and in the deepest spot I lost my footing and trailed out behind like the tail of a kite. Fortunately the water revived me a little, else I would have lost my hold on the rope when we came again into the shallows on the far side. As it was, I barely managed to get my feet under me again and stagger up behind the wagon on the other bank. There the wagon halted, and I ran bump into it.

The blow sent a stab of pain wrenching through me, and I felt my knees weaken and I collapsed on the damp stones. There were men around me then, and voices. I was conscious of them, though I could not see them or even be sure that I heard all that they said.

"Th' Gener'l? Th' devil ye say!" said one, as from a great distance. "They got th' ol' bugger then?"

" 'Oo's this 'un?" came another voice from far away. "Wot's 'e doin' 'ere?"

There was a long series of mumbles, and then I heard Orme's voice above me, clear and steady.

"Here! he helped us with the General. Pass that man up here!"

I felt hands grasp me and lift me and felt others take me and draw me in over the tailboard and drop me on the straw that covered the bottom. Nearby, in the darkness I heard a heavy body roll restlessly, and a voice say, "Who would have thought it? Who would have thought it?" Then in a moment a whip cracked up forward. Beneath me the straw lurched and thumped, and all at once I knew no more.

THE MASSACRE AT FORT WILLIAM HENRY

by JAMES FENIMORE COOPER

DURING THE RAPID MOVEMENT from the block house and until the party was deeply buried in the forest, each individual was too much interested in the escape to hazard a word, even in whispers. The scout resumed his post in the advance, though his steps, after he had thrown a safe distance between himself and his enemies, were more deliberate than in their previous march, in consequence of his utter ignorance of the localities of the surrounding woods. More than once he halted to consult with his confederates, the Mohicans, pointing upward at the moon, and examining the barks of the trees with care.

When the banks of the little stream were gained, Hawkeye made another halt; and taking the moccasins from his feet, he invited Heyward and Gamut to follow his example. He then entered the water, and for near an hour they traveled in the bed of the brook, leaving no trail. The moon had already sunk into an immense pile of black clouds, which lay impending above the western horizon, when they issued from the low and devious water-course to rise again to the light and level of the sandy but wooded plain. Here the scout seemed to be once more at home, for he held on his way with the certainty and diligence of a man who moved in the security of his own knowledge. The path soon became more uneven, and the travelers could plainly perceive that the mountains drew nigher to them on each hand, and that they were, in truth, about entering one of their gorges. Suddenly, Hawkeye made a pause, and, waiting until he was joined by the whole party, he spoke, though in tones so low and cautious, that they added to the solemnity of his words, in the quiet and darkness of the place.

"It is easy to know the pathways, and to find the licks and water-courses of the wilderness," he said; "but who that saw this spot could venture to say, that a mighty army was at rest among yonder silent trees and barren mountains?"

"We are, then, at no great distance from William Henry?" said Heyward, advancing nigher to the scout.

"It is yet a long and weary path, and when and where to strike it is now our greatest difficulty. See," he said, pointing through the trees to-

From: *The Last of the Mohicans.*

ward a spot where a little basin of water reflected the stars from its placid bosom, "here is the 'bloody pond'; and I am on ground that I have not only often traveled, but over which I have fou't the enemy, from the rising to the setting sun."

"By heaven, there is a human form, and it approaches! Stand to your arms, my friend; for we know not whom we encounter."

"Qui vive?" demanded a stern, quick voice, which sounded like a challenge from another world, issuing out of that solitary and solemn place.

"What says it?" whispered the scout; "it speaks neither Indian or English."

"Qui vive?" repeated the same voice, which was quickly followed by the rattling of arms, and a menacing attitude.

"France!" cried Heyward, advancing from the shadow of the trees to the shore of the pond, within a few yards of the sentinel.

"L'où venez-vous—où allez-vous, d'aussi bonne heure?" demanded the grenadier, in the language and with the accent of a man from old France.

"Je viens de la découverte, et je vais me coucher."

"Etes-vous officer du roi?"

"Sans doute, mon camarade; me prends-tu pour un provincial! Je suis capitaine de chasseurs (Heyward well knew that the other was of a regiment in the line;) j'ai ici avec moi, les filles du commandant de la fortification. Aha! tu en as entendu parler! je les ai fait prisonnieres près de l'autre fort, et je les conduis au général."

"Ma foi! mesdames; j'en suis faché pour vous," exclaimed the young soldier, touching his cap with grace; "mais—fortune de guerre! vous trouverez notre général un brave homme, et bien poli avec les dames."

"C'est le caractère des gens de guerre," said Cora, with admirable self-possession. "Adieu, mon ami; je vous souhaiterais un devoir plus agréable à remplir."

The soldier made a low and humble acknowledgment for her civility; and Heyward adding a "Bonne nuit, mon camarade," they moved deliberately onward, leaving the sentinel pacing the banks of the silent pool, little suspecting an enemy of so much effrontery, and humming to himself those words which were recalled to his mind by the sight of women, and perhaps, by recollections of his own distant and beautiful France:

"Vive le vin, vive l'amour," etc., etc.

" 'Tis well you understood the knave!" whispered the scout, when they had gained a little distance from the place, and letting his rifle fall into the hollow of his arm again; "I soon saw that he was one of them uneasy Frenchers, and well for him it was that his speech was friendly and his wishes kind, or a place might have been found for his bones among those of his countrymen."

He was interrupted by a long and heavy groan which arose from the little basin, as though, in truth, the spirits of the departed lingered about their watery sepulcher.

"Surely it was of flesh," continued the scout; "no spirit could handle its arms so steadily."

"It was of flesh; but whether the poor fellow still belongs to this world may well be doubted," said Heyward, glancing his eyes around him, and missing Chingachgook from their little band. Another groan more faint than the former was succeeded by a heavy and sullen plunge into the water, and all was still again as if the borders of the dreary pool had never been awakened from the silence of creation. While they yet hesitated in uncertainty, the form of the Indian was seen gliding out of the thicket. As the chief rejoined them, with one hand he attached the reeking scalp of the unfortunate young Frenchman to his girdle and with the other he replaced the knife and tomahawk that had drunk his blood. He then took his wonted station, with the air of a man who believed he had done a deed of merit.

The scout dropped one end of his rifle to the earth and leaning his hands on the other, he stood musing in profound silence. Then shaking his head in a mournful manner, he muttered:

" 'Twould have been a cruel and an unhuman act for a white skin; but 'tis the gift and natur' of an Indian and I suppose it should not be denied. I could wish, though, it had befallen an accursed Mingo, rather than that gay young boy from the old countries."

"Enough!" said Heyward, apprehensive the unconscious sisters might comprehend the nature of the detention, and conquering his disgust by a train of reflections very much like that of the hunter; " 'tis done; and though better it were left undone, cannot be amended. You see, we are, too obviously, within the sentinels of the enemy; what course do you propose to follow?"

"Yes," said Hawkeye, rousing himself again; " 'tis as you say, too late to harbor further thoughts about it. Aye, the French have gathered around the fort in good earnest and we have a delicate needle to thread in passing them."

"And but little time to do it in," added Heyward, glancing his eyes upwards, towards the bank of vapor that concealed the setting moon.

"And little time to do it in!" repeated the scout. "The thing may be done in two fashions, by the help of Providence, without which it may not be done at all."

"Name them quickly, for time presses."

"One would be to dismount the gentle ones and let their beasts range the plain, by sending the Mohicans in front, we might then cut a lane through their sentries and enter the fort over the dead bodies."

"It will not do—it will not do!" interrupted the generous Heyward; "a soldier might force his way in this manner, but never with such a convoy."

" 'Twould be, indeed, a bloody path for such tender feet to wade in," returned the equally reluctant scout; "but I thought it befitting my manhood to name it. We must, then, turn in our trail and get without the line of their lookouts, when we will bend short to the west and enter the mountains; where I can hide you, so that all the devil's hounds in Montcalm's pay would be thrown off the scent for months to come."

"Let it be done and that instantly."

Further words were unnecessary; for Hawkeye, merely uttering the mandate to "follow," moved along the route by which they had just entered their present critical and even dangerous situation. Their progress, like their late dialogue, was guarded and without noise; for none knew at what moment a passing patrol, or a crouching picket of the enemy, might rise upon their path.

Hawkeye soon deviated from the line of their retreat, and striking off towards the mountains which form the western boundary of the narrow plain, he led his followers, with swift steps, deep within the shadows that were cast from their high and broken summits. The route was now painful; lying over ground ragged with rocks and intersected with ravines and their progress proportionately slow. As they gradually rose from the levels of the valleys, the thick darkness which usually precedes the approach of day began to disperse, and objects were seen in the plain and palpable colors with which they had been gifted by nature. When they issued from the stunted woods which clung to the barren sides of the mountain, upon a flat and mossy rock that formed its summit, they met the morning, as it come blushing above the green pines of a hill that lay on the opposite side of the valley of the Horican.

The scout now told the sisters to dismount; and taking the bridles from the mouths and the saddles off the backs of the jaded beasts, he turned them loose to glean a scanty subsistence among the shrubs and meager herbage of that elevated region.

"Go," he said, "and seek your food where natur' gives it to you; and beware that you become not food to ravenous wolves yourselves, among these hills."

"Have we no further need of them?" demanded Heyward.

"See and judge with your own eyes," said the scout, advancing toward the eastern brow of the mountain, whither he beckoned for the whole party to follow; "if it was as easy to look into the heart of man as it is to spy out the nakedness of Montcalm's camp from this spot, hypocrites would grow scarce and the cunning of a Mingo might prove a losing game, compared to the honesty of a Delaware."

When the travelers reached the verge of the precipices they saw, at a glance, the truth of the scout's declaration and the admirable foresight with which he had led them to their commanding station.

Directly on the shore of the lake and nearer to its western than to its eastern margin, lay the extensive ramparts and low buildings of William Henry. Two of the sweeping bastions appeared to rest on the water which washed their bases, while a deep ditch and extensive morasses guarded its other sides and angles.

But the spectacle which most concerned the young soldier was on the western bank of the lake, though quite near to its southern termination. On a strip of land, which appeared from his stand too narrow to contain such an army, but which, in truth, extended many hundreds of yards from the shores of the Horican to the base of the mountain, were to be seen the white tents and military engines of an encampment of ten thousand men. Batteries were already thrown up in their front, and even while the spectators above them were looking down, with such different emotions on a scene which lay like a map beneath their feet, the roar of artillery rose from the valley and passed off in thundering echoes along the eastern hills.

"Morning is just touching them below," said the deliberate and musing scout, "and the watchers have a mind to wake up the sleepers by the sound of cannon. We are a few hours too late! Montcalm has already filled the woods with his accursed Iroquois."

"The place is, indeed, invested," returned Duncan; "but is there no expedient by which we may enter? Capture in the works would be far preferable to falling again into the hands of roving Indians."

"See!" exclaimed the scout, unconsciously directing the attention of Cora to the quarters of her own father, "how that shot has made the stones fly from the sides of the commandant's house! Ay! These Frenchers will pull it to pieces faster than it was put together, solid and thick though it be!"

"Heyward, I sicken at the sight of danger that I cannot share," said the undaunted but anxious daughter. "Let us go to Montcalm and demand admission; he dare not deny a child the boon."

"You would scarce find the tent of the Frenchman with the hair on your head"; said the blunt scout. "If I had but one of the thousand boats which lie empty along that shore, it might be done! Ha! Here will soon be an end of the firing, for yonder comes a fog that will turn day to night and make an Indian arrow more dangerous than a molded cannon. Now, if you are equal to the work and will follow, I will make a push; for I long to get down into that camp, if it be only to scatter some Mingo dogs that I see lurking in the skirts of yonder thicket of birch."

"We are equal," said Cora, firmly; "on such an errand we will follow to any danger."

The scout turned to her with a smile of honest and cordial approbation, as he answered:

"I would I had a thousand men, of brawny limbs and quick eyes, that feared death as little as you!"

He then waved his hand for them to follow and threw himself down the steep declivity with free, but careful footsteps. Heyward assisted the sisters to descend and in a few moments they were all far down a mountain whose sides they had climbed with so much toil and pain.

The direction taken by Hawkeye soon brought the travelers to the level of the plain, nearly opposite to a sally-port in the western curtain of the fort, which lay itself at the distance of about half a mile from the point where he halted to allow Duncan to come up with his charge. In their eagerness and favored by the nature of the ground, they had anticipated the fog, which was rolling heavily down the lake, and it became necessary to pause, until the mist had wrapped the camp of the enemy in their fleecy mantle. The Mohicans profited by the delay, to steal out of the woods, and to make a survey of surrounding objects. They were followed at a little distance by the scout, with a view to profit early by their report, and to obtain some faint knowledge for himself of the more immediate localities.

In a very few moments he returned, his face reddened with vexation, while he muttered his disappointment in words of no very gentle tone.

"Here has the cunning Frenchman been posting a picket directly in our path," he said; "red skins and whites; and we shall be as likely to fall into their midst as to pass them in the fog!"

"Cannot we make a circuit to avoid the danger," asked Heyward, "and come into our path again when it is passed?"

"Who that once bends from the line of his march in a fog can tell when or how to turn to find it again! The mists of Horican are not like the curls from a peace pipe, or the smoke which settles above a mosquito fire."

He was yet speaking, when a crashing sound was heard, and a cannon-ball entered the thicket, striking the body of a sapling and rebounding to the earth, its force being much expended by previous resistance. The Indians followed instantly like busy attendants on the terrible messenger and Uncas commenced speaking earnestly and with much action, in the Delaware tongue.

Heyward perceiving that, in fact, a crisis had arrived, when acts were more required than words, placed himself between the sisters and drew them swiftly forward, keeping the dim figure of their leader in his eye. It was soon apparent that Hawkeye had not magnified the power of the fog, for before they had proceeded twenty yards, it was difficult for the different individuals of the party to distinguish each other in the vapor.

They had made their little circuit to the left and were already inclining toward the right, having, as Heyward thought, got over nearly half the distance to the friendly works, when his ears were saluted with the fierce summons, apparently within twenty feet of them, of:

"Qui va là?"

"Push on!" whispered the scout, once more bending to the left.

"Push on!" repeated Heyward; when the summons was renewed by a dozen voices, each of which seemed charged with menace.

"C'est moi," cried Duncan, dragging rather than leading those he supported swiftly onward.

"Bête!—qui?—moi!"

"Ami de la France."

"Tu m'as plus l'air d'un ennemi de la France; arrête ou pardieu je te ferai ami du diable. Non! feu, camarades, feu!"

The order was instantly obeyed and the fog was stirred by the explosion of fifty muskets. Happily, the aim was bad and the bullets cut the air in a direction a little different from that taken by the fugitives; though still so nigh them, that to the unpracticed ears of David and the two females, it appeared as if they whistled within a few inches of the organs. The outcry was renewed and the order, not only to fire again, but to pursue, was too plainly audible. When Heyward briefly explained the meaning of the words they heard, Hawkeye halted and spoke with quick decision and great firmness.

"Let us deliver our fire," he said; "they will believe it a sortie and give way, or they will wait for reinforcements."

The scheme was well conceived, but failed in its effect. The instant the French heard the pieces, it seemed as if the plain was alive with men, muskets rattling along its whole extent, from the shores of the lake to the furthest boundary of the woods.

"We shall draw their entire army upon us and bring on a general assault," said Duncan; "lead on, my friend, for your own life and ours."

The scout seemed willing to comply; but, in the hurry of the moment, and in the change of position, he had lost the direction. In vain he turned either cheek toward the light air; they felt equally cool. In this dilemma, Uncas lighted on the furrow of the cannon ball, where it had cut the ground in three adjacent ant hills.

"Give me the range!" said Hawkeye, bending to catch a glimpse of the direction, and then instantly moving onward.

Cries, oaths, voices calling to each other and the reports of muskets were now quick and incessant and, apparently, on every side of them. Suddenly a strong glare of light flashed across the scene, the fog rolled upward in thick wreaths and several cannon belched across the plain and the roar was thrown heavily back from the bellowing echoes of the mountain.

"'Tis from the fort!" exclaimed Hawkeye, turning short on his tracks; "and we, like stricken fools, were rushing to the woods, under the very knives of the Maquas."

The instant their mistake was rectified, the whole party retraced the error with the utmost diligence. Duncan willingly relinquished the support of Cora to the arm of Uncas and Cora as readily accepted the welcome assistance. Men, hot and angry in pursuit, were evidently on their footsteps, and each instant threatened their capture, if not their destruction.

"Point de quartier aux coquins!" cried an eager pursuer, who seemed to direct the operations of the enemy.

"Stand firm and be ready, my gallant 60ths!" suddenly exclaimed a voice above them; "wait to see the enemy, fire low and sweep the glacis."

"Father! Father!" exclaimed a piercing cry from out the mist; "it is I! Alice! Thy own Elsie! Spare, oh! Save your daughters!"

"Hold!" shouted the former speaker, in the awful tones of parental agony, the sound reaching even to the woods and rolling back in solemn echo. "'Tis she! God has restored me my children! Throw open the sally port; to the field, 6oths, to the field; pull not a trigger, lest ye kill my lambs! Drive off these dogs of France with your steel."

Duncan heard the grating of the rusty hinges and darting to the spot, directed by the sound, he met a long line of dark red warriors, passing swiftly toward the glacis. He knew them for his own battalion of the Royal Americans, and flying to their head, soon swept every trace of his pursuers from before the works.

For an instant, Cora and Alice had stood trembling and bewildered by this unexpected desertion; but before either had leisure for speech, or even thought, an officer of gigantic frame, whose locks were bleached with years of service, but whose air of military grandeur had been rather softened, then destroyed by time, rushed out of the body of mist and folded them to his bosom, while large scalding tears rolled down his pale and wrinkled cheeks and he exclaimed, in a peculiar accent of Scotland: "For this I thank thee, Lord! Let danger come as it will, thy servant is now prepared!"

☆
☆   ☆

A FEW SUCCEEDING DAYS were passed amid the privations, the uproar and the dangers of the siege, which was vigorously pressed by a power, against whose approaches Munro possessed no competent means of resistance.

It was in the afternoon of the fifth day of the siege and the fourth of his own service in it, that Major Heyward profited by a parley that had just been beaten, by repairing to the ramparts of one of the water bastions, to breathe the cool air from the lake and to take a survey of the progress of the siege. He was alone, if the solitary sentinel who paced the mound be excepted; for the artillerists had hastened also to profit by the temporary suspension of their arduous duties.

The scene was at once animated and still. All that pertained to nature was sweet, or simply grand; while those parts which depended on the temper and movements of man were lively and playful.

Two little spotless flags were abroad, the one on a salient angle of the fort and the other on the advanced battery of besiegers; emblems of the truce which existed, not only to the acts, but it would seem, also, to the enmity of the combatants.

Behind these again swung, heavily opening and closing in silken folds, the rival standards of England and France.

Duncan had stood in a musing attitude, contemplating this scene a few minutes, when his eyes were directed to the glacis in front of the sally port already mentioned, by the sounds of approaching footsteps. He walked to an angle of the bastion, and beheld the scout advancing, under the custody of a French officer, to the body of the fort. The countenance of Hawkeye was haggard and careworn, and his air dejected, as though he felt the deepest degradation at having fallen into the power of his enemies. He was without his favorite weapon and his arms were even bound behind him with thongs, made of the skin of a deer. The arrival of flags to cover the messengers of summons, had occurred so often of late, that when Heyward first threw his careless glance on this group, he expected to see another of the officers of the enemy, charged with a similar office, but the instant he recognized the tall person and still sturdy though downcast features of his friend the woodsman, he started with surprise, and turned to descend from the bastion into the bosom of the works.

The sounds of other voices, however, caught his attention, and for a moment caused him to forget his purpose. At the inner angle of the mound he met the sisters, walking along the parapet, in search, like himself, of air and relief from confinement. They had not met from that painful moment when he deserted them on the plain, only to assure their safety. He had parted from them worn with care and jaded with fatigue; he now saw them refreshed and blooming, though timid and anxious.

☆   ☆   ☆   ☆

The young man threw himself down the grassy steps of the bastion and moving rapidly across the parade, he was quickly in the presence of their father. Munro was pacing his narrow apartment with a disturbed air and gigantic strides as Duncan entered.

"You have anticipated my wishes, Major Heyward," he said; "I was about to request this favor."

"I am sorry to see, sir, that the messenger I so warmly recommended has returned in custody of the French! I hope there is no reason to distrust his fidelity?"

"The fidelity of 'The Long Rifle' is well known to me," returned Munro, "and is above suspicion; though his usual good fortune seems, at last, to have failed. Montcalm has got him and with the accursed politeness of his nation, he has sent him in with a doleful tale of 'knowing how I valued the fellow, he could not think of retaining him.' A jesuitical way, that, Major Duncan Heyward, of telling a man of his misfortunes!"

"But the general and his succor?"

"Did ye look to the south as ye entered and could ye not see them?" said the old soldier, laughing bitterly. "Hoot! Hoot! You're an impatient boy, sir, and cannot give the gentlemen leisure for their march!"

"They are coming then. The scout has said as much."

"When? And by what path? For the dunce has omitted to tell me this. There is a letter, it would seem, too; and that is the only agreeable part of the matter. For the customary attentions of your Marquis of Montcalm—I warrant me, Duncan, that he of Lothian would buy a dozen such marquisates—but if the news of the letter were bad, the gentility of this French monsieur would certainly compel him to let us know it."

"He keeps the letter then, while he releases the messenger?"

"Ay, that does he, and all for the sake of what you call your 'bonhommie,' I would venture, if the truth was known, the fellow's grandfather taught the noble science of dancing."

"But what says the scout? He has eyes and ears and a tongue. What verbal report does he make?"

"Oh, sir, he is not wanting in natural organs and he is free to tell all that he has seen and heard. The whole amount is this: There is a fort of his majesty's on the banks of the Hudson, called Edward, in honor of his gracious highness of York, you'll know; and it is well filled with armed men, as such a work should be."

"But was there no movement, no sign of any intention to advance to our relief?"

"There were the morning and evening parades; and when one of the provincial loons—you'll know, Duncan, you're half a Scotsman yourself—when one of them dropped his powder over his porretch, if it touched the coals, it just burned!" Then suddenly changing his bitter, ironical manner, to one more grave and thoughtful, he continued: "And yet there might, and must be, something in that letter which it would be well to know!"

"Our decision should be speedy," said Duncan, gladly availing himself of this change of humor, to press the more important objects of their interview; "I cannot conceal from you, sir, that the camp will not be much longer tenable; and I am sorry to add that things appear no better in the fort; more than half the guns are bursted."

"And how should it be otherwise? Some were fished from the bottom of the lake; some have been rusting in woods since the discovery of the country; and some were never guns at all—mere privateersmen's playthings! Do you think, sir, you can have Woolwich Warren in the midst of a wilderness, three thousand miles from Great Britain?"

"The walls are crumbling about our ears and provisions begin to fail us," continued Heyward, without regarding this new burst of indignation; "even the men show signs of discontent and alarm."

"Major Heyward," said Munro, turning to his youthful associate with the dignity of his years and superior rank; "I should have served his majesty for half a century and earned these gray hairs in vain, were I ignorant of all you say, and of the pressing nature of our circumstances; still, there is everything due to the honor of the king's arms, and something to ourselves. While there is hope of succor, this fortress will I defend, though it be done with pebbles gathered on the lake shore. It is a sight of the letter, therefore, that we want, that we may know the intentions of the man the earl of Loudon has left among us as his substitute."

"And can I be of service in the matter?"

"Sir, you can; the marquis of Montcalm has, in addition to his other civilities, invited me to a personal interview between the works and his own camp; in order, as he says, to impart some additional information. Now, I think it would not be wise to show an undue solicitude to meet him, and I would employ you, an officer of rank, as my substitute; for it would but ill comport with the honor of Scotland to let it be said one of her gentlemen was outdone in civility by a native of any other country on earth."

Without assuming the supererogatory task of entering into a discussion of the comparative merits of national courtesy, Duncan cheerfully assented to supply the place of the veteran in the approaching interview. A long and confidential communication now succeeded, during which the young man received some additional insight into his duty, from the experience and native acuteness of his commander, and then the former took his leave.

As Duncan could only act as the representative of the commandant of the fort, the ceremonies which should have accompanied a meeting between the heads of the adverse forces were, of course, dispensed with. The truce still existed, and with a roll and beat of the drum, and covered by a little white flag, Duncan left the sally port, within ten minutes after his instructions were ended. He was received by the French officers in advance with the usual formalities, and immediately accompanied to a distant marquee of the renowned soldier who led the forces of France.

The general of the enemy received the youthful messenger, surrounded by his principal officers and by a swarthy band of the native chiefs, who had followed him to the field, with the warriors of their several tribes.

Heyward paused short when, in glancing his eyes rapidly over the dark group of the latter, he beheld the malignant countenance of Magua, regarding him with the calm but sullen attention which marked the expression of that subtle savage. A slight exclamation of surprise even burst from the lips of the young man; but instantly recollecting his errand, and the presence in which he stood, he suppressed every appearance of emotion and turned to the hostile leader, who had already advanced a step to receive him.

"Monsieur," said the latter, "j'ai beaucoup de plaisir e—bah!—où est cet interprête?"

"Je crois, monsieur, qu'il ne sera pas nécessaire," Heyward modestly replied; "je parle un peu français."

"Ah! j'en suis bien aise," said Montcalm, taking Duncan familiarly by the arm and leading him deep into the marquee, a little out of earshot; "je déteste ces fripons là; on ne sait jamais sur quel pié on est avec eux. Eh, bien! monsieur," he continued, still speaking in French, "though I should have been proud of receiving your commandant, I am very happy that he has seen proper to employ an officer so distinguished, and who, I am sure, is so amiable, as yourself."

Duncan bowed low, pleased with the compliment, in spite of a most heroic determination to suffer no artifice to allure him into forgetfulness of the interest of his prince; and Montcalm, after a pause of a moment, as if to collect his thoughts, proceeded:

"Your commandant is a brave man and well qualified to repel my assault. Mais, monsieur, is it not time to begin to take more counsel of humanity and less of your courage? The one as strongly characterizes the hero as the other."

"We consider the qualities as inseparable," returned Duncan, smiling; "but while we find in the vigor of your excellency every motive to stimulate the one, we can, as yet, see no particular call for the exercise of the other."

Montcalm, in his turn, slightly bowed, but it was with the air of a man too practiced to remember the language of flattery. After musing a moment, he added:

"It is possible my glasses have deceived me, and that your works resist our cannon better than I had supposed. You know our force?"

"Our accounts vary," said Duncan, carelessly; "the highest, however, has not exceeded twenty thousand men."

The Frenchman bit his lip and fastened his eyes keenly on the other as if to read his thoughts; then, with a readiness peculiar to himself, he continued, as if assenting to the truth of an enumeration which quite doubled his army:

"It is a poor compliment to the vigilance of our soldiers, monsieur, that, do what we will, we never can conceal our numbers. If it were to be done at all, one would believe it might succeed in these woods. Though you think it too soon to listen to the call of humanity," he added, smiling archly, "I may be permitted to believe that gallantry is not forgotten by one so young as yourself. The daughters of the commandant, I learn, have passed into the fort since it was invested?"

"It is true, monsieur; but, so far from weakening our efforts, they set us an example of courage in their own fortitude. Were nothing but resolution necessary to repel so accomplished a soldier as M. de Montcalm, I would gladly trust the defense of William Henry to the elder of those ladies."

"We have a wise ordinance in our Salique laws, which says, 'The crown of France shall never degrade the lance to the distaff,'" said Montcalm, dryly, and with a little hauteur; but instantly adding, with his former frank and easy air: "As all the nobler qualities are hereditary, I can easily credit you; though, as I said before, courage has its limits and humanity must not be forgotten. I trust, monsieur, you come to treat for the surrender of the place?"

"Has your excellency found our defense so feeble as to believe the measure necessary?"

"I should be sorry to have the defense protracted in such a manner as to irritate my red friends there," continued Montcalm, glancing his eyes at the group of grave and attentive Indians, without attending to the other's question; "I find it difficult, even now, to limit them to the usages of war."

Heyward was silent; for a painful recollection of the dangers he had so recently escaped came over his mind, and recalled the images of those defenseless beings who had shared in all his sufferings.

"Ces messieurs-là," said Montcalm, following up the advantage which he conceived he had gained, "are most formidable when baffled; and it is unnecessary to tell you with what difficulty they are restrained in their anger. Eh bien, monsieur! Shall we speak of the terms?"

"I fear your excellency has been deceived as to the strength of William Henry and the resources of its garrison!"

"I have not sat down before Quebec, but an earthen work, that is defended by twenty-three hundred gallant men," was the laconic reply.

"Our mounds are earthen, certainly—nor are they seated on the rocks of Cape Diamond; but they stand on that shore which proved so destructive to Dieskau and his army. There is also a powerful force within a few hours' march of us, which we account upon as a part of our means."

"Some six or eight thousand men," returned Montcalm, with apparent indifference, "whom their leader wisely judges to be safer in their works than in the field."

It was now Heyward's turn to bite his lip with vexation, as the other so coolly alluded to a force which the young man knew to be overrated. Both mused a little while in silence, when Montcalm renewed the conversation, in a way that showed he believed the visit of his guest was solely to propose terms of capitulation. On the other hand, Heyward began to throw sundry inducements in the way of the French general, to betray the discoveries he had made through the intercepted letter. The artifice of neither, however, succeeded; and after a protracted and fruitless interview, Duncan took his leave, favorably impressed with an opinion of the courtsey and talents of the enemy's captain, but as ignorant of what he came to learn as when he arrived. Montcalm followed him as far as the entrance of the marquee, renewing his invitations to the commandant of the fort to give him an immediate meeting in the open ground between the two armies.

There they separated and Duncan returned to the advanced post of the French, accompanied as before; whence he instantly proceeded to the fort and to the quarters of his own commander.

☆

☆   ☆

Major Heyward found Munro attended only by his daughters. It seemed as if they had profited by the short truce, to devote an instant to the purest and best affections; the daughters forgetting their fears, and the veteran his cares, in the security of the moment. On this scene, Duncan, who, in his eagerness to report his arrival, had entered unannounced, stood many moments an unobserved and delighted spectator. But the quick and dancing eyes of Alice soon caught a glimpse of his figure reflected from a glass, and she sprang blushing from her father's knee, exclaiming aloud:

"Major Heyward!"

"What of the lad?" demanded her father; "I have sent him to crack a little with the Frenchman. Ha, sir, you are young and you're nimble! Away with you, ye baggage; as if there were not troubles enough for a soldier, without having his camp filled with such prattling hussies as yourself!"

Alice laughingly followed her sister, who instantly led the way from an apartment where she perceived their presence was no longer desirable.

☆   ☆   ☆   ☆

It is unnecessary to dwell upon the evasive though polite manner with which the French general had eluded every attempt of Heyward to worm from him the purport of the communication he had proposed making, or on the decided, though still polished message, by which he now gave his enemy to understand that unless he chose to receive it in person, he should not receive it at all. As Munro listened to the detail of Duncan, the excited feelings of the father gradually gave way before the obligations of his station and when the other was done, he saw before him nothing but the veteran, swelling with the wounded feelings of a soldier.

"You have said enough, Major Heyward!" exclaimed the angry old man; "enough to make a volume of commentary on French civility. Here has this gentleman invited me to a conference, and when I send him a capable substitute, for ye're all that, Duncan, though your years are but few, he answers me with a riddle."

"He may have thought less favorably of the substitute, my dear sir; and you will remember that the invitation, which he now repeats, was to the commandant of the works and not to his second."

"I will meet the Frenchman and that without fear or delay; promptly, sir, as becomes a servant of my royal master. Go, Major Heyward, and give them a flourish of the music; and send out a messenger to let them know who is coming. We will follow with a small guard, for such respect is due to one who holds the honor of his king in keeping; and hark'ee, Duncan," he added, in a half whisper, though they were alone, "it may be prudent to have some aid at hand, in case there should be treachery at the bottom of it."

The young man availed himself of this order to quit the apartment; and, as the day was fast coming to a close, he hastened without delay to make the necessary arrangements. As soon as the usual ceremonials of a military departure were observed, the veteran and his more youthful companion left the fortress, attended by the escort.

They had proceeded only a hundred yards from the works, when the little array which attended the French general to the conference was seen issuing from the hollow way which formed the bed of a brook that ran between the batteries of the besiegers and the fort. From the moment that Munro left his own works to appear in front of his enemies, his air had been grand and his step and countenance highly military.

"Speak to the boys to be watchful, sir," he said, in an undertone, to Duncan; "and to look well to their flints and steel, for one is never safe with a servant of these Louis'; at the same time, we shall show them the front of men in deep security. Ye'll understand me, Major Heyward!"

He was interrupted by the clamor of a drum from the approaching Frenchmen, which was immediately answered, when each party pushed an orderly in advance, bearing a white flag, and the wary Scotsman halted with his guard close at his back. As soon as this slight salutation had passed, Montcalm moved toward them with a quick but graceful step, baring his head to the veteran and dropping his spotless plume nearly to the earth in courtesy. Neither spoke for a few moments, each regarding the other with curious and interested eyes. Then as became his superior rank and the nature of the interview, Montcalm broke the silence. After uttering the usual words of greeting, he turned to Duncan, with a smile of recognition, speaking always in French:

"I am rejoiced, monsieur, that you have given us the pleasure of your company on this occasion. There will be no necessity to employ an ordinary interpreter; for, in your hands, I feel the same security as if I spoke your language myself."

Duncan acknowledged the compliment, when Montcalm, turning to his guard, which in imitation of that of their enemies, pressed close upon him, continued:

"En arrière, mes enfants—retirez-vous un peu."

Before Major Heyward would imitate this proof of confidence, he glanced his eyes around the plain and beheld with uneasiness the numerous dusky groups of savages, who looked out from the margin of the surrounding woods, curious spectators of the interview.

"Monsieur de Montcalm will readily acknowledge the difference in our situation," he said, with some embarrassment, pointing at the same time toward those dangerous foes, who were to be seen in almost every direction. "Were we to dismiss our guard, we should stand here at the mercy of our enemies."

"Monsieur, you have the plighted faith of 'un gentil homme Français,' for your safety," returned Montcalm, laying his hand impressively on his heart; "it should suffice."

"It shall. Fall back," Duncan added to the officer who led the escort; "fall back, sir, beyond hearing, and wait for orders."

Munro witnessed this movement with manifest uneasiness; nor did he fail to demand an instant explanation.

"Is it not our interest, sir, to betray no distrust?" retorted Duncan. "Monsieur de Montcalm pledges his word for our safety and I have ordered the men to withdraw a little, in order to prove how much we depend on his assurance."

"It may be all right, sir, but I have no overweening reliance on the faith of these marquesses, or marquis, as they call themselves. Their patents of nobility are too common to be certain that they bear the seal of true honor."

"You forget, dear sir, that we confer with an officer, distinguished alike in Europe and America for his deeds. From a soldier of his reputation we can have nothing to apprehend."

The old man made a gesture of resignation, though his rigid features still betrayed his obstinate adherence to a distrust, which he derived from a sort of hereditary contempt of his enemy, rather than for any present signs which might warrant so uncharitable a feeling. Montcalm waited patiently until this little dialogue in demi-voice was ended, when he drew nigher and opened the subject of their conference.

"I have solicited this interview from your superior, monsieur," he said, "because I believe he will allow himself to be persuaded that he has already done everything which is necessary for the honor of his prince and will now listen to the admonitions of humanity. I will forever bear testimony that his resistance has been gallant and was continued as long as there was hope."

When this opening was translated to Munro, he answered with dignity, but with sufficient courtesy:

"However I may prize such testimony from Monsieur Montcalm, it will be more valuable when it shall be better merited."

The French general smiled, as Duncan gave him the purport of this reply, and observed:

"What is now so freely accorded to approved courage may be refused to useless obstinacy. Monsieur would wish to see my camp and witness for himself our numbers and the impossibility of his resisting them with success?"

"I know that the king of France is well served," returned the unmoved Scotsman, as soon as Duncan ended his translation; "but my own royal master has as many and as faithful troops."

"Though not at hand, fortunately for us," said Montcalm, without waiting, in his ardor, for the interpreter. "There is a destiny in war, to which a brave man knows how to submit with the same courage that he faces his foes."

"Had I been conscious that Monsieur Montcalm was master of the English, I should have spared myself the trouble of so awkward a translation," said the vexed Duncan, dryly; remembering instantly his recent by-play with Munro.

"Your pardon, monsieur," rejoined the Frenchman, suffering a slight color to appear on his dark cheek. "There is a vast difference between understanding and speaking a foreign tongue; you will, therefore, please to assist me still." Then after a short pause, he added: "These hills afford us every opportunity of reconnoitering your works, messieurs, and I am possibly as well acquainted with their weak conditions as you can be yourselves."

"Ask the French general if his glasses can reach to the Hudson," said Munro, proudly; "and if he knows when and where to expect the army of Webb."

"Let General Webb be his own interpreter," returned the politic Montcalm, suddenly extending an open letter toward Munro as he spoke; "you will there learn, monsieur, that his movements are not likely to prove embarrassing to my army."

The veteran seized the offered paper, without waiting for Duncan to translate the speech and with an eagerness that betrayed how important he deemed its contents. As his eye passed hastily over the words, his countenance changed from its look of military pride to one of deep chagrin; his lip began to quiver; and suffering the paper to fall from his hand, his head dropped upon his chest, like that of a man whose hopes were withered at a single blow. Duncan caught the letter from the ground and without apology for the liberty he took, he read at a glance its cruel purpose. Their common superior, so far from encouraging them to resist, advised a speedy surrender, urging in the plainest language, as a reason, the utter impossibility of his sending a single man to their rescue.

"Here is no deception!" exclaimed Duncan, examining the billet both inside and out; "this is the signature of Webb and must be the captured letter."

"The man has betrayed me!" Munro at length bitterly exclaimed; "he has brought dishonor to the door of one where disgrace was never before known to dwell and shame has he heaped heavily on my gray hairs."

"Say not so," cried Duncan; "we are yet masters of the fort and of our honor. Let us then sell our lives at such a rate as shall make our enemies believe the purchase too dear."

"Boy, I thank thee," exclaimed the old man, rousing himself from his stupor; "you have, for once, reminded Munro of his duty. We will go back and dig our graves behind those ramparts."

"Messieurs," said Montcalm, advancing toward them a step, in general interest, "you little know Louis de St. Vèran if you believe him capable of profiting by this letter to humble brave men or to build up a dishonest reputation for himself. Listen to my terms before you leave me."

"What says the Frenchman?" demanded the veteran, sternly; "does he make a merit of having captured a scout, with a note from headquarters? Sir, he had better raise this siege, to go and sit down before Edward if he wishes to frighten his enemy with words."

Duncan explained the other's meaning.

"Monsieur de Montcalm, we will hear you," the veteran added, more calmly as Duncan ended.

"To retain the fort is now impossible," said his liberal enemy; "it is necessary to the interests of my master that it should be destroyed; but as for yourselves and your brave comrades, there is no privilege dear to a soldier that shall be denied."

"Our colors?" demanded Heyward.

"Carry them to England and show them to your king."

"Our arms?"

"Keep them; none can use them better."

"Our march; the surrender of the place?"

"Shall all be done in a way most honorable to yourselves."

Duncan now turned to explain these proposals to his commander, who heard him with amazement and a sensibility that was deeply touched by so unusual and unexpected generosity.

"Go you, Duncan," he said; "go with this marquess, as, indeed marquess he should be; go to his marquee and arrange it all. I have lived to see two things in my old age that never did I expect to behold. An Englishman afraid to support a friend and a Frenchman too honest to profit by his advantage."

So saying, the veteran again dropped his head to his chest and returned slowly toward the fort, exhibiting, by the dejection of his air, to the anxious garrison, a harbinger of evil tidings.

From the shock of this unexpected blow the haughty feelings of Munro never recovered; but from that moment there commenced a change in his determined character, which accompanied him to a speedy grave. Duncan remained to settle the terms of the capitulation. He was seen to re-enter the works during the first watches of the night and immediately after a private conference with the commandant, to leave them again. It was then openly announced that hostilities must cease— Munro having signed a treaty by which the place was to be yielded to the enemy, with the morning; the garrison to retain their arms, the colors and their baggage, and consequently, according to military opinion, their honor.

☆
☆   ☆

THE HOSTILE ARMIES, which lay in the wilds of the Horican, passed the night of the ninth of August, 1757, much in the manner they would had they encountered on the fairest field of Europe. While the conquered were still, sullen and dejected, the victors triumphed. But there are limits alike to grief and joy; and long before the watches of the morning came, the stillness of those boundless woods was only broken by a gay call from some exulting young Frenchman of the advanced pickets, or a menacing challenge from the fort, which sternly forbade the approach of any hostile footsteps before the stipulated moment. Even these occasional threatening sounds ceased to be heard in that dull hour which precedes the day, at which period a listener might have sought in vain any evidence of the presence of those armed powers that then slumbered on the shores of the "holy lake."

A very different scene presented itself within the lines of the Anglo-American army. As soon as the warning signal was given, it exhibited all the signs of a hurried and forced departure. The sullen soldiers shouldered their empty tubes and fell into their places, like men whose blood had been heated by the past contest, and who only desired the opportunity to revenge an indignity which was still wounding to their pride, concealed as it was under the observances of military etiquette. Women and children ran from place to place, some bearing the scanty remnants of their baggage and others searching in the ranks for those countenances they looked up to for protection.

Munro appeared among his silent troops firm but dejected. It was evident that the unexpected blow had struck deep into his heart, though he struggled to sustain his misfortune with the port of a man.

Duncan was touched at the quiet and impressive exhibition of his grief. He had discharged his own duty and he now pressed to the side of the old man to know in what particular he might serve him.

"My daughters," was the brief but expressive reply.

"Good heavens! Are not arrangements already made for their convenience?"

"Today I am only a soldier, Major Heyward," said the veteran. "All that you see here claim alike to be my children."

Duncan had heard enough. Without losing one of those moments which had now become so precious, he flew toward the quarters of Munro in quest of the sisters. He found them on the threshold of the low edifice, already prepared to depart, and surrounded by a clamorous and weeping assemblage of their own sex, that had gathered about the place, with a sort of instinctive consciousness that it was the point most likely to be protected. Though the cheeks of Cora were pale and her countenance anxious, she had lost none of her firmness; but the eyes of Alice were inflamed, and betrayed how long and bitterly she had wept. They both, however, received the young man with undisguised pleasure; the former, for a novelty, being the first to speak.

"The fort is lost," she said, with a melancholy smile; "though our good name, I trust, remains."

" 'Tis brighter than ever. But, dearest Miss Munro, it is time to think less of others and to make some provision for yourself. Military usage—pride—that pride on which you so much value yourself, demands that your father and I should for a little while continue with the troops. Then where to seek a proper protector for you against the confusion and chances of such a scene?"

"None is necessary," returned Cora; "who will dare to injure or insult the daughter of such a father at a time like this?"

"I would not leave you alone," continued the youth, looking about him in a hurried manner, "for the command of the best regiment in the pay of the king. Remember, our Alice is not gifted with all your firmness and God only knows the terror she might endure."

"You may be right," Cora replied, smiling again, but far more sadly than before. "Listen! Chance has already sent us a friend when he is most needed."

Duncan did listen and on the instant comprehended her meaning. The low and serious sounds of the sacred music, so well known to the eastern provinces, caught his ear, and instantly drew him to an apartment in an adjacent building, which had already been deserted by its customary tenants. There he found David, pouring out his pious feelings through the only medium in which he ever indulged.

Heyward was fain to wait until the verse was ended; when, seeing

David relieving himself from the spectacles and replacing the book, he said:

"It will be your duty to see that none dare to approach the ladies with any rude intention or to offer insult or taunt at the misfortune of their brave father. In this task you will be seconded by the domestics of their household."

"Even so."

"It is possible that the Indians and stragglers of the enemy may intrude, in which case you will remind them of the terms of the capitulation, and threaten to report their conduct to Montcalm. A word will suffice."

"If not, I have that here which shall," returned David, exhibiting his book, with an air in which meekness and confidence were singularly blended. "Here are words which, uttered, or rather thundered, with proper emphasis, and in measured time, shall quiet the most unruly temper:

"'Why rage the heathen furiously?'"

"Enough," said Heyward, interrupting the burst of his musical invocation; "we understand each other; it is time that we should now assume our respective duties."

Gamut cheerfully assented and together they sought the females. Cora received her new and somewhat extraordinary protector courteously, at least; and even the pallid features of Alice lighted again with some of their native archness as she thanked Heyward for his care. Duncan took occasion to assure them he had done the best that circumstances permitted and, as he believed, quite enough for the security of their feelings; of danger there was none. He then spoke gladly of his intention to rejoin them the moment he had led the advance a few miles toward the Hudson and immediately took his leave.

By this time the signal of departure had been given and the head of the English column was in motion. The sisters started at the sound and glancing their eyes around, they saw the white uniforms of the French grenadiers, who had already taken possession of the gates of the fort. At that moment an enormous cloud seemed to pass suddenly above their heads and looking upward, they discovered that they stood beneath the wide folds of the standard of France.

"Let us go," said Cora; "this is no longer a fit place for the children of an English officer."

Alice clung to the arm of her sister and together they left the parade, accompanied by the moving throng that surrounded them.

As they passed the gates, the French officers, who had learned their rank, bowed often and low, forbearing, however, to intrude those attentions which they saw, with particular tact, might not be agreeable.

The advance, with Heyward at its head, had already reached the defile, and was slowly disappearing, when the attention of Cora was drawn to a collection of stragglers by the sounds of contention. A truant provincial was paying the forfeit of his disobedience by being plundered of those very effects which had caused him to desert his place in the ranks. The man was of powerful frame and too avaricious to part with his goods without a struggle. Individuals from either party interfered; the one side to prevent and the other to aid in the robbery. Voices grew loud and angry and a hundred savages appeared, as it were by magic, where a dozen only had been seen a minute before. It was then that Cora saw the form of Magua gliding among his countrymen, and speaking with his fatal and artful eloquence. The mass of women and children stopped and hovered together like alarmed and fluttering birds. But the cupidity of the Indian was soon gratified and the different bodies again moved slowly onward.

The savages now fell back and seemed content to let their enemies advance without further molestation. But as the female crowd approached them, the gaudy colors of a shawl attracted the eyes of a wild and untutored Huron. He advanced to seize it without the least hesitation. The woman, more in terror than through love of the ornament, wrapped her child in the coveted article and folded both more closely to her bosom. Cora was in the act of speaking, with an intent to advise the woman to abandon the trifle, when the savage relinquished his hold on the shawl and tore the screaming infant from her arms. Abandoning everything to the greedy grasps of those around her, the mother darted, with distraction in her mien, to reclaim her child. The Indian smiled grimly and extended one hand, in sign of a willingness to exchange, while with the other he flourished the babe over his head, holding it by the feet as if to enhance the value of the ransom.

"Here—here—there—all—any—everything!" exclaimed the breathless woman, tearing the lighter articles of dress from her person with ill-directed and trembling fingers; "take all, but give me my babe!"

The savage spurned the worthless rags and perceiving that the shawl had already become a prize to another, his bantering but sullen smile changing to a gleam of ferocity, he dashed the head of the infant against a rock and cast its quivering remains to her very feet. For an instant the mother stood, like a statue of despair, looking wildly down at the unseemly object, which had so lately nestled in her bosom and smiled in her face; and then she raised her eyes and countenance toward heaven as if calling on, God to curse the perpetrator of the foul deed. She was spared the sin of such a prayer for, maddened at his disappointment, and excited at the sight of blood, the Huron mercifully drove his tomahawk into her own brain. The mother sank under the blow, and fell, grasping at her child, in death, with the same engrossing love that had caused her to cherish it when living.

At that dangerous moment, Magua placed his hands to his mouth and raised the fatal and appalling whoop. The scattered Indians started at the well-known cry, as coursers bound at the signal to quit the goal; and directly there arose such a yell along the plain and through the arches of the wood as seldom burst from human lips before. They who heard it listened with a curdling horror at the heart, little inferior to that dread which may be expected to attend the blasts of the final summons.

More than two thousand raving savages broke from the forest at the signal and threw themselves across the fatal plain with instinctive alacrity. We shall not dwell on the revolting horrors that succeeded. Death was everywhere and in his most terrific and disgusting aspects. Resistance only served to inflame the murderers, who inflicted their furious blows long after the victims were beyond the power of their resentment. The flow of blood might be likened to the outbreaking of a torrent; and as the natives became heated and maddened at the sight, many among them even kneeled to the earth and drank freely, exultingly, hellishly, of the crimson tide.

The trained bodies of the troops threw themselves quickly into solid masses, endeavoring to awe their assailants by the imposing appearance of a military front. The experiment in some measure succeeded, though far too many suffered their unloaded muskets to be torn from their hands in the vain hope of appeasing the savages.

In such a scene none had leisure to note the fleeting moments. It might have been ten minutes (it seemed an age) that the sisters had stood riveted to one spot, horror-stricken and nearly helpless. When the first blow was struck, their screaming companions had pressed upon them in a body, rendering flight impossible; and now that fear or death had scattered most, if not all, from around them, they saw no avenue open, but such as conducted to the tomahawks of their foes. On every side arose shrieks, groans, exhortations and curses. At this moment, Alice caught a glimpse of the vast form of her father, moving rapidly across the plain in the direction of the French army. He was, in truth, proceeding to Montcalm, fearless of every danger, to claim the tardy escort for which he had before conditioned. Fifty glittering axes and barbed spears were offered unheeded at his life, but the savages respected his rank and calmness, even in their fury. The dangerous weapons were brushed aside by the still nervous arm of the veteran, or fell of themselves, after menacing an act that it would seem no one had courage to perform. Fortunately, the vindictive Magua was searching for his victim in the very band the veteran had just quitted.

"Father—father—we are here!" shrieked Alice, as he passed, at no great distance, without appearing to heed them.

"Come to us, father, or we die!"

The cry was repeated and in terms and tones that might have melted a heart of stone, but it was unanswered. Once indeed the old man appeared to catch the sounds, for he paused and listened; but Alice had dropped senseless on the earth, and Cora had sunk at her side, hovering in untiring tenderness over her lifeless form. Munro shook his head in disappointment and proceeded, bent on the high duty of his station.

"Lady," said Gamut, who, helpless and useless as he was, had not yet dreamed of deserting his trust, "it is the jubilee of the devils and this is not a meet place for Christians to tarry in. Let us up and fly."

"Go," said Cora, still gazing at her unconscious sister; "save thyself. To me thou canst not be of further use."

David comprehended the unyielding character of her resolution, by the simple but expressive gesture that accompanied her words. He gazed for a moment at the dusky forms that were acting their hellish rites on every side of him and his tall person grew more erect while his chest heaved, and every feature swelled, and seemed to speak with the power of the feelings by which he was governed.

"If the Jewish boy might tame the evil spirit of Saul by the sound of his harp and the words of the sacred song, it may not be amiss," he said, "to try the potency of music here."

Then raising his voice to its highest tones, he poured out a strain so powerful as to be heard even amid the din of that bloody field. More than one savage rushed toward them, thinking to rifle the unprotected sisters of their attire and bear away their scalps; but when they found this strange and unmoved figure riveted to his post, they paused to listen. Astonishment soon changed to admiration and they passed on to other and less courageous victims, openly expressing their satisfaction at the firmness with which the white warrior sang his death song. Encouraged and deluded by his success, David exerted all his powers to extend what he believed so holy an influence. The unwonted sounds caught the ears of a distant savage, who flew raging from group to group, like one who, scorning to touch the vulgar herd, hunted for some victim more worthy of his renown. It was Magua, who uttered a yell of pleasure when he beheld his ancient prisoners again at his mercy.

"Come," he said, laying his soiled hands on the dress of Cora, "the wigwam of the Huron is still open. Is it not better than this place?"

"Away!" cried Cora, veiling her eyes from his revolting aspect.

The Indian laughed tauntingly, as he held up his reeking hand, and answered: "It is red, but it comes from white veins!"

"Monster! There is blood, oceans of blood, upon thy soul; thy spirit has moved this scene."

"Magua is a great chief!" returned the exulting savage, "will the dark-hair go to his tribe?"

"Never! Strike if thou wilt and complete thy revenge."

He hesitated a moment and then catching the light and senseless form of Alice in his arms, the subtle Indian moved swiftly across the plain toward the woods.

"Hold!" shrieked Cora, following wildly on his footsteps; "release the child! Wretch! What is't you do?"

But Magua was deaf to her voice; or, rather, he knew his power, and was determined to maintain it.

"Stay—lady—stay," called Gamut, after the unconscious Cora. "The holy charm is beginning to be felt and soon shalt thou see this horrid tumult stilled."

Perceiving that, in his turn, he was unheeded, the faithful David followed the distracted sister, raising his voice again in sacred song and sweeping the air to the measure with his long arm, in diligent accompaniment. In this manner they traversed the plain, through the flying, the wounded and the dead. The fierce Huron was, at any time, sufficient for himself and the victim that he bore; though Cora would have fallen more than once under the blows of her savage enemies, but for the extraordinary being who stalked in her rear and who now appeared to the astonished natives gifted with the protecting spirit of madness.

Magua, who knew how to avoid the more pressing dangers, and also to elude pursuit, entered the woods through a low ravine, where he quickly found the Narragansetts, which the travelers had abandoned so shortly before, awaiting his appearance, in custody of a savage as fierce and malign in his expression as himself. Laying Alice on one of the horses, he made a sign to Cora to mount the other.

Notwithstanding the horror excited by the presence of her captors, there was a present relief in escaping from the bloody scene enacting on the plain, to which Cora could not be altogether insensible. She took her seat and held forth her arms to her sister, with an entreaty and love that even the Huron could not deny. Placing Alice, then, on the same animal with Cora, he seized the bridle, and commenced his route by plunging deeper into the forest. David, perceiving that he was left alone, utterly disregarded as a subject too worthless even to destroy, threw his long limb across the saddle of the beast they had deserted, and made such progress in the pursuit as the difficulties of the path permitted.

They soon began to ascend; but as the motion had a tendency to revive the dormant faculties of her sister, the attention of Cora was too much divided between the tenderest solicitude in her behalf, and in listening to the cries which were still too audible on the plain, to note the direction in which they journeyed. When, however, they gained the flattened surface of the mountain top and approached the eastern precipice, she recognized the spot to which she had once before been led under the more friendly auspices of the scout. Here Magua suffered them to dismount; and notwithstanding their own capacity, the curiosity which seems inseparable from horror, induced them to gaze at the sickening sight below.

WOLFE AT QUEBEC
by PAUL LELAND HAWORTH

AFTER THEY HAD EMBARKED in the canoe, Barnaby paddled out into the middle of the river and then turned the bow upstream.

" 'T is a strange world we live in, Charles," he said, in a low voice, as he plied his paddle against the current. "You an' I have seen strange sights an' suffered some trials since we went with Major Washington to Fort Le Bœuf. An' yet it seems kinder natural that we should be here together. I wonder often how it'll all end. Sometimes I feel as if I could scarcely wait."

"In prison, Barnaby," said Randolph, "I gave up hope—but not for

From: *The Path of Glory.*

long. I resolved that everything must turn out well for both of us. Somehow I still feel that it will."

"Please God it may!" said Barnaby, in a half-choked voice.

For some time he paddled steadily onward between the two black blurs that hemmed the river in. Presently they came in sight of the indistinct outlines of a vessel swinging at anchor in mid-stream.

" 'T is the sloop-of-war *Hunter*," said Barnaby. " 'T was from her I started on the scout."

"Ahoy there!" boomed forth the voice of a son of Neptune. "What boat is that?"

Barnaby gave a countersign and paddled alongside. A rope ladder was lowered to them, and soon they stood upon the deck. Barnaby explained who Randolph was; and a petty officer then led the way to a cabin, where the Virginians turned in and were allowed to sleep undisturbed. Soon after day break they were astir again, and by request joined the ship's officers at breakfast. There Randolph was introduced to Captain Smith, a bluff man with the brine of the sea in his talk, to the officers under him, and to Captain John Knox òf the army, a courteous, well-read gentleman, whose *Journal* was to give later generations much of their knowledge of the campaign. In reply to interested queries, Randolph told the manner of his escape, suppressing, however, many of the details, for he feared that the story might leak through the French lines and bring trouble upon the heads of his benefactors.

"Your health, Captain Randolph!" cried Captain Smith, when the story was finished. "Why, damn my eyes, if ever I heard of such a tale!"

When the toast had been drunk, Randolph asked some questions in his turn. "I have often wondered," he said, "whether you had serious trouble in coming up the river. Last winter the French boasted that no English fleet would ever be able to get up."

"Damme, 't was not difficult!" declared Captain Smith. "When Admiral Durell drew abreast of Bic with the advance squadron, he enticed French pilots aboard; but they were little help. We could've got up without one of 'em. To be sure, there's a variation of twenty degrees between Louisburg and Quebec and some rather ticklish cross currents besides a few ledges and shoals. But we kept sounding boats always ahead and lookout men aloft to watch the color of the water, and we came through handsomely."

"Tut, tut, Captain Smith!" said Captain Knox chidingly. "You make mountains into mole-hills. As a soldier, I have the right to say that the feat was a far greater one than has so modestly been described. The

French pilots were vastly astonished at the skill of our seamen. When we neared the Traverses, which is the worst place, the pilot on the transport I was on, gasconaded at a great rate. He declared the place would be the grave of the fleet, and that what vessels escaped would have a dismal tale to tell in England. He added that he expected that the walls of Quebec would soon be decorated with our scalps.

" 'Damn your eyes, you porpuss-faced swab, you ought to be tucked up to a yard's arm for such lies!' roared old Killick, the master. 'Damn my blood, I'll take the vessel through myself!' He wouldn't let the pilot so much as say a word, but fixed the mate at the wheel, and then went to the fo'c'sle with his trumpet. The Frenchman swore we would be lost, for no ship ever presumed to attempt to pass through without a pilot. 'Ay, ay, my dear frogeater,' growled Killick, 'but I'll convince you that an Englishman can go where a Frenchman dare not show his nose.' By watching the ripple and color of the water, hang me, if he didn't bring us through without so much as touching a sandbank. The pilot then said that surely Killick had been up the river before. When he was told 'No,' he lifted hands and eyes to heaven and crossed himself the way these popish rascals have of doing, when they see something they believe is uncanny.

"This, however, was but the beginning of the notable and important services that have been rendered by Admiral Saunders and his skillful men," continued Knox. "Twice the French have endeavored to burn the fleet, but each time our Jack-tars have foiled their efforts. The last time the enemy sent down a most formidable fire-craft, which consisted of a parcel of schooners, shallops, and stages chained together. It could not have been less than a hundred fathoms in length, and was covered with grenades, old swivels, gun and pistol barrels loaded up to their muzzles, and various other devilish inventions and conbustible matters. But this attempt, like the previous one, happily miscarried, for our gallant seamen, with their usual expertness, went out in small boats, grappled the raft before it got down above a third part of the basin, towed it safe ashore, and left it at anchor to burn and sputter and explode as it would. As they were returning to their vessels I heard one sailor ask his mate: 'Damme, Jack, didst ever take hell in tow before?' "

"Ay, ay," growled Captain Smith pessimistically, "we have all done our duty this venture, but we have been unfortunate. 'British colors on every French fort, post, and garrison in America,' was the toast we drunk as we sailed out of the harbor in Louisburg; but damn my eyes, we'll have to bestir ourselves if we're to see any of it come true. This fleet can't stay in the river forever with winter coming on."

"A few days sometimes work wonders," said Randolph hopefully. "Gentlemen, let us drink to that toast now!"

And they did it, standing, though it was evident to the Virginians that the others did so with little confidence.

Half an hour later Barnaby and Randolph bade good-by to their new-found friends and entered a boat which was to carry them to the ship *Sutherland,* where Barnaby was to make his report. It was a dismal, rainy morning; but, between the gusts of rain, Randolph could see two or three miles down the river the promontory of Quebec, which he had first beheld twelve months before, and just opposite it Point Lévis, above which clouds of white cannon smoke were rising from the English batteries. Closer at hand, an indentation in the cliff wall on the northern shore marked the Foulon, while on the southern shore and somewhat above, at the mouth of the little river Etchemin, appeared the white tents of a force of English. From time to time the boat passed warships and transports, all alive with bluejackets and redcoats.

In the contemplation of these scenes Randolph was suddenly interrupted by an exclamation from Currin. "It's losin' my memory I must be," said the Irishman self-accusingly. "I have n't once before remimbered that I have a letter for you, Charles."

"A letter? from whom?"

"From Colonel Washington. I got it 'way back in June. He was expectin' us to reach Quebec, and wrote me he thought mebee I'd get a chanst to deliver it to you. He's went an' got married."

He fumbled in the fold of his hunting-shirt, and presently produced the letter and handed it to Randolph. Randolph eagerly broke the seal and read:

"MOUNT VERNON, VIRGINIA, 27 April, 1759.

"DEAR CHARLES,—I heard with great Concern of your mishap at Ticonderoga, and was much rejoiced when the welcome news came that you were only slightly wounded, had recovered, and had been sent to Quebec on Parole. I venture to believe that *you* will find *your* Stay in that City less intolerable than would some Others.

"As you have doubtless heard long ere this, we have at last, after many Disappointments, managed to master Fort Duquesne and scatter the hellish Bands who have so cruelly Harried our Borders. For a Time, owing to the Difficulties attendant upon completing a new Road, it appeared as if we would not be able to strike a Blow. When we reached Loyal Hanna within fifty Miles of the Fort, a Council of War determined that it would be inadvisable to attempt to advance further; but at this critical Juncture we learned from three Prisoners who providentially fell into our Hands that the Enemy was very weak, so we marched without Tents or Baggage, and with only a light Train of Artillery. After letting us get within a Day's March, the Enemy burned the Fort and ran away by the Light of it. We took Possession and rechristened the Place Pittsbourgh, in Honour of the Great Minister who is doing so much for the Glory of Britain. General Forbes, who was frightfully ill during most of the Campaign but persevered in spite of his Suffering, died soon after he returned to Philadelphia.

"My own Health having long been indifferent, the Enemy being at last driven from our Border, and I having been elected to the Burgesses, I concluded to retire from the Service, and did so on reaching Home. On the sixth of January I had the Happiness to be married to Mrs. Martha Custis, with whom you are acquainted. She unites with me in sending warm Regards; and we hope that when you return to Virginia, you will often honor us by your Presence at Mount Vernon.

"I am sending this in care of Lieutenant Currin in the Hope that his General will be active enough to enable him to deliver it. 'The English flag flying above Quebec' is a Toast that is frequently drunk of late. I trust that the Objects that led you and Lieutenant Currin to join the Northern Army will be soon and happily realized. Permit me to close by saying that if yet another Plantation in the County of Fairfax were to have a new Mistress this year, it would be very pleasing to

"Your warm Friend and obedient Servant,

"GEORGE WASHINGTON."

By the time Randolph had finished the letter, the boat had drawn near a ship-of-the-line with two tiers of black-muzzled guns frowning from her oaken sides and the flag of a rear-admiral of the blue flying at her masthead. Soon the Virginians were on board. The rain had not yet ceased; and a gusty northeast wind, rushing up between the cliffs that walled the river in, whistled lugubriously through the rigging and dashed the rain through the port-holes. A petty officer at once conducted them to a cabin and knocked on the door. A voice bade them enter; and, with Barnaby leading, the Virginians stepped inside.

Randolph found himself in the presence of a young officer of perhaps thirty-two, who had just risen from a table upon which lay scattered a number of maps and papers. His hair was red; his complexion sandy; his eyes blue; his nose slightly upturned; and his forehead and chin somewhat receding. A bit of black ribbon secured his hair in a queue behind; and a scarlet coat, broad of cuffs and flowing in skirt, covered his slender body, narrow shoulders, and long thin limbs. On his left arm was a band of black crepe; and about his body, in bandolier fashion, was tied the silken scarf then worn by officers for use in carrying them, when wounded, from the field. His look was that of one on whom some chronic illness had laid its insidious hand; but from his eyes shone a vigorous and enterprising soul—too strong for the frail tenement it tenanted.

When they first entered, it was evident from the droop of his shoulders and the cloud on his face that his mood was in accord with the weather outside; but when his eyes fell upon Barnaby, he seemed to brighten, and cried:

"Egad! Lieutenant Currin, I'm glad to see you back safely. After you were gone I almost reproached myself for having sent you on such a dangerous mission. But who is this you have with you?"

" 'Tis a prisoner I took by the way," said Barnaby, without blinking an eyelid.

"Indeed! But though he has on some sort of French cloak, I see that underneath he wears the uniform of a captain of our own provincial forces."

"Faith, Gineral Wolfe, there's no misleadin' you," replied Barnaby. "You're right in thinkin' he's no Frencher. To be plain, he's Captain Charles Randolph of the Sixtieth Regiment of Royal Americans, and my immediate superior officer. And yet I told the truth. I took him prisoner."

"Well, well, that is droll. But explain the riddle."

Barnaby described the meeting on the plateau, the conflict, and the sudden recognition, not neglecting in skillful asides to mention some of Randolph's services during the war.

"Wonderful! perfectly wonderful!" exclaimed the young commander in astonishment. "Why, 't is like a page from *Plutarch* or the *Æneid*. Captain Randolph, I heartily congratulate you upon your escape and am happy to meet you. I have heard your name before. Some weeks ago, through a mistake, we captured a number of high-born French ladies, whom as soon as we conveniently could we sent back under a flag to their relatives and friends. At a dinner given in their honor a number of them spoke of you and seemed very eager to learn whether you had escaped to my army."

"I have lain hidden near Quebec," said Randolph. "I did not attempt to go down the St. Lawrence as they supposed. Only a long illness has prevented my joining you sooner. But I am happy that I am here at last, and I hope that I shall be allowed to take part in the final blow for the capture of the city."

"Gad's life!" cried Wolfe delightedly, "that is the proper spirit. I like

it, I do indeed! I shall surely see that you have work to do. Having been
so lately a prisoner you would be excusable if you were somewhat chary
about making another venture so soon."

"General Wolfe," said Randolph earnestly, "Lieutenant Currin and
I saw this war begin. We were with Washington when he took Jumonville's party. If you were to search the colonies through, you could not
find two men more anxious for the capture of Quebec."

"Amen to that!" said Barnaby.

"Captain Randolph," replied Wolfe, "I had something of your story
from the ladies. I know also the wrongs suffered by Lieutenant Currin.
What you say is true, and in a manner I am not sorry it is so, for I see
that I can trust you both. Lieutenant Currin, what have you to report?"

"Gineral Wolfe," said Barnaby, "Captain Randolph an' me scoured the
plateau well-nigh to the walls of the city *an' there is but the one post.*"

"And the cliff?" demanded the general, with kindling look.

"It can be climbed. Leastways I think so. But here is Captain Randolph, who knows more of regular operations than I. Ask him."

Wolfe turned questioning eyes upon Randolph.

"My friend is much too modest," said Randolph. "I have been with
him since the beginning of the war, and I have never known his judgment in a matter of this sort to be in error in the slightest particular.
I heartily concur in his belief that a regiment or an *army* can scale the
cliff with ease. The undertaking is far less formidable than it looks. Only
the presence of a considerable force at the top could defeat the attempt.
As to the likelihood of there being such a force, I can add one important
detail which Lieutenant Currin, owing to his inability to understand
French, did not discover."

He then related in some detail the interview which the two had witnessed between Vergor and Reparti regarding the number of Vergor's
troops and Vaudreuil's countermanding Montcalm's order for a battalion
to encamp upon the plateau.

As the Virginians told their story, a look of enterprise came into the
young commander's pale face, yet with it was still mingled something of
indecision.

"Gentlemen," he said, after a pause, "I find myself in a somewhat
peculiar situation. I see from your talk that you have penetrated what I
may as well admit was a tentative plan. Under the circumstances it will
probably be safer for me to take you into my confidence fully. And yet
not one of my brigadiers nor other officers dream that I contemplate such
a stroke as you see I do. They are older than I and have lost confidence

in my abilities. Besides, they are so wedded to conventional warfare that to them such a plan would seem that of a madman."

He paused, and for a minute or two sat bowed forward wrapt in thought. Then in a measured voice he continued:

"As you may have guessed, it was not the expectation of the government that this army unaided should capture Quebec. We were to keep the enemy employed while Amherst should march northward and effect a junction with us. But Amherst, as Lieutenant Currin reports, can hardly arrive this year. The result is two alternatives: either to give up in despair and thereby bring disgrace upon English arms and discouragement to our brave ally, the king of Prussia, or alone to make a final desperate attempt to carry a position far stronger than even we had dreamed. Ten days ago I decided that operations below the town were hopeless, and transferred much of the army above it, though endeavoring to mislead the enemy as to my intentions. I hoped to make a landing at Deschambault or Pointe-aux-Trembles, but these heavy rains have detained us and have enabled the French to prepare. Our time is short. We must either strike or go. Yesterday I thought of the little cove and the path up the cliff. Captain Randolph, can you see merit in the plan?"

It was a critical moment. Randolph saw that upon the general's decision hung the fate of the campaign, perhaps of the war.

"In my estimation," he said earnestly, "the plan you suggest is the only one by which the city can be taken. As an earnest of my conviction, I ask that Lieutenant Currin and I be allowed to guide the troops who make the first attempt. The French are so accustomed to our armies doing everything by rule that they will never dream of so bold a stroke. If we gain the plateau, we shall disarrange their plans, command their communications, and force them to give us battle on equal terms. A victory will determine the fate of Quebec and of Canada, for the defenses on that side of the city are weak and cannot resist our artillery."

"Lieutenant Currin," said the general, turning to the borderer, "I want your opinion also."

"'Tis the plan an Injun or a Buckskin would try," said Barnaby eagerly. "'Tis the best plan an English gineral has thought out this war. Try it, Gineral Wolfe, an' in five days we'll be in Quebec. An' count me in on leadin' up the cliff."

A glance at the commander's face was sufficient to show that he was much impressed. Nor was this strange. A plan that he had evolved had been commended by two men who, though neither old nor high in rank, had seen much of war, and possessed souls as ardent as his own.

"Almost," he said slowly, as if to himself, "I am persuaded to make the venture. Shall I? The plan has many merits. The troops are already properly disposed, and by a feint Bougainville can be tolled up the river.

"But, great God," he cried, springing to his feet, with a wild light in his haggard face, "it will be hazardous! If I attempt it and fail, I shall be set down as the most fool-hardy officer who ever commanded a British army. I know my officers would not approve of it, and my only purpose in taking them with me yesterday was that they might know the ground should I decide to make the trail. Yet, dangerous as is the plan, I can think of none more promising. If I go back empty-handed, I shall be a ruined man. Mad, the envious said I was, when older men were passed over and I was sent out, and they will repeat it jeeringly when I come back discredited. Worse still, another failure will be added to the long list already made by Englishmen in this war. The night before I left London I swore to our great minister that Quebec should be ours. I will not go back like other unfortunate generals to be exposed to the censures and reproaches of an ignorant populace. 'Tis true that Amherst has not given us the help we were promised; 'tis true that my wretched health might serve as some excuse; but how can I go back to William Pitt and say: 'I have failed'?

"No! no! we must take the city. This plan offers our only hope, and we will try it. Gentlemen, you shall have the honor for which you ask and in addition shall serve upon my staff on the day of battle. Come weal or woe, we will make the venture. Britannia's banner shall fly above the citadel, or be trampled in the dust!"

☆
☆   ☆

It was evening of the day following. Eight bells were striking on board the *Sutherland* when a lithe young man of twenty-four, in the uniform of a naval lieutenant, climbed the ship's side and entered the cabin. "Jacky" Jervis he was called by his fellows then, but for the deeds he afterwards performed he lives in history as one of England's greatest admirals, the Earl of St. Vincent.

"Egad, Jacky," exclaimed Wolfe affectionately, springing up and grasping the lieutenant's hand, "I'm glad to see you."

"I was told that you had sent for me," said Jervis tentatively.

"Yes, Jacky, I have a commission I want some one to undertake, and I know of no one but my old schoolmate at Swindon's to whom I wish to intrust it."

"Whatever it may be, I am yours to command."

" 'Tis somewhat somber in its nature," said Wolfe soberly. "To-night we go on a desperate undertaking. In case I should fall, I want you to see that these papers come into the proper hands. One is my will; the others are notes to my relatives and friends."

He handed the papers to the lieutenant; then, after a moment's hesitation, he opened his coat and shirt and took from next his heart a little square packet, which he proceeded to open, disclosing to view the dainty miniature of a girl with luxuriant wavy hair, sweet aristocratic face, and a full round throat, about which a dark ribbon of velvet was tied in a graceful bow.

" 'Tis Miss Lowther," said Wolfe, with feeling. "She is to wed with me if I return. If I do not, my will provides that the picture is to be set in jewels to the amount of five hundred guineas and returned to her. I want you to be my messenger. 'Twould be sad to lose her, for she is sweet and good and fair, yet somehow I feel that she is not for me."

So serious was the young commander that Jervis did not attempt to make light of his forebodings as figments of the imagination. He merely said: "If you would wear an old uniform instead of this splendid new one you have on, which is certain to catch the attention of the enemy's sharp-shooters, I should think your chances for surviving were infinitely better."

" 'Tis not that I wish to appear conspicuous, Jacky," said Wolfe. "But I feel that it will encourage the men. God knows they have had enough to shake their faith in me."

"But they are loyal still, God bless them!" said Jervis, with feeling. "They would undertake to storm Hades, with you to lead them."

All was by this time ready for the execution of the great and hazardous plan. About nightfall vessels had been sent up the river as if for an attack on Pointe-aux-Trembles, the object being to toll the French troops under Bougainville away from the vicinity of the spot appointed. The siege guns on Point Lévis were working as usual, and below the city Admiral Saunders was bombarding the Beauport lines and maneuvering flotillas of boats as if for a landing. On board the *Sutherland* and the vessels lying near her were thirty-six hundred men, and at Goreham's Post, at the mouth of the Etchemin, lay twelve hundred more in readiness to be ferried across the river if the first detachment succeeded in effecting a landing.

Time dragged slowly, as it always does on the eve of great undertakings. But about eleven o'clock seventeen hundred men were quietly embarked in some large bateaux and other boats lying alongside the squadron. One bateaux next the *Sutherland* must most engage our attention, for in it sat Wolfe and his staff (including now both Randolph and Currin), Captain Chads, the naval officer to whom the management of the landing had been intrusted, and Captain De Laune and twenty-four volunteers who were to undertake the desperate task of climbing the cliff and surprising the guard at the top.

Presently a single lantern appeared in the main topmast shrouds of the *Sutherland*.

" 'Tis the signal for the other boats to draw abreast of us," whispered Randolph to Barnaby.

Through the gloom came the soft splash of oars, and soon the whole flotilla had reached the rendezvous between the *Sutherland* and the south shore.

"What think you, Captain Chads," asked Wolfe, when this movement had been executed; "has the tide begun to ebb?"

"Not yet, but we shall not have long to wait," was the answer.

Half an hour passed; then Chads said to a petty officer who stood waiting at the rail: "You may raise the other, Williams."

The order was at once obeyed, and a second lantern appeared above the first.

"Give way," said Chads to the oarsmen; and the boat carrying Wolfe and the forlorn hope began to drop down-stream, followed by the others. Across the river at Cap Rouge the French sentinels remained blissfully unaware that the final expedition against the citadel of New France was under way.

Up to midnight the stars had shone clearly, but now the sky was mercifully overcast, and a favoring southwest breeze had sprung up. On either side, as the flotilla dropped quietly down with the ebbing tide, appeared dimly the precipitous cliffs that hemmed the river in. From far to the eastward came the roar of the batteries on Point Lévis and of Saunders's guns as he bombarded the Beauport lines from vessels lying in the Basin of Quebec, and now and again a shell trailed like some huge meteor across the heavens toward the city.

For a time all in the foremost boat sat silent, each man communing with his own thoughts. All felt the strain; all wondered what the next few hours would bring forth. Presently the melancholy ideas that oppressed him proved too much for Wolfe to endure in silence.

"Gentlemen," he said, in a deep subdued voice, "the situation we are in is so novel that one can, I suppose, be pardoned for having strange thoughts. For the last hour there has been running through my mind some lines contained in a poem recently published in a little book given me by a dear friend just before I left London. I wonder if you know it? 'Tis entitled an *Elegy Written in a Country Churchyard;* its author is one Thomas Gray."

Verse by verse he recited. The sound of the gently dipping oars and the soft ripple of the current mingled with his mellow voice but did not drown it. All listened as does an audience at some great opera, when the perfect voice of the singer expresses the supremest emotion in the gamut of passion or of suffering. And there was not one but remembered to his dying day how the young commander's feelings mastered him and how his voice broke as he quoted the immortal stanza:

> "'The boast of heraldry, the pomp of power,
> And all that beauty, all that wealth e'er gave,
> Await alike th' inevitable hour:
> The paths of glory lead but to the grave.'"

He made no attempt to recite more. "Gentlemen," he said, after a pause, "I would rather have written those lines than take Quebec tomorrow."

Out of the blackness ahead loomed the dark outlines of a vessel lying in the center of the stream.

"'Tis the sloop *Hunter,*" said Captain Chads, when the foremost boat was within half a cable's length. "Great God! what are the crew doing?"

"I believe they take us for the enemy," Wolfe exclaimed, in great alarm. "See, they are running to quarters and seem to be training guns on us. If they fire, our enterprise is ruined."

"What boats are those?" demanded a hoarse voice from the *Hunter.*

"British; for God's sake, don't fire!" cried Chads.

"Stand off till I make sure," came the stern order. "What is the countersign?"

"Victory," said Chads quickly.

"Come nearer," said the speaker, evidently still unconvinced.

Willingly enough, Wolfe's boat drew alongside. "We are friends, Captain Smith," called the commander. "I am General Wolfe. We are on a secret expedition."

"Gad!" exclaimed the captain. "You had a close call! I came near giving you a broadside without troubling to challenge you. I took you for a provision convoy that a couple of deserters say the French are expecting down the river to-night."

After the boats left the *Hunter,* it became necessary for them to steer in toward the north shore in order not to be swept past their destination.

"Qui vive!" sharp and menacing came a challenge from the darkness at the foot of the cliff.

It was a breathless moment. Discovery spelt failure. But there was in the nearest boat a quick-witted Highland officer who, having served on the Continent, knew French perfectly. He had also heard the colloquy with the captain of the *Hunter.*

"France!" he responded without hesitation.

"A quel regiment!" demanded the voice.

"De la Reine," replied the Highlander, in subdued tones.

Probably the sentinel did not hear the answer, for he said: "Why do you not speak louder?"

"Keep quiet, comrade," said the Highlander, still in French. "These are the provision boats. I fear we shall be heard."

Satisfied with this plausible answer, the sentinel said no more. Vastly relieved, the English passed on. Randolph and Currin directed the midshipman at the tiller where to steer, and in a few minutes Wolfe's boat grated upon the narrow beach. The general himself was the first man to spring ashore, closely followed by Randolph, Currin, and Captain De Laune, and the twenty-four volunteers. Three light infantry companies under Colonel Howe, brother of him who had fallen at Ticonderoga, were landed to support the attempt.

The critical moment had now come. Above towered the bold cliff which must be scaled and mastered. In many hearts were doubts and misgivings, but two lithe figures stepped to the head of the volunteers and led the way toward the rocky spur up which the attempt was to be made. Who were these figures? Who should they be but those two comrades whom we have followed in hazardous marches along the Rivière aux Bœufs, beside the swift Monongahela, and down this very cliff that frowns so blackly before us? Creeping through the thicket that skirted it, the party arrived at the foot of the spur.

"Take your time, men," said Randolph, in a low voice. "Keep cool and avoid loose stones. We shall reach the top with ease."

With muskets slung at their backs, the volunteers followed the two Virginians. Roots, bushes, and the trunks of trees furnished welcome assistance. Now and again some dislodged rock went tumbling down the cliff, but the splash of the falls of the little brook Saint Denis mercifully deadened the noise. In five minutes Randolph, Currin, and Captain De Laune were on the summit. The men were following close behind them.

From along the cliff came again the challenge:

"*Qui vive!*"

"*France,*" said Randolph, anxious to gain even a minute's delay. Barnaby dropped back into the shadow.

"*Le mot d'ordre?*"

"*La victoire,*" replied Randolph, mumbling the words so that they were unintelligible. "I command a relieving party, *mon enfant.* You may call off the other guards. We will care for *les Anglais* if any come."

Fortunately the sentinel was a slow-witted *habitant,* unaccustomed to the usages of war. Though still suspicious, he waited until other dark forms began to appear over the brow of the cliff, and one man, unaware of the sentinel's proximity, uttered an incautious British oath.

Instantly the sentinel raised his fusil. But before he could fire there leaped out from behind a neighboring tree an agile form. The sentinel went to earth with his throat clutched in the iron grasp of Barnaby Currin. In a minute the astonished man was bound and gagged.

In the time thus gained all the volunteers and part of the light infantry had reached the summit. Then from further up the cliff arose the wild shout:

"*Les Anglais! aux armes! aux armes! les Anglais!*"

Two or three shots rang out. The volunteers and Howe's infantry sprang toward the white tents that were becoming faintly visible in the increasing morning light. There were confused cries, a volley of shots, a glimpse of scurrying, half-dressed forms; and the camp was taken. To the anxious army below went down a hearty British cheer.

Soon the men came swarming up the cliff. The path was cleared. The remaining troops on the ships—which had dropped down the river with the tide—and the detachment from Goreham's Post were landed and likewise climbed the cliff. The Samos battery above the cove bellowed harshly for a time, but was stormed by Howe and his light infantry. By a little after sunrise the British army was drawn up in order of battle on the Heights of Abraham.

At last Fortune had smiled!

☆
☆   ☆

Resplendent in his new uniform and attended by his staff, including Randolph and Barnaby, General Wolfe was moving down his line of battle.

"Our chance has come," he said exultantly to the commander of each regiment he passed, "at last we are where they must fight us! Let every man do his duty, and this will be a glorious day for England. Double-shot your muskets. But do not fire until the enemy are within forty paces. After the first volley, reload, advance twenty paces, fire again, then charge!"

The men caught his spirit. Despite discouraging failures, they had never yet lost faith in their ardent young leader. Presently a company of the Forty-seventh struck up to the tune of *Lilies of France* a song which had been much heard during the early days of the campaign, but which had fallen into disuse since the disastrous repulse at the heights of the Mont-morency, where its composer, Sergeant Ned Botwood, had fallen. Soon the whole battle line was singing:

> "Come, each death-doing dog who dares venture his neck,
> Come, follow the hero who goes to Quebec;
> Jump aboard of the transports, and loose every sail,
> Pay your debts at the tavern by giving leg-bail;
> And ye that love fighting shall soon have enough:
> Wolfe commands us, my boys, we shall give them Hot Stuff!

> "Up the River St. Lawrence our troops shall advance,
> To the Grenadiers' March we will teach them to dance.
> Cape Breton we've taken, and next we will try
> At their capital to give them another black eye.
> Vaudreuil, 'tis in vain you pretend to look gruff,—
> Those are coming who know how to give you Hot Stuff!

> "With powder in his periwig, and snuff in his nose,
> Monsieur will run down our descent to oppose;
> And the Indians will come: but the light infantry
> Will soon oblige *them* to betake to a tree.
> From such rascals as these may we fear a rebuff?
> Advance, grenadiers, and let fly your Hot Stuff!

> "When the Forty-seventh regiment is dashing ashore,
> While bullets are whistling and cannons do roar,
> Says Montcalm: 'Those are Shirley's,—I know the lapels.'
> 'You lie,' says Ned Botwood, 'we belong to Lascelles'!
> Tho' our clothing is changed, yet we scorn a powder-puff;
> So at you, ye b——s, here 's give you Hot Stuff!' "

While the refrain still rose along the line the ridge ahead began to be thronged with white uniforms. Randolph looked attentively at the standard fluttering over them, and saw that, in the language of heraldry, it was quarterly first and fourth *feuille-morte,* second and third *vert;* over all a white cross.

"Those troops belong to the battalion of Guienne. I recognize the standard," he said to Wolfe.

"Let them come," said the commander gayly. "I am happy to see them."

The white-coated gentry extended themselves along the ridge, but otherwise made no hostile demonstration. Swarms of Indians and Canadians soon made their appearance, however, and, creeping along under cover of the woods and thickets, opened a galling fusillade on the English wings.

At this Barnaby began to grow restive. "If I had my old rifle here," said he to Randolph, "I would kinder like to mix in that."

"Be patient," said Randolph, laughing, " 'tis not often that one can serve on the staff of a major-general. For this once you must fight according to the rules."

Presently the firing of these sharpshooters became so heavy that Wolfe threw out skirmishers to oppose them and ordered the regiments that were most exposed to lie down. Light showers fell at intervals, but the men continued in high spirits, and patiently awaited the event. Meanwhile every eye watched keenly the crest of the halfway ridge. More columns of regulars and of motley clothed militia came in sight and deployed. Artillery began to ply the English lines with grape-shot. At intervals the solitary English six-pounder that had been dragged up the cliff bellowed a defiant reply.

" 'Tis evident they mean to fight!" cried Wolfe delightedly. "We shall not have long to wait."

It was now near ten o'clock. The clouds which hitherto had obscured the sky were passing away and giving place to a flood of warm sunshine that lit up the brilliant uniforms and glittering weapons of the two armies and illumined the gorgeous crimson, yellow, and purple foliage of the woodlands in the stupendous amphitheatre in which one of the great scenes of history was about to be enacted. The plateau on which the armies stood formed the stage. To the British left, gradually rising tier upon tier, lay the northern range of the blue pine-clad Laurentians; while to their right stretched away league upon league of undulating upland sweeping up to the yet more distant southern range, whose wider semicircle curved in to meet its northern counterpart and make the vast mountain ring complete. Across the arena to the right the great river, full-charged with Britannia's might, ebbed and flowed past the Rock of Quebec—the bulwark of New France and the prize of victory!

As he watched the enemy's lines Randolph saw ride out from them, on a splendid black charger, a cavalier wearing a shining cuirass and the full uniform of a lieutenant-general of the French king. For some minutes the officer surveyed the English position, which was only partly visible because of the rough ground; then he turned and rode slowly down the front of his own line, brandishing his drawn sword, and apparently calling on his men to do their utmost. And from the waiting ranks came thunderous cheers of:

"*Montcalm! Montcalm! Vive notre général! Montcalm!*"

No Roman emperor ever received such a salute from gladiators about to die. A lump rose in Randolph's throat; he felt strangely troubled. "Should either leader fall," thought he, "I shall be sad, for I love them both!"

Before Montcalm finished his course, the English line, at an order from Wolfe, moved forward a hundred paces in order to commit both armies to close and decisive action. Then, with Randolph and Currin and other aides, the English general moved once more along the front of his line.

"Be firm, my lads," he kept saying to the men. "Do not return a shot till they are within forty yards of your guns. Then you may fire."

And as he passed on huzzas that rivaled the cheers which greeted his great opponent rent the air. Shouldering their muskets, the men stood as if on parade.

The bullets fired by the Canadian and Indian sharp-shooters were now flying thicker than ever, and as Wolfe turned to come back from the left, one struck him in the wrist. Wrapping a handkerchief which bore the monogram "K. L." around the wound, he kept on without a word of complaint. From behind bushes and knolls, and from the edge of corn-fields, puffs of smoke shot incessantly, for more than one skilled rifleman had marked the young commander as his prey. Near the middle of the line Randolph and Barnaby saw him stagger; but to their anxious questioning he gave no answer, and, heedless of a bullet in the groin, kept on down the line, pouring out his spirit in the animated exhortations that spring from that deep emotion which none but warriors can feel and none but heroes can utter. At last he took his stand on a little knoll between the Twenty-eighth and the Louisburg Grenadiers, whence he commanded a view of nearly his whole line.

From this point Randolph and Barnaby saw the enemy sweep proudly down from the ridge. The French regulars—victors of Oswego, of William Henry, of Ticonderoga—were in the center; the Canadian regulars and militia were on the wings. As they moved forward, the French shouted loudly and waved their weapons. The English six-pounder, daringly planted in front of the line, plied them with grape, and the bagpipes of the Highlanders sent back a shrill defiance; but the English troops stood in ominous silence, waiting.

"There he is!" cried Barnaby, whose keen eyes had been seeking the approaching array for a hated figure.

"Where?" demanded Randolph, with no less eagerness.

Barnaby silently pointed to a gigantic figure that strode ahead of a battalion of colonial troops, over whom waved a banner which Randolph recognized as that of Montreal.

"Good!" said Randolph grimly. "He is almost opposite us." And he drew his sword.

The French advanced rapidly at first; their onslaught bade fair to be furious. But it was not long before the very silence of their opponents had its effect. The Canadians had not advanced a hundred paces when they began to fire without orders, and then to throw themselves on the ground to reload. These tactics impeded the advance without causing the British much loss, disorganized the line of battle, and furnished an opportunity for those who were disinclined to come to close quarters to slink off and join in the skirmishing attacks upon the British wings. Randolph and Barnaby saw Reparti and other officers remonstrating with their followers, but so averse were the Canadians to a fight in the open that they melted away like snow beneath a summer sun. The battalions of French regulars kept bravely on, but soon their own ranks broke out in disorderly long-range firing.

Undismayed, the French officers led their man forward, waving their long espontoons and shouting words of encouragement. Fearful for their now exposed flanks, the two battalions on the left inclined to the left, and the three on the right to the right; thus, split in two, the densely massed French line of battle moved forward with less assurance toward the waiting lines of British bayonets. This movement threw the small remnant of Canadians who had gathered round Reparti further to the English right, and brought the battalion of Royal Roussillon opposite the knoll where stood Wolfe and his staff. Rapidly the distance diminished.

Randolph could see the battalion colors of blue, red, yellow, and green, with white crosses upon which were embroidered golden fleur-de-lis, and the black three-cornered hats, red and blue collars, and black stocks of the men. The surging ranks broke forth in wild bursts of smoke, and now and again some stricken British soldier sank with clattering gun to earth. But the British discipline was wonderful. Now the French were within a hundred yards, yet not a shot had been fired by that grim battle line. Eighty yards . . . sixty . . . fifty . . . forty-five . . . forty . . .

"Fire!" rang out the voice of Wolfe.

The British muskets rose, and there thundered forth a volley so perfectly delivered that it sounded like a cannon shot. Again, with the precision of clock-work, the well-drilled men reloaded and moved twenty paces forward. The dense smoke of the first volley had lifted somewhat, disclosing a scene of havoc. Again belched forth a terrible volley. The French went down by hundreds. Their ranks began to crumble.

"Charge!" shouted Wolfe, springing in front of the Louisburg Grenadiers.

The English regiments gave a mighty cheer and dashed in with the bayonet; the Highlanders shouted their fierce slogan and fell to with the claymore. Some brave Frenchmen endeavored to stem the rush, but not many. Most who had not fallen raised the *sauve qui peut!*

> "When the Forty-seventh regiment is dashing ashore,
> While bullets are whistling and cannons do roar,
> Says Montcalm: 'Those are Shirley's,—I know the lapels.'
> 'You lie,' says Ned Botwood, 'we belong to Lascelles'!
> Tho' our clothing is changed, yet we scorn a powder-puff;
> So at you, ye b——s, here 's give you Hot Stuff!' "

Randolph and Barnaby were dashing madly forward with the grenadiers in the hope of meeting Reparti. But the longed for encounter which a few minutes before had seemed probable had been rendered impossible by the split in the French line. The few Montreal militia who advanced in the final charge were thrust far aside toward the river by the battalion of Royal Roussillon. Before this battalion gave way, the militia fled from the field, bearing Reparti with them. Balked of their hoped for prey, the disappointed Virginians fought in the *mêlée* with whomever opposed them, and came presently upon two British grenadiers thrusting savagely at a young officer who was defending himself with his sword. The combat was too unequal to be long maintained. One of the grenadiers ran his

bayonet through the officer's left arm; the other was about to give a finishing thrust, when Randolph caught the musket.

"Yield, Lieutenant Lusignan, for the sake of those who love you!"
he cried.

Reluctantly the young officer gave up his weapon. *"Mon Dieu!* I may
as well," he said bitterly, "for the day is lost."

It was true. The whole French army was a disorderly mob flying
wildly for safety, and from all parts of the field arose the cry *"Miséri-
corde!" In five minutes the fate of a continent had been decided!*

With Barnaby's assistance, Randolph helped Lusignan back from the
shambles toward the rear. They had not gone far ere they came upon a
little knot of men gathered round a prostrate form lying upon the coat
of a grenadier.

"Who is it?" asked Randolph, but even as he uttered the words he
saw the officer's face—and it was the face of him who but a few hours
before had said: "The paths of glory lead but to the grave."

"He was struck just as the charge began," said Captain Curry of the
Twenty-eighth. "The wound is mortal."

A surgeon was doing what he could, but the young general's head
was sunk forward on his breast, and in his unseeing eyes was that glassy
look that accompanies dissolution.

Suddenly, from a little knoll in front, some one shouted: "See how
they run!"

"Who run? asked Wolfe, rousing himself.

"The French, sir. Egad, they have given way every where!"

"Go, one of you, to Colonel Burton," said the dying man; "tell him
to march Webb's regiment down to Charles River to cut off their retreat
from the bridge. Now—God be praised—I will die in peace!"

A moment more and his soaring spirit took its flight.

THE HIGHLANDERS' RELIEF AT FORT PITT

by NEIL H. SWANSON

A DRUMMER BOY in a red coat lay asleep on the bench inside of the governor's office, one arm curled round his drum.

The trim orderlies were gone; the loopholes needed every man. For two days and a night, the tow-headed drummer had been the governor's whole staff.

Now, across the stump of a candle on the table, Ecuyer looked at him heavily. The greasy light gave the boy the face of a corpse—yellowish, with hollows where his cheeks should be. The soldier's lips moved as his mind moved, slowly, putting into orderly ranks the words he would set down in his report for the day. There was no one to read the report; it had become very plain, these last two days, that unless help came quickly no one would ever read it. But his majesty's regulations called for those daily entries in the journal. Captain Ecuyer began to write.

"29th July,

"Continued firing on the fort, the whole day, from the Ohio bank, they kept up a very smart fire, this day a number of shells thrown to disperse them, but they only shifted places, this day and yesterday about 1,500 small arms fired on them from the fort. Wounded this day: Marcus Huling's leg broken, Sergeant Hermon shot through the lungs, a grenadier shot through the leg, fired three shots from a six pounder, as they were passing the river in canoes; obliged them once to throw themselves into the river, one of them said to be cut in two by one of the shot. These two days killed several of them from the fort, one of them wounded and drowned in the river, attempting to swim over and five more seen carried out of the canoe on the farther side of the Ohio, supposed to be wounded. The roofs of the Governor's House and the Barracks much hurt by the enemy's fire." *

He turned the page; his lips began to move again, helping his brain trudge on through its clogging weariness. His eyes, having no part in the task, ran to queer scenes; they made him see feet in column, feet in gaiters, trudging through a road that was deep mud. The mud clung to the feet, pulling them back, clogging them. His mind, for a moment,

* From the official journal of Captain S. Ecuyer, commandant of Fort Pitt, preserved in the British Museum.

From: *The Judas Tree.* Copyright 1933 by the author. G. P. Putnam's Sons.

played him tricks; he saw his thoughts plodding along, absurdly, in muddy gaiters; it took an effort to lift them and move them forward. The desire to sleep clung to them.

He shook his head, jerking his thoughts, shaking off the sense of thick, sticky weight. His eyes turned to the sleeping boy again, and saw that he was smiling in his sleep; then, peering intently, they saw that it was not a smile at all. The drummer's face was so thin that the skin seemed stuck to his cheek bones; sticking there, it pulled his lips up from his teeth. Thin . . .

Ecuyer's quill began to scratch on the fresh page:

"I have at present four legs of beef and no flour. (A relief expedition must) bring a great deal of it or the jaws will rest immovable."

Fort Pitt, with its three hundred men, its hundred women, its hundred children, was just that close to starvation on Diantha's wedding day. The commandant's lips twitched as he sanded the page; he looked, for a moment, as if he smiled. Then his mouth set itself and hid his teeth. He got up, supporting himself with his hands on the table edge, easing his weight to his wounded leg, listening to the muffled thudding of muskets beyond the walls. The besiegers in their burrows were still at it. Sixty days . . . by the good God, for sixty days they had been around him, and they were still at it. He thought of the musket flashes he had watched through the past night, circling the fort, closing in. It was asking much of a man . . . to ask him to go out there, alone. He grimaced again, and walked slowly, limping, past the bench and the sleeping drummer boy, through the door into the outer office. His hand, fumbling, touched the shoulder of a man who lay on a plank bed against the wall.

"Major Leslie. . . ."

"Ay." The puncheons creaked. "Good evening, Captain. Are we ready?"

"You have not slept?"

"A little. Enough." Leslie swung his feet to the floor and stood up. "The firing stays about the same."

"Ja. They are a little closer on the garden side, where Captain Bassett's house was. No rush yet tonight. You are sure," he hesitated, "you do not wish to tell your wife good-by?"

"No." Leslie moved toward the lighted doorway. "Let her sleep. I have left a letter for her, with her brother. And a will. You will remember, if neither he nor I get through alive, that I leave everything to her." He chuckled. "Everything. A bed, a trunk, a dressing table, and three thousand acres of wild land, to the Duchess of Strangden. How much time is there?"

Ecuyer tugged at the fob adangle under his tunic, and looked at his watch.

"Ten minutes, Major. Carre will open on them at a quarter to ten, and then Phillips on the opposite wall; no volleys, every second man firing five rounds as he pleases. Five minutes after Carre starts it, the Ohio bastion will fire three rounds of canister to sweep the ditch. Then the Flag bastion three; then the Ohio again, so they will not see that we are concerned especially with the ditch where it runs down to the Mon'. Nine rounds, you understand, Leslie. After that, the two howitzers in the Grenadier bastion will put four rounds of canister into the moat, toward the Mon'; if they are in the ditch, that should clear them out, for a little while."

"Long enough," said Leslie cheerfully, "to get down to the water."

"Remember, Major . . . nine rounds before the Grenadier bastion fires at all; you had best slip into the tunnel then. Captain Arnold is waiting for you at the sally port."

"Arnold?"

"*Ja*. He feels that he has done you ill. He asked, himself, to go out with you, to make some amends. These women, they set us a little wild inside, no? I think, Major, he has regrets now. He said, if there should be some of the Indians left in the moat, a man going with you might keep them off until you should have time to get away."

Leslie shrugged. It was, after all, Valentine Arnold who had killed Robin; it was Valentine Arnold's order to put out the bear that had driven Fritz over the wall; it was Arnold who would have branded Arnett Leslie for deserter and coward to aid his own wooing. It was hard, now, to think of him as wanting to make amends.

"The canister will clear them out," he said curtly.

"You will have a little help, too, from the south wall," Ecuyer told him. "A few shots—not enough to stir them up; enough to hold their attention, only. I thought, if that side of the fort did not fire at all . . ."

"Yes. Yes. That is better. Thank you."

"Your friend Price picked the men to fire."

"Good. Thank him for me, will you? The pack . . . ?"

"Arnold has it. Ha . . .! It commences."

Behind the closed shutters, the glass rattled in the windows of the governor's room. The first cannon shot from the Ohio bastion slugged the close air and pushed it against the eardrums, a dull shock. Ecuyer blew out the candle and opened the door. They went together down the steps of the governor's house, where Diantha had sat on Leslie's knee to wash her feet and put on her stockings, where she had stood and watched Leslie pass by, a prisoner, on his way to be tried for a coward. The Flag bastion began to fire.

They walked quickly along the front of the governor's house and past the officers' barracks . . . past the door where Barent had made love to a bond maid and drawn his sword on the shabby stranger who intervened . . . past the door where Diantha lay asleep across the foot of the canopied bed, at Bob Gaillard's feet. Duchess of Strangden . . . niece of a prince . . . countess of the Austrian empire . . . Mrs. Arnett Leslie of nowhere. Arnett Leslie walked steadily past the closed door. At the end of the barracks, he said:

"Captain Ecuyer, tomorrow, please, tell her I was thinking of her. Say I thought it was easier to go this way—that I will get through safe."

"Ja! Ja!"

They turned into the dark space between the brick buildings and saw Arnold waiting at the entrance to the tunnel under the south wall. Arnold held out a small pack, rolled tightly.

"I tried both pistols," he told Leslie. "They have fresh flints, and the muzzles and the vents are plugged. The quartermaster cut the plugs, and we tried them; they will keep the charges dry. Prime them, and they will fire, if you have need of them quickly."

"Thank you."

In the pent-up, triangular space between the two barracks and the rampart, the heated air was vibrant. The successive shocks of the cannon made the ears ring. It was difficult to listen, or to talk. Leslie cared to do neither. He loosened the strings of his hunting shirt and stripped it off; untied the leather latchets that held the tops of his leggings to his breechclout belt, and stood naked in clout and mocassins. His body, blackened again with gunpowder, remained invisible in the dark; Arnold's face and Ecuyer's made fleeting blurs when they moved, but Leslie's dark skin was as little white as any Indian's where the sun had touched it.

Ecuyer took the bundle and tied it firmly to the beaded belt, behind. Absently, without enthusiasm, Leslie heard Arnold speaking of moccasins, powder and ball for the pistols at the center of the small pack, food. Without enthusiasm, he saw the Royal American stoop and slip off first one boot and then the other.

"Ready?"

"Ready."

Arnold's stockinged feet rustled on loose gravel; Leslie bent double and followed him into the tunnel.

"God be . . ." The first blast from the howitzer sweeping the river end of the moat cut the governor's good-by in two. It was cooler in the passage under the wall, and quieter. At the iron-bound door that opened into the moat, Arnold was waiting, and his hand, fumbling, closed over Leslie's forearm.

". . . damnation sorry," he was saying, in a high, rapid whisper. ". . . make public apology when you get back. . . ."

"Yes. Yes." Leslie was impatient. What Valentine Arnold thought concerned him so little he did not know what he was saying. He had never, he realized, been so reluctant in the presence of danger. He did not wish to go out through that safe and solid door; he wanted, just now, to live. The captain began to undo the bars that fastened the door, and they slid back with the faintest scraping of wood on the iron hasps. *Lord,* it was through the sally port that he had gone out one morning seeking Fritz, and come back to find that Valentine Arnold had shot poor Robin. He thought, coldly, that if he got through the savages on the river bank and came safely ashore upstream under the bluff he had in mind, he would look to those fresh flints Arnold had set in his pistol locks.

Where the door had been, a dully luminous rectangle took shape in the solid blackness. Then it glowed red, and lost itself as the night snapped back behind the flash of the howitzer. Together, they stepped out into the moat.

Flash . . . *jar.* Shocked air buffeted their faces. Echoes beat themselves to pieces on the cliffs across the Mon'.

Leslie moved quickly along the base of the brick rampart, around the rough stone blocks that marked the first angle of the Grenadier bastion, into the largest section of the ditch. The officers of the garrison had played at bowls there the day he came to Pitt's Town. Now the Royal Artillery, twelve feet over his head, was playing at bowls with whatever savages were lurking in its deep shadows. He stopped, close under the gunport, waiting. Seventy yards to the right, the moat ran out through the river bank onto the open shore. On either side of it there were burrows where the Shawnees lay; he had marked, last night, that the line of rifle flashes ran far up the Monongahela, almost beyond range of the fort. There were so many warriors in the besieging army now that there was not room for all of them on the firing line that circled the walls;

they spread out wherever they could find a hiding place from which to shoot, though their balls fell short of the palisades.

Flash . . . *jar*. The gunners overhead fired their fourth shot.

The red glow lighted the bottom of the ditch; winked out. Leslie, running for the river, heard the clang and screech of fragments tearing at the baked earth; heard the slough and slither of falling dirt; a long-drawn howl, more animal than human; yells. Behind him, he heard Arnold carom into the wall of the ditch. *Damn him!* He might be sincere about making amends, but the naked man running soft-footed toward the river bank and its crackling rifle pits cursed him for not keeping them inside the fort where they belonged. *Fool!* If he fell and made a clatter, he would have the Shawnee pack jumping down onto their backs. Raging inwardly, he stopped. Two strides away, he could hear the regular's loud breathing. He put out his hand and clutched Arnold by the tunic.

"Back . . . go back!" he whispered.

There was the beginning of a whispered answer. Arnold never finished it. They knew, a split second before the knife drove at Leslie's ribs, that they were not alone in the moat. There was a place where the darkness was darker, solid; it leaped at them. Arnold's arm, flung up, missed the Indian's blade and struck his wrist. His other hand, clutching, felt bare skin sticky with paint.

His voice was a hoarse breath:

"Go! Quick! I'll take this one!"

Leslie left him there. Heard, as he began to run again, the sound of strangling.

Ten yards from the river bank, the bottom of the moat was no longer smooth. The canister had gouged it and strewn it with clods. They crushed under his moccasins with a gritting noise and made him stumble; he stopped running; ahead, close, he saw the black sheen of the Monongahela sliding by.

Abreast of the firing line, the din of the Shawnee muskets told him he had a chance; they were blazing away at the fort in a frenzy of haste, shooting at the flashes as Price's picked riflemen let go at random. Leslie walked out of the ditch onto the flat shore so close to a warrior that he could have touched him; the Shawnee, plastered against the bank, was staring along his musket barrel toward the stockade, waiting for another flash to give him a target. The high bank blunted the battle noises; the white man, walking steadily across the dried silt of the shrunken river, heard minor sounds in undertone—the tump-tump of a ramrod on a ball, a skitter of clay down the bank as an Indian squirmed in his burrow, harsh voices. A little way down the stream, some of the Indians had built a fire and were standing around it, eating; it cast a glow over the sliding water, and made objects blackly visible along the shore.

Leslie walked slowly into the water. He did not dare to hurry, or make a splash. He was wading. Knee-deep; thigh-deep; waist-deep. Then the river took him soundlessly.

He began to swim with the current, edging out little by little from the shore; it carried him below the fort, well out into the joined rivers, before he passed midstream. Sinking, he untied his moccasins and kicked them off. Then he settled himself into the dark water and swam with all his strength up the Monongahela.

For half an hour he could see the red, darting flashes drawing their circle around Fort Pitt.

☆

☆   ☆

Arnett Leslie had no very clear idea how he had come to Tomahawk. He saw it, lying below him, no larger than a dirty handkerchief dropped in the immensity of the great valley.

Old Iron Head had cut that square patch out of the wilderness years ago, and hemmed it with a palisade of logs. Leslie recognized the place; he had camped there with Fritz, and Fritz' thieving bear had stolen the last of the cornbread while they slept. He looked down at it with a dull surprise; it should not be there, it should be farther to the east, miles farther, hours farther. It was quite impossible that he should have come, before midday, to Tomahawk. He watched the dirty handkerchief grow as he ran down the mountain. Running had become a habit; it was easier to run than to walk; when he walked, his body had acquired a queer, annoying trick of weaving from side to side, making his feet stumble on the edges of the wheel-track. Running, he was able to work a counter-trick on his body; he simply let it hang forward, as if it was going to fall; each time before it fell, one foot or the other swung ahead and caught it. The trick made running automatic; he thought, foolishly, that if he found Bouquet and the army he would not be able to stop and tell them about Fort Pitt; he would go running past, first one foot and then the other catching his body just before it fell down.

He considered the problem seriously. Half way down the mountain, he decided what he would do when he met Bouquet. He would simply make his feet stop, and let his body fall down. Colonel Bouquet would have to pick him up out of the road to let the army go by; when the colonel picked him up he would tell the army that it would have to hurry to keep Diantha from worrying.

When he came out into the clearing, among the stumps, he saw why Tomahawk had looked like a dirty handkerchief. The Indians had been there, too, and burned it; even the grass was scorched and yellow, and smeared with black splotches that had been cabins in April.

Leslie passed at his shuffling run. He felt, for a moment, exultant. It had been midnight when he climbed the bluffs above the Monongahela, with the warm river water streaming down his body into the fresh moccasins he had donned from the pack at his belt; it had been daybreak when he had swung away from Forbes' road, plunging through the forest in a great semi-circle to avoid Ligonier and the savages lurking around the stockade; by the sun in his face, it was yet not much past ten o'clock. He had come, in ten hours, more than sixty miles. Ahead, miles ahead, hours ahead, the Allegheny Mountains stood purple-blue against the sky. He saw them now, immense as the valley had been immense when he looked down into it from the ridge above Tomahawk; when he crossed the valley and the mountains, he would come to Fort Bedford, and find the army.

Yes, the army would be at Bedford. It had to be.

Arnett Leslie put out his tongue and tried to moisten his dried lips. Lips and tongue, they only scraped each other; he grimaced, contorting his cheeks, trying to squeeze out the saliva. *God,* the army *must* be at Bedford. Today or tomorrow, the women and children in Fort Pitt would eat for the last time. After that . . .

He ran on. He must climb that mountain. He must get to Fort Bedford, and find Bouquet, and the army. He must find them quickly.

But the army was not at Fort Bedford.

Arnett Leslie came to Stony Creek a little after noon. He knew it was past midday because his shadow got to the creek before he did and was lying in the water when he dropped down on hands and knees to drink. Kneeling, he could look up through the swamp grass on the opposite bank and see the mountain. The mountain had come definitely closer; it was more green than blue; across it on a long slant ran the dark scar of road. Leslie drank again, sparingly, and thrust head and face into the water; when he raised his head with a jerk to throw the wet hair out of his eyes, he saw that the scar had changed. It was no longer dark; it moved.

It was, he decided, very much like the scar of the Shawnee hatchet on his own breast—the old, dry scar, not the new one. He looked down at himself, mildly curious, mildly pleased to find the comparison was not inapt. The long, slanting scar was lighter than the rest of his body; the skin that covered it had a thin, brittle look, like parchment, and when he moved his arm and the chest muscles moved with it, the parchment-like tissue rippled and glistened. When he looked back at the mountain, he saw that its scar was rippling and glistening, too. It was brighter, if anything, than the gash on his own flesh. He was on his feet, wading, half way across the stream, before he realized what had happened to the road to make it seem to move, to flow, to ripple and glisten in the sun. He stopped, dead still, knee deep in the tugging water.

The brightness on the mountain side was made of the white covers of baggage wagons. The glistening was bayonets. The flowing was men . . . men . . . men . . . horses . . . more men.

The army was not at Bedford. The army was there on the mountain, thirty miles closer than he had dared to hope. Bouquet was coming! Arnett Leslie floundered through the water and began to run.

He seemed, in the undulant immensity of valley, not to run at all. To crawl, rather. His shadow lengthened ahead of him until it was as tall as he; and he took a queer notion that his body finally had tricked him and had fallen down. It required, now, a deliberate effort to move his feet, as much of an effort as if his body actually lay there on the ground ahead of him and he had to push it. He watched the shadow's head, measuring how far it moved with each push, picking out marks along the road, saying to himself: *Ten pushes will put it past that tree.* And after the tree: *Four pushes will bring it to that plantain stalk.* Sometimes it took five pushes instead of four, and he swore, croaking, hating the useless burden of his shadow.

He was watching it when it crawled grotesquely up a fringed legging yellow with dust, up over a dangling powder horn, into a fringed beard yellow with tobacco drip. He stopped, swaying, but he did not fall down; It was fortunate, he thought, that the man with the yellow beard was there to hold his shadow up. Looking past him, he saw Forbes' road full of kilts and bayonets.

"Name o' th' Lord!" said the scout. "Be you from Ligonier? Have they took it yet?"

"No. From Fort Pitt," Leslie mouthed at him, and heard nothing. He tried again: "From Fort Pitt. Where is Bouquet?" This time he heard the words.

The bearded man raised his rifle arm's length above his head and flourished it. His mouth, wide open, showed four black snags of teeth. His voice rose in a shrill hail, and Leslie saw other riflemen trotting toward them, thrums bobbing, weapons at trail. They passed with quick, curious glances, with flung questions.

"From Pitt's Town," the scout told them. "It's still holdin' out."

They trotted on, keeping their distance ahead of the kilted column. After them came a horse, galloping—a gray horse with a red rider, red and black kilt flapping, red jacket perking up at every jump. Leslie took a step to meet the gray horse.

"Ye've taken a bad sun scald, Robin," he croaked. "Have ye no goose grease handy?"

Robin Stuart gaped at the naked wretch who called him by name and pulled his lips back from his teeth, smiling horribly through dust-caked hair that dangled down his cheeks.

"Arnett Leslie! It's never Major Leslie?"

"Ay. For God's sake, Robin, have them to hurry."

Stuart flung himself out of the saddle.

"Arnie, man, I canna believe. . . . What have they done to ye?"

He did not wait for the answer. The urgency in the blood-rimmed eyes was answer enough. He got his arm around the sweat-streaked back.

"Here, Arnie. Can ye mount? Bouquet's just down the road. There . . . foot in the stirrup. Man, ye're barefoot; there's nought but rags o' leather, and y'r feet all bloody."

Leslie looked down at them curiously; they had not hurt at all. He shoved them hard against the stirrup iron as the horse began to move, and saw black blood well from a cut he had not known was there. Stuart's hand lay on his grimed thigh, steadying him. The ground rose and fell in waves. At the top of the first wave they passed more of the shirtmen, a straggling squad, long rifles criss-cross against the sky, eyes squinting into the sun, watching the thin fringe of scouts flung out ahead.

Riding up the next slope, Leslie saw the crest of it break suddenly into blinding, sparkling foam. The foam ran down to meet him, all polished steel, two hundred steel blades flashing above the polished muskets. They flowed by. From the saddle, he looked down between them and saw, underneath, a dark current of black knapsacks swaying above dust-dark kilts. Through the current ran dull gleams of red as the highland jackets swung unbuttoned from the bent, plodding bodies. From the highland bonnets, long feathers danced in a dizzying, criss-cross pattern, bobbing along on the current. The naked man on the horse closed his eyes to shut out their dancing; it made the mountain and the valley and the horse dance too.

There was an empty place in the road, and then more sparkling steel, more swinging kilts, a gleam of Lochaber axes swaying, a turgid current of tired legs and drifting dust. Then the road was empty again, except for clumsy bat wagons heaving in the ruts, and two strung-out lines of pack horses. Leslie thought he had dozed. While his eyes were closed, the army had gone by. He put his hands together, tight, on the saddle horn, and leaned to Robin's bonnet:

"Is that . . . all?"

Stuart looked up.

"Ay. That's all. Four hundred thirty, and half o' them more fit for bed than marching. Here comes the colonel."

Bouquet came up at a gallop along the crawling baggage train.

"What is it? A message, Stuart?"

Stuart saluted; Leslie lifted one hand from the saddle horn and put it back quickly; the gray horse stood still, but the ground would not.

"Major Leslie, colonel, from Fort Pitt," Robin said.

"Pitt! After five weeks . . . When did you leave the Forks?"

"Last night."

"*Last night?* Seventy miles?" He swung to Stuart.

"Look at his feet, colonel. He's not lying. Do ye not recollect him from '58, with the Maryland men?"

Bouquet ranged his black mount along the gray's neck.

"Leslie! Yes. Yes. I ask pardon, Major. We have all been frantic. Rumors. Rumors. Fort Pitt holds on?"

"Yes." Leslie closed his eyes to shut out the scarlet coat and the black horse. Red . . . black; red . . . black; fire . . . night . . . roofs crackling . . . hatchets licking in between the scorched palisades . . . a girl crouching against the flimsy wall. . . .

"It can yet hold on?"

"Yes." *It can yet hold on!* Leslie felt a blurred rush of hatred for the calm, calculating Swiss. It was easy to say "Hold on," sitting there in trim bright tunic, in ribboned wig, in crisp white spatter-dashes. He forced his eyes to stare at the full, handsome face. "Yes. There was food, yesterday, for one day more. There has been a continuous assault for three days. The barracks were on fire five times yesterday. Ecuyer is wounded. Yesterday they brought our last messenger and showed him to us, naked for the stake, on the river bank, and sent Ecuyer's letter back to him. There are six hundred of them. . . ."

"Six hundred. So. And Ligonier . . . you came that way?"

"I heard firing there this morning."

"Good. Good."

The wagons, stolid, crept like snails. The soldier, stolid, watched them creeping.

"Good! Good!" Leslie heard his own voice, croaking, mocking. It would take those crawling wagons weeks to reach the Forks of the Ohio. He said so, furiously.

"You say they have no food," Bouquet answered, his eyes on the creeping rear guard. "To go there without food is impossible."

"There will be none left to eat it," Leslie told him harshly. The Swiss soldier of fortune put out one hand and touched his shoulder.

"Good. It is so bad as that. That is what I wish to know. We will go there in time. See to him, Captain Stuart." Even then he did not move, sitting there massively calm, watching the red jackets of the light infantry toiling through the dust cloud behind the baggage train.

Robin hailed a wagon. Heaving, complaining, it lurched up out of the ruts and came to a halt in the brush alongside. The wagon box was filled to the tops of its high sides with sacks of corn meal. Robin and the teamster plucked Leslie out of the saddle and laid him on a blanket spread across the sacks, and the wagon jolted down into the ruts again. Stuart, squatting in the low space under the canvas cover, produced from his sporran a gnawed heel of wheat bread and a slice of bacon.

"Here, Arnie. Lie back; I'll feed ye." He broke the bread. "Man, man, I canna believe. . . . D'ye recall, Arnie, I said I would think of ye when I rode through these mountains ye had fought in?"

"Ay." The sun came strained and thin through the wagon cover; the rakish highland bonnet set dour shadows on Robin Stuart's face and sunk his eyes deeply into their thickets of black hair. "Ay. I named a dog for you, Robin."

"Did ye, now? A snappin', snarlin' beast, I warrant. Look ye, Arnie: ye haven't said, but the sweet lady ye were goin' to wed . . . she'll never be yonder, in Fort Pitt?"

"Ay."

"And ye came away. That wanted courage, man, hers and yours. I remember that day, on shipboard, when that wastrel Lawless railed at ye for a coward, and ye had the courage not to fall in with his wicked dueling until he misnamed y'r lady, and then stood his fire and put y'r bullet in the air. Be easy in y'r mind, Arnie. Bouquet is a grand soldier, for all he sits like a mountain."

"Lawless is there, too," Leslie told him.

"Yonder? In Fort Pitt? Damme, did he quarrel with ye again, that you scared him out of Maryland, and sought him . . . ?"

"No. 'T was he came hunting me. You see, Robin, I did not wed the lady I told you of."

"Ye did not?"

"No. She was already wed. And I am wed to that girl I bought, that day on the *New Adventure.*"

"Ye're never! And Lawless came seekin' ye, to do ye hurt for it?"

Leslie smiled, and took what was left of the bread and bacon out of Stuart's fingers.

"He did me, first and last, the two best services of any man. I would not have bought her but for him; I would not have wed her had he not come hounding me and let her see I was not the beast she thought me."

While the floundering wagons inched their way across the valley, Robin Stuart heard how a bond maid became a fine lady, a duchess, a countess and a wife in the midst of hunger and death; and must clamber out over the corn-meal sacks to tell the tale to Bouquet. He came back, hours later, to tell Leslie that a flying column would ride for Ligonier that night, and that Bouquet would leave the baggage wagons and press on with such food as could be carried on the pack saddles of three hundred horses.

Thirty men rode out of Tomahawk after sunset on the night dash for Ligonier. Somewhere in the darkness on Laurel Ridge, they became thirty-one. At daybreak, when they broke from the forest edge and rushed for the log gates of the beleaguered fort, they were only thirty again. Two miles beyond the stockade, Arnett Leslie turned on the bare back of his stolen horse and listened to the distant rattle of musketry as Bouquet's flying column ran the gauntlet of the besiegers. The firing lasted five minutes, and ceased. The thirty men were safe. Leslie kicked his horse into a shambling run up the valley of the Loyal Hanna. No matter how hard Bouquet drove his little army, it would not get to Fort Pitt for three days. When they got there, they would be outnumbered. The three hundred men inside Fort Pitt could help them, if they had word in time. He rode with a growing eagerness, a growing exultation. When he came to the weed-grown ovens and the old log breastworks of Twelve-Mile Camp, where Bouquet had fought the Shawnees seven years before, he was seeing again the limestone manor house he would build for Diantha. He heard her whispering against his cheek:

". . . and let me be your scullery maid, and give me a kiss each night and morning for my wage."

They had had, so far, only such hasty kisses.

He saw, too late, the roached scalplock rising from the laurel smother between two cat-clay ovens; saw brown smoke jetting; felt, instantly, the sag and quiver of the horse. While the beast staggered a dozen steps, he searched the brush, the breastworks, the encroaching forest growth, and saw only the one warrior rushing toward him. A youngster, Leslie told himself, unblooded and thirsty for his scalp. He let himself fall with the horse, drawing his pistol as he fell; lying with one cheek to the grass, he saw the Shawnee leap a stump and plunge at him with lifted hatchet. The misericord slipped softly through the gay band of yellow that ran like a belt around the copper belly. The hatchet cut the sod six feet away. The yellow paint turned red. In cold anger Leslie took the scalp; he was not sure whether he or the tyro warrior had been the greater fool; altogether, they had almost destroyed the limestone manor before it was even started. Reluctantly, Leslie left the road, running southwestward through the hills, fiercely resentful of the delay.

In the end, it was the delay that saved him.

Two miles from the trail he turned north again. From a hazel copse, late in the afternoon, he looked out across a rolling valley and saw the road far ahead, winding westward through Crab Tree Bottom. It vanished into distance, into a purple gash between blue ridges. Fifteen miles beyond the ridges, through the twisting defiles of Turtle Creek, lay Braddock's battlefield; beyond that, four miles northwestward, lay Fort Pitt. Leslie wiped the streaming sweat out of his eyes and ran on; the linsey leggings and the fresh mocassins Robin Stuart had found for him were drenched black; the deerskin shirt Robin borrowed for him he had discarded hours before, except for a long strip cut from the skirts of it to bind his feet when the moccasins gave out.

He ran cautiously, from cover to cover, following the windings of dry creek-beds, seeing the sunset a red glare above the gap at Turtle Creek, seeing it fade and leave the ridges charred black against the sky. A ravine with steep banks shut out the hills; stars came and looked down at him between the leaning willows. When the ravine lost itself at last in a dried-out swamp, he saw that the charred ridges had been rekindled.

A red glare hung again over the deep gash of Turtle Creek. Through the hot, pressing night he heard the jingle of sleigh bells. He stopped running. Began, instead, a stealthy creeping up the steep ridge. Came, step after slow step, to the brink of the defile. Saw the red gut of valley teeming, churning, swarming with savages.

Their fires stretched for a mile, staining the dark reaches of the creek, dancing on the dark walls of the ravine. Around the fires, the warriors were dancing also, whorls of black bodies, blackly shadowed, redly lighted. Each writhing, leaping circle swirled around its own vortex of leaping flame. A phrase leaped into Leslie's brain. He had heard Peter Lanness describe a war dance of the Ottawas:

Hell gone for a sleigh ride!

Out of the hellish ravine, out of the obscene yelling, rose the jingle of the bells. Fire glistened on them where they hung to the clout belts of howling Delawares. A naked, copper leg, thrust suddenly into the glare of fire, showed anklets studded with a double row of white man's sleigh bells. Leslie crept over the brink of the defile, crept down the rock-strewn bank. When he was close enough to be sure that there were no white men pinioned, waiting for death, no fresh scalps dangling on coup sticks in the frenzied dances, no white women's clothing on the squaws banked beyond the fires, he crept up to the brink again.

He had been, once more, too confident—so confident the Forbes road was unwatched that the lone Shawnee had almost shot him from his horse, so confident Bouquet would save Fort Pitt that he had begun to dream again of South Mountain, and Diantha, and the wage she had bargained for.

With a groan, he turned his back on the distant Forks and slipped down the ridge. If he would save Diantha, he must warn Bouquet.

A little after daylight, at a turn of road beside the Loyal Hanna, a startled scout threw his rifle to his shoulder, and dropped it at the sound of a white man's voice. Leslie, shuffling past him, saw black snags of teeth above a yellowed beard.

Under a burning sun, in moving dust, the army dragged itself seventeen miles in one afternoon. After the first three hours, its canteens were empty. The springs were dry; the streams were twists of bare sand, of mud baked and cracked into mosaics. At intervals the red-kilted pipers of the Black Watch flung their wild "Come to the Feast" into the hills ahead; at intervals the big drum tolled the marching cadence; behind the pipes and the drum, the colors drooped, moving as the men moved, bent forward, listless. Around them hung the dust; the regimental flag, buff silk with the gold "XLII" upon it, took on the hue of the dust; the very roses and thistles, twined around the Roman numbers, turned brown as if they were wilting in the heat.

Half a mile ahead, the fringe of scouts appeared out of the valley, moving slowly up rounded hills. They made a ragged line of dots; the dots seemed to jump about, now here, now there, though actually each dot barely crawled; a dot vanished into a fold of earth, and abruptly, away to one side, a similar dot come out of a clump of trees. Watching them was a dizzy business. Leslie, riding with Robin Stuart in the gap between the rear of the Black Watch and the leading company of the Seventy-seventh, found the dots blurring and losing themselves against the parched brown hills. The Forty-second began to climb. "Are ye sure there *is* any Bushy Run?" Robin asked him, the burr of his voice thicker with the dust in his throat.

"Just over this line of hills. We'll be atop it in ten minutes, and drinking in half an hour. How long d'you think Bouquet will wait there?"

"Only until dark, Arnie. We'll march off and leave the campfires burning, to make y'r red friends think we're set there for the night. Did I not tell ye, man, he is a grand soldier? *Whush!* Did ye hear that?"

The two plodding regiments heard it, a single shot. Heads went up. A quick stir ran down the column like a shiver. Then the files stiffened; the ripple of bayonets above the feathered bonnets swung into a tight, quick rhythm. Over the hill, another shot cracked out . . . another . . another. A dozen burst in a straggling volley. Up ahead, the knot of shirtmen who marched behind the fringe of scouts spread out, like a fan flipped open, and went running into the brush. Bouquet whirled by at a gallop. The pipers wheeled out to the side of the road. Two companies of the Forty-second, light infantry, went up the hill at the double. Just under the crest, still running, they wheeled, one company to the right, one to the left; wheeled again, up the slope into line. The line, steel tipped, went out of sight.

The shots blended into a crackle that was like flames crackling through dry brush, uneven but unceasing.

Panting, with sweat streaming, with claymores clacking against their thighs, with bearskin helmets slanting forward, the grenadiers of the Black Watch left the column and swung into line of battle. They met, as they crossed the hilltop, a fusillade that hung the scrub oaks to their right with balls of smoke. Steadily, precisely, the double rank of bearskins turned on its flank, hung an instant, fired once, and charged. Behind them, from other scrub oaks, a volley blazed into their backs. Panting, half blind with sweat, the light infantry that was left of the Forty-second deployed in the hazel brush to the left of the road and charged the woods from which the volley came. On both sides of the hill the firing redoubled; smoke rose above the stunted oaks; out of the smoke came a frenzied yelping.

"Come to the Feast!" shrilled the pipes of the Black Watch, playing the Seventy-seventh up the slope. As it came, the woods on both sides blazed and spewed smoke. Men fell. The column shrank in upon itself. A line of naked, bounding bodies broke from the cover of the hazel scrub and came on, yelling.

Commands. A stiffening. A level flash of light as the muskets of the Seventy-seventh came up together. A rolling crash. A roll of smoke smothering the road. Out of the smoke a rush of men.

The Montgomery Highlanders, charging, met the Shawnee hatchets with the bayonet. Grenadiers to the left of the road, light infantry to the right, they cleared the scrub oaks for three hundred yards. Bounding, howling, the Shawnees fled before them. Bounding, howling, they came back again as the Highland line drew off.

Up the road at a gallop came the pack train. Behind it burst a new clamor. Two companies of the Seventy-seventh went down to help the hard-pressed rear-guard; between them, plunging, squealing, colliding, the loaded horses stormed up the hill. Packs, ripped open, strewed corn meal in the trampled road. Shots from the forest edge tumbled beast after beast out of the jostling herd.

A teamster on a tall bay galloped through the brush to check the stampede at the hill top; a ball gouged through the horse just back of the ribs; he reared, spouting blood, and swung at a mad run toward the crackling woods. The teamster, sawing at the reins, tried desperately to stop him, gave up, flung himself out of the saddle. His foot caught in the stirrup and he fell and was dragged. His jacket pulled up over his head, and then his shirt. When a second shot stopped the horse, he got up blindly, clawing at the garments about his face, his back streaming from a dozen gashes. Three Indians pounced upon him as he stood there pawing; two struck him with their hatchets, but the third jerked off the coat and shirt and scalped him while he stood erect. He fell, still shriek-ing, and a grenadier, prone behind a stump, shot down the warrior who held the scalp.

Soldiers and shirt-men, wagoners with long whips and sergeants with bright axes swinging, they got the remnant of the horses into the scanty shelter of a locust grove to the right of the road. Firing, loading, firing again, the Highlanders got themselves somehow into a circle around the hill, half way down the slope, their backs to the pack train, their bayonets to the swarming woods that hemmed them in.

Arnett Leslie, a dead man's musket in his hand, came back with Robin's company from a headlong charge and dropped where a tree, uprooted, had left a pocklike hollow. Along the fallen trunk, a squad of the Black Watch crouched. Toward them, through the hazel clumps, a flood of painted Ottawas welled up across the ground the white men had abandoned. They fired as they came. Behind the log, the ramrods slid home, the musket barrels slid out; the grenadiers fired, scrambled over the fallen trunk, and charged with a wild, high cry. Leslie, running with them, saw a head with horns and fur above a crimson face, fired from the hip, and saw the horns root the grass as the Ottawa kicked and flopped about in dying. The pack fled howling; the grenadiers turned back; after them, when they had reloaded, came the horned, daubed warriors.

That was the battle.

There was the round knob of hill, parched and waterless. There was the road, running across its rounded top, running down to Bushy Run and plenty of water, half a mile away. There was the locust grove, a little below the crest, where frightened teamsters fought to hold the frightened horses, stripped off the packs, heaped them into a crude fence, a crude barricade. There were the clumps of stunted oaks, the tangles of laurel, the patches of hazel brush. There was, below them, a strip of open ground, and then, at the bottom of the hill, thick woods whence came a ceaseless yelling, a ceaseless fire; whence came, also, one rush after another that must be driven back.

Through the burning afternoon the two regiments—they were, actually, not one full regiment—endured the fire, the thirst, the certainty that they were surrounded and outnumbered. They knelt, fired, rose, charged down the open slope. The long, dry grass was slippery; the men's shoes were worn slick from a hundred and eighty miles of Old Iron Head's road. Charging, they slipped and staggered; turning when the savages fled before them, they slipped and fell, clawing at the grass, squirming for safety. Some of them died under the Indian knives and mauls before they could gain their feet, and those who survived looked down from the thin firing line at their scalped and bloody heads.

Men's bodies ran with sweat. The white, red and green checkers of the Highland bonnets turned black with it. The scarlet jackets turned black; the kilts hung soaked and clinging around sun-scalded thighs. Dust caked on streaming faces, and the streams dug furrows through it; bloom from the dry grass caught in the sweat drops under the eyes, under the lower lip; the cartridges drew black rings around straining mouths.

There was the taste of fur, the bite of powder gas in the throat and nose. The sun slid down behind the Bushy Run ravine and left the four hundred men inside the ring of death.

Not all of the four hundred were thirsty. There were more than thirty dead. But the wounded made up for those who were dead in the agony of their thirst; there were more than forty of the wounded; they lay among the sacks of flour and corn meal, among the trampling horses, and moaned and cried for water.

In the dark, Bouquet called his officers together. They sat on the sacks and talked. Not much; there was not much to say. Without the food and the wounded, the men who were left might cut their way through to Fort Pitt, or back to Bedford. If they left the food behind, Fort Pitt would starve, and they with it. If they retreated to Bedford, Fort Pitt must surrender, or fight on until, starving, its men grew too weak to stop the rushes, the women too weak to quench the fires. There was no talk of leaving either the food or the wounded; the Black Watch, the Seventy-seventh would not save themselves. There was a word or two about the thought in every man's mind: Braddock's battlefield lay off there to the west, a short day's march away. Braddock had gone into the battle of the Monongahela with twelve hundred men, with cannon; four hundred savages had destroyed him. Bouquet had now on this hill above Bushy Run something less than three hundred and fifty men. He asked Arnett Leslie, calmly, how many warriors he thought were around him.

"All the Shawnees, probably," Leslie answered, "from Fort Pitt, with all the Delawares and all the Mingoes. Say five hundred men. The Forty-second had Ottawas in front of them this afternoon."

"The jolly fellows with the horns," Robin said from the next meal sack. "They sounded hoarse."

"Their voices are harsher," Bouquet put in. "Glaywyn * should be glad to be rid of them. Who else?"

"Wyandottes—not many, probably—and a few young bucks from the Miamis. Perhaps," his throat tightened at what he saw when he thought of them, "a few Ojibway from Major Gladwyn's neighborhood. I saw none, but they have been at Pitt's Town."

"Altogether?"

"Altogether, six hundred warriors."

"If Ecuyer could strike them from the rear with the Fort Pitt garrison," a captain of Montgomery Highlanders suggested.

* Gladwyn, commandant at Detroit, in the Ottawa and Ojibway country.

"I will try to get through," said Leslie, and felt Robin's hand objecting, plucking at his arm.

"No." Bouquet spoke decisively. "If the attempt failed, it would doom Fort Pitt."

"It is doomed," some one said grimly out of the dark, and went unrebuked. Around the foot of the parched hill, the yelling burst suddenly into a triumphant chorus.

Leslie turned to face Bouquet across the faint sheen of Robin's crossbelts:

"I am not a soldier in fact, Colonel. I am only a former major of militia, here by your courtesy. May I recall to you how you beat the French Indians at the Loyal Hanna?"

"Of course, Major. The Maryland men earned the right to speak at any council. Did you know Shelby, who fought and killed a chief outside the barricade that day?"

"Ay. It was outside the barricade I was thinking of. You fought them first outside, and then retreated, and when they came on, hot and yelling, you turned on them at the palisade and whipped them. Both you and Shelby were audacious that day."

"Which is to say, Leslie, that you would risk a retreat here to draw them on and trap them, eh?"

"Something like that, sir." Startled voices jumped out at him. Bouquet said, in his blunt, calm way:

"Good. Good. We shall talk about that."

There was no sleep on the hill that night. The yelling and the moaning never ceased. At down the moans were fainter, but the howls redoubled. Men looked to the priming in their pans, looked down at the ring of woods where painted bodies capered just out of range, looked at each other, croaked, swallowed at their furred tongues or at the hearts in their throats. Leslie, walking with Bouquet and Stuart along the firing line, saw the trim Highland regulars dirty and unkempt as his hardbitten militiamen behind the palisades of Fort Pitt. Before the sun was level with the tops of the scrub oaks, the hill was hot. It was possible, in the clear, bright air, to see a long way.

The Forbes road, running through the circle of beleaguered men, stretched away east and west, empty, peaceful. Standing in the wheel tracks, it was difficult to believe that to walk along them down the brown hillside was to die. The road, homely and familiar, strengthened the sense of isolation. It was as if, still alive, these two regiments were already in the region of the dead. Beyond them, along those ruts they had trod, was the land of the living, remembered, almost visible, but out of reach. Even the water was out of reach, and thirst intensified to torture.

The sun mounted, the heat increased, the fight began again. Rush, counter-rush, retreat, it repeated itself. There were more dead, more wounded. Sure that their trapped prey could not escape, the Indian warriors would not face a charge. They ran, yelping, ahead of the bayonets; and when the bayonets went back to fill the gap they had left in the firing line, they sucked the Indians back with them.

"We beat them every time, but we never win," Robin panted. He looked down at the blood dripping from his finger ends, and held out his left arm to Leslie. "Damme, they burned me, Arnie. Ye'd think I was a gentleman, fighting a duel before breakfast. 'T was in the left elbow y'r noble Lord Dick furrowed ye, was it not?"

"Ay, and we had a drink on it," said Leslie, smiling.

"The devil fly away with ye! Will ye have done with speakin' of drinks, man? 'T is all right for Bouquet to tease these red devils into thinkin' we're about to howl king's cruse, but I canna stand teasin' concernin' liquid."

"I think," said Leslie as he cut away the sleeve of Robin's jacket and bound a strip of shirt around the gash in his elbow, "I think Bouquet's about done with teasing them."

In the locust grove where the pack horses jerked at their pickets and the wounded who could still hold a musket lay waiting with their shoulders to the barricade of sacks, the pipers of the Black Watch began to play:

> Fareweel to Lochaber,
> Fareweel to my Jean,
> Where heart-some wi' her,
> I hae mony days been. . . .

Around the firing line, men licked their lips, loosened the claymores in their scabbards, wiped sleeves across their eyes to see. High and plaintive, the pipes sang:

> Lochaber no more.
> Lochaber no more.
> We'll maybe return to Lochaber no more.

From the woods below the north slope, a surge of naked bodies swept up the hill; a company of grenadiers fired, charged, and swept it back. The pipes played on.

Stuart spoke softly to his crouching men. The lament changed, the music quickened; the pipers went screaming into the shrill defiance of "Come to the Feast."

"They're coming," Robin said hoarsely, and drew his claymore clear.

Out of the woods that lay between the white men and Bushy Run leaped another howling rush. Stuart waved his hand; behind the next company a bearded officer waved back.

"Present, *firelocks!*" The pipes stopped on a high, wailing cry. "Remember, it's fire and run this time. Take aim . . . *fire!*"

The two light companies got to their feet in the hanging smoke. Instead of charging, they began to break and fall back. They straggled, drifted along the face of the hill, began to run. Behind them, the rushing warriors raised a yell of triumph. Around them, the companies that had not broken began to move back, shortening the line, closing the gap in the circle. The whole front facing Bushy Run bent in, retreating as the torrent of painted bodies poured up the hill. The whole front gave way . . . except that on one side of the hill a company of grenadiers, crouching, running, sped through the hazel coverts *toward* the oncoming savages . . . except that on the opposite side of the hill, a company of light infantry did the same thing.

Between them, pell-mell, rushed the howling pack, straight for the baggage train.

Ahead of the rush, in full flight, Robin Stuart's company and the other that had broken with it ran headlong to the rear, toward Ligionier. They met, those two broken companies, at the far end of the baggage park. Met, fell with the cool discipline of veterans into line, wheeled, went at a dead run southward along a wooded spur that stuck out from the knob of the hill.

The white man's two traps were set.

Bouquet sprang one of them as the Indian charge reached the floursack barricade.

From both sides, the companies that had run crouching into ambush in the hazel brush rose and fired point-blank into the huddled mass, loaded, fired, and charged with the bayonet.

On the wooded spur Robin Stuart's two companies wheeled right again to face the west. As the second volley from the ambushed companies crashed into the trapped Indians inside the circle, Stuart sprang the second trap. In close order, with leveled bayonets, the light infantry burst out of the woods along the spur and struck the flank of the Indian firing line outside the circle.

There was, ahead of them, a strip of brush, a scatter of stunted oak, an open space, and then the woods. High and fierce as the Shawnee scalp yell, the Highland pibroch rose above the crash of firing. Thrusting, stabbing, the two companies ripped through the brush and the oak scrub. They swept into the open ground a score of screeching, hacking Delawares. The left flank company, plunging into the woods, drove out another score. The Black Watch had them hand to hand at last. Feathered bonnets flew to meet feathered scalplocks. Under tartan kilts, bare legs locked with legs that were bare from breechclout to moccasin.

Leslie, fighting with clubbed musket, saw a Shawnee dodge a soldier's bayonet thrust, knock up the gun barrel, and throw the man off his feet with a hand grappled in the badger fur of his sporran. Striking with the butt, Leslie missed, went to his knees, and got the savage by the buffalo hair of his own war-sack and wrenched him clear. The Highlander's bayonet ripped the red throat open.

Up and down the brown slope the mêlée spread. Knife against claymore, gun butt against gun butt, it swirled west around the turn of the hill toward Bushy Run. It met, in full retreat, the horde that had rushed the baggage train and found itself caught between two fires. There was, for a headlong moment, a crush of two hundred men fighting body to body.

A sergeant of the Black Watch took a Delaware maul full in the face and went down, his Lochaber ax flying from his grasp. His hand, groping, closed on a dry mullein stalk. As he dragged himself toward it, scrambling for a footing on the slippery grass, a greased and red-daubed warrior snatched up the ax and whirled it. The blade fell once on the clutching hand and severed it, fell again on the neck of the red jacket and stuck there. The sergeant sprawled face down, twitching, the severed hand still clenched around the mullein stalk. Robin, his broken claymore in his fist, broke through the press and snatched up the ax; whirling, it crushed the head of the Delaware stooping with his knife at the sergeant's hair. Three warriors closed in; the reddened ax swung again and sent one of them staggering; the others leaped under the haft and gripped Robin by the arms and waist. Leslie saw him fight free of the mêlée, the ax gone, his fingers on one painted throat; saw him break the other's grip and swing away; saw that the reeling Indian had his kilt gripped in both hands. The kilt, unwinding, spun Robin full about; his fingers slipped; spinning helplessly, he flew down the slope like a boy thrown loose from a children's game of crack-the-whip.

"Robin!" Leslie cried at him. "Robin, I'm coming!"

The stock of his clubbed musket broke off short on a shaven skull.

A knife drove for his ribs. A hatchet, whirling, struck him on the head. Falling, he saw Robin go down under another lifted hatchet.

The grenadiers of the Forty-second, roaring, came down the hill and swept the mêlée into the woods below it.

☆

☆   ☆

THE SILENCE, for most of the men and women in Fort Pitt, was harder to bear than the waiting.

They knew, after the seventh day of August, that something stark and terrible had happened in the hills beyond Braddocks's field. On that day, a horde of Indians poured past the fort.

They flourished scarlet jackets and feathered bonnets. They carried, on long poles, fresh and ghastly scalps. They waved like banners the long tartan kilts of Highland soldiers. They shouted, brandishing their trophies, taunting the haggard garrison that lined the palisades. But they did not stop.

Men, women, horses and baggage, they streamed across the Allegheny a half mile upstream and vanished into the hills.

Ecuyer, stubborn and cautious, kept the gates closed and the drawbridge up. The five hundred pent up inside the walls lived on with their hunger, with the sickening stenches, with the burning heat. After the days and nights of ceaseless musketry, the silence was unbelievable. Women, face to face at the ovens where there was nothing to cook, screamed at each other to make themselves heard, and felt their nerves jump and quiver when the sound struck their ears and pierced them.

Diantha smiled wanly at her brother and shook her head.

"Please, Bob. Don't argue. There can be no more danger. I shall go mad if I stay here, listening, listening."

She pulled the limp skirts of the blue gown out through the pocket holes, and heard Bob rally her:

"Primping again, though your feet are bare. D'you mean to crape your hair, too, so that you may pick nettles in style?"

She made a face at him, and sobered.

"I keep thinking of Peg. The day Arnett was tried for being a coward, she said to me, here in this room: *I lie awake at night, praying that Valentine Arnold will be shot; I want him to be hurt, so that he will need me and want me again.* Now she has her wish, and I envy her. I envy her, Bob. I keep praying for Arnett to be wounded—oh, even terribly wounded—so that they will bring him back and let me care for him. Even with that awful gash across Val's face, she is happy; she has him . . . safe. I have nothing but the listening."

She went out into the unbelievable silence.

Tom Yeardley sat on the wood frame of the well, one foot drawn up across his thigh and cradled in both hands. He untangled himself and came lumbering to meet her.

"Will he . . . ?"

Tom shook his head, his face screwed up into wrinkles, like a baby on the verge of crying.

"No, Diantha. I've just come from Ecuyer. He'll not let a man go out of rifle shot. He says, if there is any army to be found by a scout on the Forbes road, it will come marching in sooner or later. He'll not risk another man to go looking for it."

"I knew he would not. No . . . no . . . I am all right, Tom."

She smiled, and went quickly toward the covered way.

In front of the guardhouse, Captain-lieutenant Phillips stood with heels precisely together, watching while a sergeant with his coat in rags and his halberd polished to mirror brightness dressed a company of the Royal Americans into rigid perfection. The Royal Americans were very gaunt and very threadbare, but they were regulars. Such buttons as they still possessed shone like the sergeant's halberd.

Phillips, facing about, saw Diantha in the group of women clustered below the Flag bastion, and raised his hand in salute. As he brought it smartly down, he called out to her:

"Today. I feel it."

"'T is the soup you feel," she flashed at him. "They tell me the king himself will have nettle broth for his dinner when he hears of it."

Phillips gave her a silent cheer as he went by at the head of the rhythmic column. The steadiest regiment that bore the king's cypher could teach Diantha Leslie nothing about courage.

The drawbridge swung slowly down with a great clatter and shriek of chains. The musket stocks struck with a precise slap against hands weak with sleeplessness and hunger; threadbare gaiters swung into unison through the gates and out across the cracked mud of the King's Highway. After them trooped the women with baskets on their arms, with knives and shears and sickles. The regulars wheeled smoothly toward the river bank, deployed, and ran into skirmish line among the naked chimneys.

Between the picket line and the watching gunners on the walls, the women fell to snipping the tops from the nettles growing rank behind the ruined cabins. They talked a little. Once there was a laugh, quickly smothered. It seemed, in the unnatural quiet, like blasphemy.

There was nothing, no loud talking, no heedless laughter, to keep out the sound that came, faint and far, across Massacre pond and the hills above it. The click of shears stopped. The baskets lay forgotten among the nettles. The picket line heard it and stood staring toward Grant's Hill. The women came out of the weeds and stood behind the pickets.

High and clear, the music of bagpipes came out of the forest and shook the silence to pieces. The walls of Fort Pitt filled with men; the drawbridge swayed with the stampede of a shouting, weeping, jostling crowd. From the walls and from the baked roadway where the women stood rose a murmur that swelled and swelled.

Out through the forest wall came the swing of red kilts. Behind them came the glint of steel.

The murmur rose into a formless sound that was like a great laugh and a great sob at once.

The red kilts came down over the hill, between the first skeleton chimneys. They came with a jaunty, victorious swing, the big drum thundering ahead, the pipers blowing with all their might. Wave after wave, shining in the sun, the bayonets of the Seventy-seventh dipped down to the ford and poured along the King's Highway. Behind them, wave after wave, the Black Watch filled the road between the ruined cabins, steel blades like a burnished hedge above them, feathers cockily aslant, red jackets bobbing, sporrans swinging.

The formless shouting grew into a roar. On the crazy, jack-straw walls, men swung their hats, flourished their muskets overhead, and cheered in a paroxysm of relief.

THE REVOLUTION

1775–1783

THE REVOLUTION
1775-1783

During the terrible encampment at Valley Forge, a committee of Congress worked out with Washington a plan for reorganization of the Continental Army. Baron von Steuben and General Greene took posts respectively as inspector-general and quartermaster-general; discipline of the strictest sort hammered out an army, the Continentals, after three years of alternate cajoling and cursing of unreliable, if willing warriors, by their commanding officers. The old days of reliance upon wayward militia—whose officers were selected by every means from pot-house popularity to downright bribery—were at an end. After the institution of the Continental Army, Washington no longer was forced to count upon miracles to win military success.

Bennington is an admirable example of the militia system performing at its best, against bull-headed troops and officers of the XVIIIth century school professional type, functioning at their worst. Freeman's Farm—or Saratoga—on the other hand, exposes brilliantly the breakdown of morale and efficiency resultant from an excess of private judgment and lack of authority. Saratoga was a triumph, not of tactics or strategy, but of pure personality with the headlong, insubordinate Arnold leading an inspired armed mob.

For a further contrast, one perceives how the small, disciplined core of Herkimer's army stopped St. Leger at Oriskany. The account of Yorktown may seem out of place in this collection because of the prim precision of the author's XVIIIth century prose. One wonders what a modern novelist would do with a girl who served undetected in the Continental Army?

This account incidentally, is the earliest known novel which describes American military history from the point of view of an American and so has at least a museum value.

BREED'S HILL
by F. VAN WYCK MASON

THE 4TH SQUAD of Captain Knowlton's company was busy making as many cartridges as it could from a miserably insufficient issue of powder. When each man drew only a gill of the coarse black stuff, David cocked his eyebrow.

"Is that all? God's teeth! Down in Virginia a man takes more than this to a turkey shoot!"

"Wish to God we was going turkey shooting," Haskins grunted. "How's that Tower musket you drew?"

A few choice blasphemies expressed David's contempt of all smooth bore muskets in general and of this specimen in particular.

"How in blazes do the British expect a man to hit anything with no rear sight?" he fumed. "Damn' thing weighs fifteen pounds and won't shoot straight beyond sixty yards. You can't hit the broad side of a barn with this damned thing."

Curious, Billy Colgate came over. "What you doing with that wire?"

"Rigging a rear sight of sorts," snapped the Virginian, twisting some strands of copper wire into a loop just forward of the lock. "It's mighty poor, but it's better than nothing." He sighted down the cumbersome brown barrel. What wouldn't he give to lay hands on the long-barreled Deckhard he had left in Tom MacSherry's care? Up to two hundred yards he could give these serious-talking Yankees a shooting lesson.

Johnny from the next room called, "Hi! Any cartridge paper in there? We're fresh out."

Around five of the afternoon an orderly, running streams of sweat from under his wig, came clumping up into the North Entry of Hollis Hall and inquired for the commanding officer. Alert in an instant, Knowlton came out, thin-lipped mouth still full of bread and honey.

"What is it?"

"General Ward says you should fall in your men on the parade ground right away," the orderly puffed. "No fifes or drums. Bring along

From: *Three Harbours*. Copyright 1938 by the author. J. B. Lippincott Company.

any axes or spades you've got." With that the messenger spun on his heel and went clumping off. He walked on the side of his boots as if his feet hurt.

"That's a newfangled way of delivering marching orders," Captain Knowlton complained. "Bellinger!" He licked his fingers free of honey and went behind his desk. "The company will fall in within fifteen minutes. Every man will carry at least five flints and as much powder and ball as he can lay hold of. Lieutenant Bisley will take command of this detachment. I'm riding over to Inman's farm."

"Hey! What about food, Cap'n?" called Billy Colgate from the stairs.

"Let the men bring whatever is handy," Knowlton advised. "They may get fed—but more likely they won't."

Drums rattled in all directions. Voices shouted. The Harvard Yard began to fume with activity. Out on the edge of town conch shells, carried as bugles by the Salem company, began to moan. They made an eerie sound.

"Say, Cap'n, where are we goin' to?" presently demanded Bellinger. Tucking a pen above his ear, he handed over a page of instructions written in a flowing hand. It was as neat as copperplate.

"'We?' You're not going," Knowlton said shortly, buckling on his sword.

Bellinger's permanently rounded shoulders bent and when he straightened, he had in his hand a huge bell-mouthed blunderbuss such as boarding parties on men-of-war carried.

Said he, squinting over the square lenses of his spectacles, "Listen to me, Tom Knowlton; them Britishers' damned stamp tax ruined my stationery business and last month they broke my press to bits. If you think I'm not going along, you're plumb addled!"

The captain started to get mad, but being a good officer, laughed instead. "Very well, get your tail shot off, then!"

"Where we heading?" Bellinger persisted, cramming into his pockets a supply of cartridges.

"Your guess is as good as mine, Joe. This may be only one of those practice marches General Putnam is always hollering for."

An interval of more or less orderly haste ensued. It was punctuated by the frantic curses of soldiers searching their bedding straw for items of equipment.

Some found it strange that the company's newest recruit, though penniless and with only a swollen jaw and a missing tooth to show for a night's fun, should turn up so completely outfitted. Knowlton merely smiled. He felt small concern regarding Shaun Mahoney's ability to look out for himself. In the regulars soldiers got that way.

Already the parade ground swarmed with militiamen attempting to locate their units. Fanning themselves with wide farmer's hats and sober black tricornes, the Provincial army stood mustered in long lines, subdivided into companies and regiments. Bits of straw sticking to their clothes gave a lot of them a ludicrous, bucolic appearance. Not a few had caught chaff in their hair.

Self-important junior officers walked about, scarlet-faced, bellowing through cupped hands. "Shake a foot, you dunderheads!" "Gerrish's regiment this way!" "Whitcomb's men here!" "Prescott's men fall in here!"

Under a big maple stood old General Artemas Ward; he was too sick to sit a horse. Nervously he tapped the ground with an ivory-headed walking stick. Now and then he would bend over and trace a design on the earth to illustrate some point to one of his staff.

Three-deep, hot and excited officers clustered about the Commander-in-Chief. Dumpy little Colonel Bridge, blowing out his fat cheeks; General Putnam, hearty, big-faced and bellicose; Colonel Samuel Gerrish dressed to the nines in a snowy white tie wig, mulberry suit and an elegant French walking sword; Joseph Frye, newly appointed, but not yet commissioned Major-General. He looked somber and uneasy with this unfamiliar responsibility. Of more soldierly appearance was Colonel Gridley, hatchet-faced and standing very straight, as befitted a veteran of the Indian wars. He had just been designated commandant of "the regiment of the train"—of artillery.

Longest of all General Ward's head remained close to the white wig of Colonel William Prescott, a bold-appearing man with dark eyes and swarthy complexion. David almost laughed aloud when he first saw the Massachusetts Army's principal colonel. Of all things to wear on a march, Prescott had elected to don a bright blue and tan banyan—a sort of dressing gown! Around this he had fastened a belt very tight and had jammed under it a long French dueling rapier; even in its scabbard the weapon looked scarcely thicker than a tooth pick.

There were other colonels; David Brewer, Paul Sargent, Jonathan Ward were standing under the maple in a big hayfield northwest of the village—lately the troops had taken to parading around it. The sunset dappled their solemn expressions. All the staff was in civilian clothes except General Ward. No doubt he had felt it his duty, as Commander-in-Chief, to put on a militia uniform of faded blue.

Johnny bent forward from his place in the adjoining squad. "Hey, David! There they are! That's where we ought to be!"

"Wal, burn my pants! Ain't they pretty!" "Bet the redcoats runs a mile when they sees you!"

Raucous uproar followed the progress of the Wethersfield company towards their post. The Connecticut men, despite sheepish expressions, looked quite impressive and encouragingly martial in their cocked hats, blue and red uniforms and carefully pipeclayed gaiters and crossbelts. Wonder of wonders, they had even been equipped with cartouche boxes and bayonets!

Johnny scowled, "Ain't this just my luck? Going to war looking like a confounded rag-picker!"

A great majority of the Provincial troops were in homespun: gray, brown and neutral. Many favored three-cornered hats. The evening being sultry, they wore their coats knotted about their waists. Hardly any type of firearm manufactured within the past hundred years was not represented in the ranks, but, as far as David could see, there was not a single rifle in sight!

An hour passed and still the Provincials waited about in the dusk. Finally, the last stragglers showed up.

"Must be at least three thousand of us," Billy Colgate cried, white-eyed.

Mahoney ran a practiced eye over the muster. "Sonny, if there is here wan man over a thousan' I'll kiss yer butt before the whole brigade." Turning solemn, the Irishman tilted his flat, rather comical face in Corporal Haskins's direction. "Faith 'tis wings ye'd best be fitting to yer feet. God help these poor bhoys whin they faces up wid regulars. *Wurrah!* If he wasn't down to his last sixpence, Shaun Mahoney would niver be finding himself here!"

A drum, then another, commenced beating the long roll, exacting silence. When they had done, General Ward, leaning heavily on his stick and looking very haggard, limped out to face an army gathered in a great half moon.

He spoke briefly, succinctly, like a soldier. He reminded them of the heavy part they and their fathers had taken in long and victorious wars against the Frenchmen and the savages. The British, he told them, must be kept penned in Boston! There, General Gage's troops could do little harm. But once they got into the open country, the eighth plague of Egypt would be as nothing. He was, on the orders of the Committee of Safety, sending them on a mission of vital importance. No man was to flinch in his duty; it was not in the English tradition to shirk. They were to march at once.

No oratory, no fire-eating, David noted. Just a plain statement of fact.

The Commander-in-Chief turned heavily to a straight, handsome old man in a black surplice.

"Dr. Langdon, will you lead us in prayer?"

The snowy-haired president of Harvard stepped forward. Removing his scholar's cap, he knelt and clasped his hands before him. Slowly he raised tight-shut eyes to the evening sky. Hats whispered off by the hundred as militiamen followed suit, saving only those adhering to some denomination which forbade kneeling.

Mahoney fumbled until he found a rosary. That was no proper priest out there, he reflected, but he might as well draw a ration of salvation with the rest. As Dr. Samuel Langdon commenced to pray, beads began to slip through the deserter's calloused fingers.

"O Heavenly Father," the old man's deep and reverent voice rang far out over the crowded field, "grant to these, Thy unworthy servants, Thy blessing. Grant to them strength each man to do his part. Comfort those which are in fear, O Lord, and support them in their hour of trial.

"Make the light of Thy Countenance to shine upon their arms, O Lord, and grant wisdom to their leaders. I do humbly beseech Thee to grant eternal salvation to any of Thy servants who may be called in judgment before Thy Awful Throne. Forgive them their many trespasses against Thy law, O Lord, and sustain Thy servants as they enter into the Valley of the Shadow of Death. For the sake of our Lord Jesus Christ, Amen."

For some instants the army, the staff beneath the maple and the townsfolk hemming them in, remained kneeling. Then, to a great rattle and clanking of accoutrements, they followed Dr. Langdon's example and got to their feet.

☆

☆   ☆

"ATTEN-*shun*! Shoulder firelocks!" bawled Lieutenant Bisley, trying to imitate Tom Knowlton's way of giving orders.

When hands slapped stocks in a quick succession of miniature reports, Johnny felt a tingle race the length of his spine. He had never stood straighter, had never shouldered a musket more smartly. His high-strung features were tense. At last! Here at last was the first thin taste of a soldier's career. It was somehow poetic, he felt, to begin as a simple private. Next week a corporal's rank; within a month a sergeancy; then, having won his spurs on the battlefield, surely a cornet's or an ensign's commission! Later would come a position on the staff. He would climb up and up, like Grand Uncle Arthur who died, a Lieutenant-General, in Seringapatam. But he wished to blazes he was wearing a certain red and blue uniform already cut out at the tailor's.

"Forward—march!"

The Connecticut detachment picked up the cadence of drums massed back of the staff. To "The Pioneer's March" they followed Colonel Prescott's fine Massachusetts regiment out of the field. The march was towards the Charles Town road, towards the British in Boston! Johnny's heart sailed like a buck clearing a windfall.

Colonel Prescott's horse got frightened and broke wind with a shattering blast. A great roar of belly laughter rang in the ranks.

"I hear Billy Prescott's brought him along a bugler," Haskins hollered, and Lieutenant Bisley glared at him.

Now that the troops were in column David had further opportunity to appreciate the extraordinary disorganization of the Provincial forces, the disparity in their numbers. In some companies marched as few as twenty or thirty men; others mustered nearly a hundred, approximately the strength of other regiments. Nowhere could he see any flags or any insignia for the officers, beyond hastily improvised brassards. A few veterans wore a blanket rolled about their shoulders and the same experienced men carried a majority of the water bottles.

The 4th squad became but a minor ripple in a black river of men streaming northeast out of Cambridge along the inland road. The sullen rumble of wagon wheels grew loud in their ears.

"Left right, left right!" Corporal Haskins, slogging along bent-shouldered, wondered where they'd be a night hence. It was queer to be up so late. It must be almost nine. Usually him and Dorcas would be sound asleep and snoring by this time. Jerusha! How Dorcas had took on when he marched away across the north field to the highroad. He missed her, too. Weren't any decent cooks in this army.

Before the troops were well clear of the village, continual halts and delays began. At such times the men would light pipes and sit by the roadside, speculating on what was likely to happen. The veterans lay down full length. Mahoney, too. Little Billy Colgate was yawning, but tried to hide it. Several men kept wanting to move their bowels.

Now and then a horseman went clumping back towards the village.

" 'Tis lucky we are 'tis a dark night," remarked Mahoney, puffing on a short clay pipe. "A blindman could see the dust we're raising clear across Amurica."

"Where's the captain?" the Reverend Edgell called.

"Gone ahead to talk with old Put," Haskins told him. "I allow we'll pick up the rest of our boys down the road a piece."

A rider came clattering up the road, bawling, "Out of my way! Out of my way! Important business!"

"That'll be Gerrish," somebody said. "The old rumble-gut's been drinking again. Bet he makes tracks if things get hot."

The farther the column marched, the slower became its progress. Towards ten o'clock all the infantry was ordered off the road and, after an interminable delay, a train of farm carts, loaded to the top with picks, shovels and spades, bumped by. Nowhere were any lanterns lit.

Though the sun had long since vanished it remained surprisingly hot, and tempers grew shorter as the slow miles unreeled. Always men kept passing up and down the column asking for this company or that regiment. It was seldom they got a right answer.

David, lying on the dew-wetted grass, became aware of an unforgettable obbligato in the tramp of feet, unnaturally lowered voices, the creak of leather gear and the occasional clank of musket barrels bumping. Fireflies danced over almost every clump of shrubbery.

From various fields along the route waiting units fell in, steadily augmenting the column's length. By the time the van of the army had passed a bridge over Willet's Creek, the river of men flowed as far back as one could see.

David decided it was typical of Knowlton and Israel Putnam that, when Mr. Inman's farm buildings hove in sight, the remainder of the Connecticut men were waiting just where they should be and ready to march. Unlike some units, they did not indulge in loud talk.

The nearer the Provincials drew to Charles Town Neck, the fewer grew the trees. Above and below the road the terrain was now composed of well-grazed pastures which soon resolved into a series of long smooth ridges.

"Golly!" Billy Colgate, who had started ahead to try to find a spring, stopped suddenly, gaping at a distant row of lights. They were small as fireflies. But they stayed put. "Look at that! Why, Boston's big as all get out!"

"—And full of Britishers, Bub."

"I ain't afeared of 'em," he called in his thin voice. But the boy wondered what he might do if a big grenadier came rushing at him with a bayonet.

From the crest of a low hill more men began to make out the lights of Boston blinking far away, across the Charles.

"No lights. No pipes," Knowlton kept warning.

It was good to have him back, David felt, and for future reference studied the Connecticut captain's bearing, his methods.

The axles of an overloaded cart began to give, creaking loudly. "Stop that wagon! You men take out the shovels!"

For the Connecticut regiment this accident proved a passport. Because they carried picks and shovels, they were passed up along shadowy lines of men who cursed with envy.

"Them Connecticut horse thieves is going ahead to dig us a back-house," drawled a nasal voice from the dark.

"No, we ain't," Haskins promptly retorted. "You twerps ain't got the decency to use one!"

A guffaw was quickly checked by Colonel Prescott's growl of, "Next man opens his mouth I'll break his jaw! How far back is Colonel Frye's regiment?"

No one knew.

The starlight was just strong enough on Charles Town Neck to let the Provincials glimpse wet boulders and seaweed littering beaches to either side. After all, the Neck was less than forty feet wide, so the army had to slow up and jam together to cross it dry shod. As the van passed on over and found room again in a wide field lying behind the loom of Bunker's Hill, some kildeers whistled. Charles Town, David learned, was built on the point of a spoon-shaped peninsula, dominated by two grassy, treeless hills.*

At the foot of Bunker's Hill General Israel Putnam and Colonels Prescott and Gridley were engaged in heated argument. Now and then one of them would refer to a map by the light of a carefully hooded dark lantern. They were in deadly earnest. When he wasn't beating the palm of his left hand with his fist, Putnam, the Connecticut general, kept pointing towards Charles Town and Boston.

---

* Due to an error on the part of certain British Army cartographers, notably Montresor, Page, and de Bernière, Breed's Hill, lower and much nearer to Boston, was mismarked "Bunker's Hill." The real Bunker's Hill stood to the rear of Breed's Hill and was the scene of no fighting at all. Thus, the Battle of Bunker's Hill should properly be known as the Battle of Breed's Hill.—Author.

"Plague take a fort on Bunker's Hill!" he was rasping. "From Breed's Hill we can fire straight into Boston and singe Gage's wig. From Bunker's the range is too great, eh, Gridley?"

The engineer nodded reluctantly. "But there are no flanks to be covered and—"

Putnam's roundish face glowed a deep red. "To hell with the flanks! Gage will be too worried getting out of our range. Look!" He sank onto his heels and began jabbing at a map with the ferrule of his scabbard. "A battery on Breed's will drive the British ships out of the Mystic, out of the Charles, out of Boston Harbour—clear down to the Castle!"

Vehemently, Colonel Frye shook his head. "Nonsense! All you will accomplish is to sting Gage into action. A redoubt on Bunker's Hill would keep him where we want him—in Boston, and it wouldn't alarm him!"

"Where I want Gage," Putnam rasped, "is charging up to our muskets! There's been too confounded much shilly-shallying. Eh?"

Colonel Bridge had shoved forward a paper. "Those are the Committee of Safety's orders. Read them again, General." He was tired and the skin was gray around his mouth. "It says, 'A strong redoubt is to be raised on Bunker's Hill.' See? There it is. *Bunker's* Hill! 'With cannon planted to annoy the enemy coming out of Charles Town—'"

All at once Prescott, run out of the same mould as Israel Putnam, stooped over. His black eyes were hard and bright as he whispered into the Connecticut general's ear. Gridley fidgeted, stared anxiously out over the Mystic. The killdeers had fallen silent and only the grunting of bullfrogs in a mill pond off to the right broke the stillness. Uneasily, the troops on the beach and on the Neck waited.

Putnam got up, a hard grin on his mouth. "Gentlemen, we will obey the Committee's orders. We *will* fortify Bunker's Hill—after we have taken possession of Breed's Hill! Colonel Prescott will attend to it."

"You're a pig-headed old fool!" snarled Frye. "You'll get us all massacred."

"Silence! You'll answer for that later!"

"So will you!" Bridge cut in. "Look! A child can see how easy it is to get out-flanked on Breed's. I know! I have been there!"

☆
☆ ☆

"QUIET, FOR YOUR LIVES!" A whispered warning passed from mouth to mouth down the column. "Men-of-war out there. They'll shoot the hell out of us if they take alarm." Last murmurs of conversation died away.

After their six-mile march along a road dusty even at night, the men were thirsty and dog-tired. They climbed Bunker's Hill in a long ragged line, sweating under picks, shovels and lugging timbers of which gun platforms would later be built.

Mahoney frowned, looked back on the Neck and the column writhing up from Fort Number Three on the mainland. "Sure and won't there be ould Satan to pay if we have to skedaddle back over this bottleneck two jumps ahead av a baynet?"

Marching in loose order, Knowlton's Company toiled over the side of Bunker's Hill and followed Prescott and Gridley down a long slope across a series of pastures separated by low fences built of glacial stones. In them cow droppings lay thick and the stones and the grass were so soaking with dew that the men were glad to get back onto a road even if it was only a cart track used at haying time. Passing under an occasional willow tree, the track led straight towards the lights of Boston.

The leading regiment proceeded in straggling fashion in two lines, each one following a rut. They passed some trees, then deserted the track once more and descended into a humid and mosquito-ridden little valley. An explanation for the pests was soon forthcoming for, in turning right, the column crossed a marshy field. The *suck-sucking* of muck sounded loud, somehow obscene. In it more than one shoe was lost. Over to the left, a few trees were dotting a long slope which rose gently towards the summit of a hill similar to, but smaller than Bunker's. None grew near the summit.

"Wait here and keep quiet!"

The Connecticut men dropped their implements, rested their muskets beside a rail fence and began to dig the marsh slime out of their footgear. After that they were only too glad to stretch out and stare up at the stars.

"Say, can anybody see a man-o'-war?" It was Bellinger, the company clerk. Though his blunderbuss was much heavier than most of the firearms, he had kept up very well considering his thin, badly bowed legs.

"There's one," Billy Colgate replied in a quivering whisper. "A great big sucker!"

"Where?" demanded a dozen voices, several of them sounded nervous.

"If you'll sight right down this little valley, you can just make her out layin' off a point."

"Ye've good eyes, Bub," Haskins croaked. "I can't see a blessed thing."

So the enemy lay with shotted guns but half a mile away! The realization stung David's scalp. Removing his black, three-cornered hat, he rolled over on his stomach. He took care not to break powder charges, neatly rolled in newspaper, that were in his coat pockets. For a long time he studied the line of beach and water, shining the dullest imaginable silver under the stars, but could make out nothing except a series of stone fences. Then all at once he saw a tall-masted man-of-war, a brig.

Suddenly she seemed to dissolve in the gloom, to vanish completely. David tried a trick taught him long ago by an old Shawnee. He dropped his eyelids briefly then suddenly reopened them. The brig was even more clearly to be seen than before; even the sails furled on her yards, the streak along her side, and the black squares of gun ports interrupting it.

God's teeth, but he felt tired! He wondered how Johnny's martial spirit was bearing up. He reached down to rub the fetter scars on his ankles; they had begun to ache. This was hard going for men ill-fed and underexercised for six months. Damn! How handy the *Assistance's* cargo would come in right now. When he remembered that he carried but eighteen rounds of ammunition he licked his lips slowly, thoughtfully.

Presently a man with a dark lantern came slipping and sliding down from the summit of Breed's Hill. It was Colonel Prescott; the men immediately recognized him by his stature and straight carriage.

"Captain Knowlton?" he hailed in a cautious undertone.

"Here, sir!"

"Take your men and their tools to the top of Breed's Hill. Report to Colonel Gridley." And he hurried along the column.

The men began to sit up and look about.

"I don't feel so good," one of the Connecticut men announced suddenly. "I got a complaint in my bowels. Maybe I'd better go back?"

"I allow what you've got, Lem Barker, is the running complaint." Corporal Haskins spoke in a fierce undertone. "Just you bide where you are!"

Unhurriedly, Captain Knowlton knotted a white handkerchief about his arm. "You can see this. Come along." He picked up a spade and started slowly to breast the slope of Breed's Hill.

The 4th squad and the rest of the platoon scrambled after him with the long wet grass licking like little tongues. It soaked right through shoes and stockings. Gasping, they gathered at last on the hilltop and felt a faint breeze off the harbour fan their faces.

"See this line?" Old Colonel Gridley was showing Lieutenant Bisley and Captain Knowlton a white cord stretched over the earth in a straight line. "This marks the east wall of a redoubt. Dig down about four feet and throw the dirt towards Boston. Hurry! It will be dawn before we know it."

Other troops—Massachusetts men—came up carrying picks, mattocks and shovels—a lot of them. Under their captain's command the men awkwardly stacked arms.

Captain Knowlton pulled off his coat, spat on broad hands and drove his spade deep into the ground, saying, "Some of you fellows are dodgasted clumsy with a firelock, but you ought to be Jimdandies with a shovel. Remember one thing—if sunrise catches us above ground, we'll be nothing but a lot of dead heroes."

Dirt flew in a dark spray. Knowlton had been entirely right. With these tools the Connecticut farmers felt right at home.

Johnny paused, tore his shirt open and, gulping for air, grinned. "My God, you'd think there was gold down there!"

With an elbow David diverted an acid trickle of sweat from his eyes. "Pity you haven't got your uniform along. You could break it in right quick."

"Hush up," warned the Reverend Edgell, "and dig."

On David's hands, softened even beyond their usual tenderness, blisters formed and broke, leaving raw patches. Though his body had become one great ache, he kept on swinging a pick. Damned if a Virginian should slack up before a pack of psalm-shouting Connecticut Yankees!

The raw earth felt comforting, was heaping higher about the little redoubt. Every now and then some militiaman's spade would strike a rock and draw sparks. Prescott and Gridley strode about encouraging, scolding. They were everywhere.

Every half hour Captain Knowlton would lift a hand and call softly, "Catch your wind a while, boys." He never seemed to get excited or tired. And he never swore.

For awhile the men would lie flat, chewing grass stems and listening to the long-drawn calls of sentries posted only twelve hundred yards away over in Boston. On men-of-war nearer but still swinging unalarmed to their anchors, the watch called, "All's well."

They were wrong. All was far from well. They'd damned soon find out, the grimy Provincials whispered. Johnny fell to wondering what was going on in the rear of the Provincial Army.

Distinctly the *plop!* of fish jumping in the river reached the diggers.

Towards dawn the dew fell so heavily Mahoney picked up his coat and wrapped it about the action of his firelock.

Said he, "Bhoys, this dew would drown the devil av a big tomcat. When the time comes, ye'd best dry yer flints and reprime entirely."

Long since, he had selected the most favorable route for his retreat. Definitely, he intended to be one of those few who would get away in time.

Farther back along the peninsula fresh groups of militia were blundering about, seeking their posts. David could catch the impatient undertones of their officers. To his right some Massachusetts men were certainly making the dirt fly.

"Time," Knowlton called. He got up and chose a pickaxe this time. Drive and swing. Drive and swing. Would Matt Phipp or John Brush or the other Norfolk patriots be willing to work like so many niggers in a ditch? Probably they would. They were in earnest, too. He would give a lot to see George Leavitt's face if he could happen by right now and find his boon companion naked to the waist and sweating like a pig.

Over in Boston a rooster crowed. Then another and another, sleepily. Not like Hannibal's fierce call. Poor Hannibal!

Somebody remarked, "It's going to get light any minute." As if to bear him out robins commenced to chirp among some apple trees at the foot of a slope to the left.

"Why don't somebody come up and spell us?" Bellinger demanded wearily.

"Yes. Why don't they?" Haskins said. "Why the hell should we do all the work for the army?"

Billy Colgate sank trembling onto a pile of dirt. "What chances for some food?"

"The hell wid food—'tis watter I want," Mahoney panted. "Ain't there no watter near?"

Captain Knowlton said to Johnny, "Gilmorin, suppose you scout around, see if you can locate a spring." The young Virginian was patently exhausted but he was so very game the captain felt sorry for him.

"Yes, sir," Johnny smiled and, after saluting, went trotting off down the slope.

A dim milky quality was invading the darkness. The sky lightened perceptibly. Then up from the river floated a noise so thin and shrill as to sound ludicrous.

"Peep! Peep! Peep!"

"Bosun's pipe," Mahoney commented. "The lobster-backs will have seen us at last. Now watch what happens."

Oars rattled and a small boat put out from the man-of-war's stern.

She was carrying a sheet anchor with which to swing the brig about. The militia stayed their tools, peered anxiously at the two-master lying so ghostly to the eastward of the Charles Town shore. Down there voices bellowed, gun tackles creaked and whined and gun-carriage wheels rumbled across the decks.

Bom-m-m! A cannon shattered the pre-dawn stillness to atoms. Its report reverberated about Boston Harbour like a stroke on a titantic kettledrum. The startled Provincials were still catching their breaths when the man-of-war's whole starboard side seemed to explode into a blinding sheet of yellow flame. In minutest detail her spars, shrouds and masts revealed themselves. Lower on the hill sounded a terrific crackle of branches. It was followed by a succession of heavy thuds.

The Provincials for the most part flung themselves flat or, in frantic haste, sought the half-finished redoubt. A few, kneeling, began to pray wildly. One man clutched his head, sobbing that he was killed.

David felt his intestines writhe like angleworms in a can and into his mouth welled a sour, bitter-tasting fluid. But he wouldn't duck, not while one Yankee stayed on his feet. *Bom-m-m!* Another whistling screech.

"Come back here, you bloody coward! Come back here!" From the top of the hill somebody was yelling, but the deserter kept on running.

"Oh Christ—save me," whimpered Billy Colgate, hiding a twitching face in his arms.

"Dig, boys." Knowlton came stalking along, his face harsh and rigid as the ceremonial mask of an Iroquois sachem. "A cannon's bark is a hundred times worse than its bite. See what Colonel Prescott thinks of them? He's an old soldier, too."

The militiamen looked up. There, walking quietly on the yielding earth of the parapet was the Massachusetts colonel! He was pointing down the slope at something and when a third broadside boomed he calmly stooped, picked up a pebble and chucked it in the direction of the enemy.

"Get busy, boys," he called. "These iron musketeers whine, but they don't sting! Captain Trevett, I believe the parapet should be higher here."

Again a thuttering roar ended in a thud below, but higher on the hillside. David felt his throat close. So that was how cannonballs sounded when they came your way! Another ship started firing. They couldn't see her, but the ruddy flare of her guns threw the shoulder of Breed's Hill into relief.

The milky-gray quality of the sky was turning pink, so the militiamen made their shovels fly. The men-o'-war Mahoney identified as the *Lively,* 20 guns; the *Symmetry,* 20 guns; and a huge ship-of-the-line, the *Somerset,* 68 guns. They maintained a noisy but almost ineffectual bombardment.

Colonel Prescott and a couple of aides remained atop the parapet watching dawn extend the scope of vision. The Massachusetts colonel seemed worried about something to the left of the redoubt. Presently an aide came running down to Captain Knowlton.

Knowlton nodded several times and before the aide had climbed up a half completed gun platform to rejoin Colonel Prescott, he called: "Get your guns and clothes, boys. We're going to be moved."

This order the 4th squad promptly obeyed. A breathing spell would come very welcome indeed. They were aching in every muscle and trembling with fatigue. When the captain led them straggling out of the redoubt and down the back of Breed's Hill, they had an opportunity to look about. David could see all three, no, there were four men-of-war! The fourth ship, a sloop, had been hidden by the buildings of Charles Town. She was lying off a little point. The ship looked so familiar he wanted to ask Johnny about it. Johnny, however, hadn't returned from hunting a spring.

David asked, "Anybody know the name of that ship?"

Mahoney spoke up. "Sure, 'tis the *Falcon.* She's fresh in from pathroll dooty."

The *Falcon!* Rubbing his forehead with a hairy wrist, David stared on her. She had brought him bad luck—plenty of it last winter. Was her presence an evil omen? He was worried. Omens! He remembered Rob. Rob was a great one for omens. He wondered how Rob would like being here? Probably all right. Rob was all-fired slow, but when he got started the grass didn't grow where he hit.

Well, for better or for worse, there in the river swung the *Falcon,* dark blue with a yellow stripe along her side and yellow topsides. In the dawn's light her furled white canvas looked bluish on the yards. Great puffs of woolly white smoke spurted regularly out of her side and often her cannon blew great hollow rings like those a smoker shapes for admiring children. On the hillside below the redoubt a series of dark brown geysers erupted, betraying the hopeless inaccuracy of her broadside.

The Connecticut men kept on down the hill, trampling daisies and buttercups and wild strawberries underfoot. Generally they carried coats and shirts over one arm and lugged powder horns and firelocks over the other. Hats were jammed on at every angle. Often stripped to the waist and streaked with earth, the Connecticut men made an odd appearance, but they had learned one thing. Colonel Prescott had been right. Cannon made an awful fuss, but did such precious little damage that no one flinched except Billy Colgate when a round shot came rolling up the hillside, ploughing up the flowering hay grass until it lost momentum.

The Connecticut regiment having reached a little meadow half-way between Breed's and Bunker's, Captain Knowlton indicated a stone wall and called out, "We are to wait here for orders. Don't stray off. Rest as much as you can. If any man has food, let him share it."

He came over to David who was trying, without much success, to bandage his blistered hands. "You've done fine, Ashton; especially when those fool cannons began. Where has your friend got to? I sent him to hunt water over an hour ago."

David sprang up, looking very tall. "Sir, I do not know where he is." His jaw took an aggressive angle. "I trust you are not implying that a friend of mine would run away?"

The captain smiled, shook his head in a tired gesture. "I imply nothing, Ashton. I merely asked."

Singly and in little bunches, the men sought a long gray wall and, resting their weapons against the smooth stones it was made of, flung themselves flat. They were damp with perspiration and terribly thirsty. A little food appeared from various haversacks and was divided with meticulous care. Bees hummed by on their way to work.

Around eight of the morning the war ships ceased firing. Their bombardment had not caused any real damage. In Prescott's little redoubt— it was hardly fifty yards on a side—the ringing thump of hammers and a hurried rasping of saws told of cannon emplacements nearing completion.

"Hurray!" someone cried excitedly. "By Crikey! Look, boys! We got cannons, too!"

Skirting the base of Bunker's Hill, progressed a short column of cannon dragged by oxen and horses. Men trotted over from adjoining fields and clustered about, staring at the harnesses of the gun teams. They were wonderful contrivances devised from odd straps, traces, and many lengths of faded and often frayed rope. No two sets were even remotely similar. The sunburned militiamen looked with some awe upon the dully shining iron tubes, but laughed at the home-made carriages upon which they were mounted. They had been built of new, unpainted oak and hand forged iron, and the clumsy wheels of farm carts had been attached to them.

A man with an axe cut in his leg limped by. "The British are coming over," he yelled.

"How d'you know?"

"On the hill you can hear drums going to beat the band over in Boston."

Johnny hammering at a gun platform up in the redoubt, heard them, too. Unable to learn where his company had gone, he reckoned he had better stay where he was. There were too many militiamen wandering aimlessly about already. Besides, he liked it up here. You could see all of Charles Town, and along the Charles River almost to Cambridge. As for Boston, the town showed up ever so clear. He counted five, six, seven steeples. One of them had a crowing cock for a weathervane. He thought it an odd design for such a nest of Puritans.

Colonel Prescott's bearing inspired him. In time he hoped he would get to be like Prescott. The Yankee colonel was so calm, all seeing, and so smart at making the best of things. It was a damned pity Colonel Prescott wasn't wearing regimentals and a real sword instead of that silly French rapier. He'd have looked grand as any picture. Every now and again the commanding officer would steal a glance over the shoulder of his banyan. He kept looking towards Bunker's Hill; obviously it was for reinforcements. A few stragglers were advancing over the grass with long-barreled guns slanting over their shoulders, but not a regiment, not even a single company!

" 'Tain't no use, Billy," called someone in a clear voice. "Those damned old women on the Committee have sent us here to die alone. We've been betrayed!"

Said Colonel Gridley, looking very frail and all of his sixty-eight years after the long night's activity, "You and Putnam were wrong, dead wrong, Prescott, in not fortifying Bunker's first. I still say you won't be able to hold this hill ten minutes against Gage's regulars."

In the fresh morning sunlight the New Englander's strong features contracted. "Nevertheless, I will hold it, Gridley. I will never retreat, so help me, God!"

But Prescott by now must have known that the engineer was right. He should never have let hot-headed old Ike Putnam talk him into taking up this position. Safely out of range British troops could slip around his flanks on both sides. To check such a move he ordered some militia to occupy Charles Town which had been all but deserted for weeks.

"If you intend staying here," Gridley was saying heavily, "you had better build a breastwork to cover this slope. So long as you can hold it, the British won't be able to enfold your redoubt."

Work on a breastwork began immediately. As the sun climbed higher, men began to shed their shirts and to put on floppy felt hats. Calls for water grew louder, more persistent. There was no water. Just a little rum. No food, either. Nor did any reinforcements appear for the three hundred men in the redoubt.

Never, Johnny was thinking as he lay on the ground before the finished parapet, could he recall a more perfect early summer day. The sky was a bright blue and clear save for a few lazily drifting cloudlets. The smell of fresh-cut hay was pleasantly strong in the air.

A shadow fell over his shoulder and someone remarked, *"Ante tubam trepidat?"*

For once Johnny's Latin served and he grinned back. "Like the devil, I tremble. Got over that hours ago. How are you, Coffin?"

"Weary with well-doing," the Nantucketer declared. "Been running messages for Prescott till I'm fit to drop. But now—" he tossed a folded coat onto the ground and took up a position on the ground beside Johnny—"I am here. *Dulce et decorem est pro patria mori.* My father, I fear, would scarcely agree that the tag bears on the situation. Have a bite?" From a piece of greasy paper he produced a hunk of cold mutton.

"You bet. Reckon I could eat fried skunk right now."

The ex-junior sophister queried, "Are the redcoats really coming out? Everybody swears old Gage has cold feet."

"He's coming out. Why, he's got to, or be called a coward! What do you reckon will most likely happen?" Johnny asked cutting off a gobbet of meat. "Think they'll try to drive us out?"

"I guess so." Nathaniel Coffin picked up the Spanish fuzee Johnny had been issued and a comical grin spread over his heated features. "Ye Gods and little fishes! From what museum did you resurrect this relic?"

Hampered by a full mouth, Johnny mumbled, "She ain't so bad as she looks. Her lock's tight and the bore is small." He threw back his head in a characteristic gesture. "Lay you two to one I can knock off a Britisher at longer range than you."

The ex-junior sophister of Harvard College promptly produced a shilling, then hesitated. "I'd take you, but it wouldn't be fair. My firelock is almost brand new. Deacon Burret out at Concord built her for me.

Kept it in my room and got rusticated two months last year. *Contra* Chapter Four, Section XVI."

Johnny handled the piece with interest. Good solid workmanship all right, but not a patch on a Kaintuck.

"Nevertheless, my friend, the bet still stands," he chuckled. Hesitating, he added, *"Sutor, ne superam cupidus."*

Nat Coffin laughed so hard everyone looked at him. "Your advice about a cobbler sticking to his last is good. Your last may be guns, but it isn't Latin. *Sutor, ne supra crepidam!"*

"Three deep bows—and still two shillings to one!"

"What's that?"

All in a moment the digging noises had stopped. Carpenters working on the gun platforms scrambled up onto the parapet. The buzz of voices swelled and swelled and swelled until men behind Breed's Hill came running to see what was the matter.

"Look there, by the North Battery! The British are going to cross! My God, will you look at all them boats?"

Johnny felt his last doubts disappear. Definitely, there would be a battle. On a long wharf bodies of troops were moving like red checkers in an intricate play. Big barges propelled by leglike oars began to crawl away from various piers and jetties, out over the Charles.

"By God, they dassant tackle Charles Town!" "They're heading for the Neck!" The breath of Panic blew over the redoubt. Colonel Prescott, sensing it, shouted,

"Stay here! They may not! They have sent no ships up the Mystic."

Breathless, the men on Breed's Hill watched hundreds of red figures climbing down into more, and still more, boats. Bells in Boston were striking a single note each. The sun beat down hotter than ever.

☆

☆　　　☆

WHEN HE BECAME CERTAIN that those long lines of barges ferrying the British army were going to put in at Morton's Point, Colonel William Prescott was at once relieved and alarmed. So General Gage wasn't going to try to seize the Neck? Good! He was throwing away his one chance for a cheap victory. But so many regulars! Prescott hadn't figured Gage would deign to send more than a regiment or two to dislodge a pack of rebels.

To General Joseph Warren, who had just come up carrying, not a sword, but a musket, he called, "You are senior, sir. Will you assume command?"

But the Boston ex-doctor shook his head. Hard running had left him gasping. "Thank you, no, Colonel. I'm here as a volunteer—no more. Wouldn't think of supplanting an officer who has accomplished so much." But he was worried all the same. Pretty soon he asked, "What do you propose doing about the interval to our left?"

Though the breastwork Colonel Gridley had suggested was nearing completion, a wide gap still existed between the end of it and the shore of the Mystic River. That it presented a dangerous flaw in the Provincial line of defense everyone could see. It was all of a hundred yards long.

Colonel Prescott, mopping his shiny features with a kerchief, countered with another question. "Did you notice any reinforcements on the way to us?"

"No, but old Put is killing a horse trying to scare up some."

From their point of vantage on the parapet, the two officers watched the first British units disembark, leisurely, on a point perhaps a quarter of a mile distant. They made an ever widening red area on the green turf out there. Far to the rear wailed the conch shell bugles of some straggling militia company.

"Don't know what I can do about that interval," said Prescott as if to himself. "I haven't any reserve, except some Connecticut men under Captain Knowlton."

"How many of them are there?" Warren wanted to know.

"Only about two hundred."

"They can't hope to hold a fence two hundred yards long. Not against British regulars."

"Of course not." Prescott's tone was bitter and he directed a baleful look at Bunker's Hill. Upon its safe height a dark swarm of men milled uselessly. "If only those careful old maids over there would send me some reinforcements! Hell's bells! I'm going to send my reserve to build up that stone wall, anyhow!"

Thus, around two o'clock of the afternoon, a runner came panting up to Captain Knowlton, comfortably smoking his pipe in the shade of a small pear tree.

"Urgent orders! The Colonel says take your men over behind the rail fence yonder. Build it higher."

Knowlton tapped the dottle from his pipe. "For some time I have been thinking that would be advisable," said he dryly.

"Reinforcements are—on way," wheezed the messenger turning away.

"Reinforcements, hell!" called a red-haired fellow lying on his belly in the deep grass. "Ward has forgotten all about us buggers."

Ten minutes later Knowlton's tired command set to work. It lent them energy to know that the British were actually landing in force farther down the peninsula. Soon they would be coming this way. The fence, as they found it, was no higher than a man's knees. It consisted of stones and two wooden rails which raised it waist high.

Crisp, calm and as resourceful as ever, Knowlton detailed half of his force to fetch rails from a fence marking the rear side of the pasture. The others were directed to gather up armloads of freshcut hay. This they stuffed between the intersections between the rails.

"Hey, Cap, where in hell do you want these?" From behind, a squad had appeared. It was handling two six-pound cannons.

"Arrah! An' thim should be a help," Mahoney sighed.

Once his men had pulled aside enough rocks to form rude embrasures, Captain Knowlton ordered the cannon trained to cover a broad meadow stretching away before his position.

"Say, that's fine," said Lieutenant Bisley. "Now, where's the shot?"

"Shot? Oh, my God!" The leader, red-faced, turned and fiercely cursed two of his men. "What you carryin' round in place o' brains? You dunderheads hev clean forgot it!"

The artillerymen looked angry, rather than ashamed. "Go stick yerself, Callender! How wuz we to know we wuz supposed to bring it? You didn't tell us so. Nor nobody else!"

"It would also be helpful if you'd brought some powder," Knowlton pointed out, "not to mention spongers and rammers."

The officer in charge cursed and hurried off to the rear. They never saw him again.

The gunner sergeant exposed gapped yellow teeth in an apologetic grin. "Shucks, Mister, don't be too hard on us. We ain't ever handled these contraptions before."

"Where are the regular gunners?"

"Made tracks, damn 'em! Along with Colonel Bridge, Lieutenant-Colonel Brickett of Prescott's own regiment went, too! They got pains in their bellies quicker'n greased lightning once the British started to row over."

David's hands began bleeding once more and soon his nails split from dislodging and replacing the smooth glacial stones of which the fence was built. Billy Colgate and Bellinger were in no better way. All three of them were on the extreme left of line. From where they stood they could see the beach and the slimy green stones on it.

Advancing along the shore of the Mystic some Provincial troops came slogging along. It turned out to be Jonathan Stark's New Hampshire regiment. Some more Connecticut men were with him. They arrived surprisingly fresh.

"Took your own blessed time getting here," Captain Knowlton observed. He had been up and on the move some thirty hours now.

Stark cast him a contemptuous glance. "You can kiss my arse. It's time you Connecticut nitwits learned that one fresh man in a battle can lick five tired ones!"

A succession of messengers came sprinting down Breed's Hill, urging the defenders of the rail fence to make haste. They said a second flotilla was crossing from Boston. Colonel Stark, fresh and keenly observant, saw how fast the tide was falling. He deduced that a considerable width of beach would be passable between the end of the rail fence and the river. By merely following the beach, a British column might sweep by and turn the Provincial position, because most of the militiamen couldn't see under the river bank. Therefore, he ordered his stocky mountaineers down onto the damp sand. From boulders all green and white with slimy growth and barnacles they commenced constructing a crude breastwork.

A rhythmic beating of drums drew David's attention. Then many fifes began to shrill "Britons Strike Home!" They were real drummers off there. Their flams fell precisely together—*a rattle-tat-tat-tat! a rattle-tat-tat-tat!* The Provincials raised heads in broad-brimmed straws and felts and tricornes, but they couldn't see anything because of the slope of ground down to the beach.

No ammunition arrived for the two field pieces.

Colonel Stark climbed up on one of the cannons, clapped his hands for attention. "You boys better form teams of three. When the first man shoots, the one next behind him will step forward and fire." He raised his voice over an insistent dull thunder raised by the fleet's broadsides. "Remember, we have very few rounds a man so every shot has got to tell! Now look alive all of you and pick out their officers. You can tell 'em by their pretty uniforms and they don't wear crossbelts. They'll have silver moons hung over their throats and will carry swords or spears. Got that? Shoot at their officers and *aim low!*"

Everyone was listening, squinting up at Colonel Stark's chunky figure up there on the gun carriage.

"Best place to hit the rest is where their white belts cross. If any man fires afore I give the word, I'll kick his pants up to his shoulders." He said it as if he meant it. "Now take your positions and remember why we're here. If the British get past us, we may as well go home and fit handcuffs on ourselves."

David, troubled by Johnny's continued absence, made up a team with Mahoney and Bellinger.

"I'm probably the best shot, so I'll take Number One," he told them, hoping his voice sounded natural. "Mahoney, suppose you take the second position. Bellinger, your blunderbuss ought to do some mean work at close range."

"If ye've niver fired wan av thim Tower muskets," Mahoney warned, "ye'd best close yer eyes forninst yez pull the trigger. Some av thim Brown Besses squirts fire from the pan."

On Morton's Point the martial shrilling of fifes grew more strident. Up on Breed's Hill breathless silence reigned. The defenders evidently were watching something.

"My God," croaked Haskins. "Look at that!"

In stately array two scarlet streams began trickling away from the great red pool collected on the grayish sand of Morton's Point. One division started climbing very slowly towards the redoubt on Breed's Hill. The other moved off trampling the beach grass and gray-white sand along the bank of the Mystic. They came straight towards the breastwork of boulders the New Hampshire men had just raised, and at the rail fence.

It was an awesome, breath-taking spectacle, a terrifying exhibition of power. In the distance British weapons gave off brief, thin, pale sparkles of light. The scarlet of their tunics as yet obscured the white of their breeches and gaiters. Formed in column, company after company swung into sight, officers marching stiff and proud alongside. The drummer boys looked like Midgets. Nobody who saw it ever forgot the spectacle of old England's troops on parade.

A veteran of the Louisburg expedition said to the Colgate boy, "If you hold spare musket balls between the knuckles of your left hand, you can save time reloading. They won't fall out, either."

For a space the 4th squad was given time to watch the British left wing deploying at the base of Breed's Hill. They were having trouble in their advance. Time and again the ruler-straight ranks were forced to break up in order to scale a pasture fence. The British pulled down the rails whenever they could, but often they had to scramble over and re-form on the far side.

"By God, they're slow as kids on the way to school," grunted a bald old man two places down from David.

"Ye'd move slow, too," Mahoney grunted. "What wid thim packs and heavy coats, ivry mother's son is carryin' a hundred pounds or better, or I'm a nigger."

The other enemy column which advanced along the beach found the going much easier. The British came steadily on behind their drums the hollow beat of which was reverberating between the two hills. Larks flew up out of the grass before them, sped low towards the rail fence, then, seeing more men there, circled terror-stricken into the blazing sky.

Gradually, Mahoney became able to identify various units.

" 'Tis the light companies on the beach. We'll tangle wid 'em, too," he predicted.

"How d'you know they're light infantry? Look all the same to me," Edgell said.

"Do yez see thim big brass plates on their caps? See the shorter skirts to their coats? Thim wid the light blue lapels is the Welch Fusiliers. Behind thim and turned up in dark blue is the King's Own. Third in column looks like the 10th, or maybe 'tis the 38th. They're both in yellow facings. 'Way over yonder goes me own ould rigiment." The deserter looked a little scared. David thought, when he saw those orange revers.

"What are those big fellows farther back with the high black hats?" Bellinger inquired in a small, dry voice. He had taken off his spectacles quite awhile back but the red mark on his nose lingered.

" 'Tis the grenadiers," the Irishman replied. "From each British regiment is picked wan company av light infantry and wan av grenadiers. Big men goes to the grenadiers, small men to the light infantry."

"We'll pick them," piped Billy Colgate, but his thin, heavily freckled face was far whiter than his shirt.

"Steady now, boys. Get down low!" Trying to look stern and unimpressed, Provincial officers began walking up and down behind the rail fence and behind the boulders on the beach below.

Still no ammunition had arrived for the cannon standing so black and threatening—and useless.

The staccato *slam-slamming* of drums grew very loud. Now David could see the cockades and lace work on some of the officers' black, three-cornered hats. Being without packs, they strode easily along and their bared swords flashed. More details quickly became visible. As Stark had promised, colonels, majors and captains were easily distinguishable because of their massive epaulets and the gold and silver braid on their hats.

"Take your finger off that trigger!" Knowlton snapped at the Reverend Edgell, and kicked him on the rear when he did not instantly obey. "There's nothing to be afraid of; nothing!"

A gorgeous officer moved over to a big patch of greenish-white grass that rose to his knees. He shouted a command. The light infantry column halted. Like some movement of a precise machine, steel rippled and a metallic rattle marked the fixing of bayonets.

"To hell with them!" Colonel Stark bellowed down the line. "If you hold your fire, boys, the bloody-backs will never get close enough to use those cheese knives!"

Like spilt water widening on a floor, tension spread behind the rail fence. The earth-marked militiamen pulled off their hats and, swallowing hard, sank low behind the tumbled stones of their fence. Many men knelt, or crouched over like a valet peeking in a key hole.

At a trot grenadier companies in tall bearskin shakoes began to deploy over the hay stubble some eighty yards away from the rail fence. Everyone could see the buttoned-back tails of their coats a-swing, and brass-tipped bayonet scabbards wagging like the tails of so many dogs. In that big meadow there didn't seem to be quite so many of them. But there were still plenty.

The big grenadiers formed a long triple line, shoulder brushing shoulder, their white-gaitered legs swinging in time to the thumping drums. They halted and the brass plates on the fronts of their hats flashed in the eyes of the Provincials, bright as the mirror of a mischievous child. Out in front of them marched white-wigged officers gleaming with gold and silver. These also halted and, turning, supervised last minute preparations.

David was only dimly aware of the fleet still thundering away at the redoubt.

Bellinger's nervousness caused him a series of spasmodic yawns. His voice sounded small and lonely when he giggled. "Promised my boys I'd fetch back one lobster-back apiece. Guess there's more'n enough out there to go 'round."

Down on the beach the British light companies had not halted. Their advance continued. It was breath-taking, unforgettable, seemingly inexorable. Still in column they resembled a long scarlet tide sweeping up along the beach. White wigs, glittering epaulets, flashing musket barrels. Stiff as posts, the officers marched many feet in advance of their men. Faces set, scarlet with heat and exertion. Closer. The swishing of their feet over the sand was clearly to be heard now.

Behind the fence the Provincials locked their teeth, tried not to look as scared as they felt and for the last time tested set-screws securing their flints. David mechanically snapped back his pan cover to make sure the priming had not sifted out. Then, like the other Number One men, he jerked out his ramrod and stuck the yard of steel handy in the ground by his knee. The men about him were shifting so as to bring their muskets to bear on the beach. The grenadiers were still lingering as if to see how the light companies would fare.

So steady, so mechanical was the British advance, David's heart began leaping like a speared fish. How little the drummer boys looked! They didn't act the least bit scared, only swung their brass mounted sticks with a flourish. Suddenly deep voices shouted out there on the meadow and the grenadiers came on again, kicking up the cut hay as they advanced. The drum beats grew deafening, sounded right on top of the fence.

In David's squad, farthest to the left along the rail fence, there was a hurried shifting of musket barrels back to the front. Let Stark's men on the beach look out for themselves! The carpet of cut hay separating the grenadiers from the rail fence was growing narrower.

From behind came Captain Knowlton's sharp, "Take *sight!*"

David rested the Tower musket on the top rail and through his improvised rear sight watched square red faces, all bright with sweat, take shape. The officer nearest him was a big hairy fellow. He was loudly cursing the heat.

The wood of David's musket felt very hot to his cheek when he settled its butt more firmly into his shoulder, but the skin on his shoulders felt cold as if they had been rubbed with ice. Swallowing hard, he swung his front sight until he saw, as if balanced upon it, the gorget of a very tall major. As in a dream he watched the Englishman's face draw near. He had a big livid scar across his chin. A curl of his wig had fetched loose from its pins and was bobbing to his every stride. All the rest of the world became obliterated by that figure in scarlet with light blue cuffs, light blue lapels and a white waistcoat. The gorget grew simply enormous.

Why in hell didn't Stark give the command? The damned British were right on top of them! *Why didn't he?* A Virginia rifle company would have fired minutes ago. Closer! Closer! The dancing half moon of gilt silver and lace jabot under it looked to be hovering right above him.

Jonathan Stark's husky voice suddenly roared out. "Pick the officers! Aim crossbelts. Ready—Fire!"

Banging reports slapped at David's cheeks like invisible hands, but he held steady on the gorget and, by tightening his whole hand, squeezed the trigger. The clumsy Tower musket kicked him like a curried horse with a ticklish belly and a swirl of rank, rotten-smelling powder smoke beat back in his face. He couldn't help a series of hard, racking coughs. A swirling hurricane of flame and smoke spurted from between the fence rails. All in an instant a gray-white miasma eclipsed nearly the whole of that glittering parade in the meadow.

"Fer the love av Mary! Get out av me way!" Mahoney was grabbing at his arm, hauling him back. At once the Irishman poked his firelock through the hay covered rails.

David remembered his ramrod and had bent forward to grab it when a rift appeared in the wall of smoke. The hatless head and hunched shoulders of an officer showed up. He was clutching his cheeks and dazedly swaying back and forth, his sword a-dangle from a knot fastening it to his wrist. Out there the lines of muskets were wavering and bayonets were swaying like steel reeds under a gale of death. More heads materialized in the murk, some streaming blood, some yelling.

Terrible, animal-like noises arose beyond the curtain of smoke. Then a puff of wind from off the Mystic brushed aside the fumes. David felt his heart heave and he gasped as if a foot had been driven into the pit of his stomach. Not over sixty feet off lay a long squirming windrow of bodies dressed in scarlet and white.

A colonel stood alone, statue-still, with sword still raised. In his paralyzed astonishment he seemed not to notice a big sergeant rolling over and over on the ground at his feet. The N.C.O. was spilling yards of grayish-red entrails onto the new hay. A corporal in his death agonies snapped blindly at the turf, like a dog in a fit.

To the left of David's position a light infantry man was stumbling around in crazy circles.

"Oh, Christ! Christ!" he screamed and kept his hands pressed tight to his forehead. Nonetheless, a fine spray of blood was squirting out between his fingers. He tripped over a pile of corpses, then staggered on until he tumbled over the edge of the bank and fell down onto the beach, among the corpses littering it. Other wounded were blindly trying to burrow among the bodies. From behind the rails a musket roared and David distinctly saw the colonel's body jolt under the savage impact of ball and buckshot. Again a pall of drifting smoke descended.

The *click! clock!* of Provincial firearms being hurriedly cocked sounded on all sides. There was need of haste. Eyes a-blaze, cheering, the second line of grenadiers was charging, hurdling their fallen comrades. David saw dark blue lapels out there this time—some white—a very few light blue. Here and there a survivor of the first wave staggered up, gray-faced, to join them. God! Too clearly he was remembering the way those deadly black holes had appeared in the tall major's gorget.

Bayonets, murderously a-twinkle, shone amid the dust and smoke. Again the rail fence spouted fire. Before the smoke shut down David, trying to tilt a powder charge into his gun, beheld the further effects of the Provincial fire.

No less effectively than before, the second volley had knocked the heavy companies backwards off their feet, had torn murderous gaps in their array. Howls, screams and curses became mixed in a fearful cacophony. As with trembling hands he poised a handful of buckshot over his musket muzzle, David watched a tough-looking grenadier's bearskin fly off. A small package fell out of it. He wondered what it contained.

Despite widening intervals in their ranks, the English bent their bodies as if walking into a stiff gale, kept on. Raising a hoarse cheer the Number Three men of the Provincial musket teams sprang forward. Foolishly, futilely swinging his hat, Bellinger was trying to fan away the blinding smoke. David, repriming in a frenzy of haste, watched the round-shouldered clerk rise, blunderbuss leveled, avidly awaiting a target to materialize. Down on the beach the slamming of reports was continual.

"Come on! Oh damn you for bloody cowards! *Come on!*" A red-coated major, wig canted over one ear, became visible in the meadow. With the side of his sword he was hammering at some privates who, hat-less, were reeling back, coughing, and black with burnt powder grains.

Bellinger, sighting deliberately, dropped that major in his tracks. "That one's for Eddie," he cackled.

It was somehow appalling for David to watch the British third line come up, carrying with it broken remnants of the first and second ranks. Again a murderous volley smashed full into hot faces a-twitch with desperation.

Off to the right the grenadiers were faring no better. David, running forward to take Bellinger's place, glimpsed a slim lieutenant—a mere lad—running along the wavering line. He grabbed reeling men by the shoulders, shoved them forward, all the while yelling in a thin high voice.

"That shot's mine," someone said.

"In God's name, don't kill him!" Edgell cried. "He is too young—"

The young lieutenant broke his sword across the shoulders of a corporal. Then mad with fury when the soldiers kept on falling back, he turned and charged at the fence with the stump of his sword. Half a dozen privates started after the boy. A fourth volley mowed down all the survivors who had kept on.

There were no more redcoats and crossbelts to shoot at. The few British left on their feet were running or staggering back over the meadow. Of all the officers who had participated in this attack, David could see only two and these were still pleading with their men to come back.

The cloying, musty-sweet smell of blood and the nauseous stench of torn entrails hung heavy in the lifeless air. Some forty feet away a drummer boy lay crumpled, his small face a pulp. In a scarlet cataract his blood was draining across the smudged head of his drum. Agonized shrieks from the pile of men on the meadow made an inferno of sound.

The young lieutenant whom David had noticed suddenly came crawling out from behind a tangled pile of bodies. On his gray and shining face was a look of awful astonishment at what had happened to him.

A wounded sergeant flopped up on one elbow, cried, "Mr. Bruère, go back! They will kill you! Go back!"

"Water! Water!" New gorget swinging, the young lieutenant came crawling on hands and knees over the grass and the daisies were not whiter than his teeth, bared in agony.

"Stop, Mr. Bruère! That's the wrong way!" yelled the sergeant and tried to wave his arm in warning, but the pinkish and jagged end of a bone was sticking out just above his elbow, and his forearm dangled dreadfully limp.

"Don't shoot," gurgled the wounded boy. "Water! Kind friends, Oh, for the love of God! Water!"

Twenty feet short of the fence the young officer slowed, stopped his crawling. Then, like a frightened cat, he humped his back. He began to vomit such incredible torrents of blood it seemed as if he must be pumping from an inexhaustible reservoir. The flying gore splashed back from the ground, spattered his face, his white waistcoat. All at once he crumpled onto his side and lay still.

There was still continued firing up on Breed's Hill, but the enemy was retreating from it, too. The slope towards Boston and the harbour was carpeted with red and white bodies. All the way to Morton's Point the dull green of the ground was dotted with running figures in red and white. Without exception officers were cursing, beating at their men, trying to slow down the retreat.

Mahoney licked his lips. "Holy Mother av God; This *can't* be so! Why, thim regulars is running! *Arrah,* may they niver come back!"

David reckoned that at least a third of the attacking force had fallen. That the enemy officers had suffered out of proportion was attested by the number of bodies in gold epaulets and golden buttons. Stark's orders had been followed. One fantastic phenomenon drew everyone's attention. Quite a few muskets flying from stricken hands had plunged bayonet-first into the ground; they remained butt upwards, wavering among the dead like hideous weeds. Caps, packs, cartouche boxes, equipment of all sorts littered the meadow.

Billy Colgate's freckles stood out very brown on his pallid forehead. He was vomiting over the trail of one of the useless cannons. The Reverend Edgell knelt, feverishly begging the Lord to forgive him for having taken so many lives—even Church of England lives.

David Ashton was gradually recovering from his first sense of horror. He wanted a drink of liquor the worst way.

☆

☆   ☆

IMMEDIATELY AFTER THE REPULSE of the British the wind died away entirely. Wounded men felt the sun grow scorching hot, howled and screamed for water. Only the sullen, futile bombardment of the redoubt by their ships and by a battery somewhere over in Boston marked any British activity.

Buff, shuffling loose-jointed and watchful over the Neck, kept a sharp lookout across a tidal millpond to his right. Yonder, some men—he didn't know which side they were fighting on—were poling two big barges into shallow water among some reeds. Each had a cannon mounted behind by a sort of wooden shield. Who-e-e! If them things started shooting, this Neck would be no place for a certain nigger. He looked up and watched a great lot of men swarming around the top of Bunker's Hill. Laws! They didn't seem to know where they was heading, no-how. Bluish heat haze, he realized, was obscuring the far end of this point of land.

A bony-faced farmer came shuffling to the rear. He was biting his lip and his face was a queer yellow-bronze color. Buff's eyes grew white. Blood dripped slowly from the farmer's shattered forearm. Eagerly, the dust closed over each drop, as if to hide it.

"Please suh, whe'h at is Cap'n Kno'len's people?" He repeated the query he had been asking all the way out from Cambridge.

"He Connecticut?"

"Yas, *suh!* He Connecticut!"

"Wal, you might come across him over there on our right—towards Charles Town. They say 'tis Massachusetts in the fort."

His information could not have been more erroneous, but Buff had no way of knowing it. The sight of that wounded arm was evoking unfamiliar, long dormant impulses. Buff's clumsy-looking fingers crept up to rub the chevrons of scars on his cheeks. He had no idea he came from a fighting tribe in Senegal, but he did know he was different from his lazy, good-natured, brown-black companions in slavery in lots of ways. "Stupid Bushmen" he called them. It was queer, but he really enjoyed a fight—a taste which had earned him shackles and many a session at Candless's whipping post. That, and the stigma of being "a bad nigger."

His conical-shaped head settled lower between his shoulders, but his step lightened. "Keep yo' eyes skinned, boy," he muttered. " 'At's a pow'ful lot o' shootin' up yander."

Along the cart track he was following came another wounded militiaman. He was profanely protesting to not less than eight chalk-faced Provincials.

"Git back to the fight, you consarned yellow-bellies! Git away from me. I don't need help half so much as the boys up to the fort." He halted and, leaning on his weapon—an old duck gun with an enormously long barrel—glared appealingly about. "Won't any of you dad-burned heroes go back?"

"Shucks," boomed a gloomy-visaged fellow in undirtied nankeens, "we ain't going to allow a suffering comrade die on the road to safety."

"Won't one of you go back?" The wounded man's face was bitter, twitching.

"Whut for? Anyhow the British have run. They're whipped."

"They'll come back—damn yer ugly eyes! They're British regulars!"

Despite greasy duroy breeches and a very dirty red and white striped jersey, Buff made an impressive figure when he came padding up on bare feet. His smooth blue-black skin was glossy with sweat and the great muscles of his chest and arms stood out like sculptured bronze. Though his features revealed nothing, he was thinking, developing a crafty scheme.

"Please, suh, Ah heered whut you jes' said. Ah sho' would admire to go an' fight, but Ah ain't got me no gun."

The wounded militiaman jerked his head at the old fowling piece. "If you'll fight, nigger, she's yours. Here are some bullets and you'd better take along my powder horn."

"Thank you, suh! Thank you, kindly." Buff ducked his head several times.

Once he had unstrung his cowhorn of powder, the wounded man

glared at the skulkers in bitter contempt. "Go on home and tell your Mas to put your diapers back on." He spat in their direction then said, "Good luck, boy, and give 'em hell!" He nodded to Buff and resumed his slow retreat.

Buff hadn't the vaguest notion about how to load a gun, but he climbed over the hot stones of a fence and took up a trot. He was heading for the gray-white roofs of Charles Town and the tree tops poking up between them.

Presently he overtook a man tramping in the same direction. This one was wearing the blue shell jacket and white canvas breeches of a mariner. When Buff asked him about loading, the seaman stared, then squirted tobacco all over a clump of fireweed before he said,

"Sure, I'll teach anybody who'll go ahead." He demonstrated with his own weapon, as they walked along. "First off, make sure there ain't no sparks left in the bar'l from your last shot. You'll get a couple fingers blowed off, else. Then pour in so much powder." He raised a cow's-horn powder flask and tilted out a half palm full of coarse black grains. "Next comes the wadding. Got any?"

"No suh, Ah doan's reckon so."

"Well, here's some paper." He fished out a lot of ragged pages torn from some book and gave them to Buff. "Crumple it up and ram it home. Keeps the powder from running out, understand?"

Buff listened hard, ducking his head beneath a big floppy hat he had "found." They were nearly across the first meadow now with uncut hay whipping about their shins.

"Take five or six buckshot—"

"Whut dat, suh?"

"Six little lead balls like these. After them goes a musket ball. Ram in another piece of paper and tamp it down hard; keeps the balls from rolling out. Now, let's see you do it."

In the shade of a little grove behind Charles Town they paused. Buff tried to remember the instructions, but it was hard work. To make matters more awkward, the duck gun's barrel was long, and five or six times the little man whose name, it appeared, was Metcalfe, had to prompt him.

"Je-sus!" he exploded. "Cant you remember nothing? I never did see such a dumb nigger! Look here, we better set down by that fence while I show you how to prime."

Eyes very round, Buff watched Metcalfe's methodical movements. After transferring shot and spare flints to his breeches, the mariner stripped off his serge shell jacket and hid it in the hollow part of an apple tree. Buff was powerful glad to sit down. Yes, suh. His feets sho' was tired, but they didn't hurt so much as before he threw away them shoes he'd hooked out of a supply wagon.

"Now watch close." The mariner's broad thumb pushed forward a section of the lock. "This here thing's called the frizzen. The flint strikes against it when it falls, and throws sparks into the pan which touch off the priming load. See this here little hole? Well, the fire squirts along it inside of the breech. It touches off that load of powder you dropped down the bar'l. See?"

"Yas, suh. Ah reckon so," Buff said. Surprisingly enough, he really had grasped the idea. Sparks into pan, fire into barrel. Powder explodes, bullets fly out. It really wasn't so hard.

Metcalfe reached up, pulled a green apple off a limb, inspected it, threw it away and got to his feet.

"What's your name?"

"Buff, suh."

"Well, come along, Buff. I guess the redcoats will have pulled themselves together by now. Maybe we can find us a bagnet or two down in Charles Town. They come in handy sometimes."

"Is 'at whe'h Cap'n Kno'len's folks is?"

"I dunno," Metcalfe grunted. He climbed over another fence and started towards the outlying houses of deserted Charles Town.

Lots of militiamen were clustered about a big well, drinking eagerly. Their leaders were vainly trying to get them away. "Shake a leg! The British are coming back!"

Hopeful all the while of catching a glimpse of Mr. David or of Mr. Johnny, Buff followed Metcalfe down a street lined with empty houses. They looked very forlorn with their doors standing open and their windows mostly smashed. Men who had been sitting in the shade of the porches were reluctantly rising and moving off towards the northeast edge of the village. It was nearest to Morton's Point.

The big negro attracted no end of curious stares with his scarred cheeks and pointed teeth. In a red and white striped jersey and carrying a six-foot ducking gun, he made quite a picture. When he saw how cannon balls had knocked in the roof of a big school house, his broad nostrils began opening faster. From a gaping hole threads of blue smoke were spiraling slowly into the cloudless sky.

Pretty soon they reached an orchard and found many Provincials gathered among the trees. They were all staring anxiously across at

Boston and at a line of boats rowing over. They were filled with red uniforms. Reserves.

Metcalfe stopped, pointed past a schooner building on some stocks at a long wharf across the water. Lying to it was a big, full-rigged ship. Her topmasts were down and her yards bare of canvas. Her water line was foul with weed.

"Look at the poor girl," Metcalfe growled with a savage oath. "I own her. God-damned Britishers wouldn't give me clearance last day before the Port Act began. That's why I am here."

Men skirmishing slowly out from Charles Town were just in time to see a second assault on the redoubt take shape. Once its reserve had been landed, the British command lumped together the decimated units which had already attacked.

As, bent well over, the Provincials advanced through a young pear orchard, they began to hear the groans of wounded British laid out on the beach in the broiling sun.

Some Provincials evidently had been in the orchard from the beginning of the battle. One of them called, "Say, friends, could you spare me a mite of powder?"

Another skirmisher lifted his head from the heart of a willow thicket. He and the three other men with him had been quite invisible. "Where are our reinforcements?"

Metcalfe told him, "There ain't reinforcements. That yellow twerp Gerrish won't move off Bunker's, come hell or high water! He's warning everybody to stay on the other side of the Neck."

"If that's so, then I guess we had better be going back pretty soon," drawled a powder-marked man. "What you doing here, Black Boy?"

Buff grinned. "Well, suh, Ah aims to collect me one ob dem pretty red coats with lots of gold onto it." But what Buff really yearned for was enough human ears to string a necklace with. Even if it was a little necklace. He could recall back home a round hut with a thatched roof—a headman showing someone a whole ramrod jammed with dried ears. He had been a great warrior.

The British drums were *slam-slamming* again, but not so evenly, and the squeaking of their fifes held hysterical overtones.

"Where would we be the most use?" Metcalfe asked of the crowd.

"Right here," said a man in a decent gray coat. "Since during the first attack we stung the British flank a lot, it stands to reason Gage will order Charles Town bombarded. We figure he will likely send troops to drive us out of here—or try to. It's my guess we will see plenty of action before long."

Buff was surprised to find how calm he felt. Who-e-e! In a little while he'd maybe be killing someone. All through the pear orchard sounded the thin slithering of steel slipping over steel; many ramrods were being driven home.

Buff felt his stomach tighten and his nostrils stiffen. He looked about and pretty soon he found what looked like a fine vantage point behind a stone well. The coping faced a rather wet cow pasture over which a British force coming to clear Charles Town must advance. Metcalfe came up to him.

"This is a dandy spot. Why, it ain't forty yards to the nearest of them dead Britishers," he grunted. "Remember to hold low."

Down on Morton's Point the British Army was taking its own sweet time. The commander was forming two wings arranged in the familiar three line pattern. Even at this distance the waiting Provincials, chewing hay grass and luxuriating in the shade, could see shakoes and hats missing. Here and there the uncovered wig on an officer glistened like snow in the fierce afternoon sunlight.

Metcalfe said suddenly, "We were smart to clear out of Charles Town, the way we did."

Buff couldn't grasp what he meant though H. M. S. *Somerset* was slowly swinging with the tide. Gradually her port battery of thirty-four guns came to bear on the shingle and clapboard houses of the village.

"In about five—" A broadside from the *Somerset* drowned out Metcalfe's remarks.

A chorus of infernal voices screeched overhead and, a split second later, came such noises as a giant might make in chopping kindling. *Bom-m-m!* Over in Boston the "Admiral's Battery" on Copp's Hill joined in showering destruction on Charles Town.

A shell shrieked by. Buff cowered. Convulsively, he clasped both hands over his head.

Metcalfe laughed. "Take it easy, Nigger. They ain't coming this way —yet."

Heart-stilling crashes sounded among the houses. Buff, shaking like a frightened colt, watched bricks fly from a chimney and fall into the street. Some of the bricks smashed windows clear across the road, scaring hell out of some militiamen. Under a steady rain of cannon balls, boards, shingles, shutters scaled up into the sky. A whole series of terrific smashing crackles reached the orchard.

Why, Buff wondered, had he ever been such a no-sense fool as to come looking for this sort of a death? Peeking around the well top, through the rough trunks of the fruit trees, he could see Provincials sprinting out of the village at a dead run. Every time a shot landed near they'd give such a funny little jump that Metcalfe and the rest of the fifty or sixty men lying hidden and safe in the orchard began to laugh.

All at once a long trail of yellow-white smoke arched itself across the deep blue sky and landed in a shipyard. Another band of smoke sprang from Copp's Hill and, crossing the first arc, sketched a gigantic, curving X. For the first time, Metcalfe noticed that the heights, roofs and docks in Boston yonder were black with onlookers. They had a perfect view of everything that was happening.

Buff's eyes bulged to see that unhealthy yellowish-green smoke begin to settle. A half finished ship took fire. In widely separated parts of the village, flames began to raise banderoles of smoke above the glassy river.

"Them must be red-hot cannon balls," Metcalfe averred, pointing to a pillar of sickly yellow smoke climbing from yet another house.

Said the man in decent gray, "What they've just now pitched into my home—" he nodded at a big, white painted house—"is a shell filled with burning sulphur. Artillerymen call it a carcass." He took out a neat metal flask and quietly reprimed his gun. "I am going to kill someone for that."

Within ten minutes Charles Town was blazing in a dozen places, then the breeze sprang up and began to blow a great blue-black pall of smoke over the Charles River and into the faces of the naval gunners. Immediately their aim got bad and some cannon balls began smashing through the young pear trees. But they hurt no one. Soon the bombardment ceased and only the fierce crackle and roar of the flames consuming Charles Town beat against Buff's eardrums.

Metcalfe emitted a startled grunt. "Look alive, boys. Here they come!"

For the second time the British Army moved off, still bent beneath heavy packs and under fixed bayonets.

"Any room here?" Singed, wild-eyed sharpshooters came panting up from Charles Town. "Bloody pigs burnt us out."

"Sure," Metcalfe, a natural leader, raised his voice. "Over behind that woodpile, shouldn't wonder. Let everybody lie low and stay hidden 'til I give the word. They can't see you in that long grass, either."

Battalion on battalion, regiment on regiment, the British, 3,400 of them, were on the move, swinging over a succession of fields, and climbing fences. Metcalfe's party on the flank could see how very slow the advance was. With livelier interest they also watched the maneuvers of a body of marines. Because of their black leggings and white lapels they were easily recognizable. In column they came tramping along the beach; obviously detailed to drive the last Provincials out of the village.

"Boys, you had better close in a mite," Metcalfe called. "There are a lot of redcoats headed this way."

And there were, nearly 200 in number. Buff, too terrified now even to run, beheld coming towards them two whole companies of marines in low caps with silvered ornaments and white facings to their scarlet tunics. That they had taken part in the first attack could be told at a glance. Some of the men wore bloodied rags tied about head or limbs. Not a few were limping. When they came closer, the Provincials in the orchard could read a sort of stunned expression on many of the sweat-bright faces.

A middle-aged, hatless officer carrying an espantoon was directing the advance. Only one other officer, a lieutenant, was to be seen. Sergeants and corporals were acting as captains and lieutenants. Many of the white breeches out there were marked with blood streaks.

A few impatient Provincials popped heads from behind the wood pile, stared mesmerized at the brilliant array moving forward across the cow pasture. The Royal Marines were now so close Metcalfe could make out an anchor and some oak leaves on their cap badges.

The officer saw the lurking skirmishers and yelled something. With a precise one-two-three the red and white ranks came to a halt. Like corn under a reaper, brown-mounted musket barrels swept down until the marines, holding their weapons waist high, were pointing in the general direction of the woodpile. Buff held his breath, cowered flatter than flat and felt his pants grow damp.

"Fire!"

The British volley struck only one of the Provincials. But he, a dark, unshaven fellow, was struck in the belly and began to scream shrilly, horribly, like a hurt horse. Whirling, rotten-smelling smoke shut out all sight of the enemy.

"Get ready, boys!" Metcalfe called out. "Aim for their belt buckles."

About sixty militiamen rose up out of the tall hay grass, some standing right up, others sighting from one knee. They took steady aim, waited for the smoke to thin out. Buff put up his duck gun and squared his shoulder against its butt. Dim figures coughed and wavered around in the gloom. The marines' second rank was slipping through the first, in a hurry to fire.

The man in gray yelled, "One—two—"

At that range the militiamen could not miss. Buff, too rattled to pull his own trigger, watched the knees of a whole row of redcoats buckle, saw their arms fly up and queer caps of scarlet cloth go spinning through air. Muskets fell every which way. The hatless officer hadn't been hit. Buff whipped up the duck gun and fired at him.

The recoil made his teeth rattle and the comb of the stock cut his thick lips. What was it a man did first to reload? As he fumbled for his powder horn, Buff peered to learn whether he had killed his man.

He had missed. The officer was running down the wavering ranks, but his wig was gone and he had lost an epaulet.

Out of the pear orchard came another slamming volley, not so heavy as the first, but it hastened a slow backward motion of the shattered lines on the pasture. Now great gaps had opened in the marine formation. Men were rolling over and writhing among the tussocks and dry cow turds out there.

"Come on, marines, for God's sake! Don't run!" The only surviving officer ran back waving his little halbert. "Come back!" But the retrograde movement was gaining momentum. "Thompson! Harker! Stop those men!" he yelled. "Oh God! Why am I condemned to lead such wretched cowards!"

In a passion the hatless lieutenant reached up and tore off his remaining epaulet.

"There, damn you! I'm no officer of yours! Don't call yourselves marines! You act like damned frog-eating pimps!"

Violently he hurled the lump of silver lace to the earth and stamped on it. A few marines turned and started slowly back, jaws set, eyes ablaze.

Followed by less than a dozen men the lieutenant charged for the pear grove. In his rage and shame the Englishman was weeping. The tears traced clean paths down his powder-blackened cheeks.

"That's better. Now—" He got no farther. The man in decent gray had raised a handsome fowling piece and fired. The heavy bullet's impact knocked the lieutenant right off his feet. His halbert flew shimmering through the air.

More Provincials, smoked out of the village, came up, but the marine detachment was in full retreat, trailed by staggering, limping wounded.

Metcalfe saw the British of General Pigot's wing still on the slope of Breed's Hill exchanging volleys with the redoubt. They were falling back a second time, however.

Buff was trying to tamp home a charge when someone who swore he came from Colonel Prescott himself ran up and told the men in the orchard to fall back. More troops had been seen embarking in Boston. This time it was certain they meant to strike Charles Town in force.

He advised, "You had better retreat along the road that runs across the back of Breed's Hill. There is a barn over there. You might make a stand in it."

Buff caught at his arm. "Misto, whea's de Connecticuters? Ah's jes' *got* to find Misto David."

"Clear around on the other side of this point," the messenger called over his shoulder.

With the other men from Charles Town, Buff retreated. He had started to skirt the rear of Breed's Hill when a terrible old man with two big horse pistols in his belt pointed to the redoubt.

"Go up there! No back talk!"

☆
☆ ☆

To DAVID, Lord Howe's second attack on the rail fence seemed but the stupid repetition of an initial error. Somehow, the unflinching discipline of those regulars in the face of certain destruction was more appalling than admirable. Good thing he felt numbed to ghastly sights and piteous sounds. In some places the grenadiers had fallen in easily discernible lines. They lay huddled like game arranged after a drive.

From everywhere arose anxious, urgent cries for powder. Captain Knowlton went striding across a gap between the end of the breastwork above and the rail fence. Some stragglers had built three crude *flèches* of rails there. He asked the sunburnt militiamen if they had any to spare.

"Jesus, no, Mister. We got less'n two rounds apiece."

Knowlton hurried back and said, "Ashton! Get up to the redoubt—find whether they have any powder to spare. Even a horn or two would help. If there's none there, wait. Somebody might think to send some forward."

As he climbed Breed's Hill, David was surprised to note that the afternoon was well advanced. Shadows were lengthening, deepening.

He found Buff hovering outside the sallyport.

"Misto David!" If Buff had had a tail he would be wagging it, thought the Virginian.

"What the devil you doing here, boy? Haven't you got good sense?"

"Oh, Misto David, is you all right? You doan' look so brash."

"I reckon I don't." David's eyes were hollow and red rimmed. His throat felt as if someone had gone over it with sandpaper. The one drink of water he'd swallowed came from a brackish pool and tasted as if it had lain overnight in an old boot.

"If you have the sense God gave a goat, Buff, you'll chase yourself as fast as you can."

"No, suh, dat don't lissen right to me, suh. Ah reckons Ah stays."

"Well, come along, then."

"Yassuh. Ah's stayin' wid·you, suh."

Colonel Prescott in his dirtied banyan was directing men to hatchet open some cartridges brought for the cannons. In very sparing fashion coarse black powder was being rationed into eagerly outstretched hats, horns and flasks. The meagre portions gave David no answer to Knowlton's hope.

As soon as they had drawn their two or three rounds apiece, the powder-blackened Provincials scrambled back into the breastwork or sat on its parapet, watching swarms of redcoats land to the windward of Charles Town. Others were reinforcing the mangled regiments on Morton's Point. Prescott's head halted its slow motion to the right. He beckoned an aide.

"Howe has finally got his artillery where it will be of use. Soon he will be able to rake our breastwork. Tell the men in it to come up here."

David was debating whether he should go back and report to Knowlton that there was slim chance of any powder being sent when Johnny Gilmorin saw him.

"Davey!" He rushed forward, barely recognizable. David couldn't help laughing. Johnny's shirt was torn half off; his long, light brown hair was unclubbed and flying wild. One naked shoulder was black and blue from the recoil of his musket. A far cry, this, from the Johnny who doted on gay cockades and wigs of the latest *ton*. His face was so coated with burnt powder grains that the whites of his eyes showed up even brighter than Buff's.

"Hi, Johnny! Did I say something about the Yankees being scared to fight?"

Cried Johnny, a fine clear flame in his eyes, "They can fight! Damned if they flinched, even when some Britishers got right up to the parapet." He lowered his voice, licked his lips in puzzled fashion. "But, hang it all, Davey, they don't seem to take any pleasure in fighting. They're so—so damn' *serious* about it!"

He broke off. David was staring at a courier who had just appeared. He was wearing a very lumpy-looking hunting shirt. While he was talking to Colonel Prescott, its tie strings came undone. Underneath the shirt, he was wearing a blue uniform turned up with red.

David, tired to the point of faintness, grinned. "My boy, doesn't that look like one of your Wethersfield peacocks?"

Johnny looked thunderstruck. He called, "Say, what's the idea covering up your regimentals like that? You ought to be ashamed!"

The Connecticut man looked sulky, blinked in the dusty sunlight of the redoubt. "Go ahead and laugh, but we don't aim to get joshed all day over some no-'count uniforms."

Johnny gaped, incredulous, shocked as he had not been by anything that had gone before. High God in His Heaven! This yokel was actually ashamed to let his reginmentals be seen! It was the last straw. All day he had been looking for war as it ought to be; a bright, gallant war. "Pray shoot first, gentlemen of France!" *Mais non, tirez les premiers, Messieurs les Anglais!*" That sort of thing.

In the right kind of war men didn't writhe about trying to cram entrails back into their bellies with dusty fingers, soldiers didn't whimper with fear like little puppy dogs, officers didn't shovel dirt until their hands were raw and slippery. Soldiers never ran away, or pretended to get taken sick so they could go to the rear—like Colonel Bridge and Lieutenant-Colonel Brickett.

Suddenly Johnny felt a thousand years old, very tired and, now that those distant drums were tapping for the third time, just a little scared. That was wrong, too. Long since, the British should have admitted that they were beaten.

David, having read a measure of his disillusion, put a hand to Johnny's damp shoulder. "One more repulse, Johnny, and even those damned brave bastards down there will have had enough. Then we can go back to quarters and get stink-o!"

"Come on up." Nat Coffin turned a profile gilded by sweat and sun. "Here's a couple of good loopholes. Find any powder? I have only three shots left."

Other voices, croaking with thirst, called, "Powder! Where in hell is some powder?" "Damned Committee's sent no powder all day!" "We've been betrayed—I told you so!"

"This time they mean business," an officer in muddied breeches said.

The British array was not so colorful. At last they had shed their heavy packs and a lot of them had removed smotheringly hot uniform coats. Not a few infantrymen had stripped to the waist, slinging over naked shoulders the crossbelts which supported their cartouche boxes and bayonets. With their tall bearskins and powdered hair the effect was grotesque.

The officers, however, had disdained to remove either coat or shirt, but their finery was sadly stained and their white leggings had taken on a pinkish hue from the bloodied grass stems which had brushed them. David, resting his musket across the berm of the earthwork, noted how motionless patches of white and scarlet dotted the slope from the crest of Breed's Hill all the way to Morton's Point.

Colonel Prescott, his blue banyan ripped and smeared, hurriedly re-arranged the defenders. Along the redoubt's south wall he placed those men who were coming up from the abandoned breastwork. Headed by General Warren, the few remaining Provincial officers began checking powder flasks. Many were quite empty and the rest so sparsely filled the officer's expressions grew strained.

"Any men having bayonets had better fix them," Warren called.

"I got a war hatchet," proclaimed a man in a buckskin shirt. "That's better'n a baynit any time!"

When the British in their long lines again started climbing that series of stone walls which had gone so far to exhaust them in their previous efforts, no drums were beating. Grenadiers and light infantry were all mixed up with the regular line companies. David saw tall shakoes stand out like dark stumps in a red and white field. The short-skirted light infantry coats looked frivolous among the longer ones of regular length.

The enemy climbed faster, much faster than before. Nathaniel Coffin's usual half mocking smile was absent as, carefully, he tucked three bullets between the knuckles of his left hand, crammed six paper wads into the top of his breeches.

David glanced sidewise. Johnny's face was pale and the too delicate line of his chin quivered. The strain was getting him. Farther over, Buff's head made a shiny black smudge against the raw oak of a gun carriage. Tense as a hound's the big negro's head was outthrust and his yellowish eyes narrowed.

"Will you look at 'em come?" somebody muttered.

The British raised a cheer and kept on without waiting to re-form every time they crossed a fence; previously they had always realigned their ranks. The officers, though they must have realized their especial peril, were again well out in front.

A recruit just up from the rear leveled his gun barrel at a very fat officer waddling along. He was using his sword as a cane when he came to a tough spot.

"Put up that gun!" Colonel Prescott roared. The recruit was too scared or too slow to obey, so the colonel jumped up on the berm and himself kicked up the barrel. "Make every shot count," he warned, jaw muscles twitching. "Let them get real close this time. Close enough to see the color of their eyes."

Down by the rail fence, Shaun Mahoney, having used the last of his powder, dropped his musket and ran like hell. He intended to get over the Neck in time.

Unhampered by packs, the English scaled the daisy and mustard flower-dotted slope almost rapidly and, at sixty yards' range, commenced firing very coolly. After each volley they would advance ten yards and fire again. The bloodied corpses among the flowering hay grass might not have been there.

The British fire intensified, for the first time became effective. Men were being hit. The Provincials crouched lower, shielding their eyes from dirt sent flying by bullets. Thousands of giant bees hummed over David's head and now and then a ricochetting bullet raised an eerie whine.

Colonel Prescott's ridiculously thin rapier wavered in the hot air. "Get set, boys. The officers first!" By the dozen, long barrels slipped over the top of the parapet.

David, peering over the tumbled earth, picked out an officer, a gross, fat-shouldered fellow with a big belly wabbling beneath a buff waistcoat. By God! That was Bouquet! The major's heavy features were shining as if lacquered and since he wore a soggy red bandage about his left arm, he must have been this way at least once before.

"Fire!"

The weird assortment of firearms in the redoubt roared and like dominoes the first rank of the British began spinning and tumbling about. But the other lines came on. A few scattered shots roared in an effort to check them. David thought of Hannibal, and took a careful bead on Major Bouquet's chest. This was the last of his powder.

In a hot rage he squeezed the trigger and must have pulled too hard. His ball merely tore some gold bullion from Bouquet's shoulder. The major roared and shook his sword at the redoubt. David had to hand it to that Englishman, the way he kept on coming!

Johnny not recognizing him, instead picked off a captain 'way down on the right. He winked at Coffin, said, "Pay me!"

"Forward, lads—got them!" Bouquet was struggling across a ditch below the parapet. He was dreadfully out of breath, but still could make himself heard. "Forward! Forward!"

The British, encouraged to be so much nearer their goal than they had ever been, set up a fierce yammering. A dozen half-naked grenadiers broke into a run; bayonets swinging, they poured into the ditch below. When more soldiers came, they began boosting each other up.

Meanwhile the Provincial fire had gone out like an old candle. The attackers, too, stopped shooting for fear of hurting their own men. To climb up onto the parapet the English were forced to use both hands. To do it some of them, unwisely, laid their muskets on the berm of the redoubt. David and some others snatched these up and began smashing at the powdered heads which came clambering up.

"Oh God, isn't there *any* more powder?" Johnny began yelling crazily. "Powder! Give me powder!"

Nat Coffin, stooping, caught up a stone. He heaved it with all his might and, catching a disheveled Englishman on the side of the head, dropped him cold.

When the other men saw that, they too dropped their useless muskets and commenced throwing stones. In astonishment the British wavered. The frontiersman sent his war hatchet spinning through the air. It split in half the face of a beefy sergeant swaying with leveled bayonet on top of the parapet. Right above David a figure scrambled into sight! Major Bouquet!

He seemed tall as the Colossus of Rhodes when he brandished his sword and roared, "Surrender, you rebels!"

"We are not rebels!" Colonel Prescott shouted.

Raising his rapier, he started forward, but Buff, crouched by a cannon's trail, heard Bouquet's voice and glimpsed him against the sky. In a flash he whipped up the duck gun and fired.

A full load of ball and buckshot struck Major Ponsonby Bouquet under his raised right arm. It ripped his scarlet coat into tatters, front and back.

"Dere's cutleries fer you!" snarled the negro, then dropped his gun and joined a mob of fugitives fighting to get out of the sallyport.

A dying British officer falling into the redoubt dropped his sword almost at Johnny's feet. A sword! He snatched eagerly at it. This was more like it. Ha! The grip, though slippery with its late owner's sweat, felt fine in his hand—reassuring. Shouting, he turned with some others to dispute the British advance.

By tens and twenties attackers swept over the parapet and jumped down behind leveled bayonets. Dust rose in blinding eddies, figures disappeared, reappeared—red, homespun, white. Thumping sounds. Curses. Johnny parried a bayonet's point and drove his blade in hard. It pierced through the fellow's throat. Why, this was easy!

"Forward! Forward!" he screamed. The captured blade shivered, but he beat aside another bayonet and slashed back. Missed this time.

An eddy of Royal Marines swept up from the right, driving a few Provincials before them. Leaping backward, the Yankees were swinging desperately with their clubbed muskets.

"Nah then, ye bleedin' rebel!" Johnny saw a towering sergeant gather himself behind his musket, and fell back a step to win elbow room. His heel struck an abandoned pickaxe and he lurched backward off balance. All the world resolved into a long brown face set with blazing blue eyes, snaggle teeth and writhing lips. A shooting star of steel materialized between him and it.

"Don't!" Johnny screamed and, using his left hand, tried to deflect the down-rushing bayonet, but the point caught on his palm, punched clean through it. Drove onwards. Johnny felt his arm slammed tight against his chest. He suffered an excruciating, unbelievable pang, then distinctly felt the grating of steel against one of his ribs. The big sergeant had all his weight behind his bayonet so, quite easily, he pinned Johnny Gilmorin to the dusty trampled ground.

Magically the tumult faded. Johnny caught a fleeting glimpse of a white-pillared mansion and of a paddock nearer at hand. Some mares and their foals stood in it, switching flies beneath a summer sun. He heard a tender, beloved voice murmur, "You must go to sleep now, Johnny. You are tired and it is very late."

Nothing more.

David, fighting alongside Colonel Prescott, was much too busy to see what had happened elsewhere. Supported by a handful of men, Prescott was trying to delay the enemy until Provincials without bayonets could escape through the sallyport. Surprisingly enough, the more he whirled his Brown Bess by its barrel, the more strength David felt welling back into his body. There was, he discovered, a fierce and unsuspected satisfaction in this business of killing people.

He made such an iron windmill of his musket that the British began to give way before him. At once some Provincials rallied and were starting forward, but a light infantryman slipped in behind David and jabbed his bayonet deep into the Virginian's right shoulder. Reeling under the shock, David dropped his musket and when the Englishman struggled to free his bayonet, he was pulled over backwards. A snarl of panting grenadiers closed in and a whole constellation of steel stars hovered above him. But a harsh voice rasped,

"Leave the wounded be, you bloody idiots! Get after the live ones, or they'll be back."

Sprawled across a litter of abandoned entrenching tools and firearms, David lay spouting blood over the floor of the redoubt. Confusedly, his half closed eyes registered the passage of many shouting men, but the picture made no impression on his brain. An icy lump came into being in his stomach, began to expand. He must be bleeding a lot—should do something about it. Couldn't. Too tired.

A gay, mocking face looked into his—Andrea Grenville's—of all people. Was that Katie's rich, throaty laughter sounding so close? Were Madelaine's cool fingertips brushing his forehead?

It wasn't so bad just to lie still, comforted by the sun's warmth. Odd, the redoubt, the sky, everything, had begun slowly to revolve. The world spun faster. Faster.

A hand grabbed his good arm and tugged him over onto his back. A tired voice directed:

"Tie a rag over that hole in his shoulder. We must take some prisoners to show for this hellish day's work."

BATTLE OF MOORE'S CREEK BRIDGE

by TIM PRIDGEN

DUNCAN WALKED HOME slowly that night. He went by the framing of his stout house. It gave him satisfaction to grasp the timbers and feel them solid in his touch. Through them he could see the stars shining. Over the creek he heard Donald Bane stamping in his stall. He went that way and took the horse out in the darkness and ran his hands over him to see that he had been rubbed properly. He sank his hands in the feedbox to see that the nag had not been chewing the cobs, had been getting enough to eat. He woke Gillie Black, who was not much surprised. Duncan these months came and went at strange times.

"Ye hae been eatin' bread and greens, as I told ye, or hae ye been eatin' meat alone as ye are wont to do?"

"Grass, Mas' Dunk—plenty o' grass, jes lak you said," Gillie smiled.

"I suspect ye lie, but ye still look hearty, so it is well."

Duncan went to bed and with a fine, serene content upon him went to sleep. The mobilization so far had meant little to him—marching, drilling, talk. In the background the Whigs scuttled through, indefinitely going places, marching, drilling, talking. Mostly talking. The Scots would march to the sea. They would join Cornwallis, and the whole crisis would fade out. He would be burning tar again in three weeks. It seemed senseless to lose the three weeks from work.

In this mood on Wednesday noon he concealed himself in the gallberry bushes on a bluff and watched the river, to see a strange sight—a little army of Whigs paddling madly down the stream. They had sixty or seventy boats. They were like a raft of things alive, holding close together.

Alexander Lillington sprawled hugely in one boat that four men paddled. John Ashe was in another. They were in no order, merely a conglomeration of paddle boats with two hundred paddles, perhaps three hundred, flashing in the sun and splashing in the water.

Duncan grinned and shook his head. It was a queer war. MacDonald's army raced down this side of the river and Moore's the other. Lillington's "navy" paddled desperately between. The one that got there first, he reckoned, would win a prize. That was a joke. He laughed aloud. It was a monstrous, curious war.

Early Friday morning Duncan stood impatient among the fog-dimmed pines on a sand ridge. He was near South River, to the east. He wore his sword and carried his rifle. He had marched since midnight to join MacDonald. Now he was ready to go. Even eager. His mind was clear on it. The muffled noise which rumbled through the mist from up the trail heralded the Scots. But for the fog on the lowlands, he could see them now. He listened, instead. Presently they would wind out of the veil at the foot of the ridge, curve back into it again.

The sun put a ghostly glamor on them when they came near enough to be seen. As though awaiting the moment, the vanguard's pipers blasted. It was a weird thing out there on the gray flatlands. The flapping kilts, colorless shadows at first, became red and green and yellow. The guns swayed on broad shoulders. The swords swung like pendulums. The men looked ahead and marched. At their head, driving doggedly, was Scalpie Campbell. Duncan suddenly was not only dutiful: he was proud. It was a grand company, Scots all, his company, marching for the Crown. He ran down the hill and took his place in line.

They marched that day over interminable sandhills. They crossed South River in the morning. They cut new roads here and there to save distance on their way to Black River. Duncan first gave attention to the new country, sandhills, swamps, creeks in white sand beds, creeks in black mud beds, the tall, gently glowing pines, the bullet-colored trunks of the bare-branched scrub oaks. Then, eventually, it all became the same. He no longer cared. It was just a march. At times they would stop and rest. Then they would march again. Then it was late afternoon, and they were at Black River. There was no bridge. Only a flat, half sunk in the water.

They marched into a field, knee-high in dead grass, and broke ranks. Other companies came up behind them. Fires started. The wagons rolled up. General Donald MacDonald and Alexander MacLeod and James Cotten and Allan MacDonald came in, riding horses. General MacDonald was tired and pale. He rode down to the narrow river and looked at the flat. Duncan and his mates gathered timber and made three fires. He stood at one and waited for supper. Scalpie Campbell came and stood beside him, smiled curiously.

"Glad tae hae ye back," Scalpie said.

"I had to go," Duncan said. "I knew there'd be no battle at Rockfish."

"Aye. All o' us kenned that."

Scalpie Campbell was a bonnie fellow. He had no thought that Duncan had left to escape a fight. "Else ye'd ha' stayed," Scalpie said.

"Aye. I'd sock the man who said not."

"Weel, there's a lot o' such talk in the line, I'm sorry tae say. The colonels and the majors are bitter."

"Aye?"

"Aye. The MacLean and ithers are most contemptuous o' General MacDonald's determination tae avoid the Whigs. He crossed the river above Rockfish to avoid Moore. He intended to recross at Elizabethtown, but the big fellow Lillington and his boatmen outstripped us, and Moore was just behind. That was twice. Then we headed for Corbett's Ferry, straight down our side o' the river and a little march across, but then we learned that troops from New Bern, under Caswell, held that. Not many, 'tis true, but General MacDonald wants nae fight at all. He has escaped three fights, and it may be that we wi' skin through, like hounds runnin' frae rabbits, and finally join Cornwallis without nickin' a Whig's hide. Perhaps it is wiser. I dinna gainsay it. But I hae na likin' f'r this seemin' retreat."

"Aye," said Duncan. "I saw Lillington scootin' down the river. They made talk o' going to Corbett's Ferry."

"Weel, they'll abandon that when they know we're crossing the Black River higher up. What's the next place they can drop back to and block our way?"

"The Widow Moore's Creek Bridge, two days' march, below."

"Weel, personally I hope tae God they make a stand there and let's hae it out wi' 'em. I'm tired o' dodging. We'll hack our way through 'em like goin' through cotton stalks."

"Aye—they winna fight."

"Na."

It took half a day next morning to raise the ferryboat. After that it was quite simple to span the stream with a pontoon bridge. Then, still seventy miles from Fort Johnston, the Highlanders again took up their march.

That day they drove through more scrub oaks and live oaks and pines, and through more swamps and across more crystal-clear and inky-black streams, and over more white sandhills. They camped in another field that night, and Donald MacDonald looked still paler and still more weary. The next day was Sunday and the march was short. The soldiers rested. Reverend John Bethune preached of the God of battle. Monday morning they marched again. Now across both rivers, with nothing but creeks between them and the waiting British ships at Wilmington, the Highlanders considered that the Whig bands would not dare face them.

At midday General MacDonald slumped from his horse, too sick to go on. They took him to a farmhouse and put him to bed. The soldiers halted solemnly in the road.

The uneasy officers stood in brown concern, the same thought in the minds of all. MacLean, Governor Josiah Martin's confidante, spoke it with some acerbity:

" 'Tis most unfortunate. Here we are, two days' march from our destination. We have dodged Whigs for a week, and now our commanding officer begins to rave with the fever. It will demoralize our men. What with suspecting that their officers fear to fight and being suddenly leader-less—"

"Gentlemen!" Colonel Donald MacLeod, who had led the Regulators, strode among them with purposeful abruptness. "If I interrupt," he said with edged sarcasm to MacLean, "please forgive me." Then he turned to the group.

"I am in command—General MacDonald's orders. My first instructions are that officers shall desist from subversive comment and co-operate with me fully in accomplishing our task according to the policies laid down."

"But," said MacLean, "how can it be by General MacDonald's orders, when he was raving—"

"Silence!"

MacLeod was an old hand in the army, and he knew when to draw an issue. He took two quick steps. He stood directly in front of the governor's friend and glared into his eyes.

"Mr. MacLean," he demanded, "if it is your intention to gain command of these troops, state your authority. If not, then you will obey my orders. My immediate command to you is to be silent!"

MacLean paled. He suppressed his anger and humiliation with an effort. "Aye, sir!" He saluted.

Colonel MacLeod continued: "Captain Pyle, you will detail a squad of twenty men under a sergeant as a bodyguard for General MacDonald. Include in this number anyone you may have with experience in attending the sick. Also cut out one of the wagons for the general's use when he shall have recovered sufficiently to continue his march. Wi' a good night's rest he will o'ertake us by tomorrow noon, no doubt."

To the others MacLeod said: "To your places, gentlemen. We will finish the day's march as planned, so that we may reach Nigger Head Point and board the King's ships tomorrow evening. March!"

Scalpie Campbell was standing only a few yards away from his Highlanders. He whirled toward them. "Whaup!" he shouted, and the line jerked into motion, their shoes sinking in the white sand. Nearly a mile up the road the teamsters were shouting to their horses, and the dull knock of the wagons sounded over the soft shuffle of feet.

They were well into the Whig country now. Lanky men, patiently bitter, sat on the porches of their cabins, long rifles across their knees. Litters of shirt-tailed children climbed to the fodder stacks and smoke-house roofs to stare. Up the long lanes to the big houses saddle horses stamped at the hitching posts. Groups of men leaned on the fences to watch the passing column. They gave the impression that they but waited for the Tories to pass before they themselves took to the saddle.

Still no one made an untoward move. The only sign was of defense, but there was no denying the hostility in the air. One weathered old woman sat on her little porch behind a rail fence and spat snuff spitefully for every company that marched before her. There was no fear. Some of the women looked merely curious. But nowhere along the road was there even a flicker of a smile as the Scots stamped through.

Colonel MacLeod rode up to Scalpie Campbell, at the head of the line. "The territory," he said, "betrays its animosity. Detach ten for an advance guard. We should take that precaution."

The first ten men moved out from the front rapidly, leaving Duncan as one of the two front men. Scalpie looked back over his shoulder and smiled. "Finally the Stuarts hae come to their own!" he called, and Duncan smiled back. Scalpie was a bonnie captain.

The scouts went faster, impressed by their new duties. They took to the woods, and one crouched and searched ahead. It brought a strange, unexplored feeling to Duncan. It was but a simple act of military precaution, and doubtless not necessary at all, but it was the first move he had seen which contemplated a lurking enemy. It fetched him into a mood for brooding. He had thought of an actual blood-and-bone fight with the Whigs only on the top of his mind. Now it gave him the loose let-go of helplessness to think that any tree might shield a Whig bushwhacker.

The country was flat and open. It was inexpressibly drab. It had no song of peace and cheer, such as he had promised Mary. The chill February winds flowed over the smooth needles of wire grass, comfortless. Dead limbs stood out from the pines like cold, twisted fingers of corpses. A buzzard sat on a tree, lone and hungry, to look down on the passing column. Duncan had a revolting thought of the old seer's raven which should drink three fulls of MacDonald blood.

They marched more than two hours, deep sand pulling at weary feet. The sun was in the west, and Colonel MacLeod called a halt. There was a vacant cabin. The officers took that. The men scattered to the woods for fuel. Sentries were ordered out. The afternoon waxed cold, and the fires grew big. Duncan did not share it, but the soldiers had a feeling of elation, of new enthusiasm, despite the general's sickness. This was the last camp of the march. Tomorrow, everyone said, they would be on ships, British ships, sailing down the river from Nigger Head Point to Fort Johnston. Duncan wasn't so sure. The surly Whigs on the road seemed each mile to become more furtive and sinister. Mary had said the Highlanders could not go to the coast without a battle. Perhaps they faced one now.

He threw off the unwelcome thought. He envisioned what majesty he would see at the fort Wednesday morning—imperial spars reaching to the sky, sails furled, flags flying, bugle calls, the sharp commands of army officers. And ships, ships filling the river, a hundred ships, laden with soldiers and supplies and cannon. Clinton—Parker—Cornwallis— in gold and broadcloth—the Crown's might personified. It was a cheering prospect, but his fit of brooding returned.

After supper the men lay on their tartans before the fires and rested their feet, cursing the sand for a nuisance for getting in their hair. Scalpie Campbell called Duncan to him, and they walked away from the men. Scalpie was worried.

"Did ye na say that we hae come back into the trail which crosses the Black River at Corbett's Ferry?"

"Aye."

"I hae given thought to it. If this Lillington caught word that we had dodged Corbett's Ferry, he might head for that creek bridge—whad'd ye call it?"

"Widow Moore's Creek Bridge?"

"Aye—how far from here?"

"Three miles, no doubt."

"Aye—and did ye see what I saw i' the road? Foot tracks, lots o' them?"

Duncan frowned. "Aye, I saw foot tracks—fresh tracks. I thought them to be those of the advance guard."

"Too many. Hunders o' men hae marched ahead o' us. I kept listenin' f'r the scouts tae report something, but they didna. We should take care before we march in the mornin'."

"Aye," Duncan agreed. He frowned and looked into the woods. "Aye!" he said again.

"Listen, Duncan—I hae said little tae ye o' the march, but I wish ye to know—"

An orderly came up hurriedly. "Colonel MacLeod's compliments, sir. He wants ye over to headquarters."

Scalpie threw his arm around Duncan's shoulder and drew him toward the cabin. Duncan did not question the gesture, taking it as an indication of the welcome camaraderie of Captain Campbell. Brave men have an unspoken language by which to know each other, and Campbell and Duncan Stuart had developed such a friendliness. Duncan was surprised, however, when Scalpie pushed him into the door and into the council of the officers.

"Flora MacDonald," laughed Scalpie, "says he is the spi't 'n' image o' Bonnie Prince Charlie, so I figgered he belonged in our councils."

Duncan prepared to be embarrassed by the laughter, but lost the feeling in the sudden air of gravity. The officers standing around the plank table were tense. They merely flicked glances to see who entered and turned back to Colonel Donald MacLeod.

"Now, let me repeat," MacLeod said, "for those who have just come in and for your own better enlightenment."

The top of the table had charcoal marks on it, and MacLeod was explaining: "This dot, here," pointing, "is our present camp site. This meandering line on our left is a creek, the Widow Moore's Creek, which flows from up the country, paralleling our route about a mile distant. Ahead of us it crosses our road and goes on into the Black River. From here to our bridge over the creek is a distance of three miles. Do you understand, gentlemen?"

No one spoke. The officers studied the rude black lines in silence.

"Now," MacLeod said impressively, "the Whigs are entrenched immediately beyond the bridge."

Duncan drew his breath. It was as though the colonel had given him the truth of what had haunted him in the bitter, secretive eyes of Whigs along the way.

MacLeod continued: "The creek at the bridge is about thirty feet wide and, with recent rains, probably six feet deep. That is our problem, gentlemen. General MacDonald is in no condition to counsel us. I will assume the responsibility, but I wish your suggestions."

"How many Whigs?" Old Hector MacNeill asked the question, and he was a regular-army man. So were Allan MacDonald and his son-in-law, Alexander MacLeod. Their opinion had weight. Duncan liked, and was lifted by, their direct, thrusting comment. They rallied him from his vague forebodings.

"We know," Colonel MacLeod answered Hector carefully, "that Lillington is there. He made good time in his boats. He arrived this morning or yesterday and has thrown up breastworks. He had Colonel John Ashe and a company of volunteers with him—about two hundred and fifty riflemen, I'd say. They were not encumbered with wagons and made much better time from the Upper Cape Fear than we did. They have no cannon in this contingent.

"Then, arriving just ahead of us was Colonel Richard Caswell's contingent from New Bern. They have at least one cannon. It may be one of those which Governor Martin dismantled just before he fled the mansion last summer. Caswell has approximately six hundred men. That makes, say, nine hundred in the two outfits. Then, I'm informed, other local companies have flocked in, and these have been joined by swampmen with squirrel rifles. We have facing us, gentlemen, at the most eleven hundred men, most of them badly trained if trained at all."

"Then how many," asked Alexander Macleod, "hae we?"

"We had more than two thousand leaving Cross Creek," Donald MacLeod said. "Our losses have been fairly constant. We have, in round numbers, fourteen hundred clansmen and two hundred and fifty to three hundred Regulators—sixteen to seventeen hundred."

"Well," Farquard Campbell asked, "what courses are open to us? What—how many different things can we do?"

"Three," said the colonel.

"Three?" demanded MacLean, the governor's friend. "I see but one."

Donald MacLeod shrugged. With his new responsibilities he could not indulge the luxury of wrath. "First," he continued, "we can hold our ground. We can camp here and wait for the British to send reinforcements, catching the rebels between us and decimate them with little loss. Thus—"

"Hold! No!" MacLean said boldly. "I may as well say now as tomorrow—gentlemen, there are no British on Tidewater. Even the old *Cruzier* was beaten back by riflemen ten days ago. No ships will meet us at Nigger Head Point. Governor Martin expects them any week, but they have not come. In the meantime the governor is in the humiliation of hiding on the old hulk, awaiting our arrival. This command is the only force in Carolina to uphold His Majesty's dignity! We must hasten to the governor, through hell or high water, for our own self-respect."

"Well—hell! Why hae ye been holding this back?" demanded Hector MacNeill.

"We've been tricked!" Farquard Campbell charged.

Donald MacLeod's knuckles bore so on the table that the bones crackled, but he forbore to vent his indignation. "I have been telling the gentlemen," he said in a low, cutting tone, "that the British would meet us there. I hope they now will understand that I was as much deceived as they.

"Now," he continued. "Second, we can deploy to the left before daylight tomorrow morning, flank the Whigs, and be below them again before they are aware. The advantage of that is that it would avoid the meeting we have so consistently prevented and would get us to the *Cruzier* without violating General MacDonald's most wise strategy. Third, we can force our way through the Whigs."

The officers looked at each other for a moment in silence. It was as though they thought rapiers and clashed suspicion with suspicion.

"For me," Scalpie Campbell said boldly, "I'm tired o' dodgin' Whigs. We've been at it f'r goin' on a week and—"

"Right!" said MacLean, smiling in triumph at Donald MacLeod. Scalpie Campbell looked at him with a frown.

"But," said Scalpie, "Colonel MacLeod is the best-equipped army man among us, and I doubt my wisdom and defer to his judgment. That is a' I hae to say."

Farquard Campbell was for the flanking movement. Hector MacNeill also was. Allan MacDonald suggested that, inasmuch as the Whigs insisted on it, they might as well be met one place as another. Alexander MacLeod agreed with him.

"Gentlemen!" said MacLean. "Are we going to make ourselves the laughingstock of the whole British Army? Here we are, with the flower of the Carolina Highlanders primed to fight, eager to fight, knowing they are in a glorious cause—and we haggle and wiggle and dodge and twist, and then let half our number of ill-equipped, untrained lowland clodhoppers throw us on our haunches. How shall we ever gain the King's favor and win promotion in his army? Gentlemen, do we tremble before the Whigs?"

MacLean looked around with a sneer. His circling eyes finally met Donald MacLeod's, and they clashed.

"Ye have left the decision to me, gentlemen." Donald MacLeod stood up, white-faced, but still gripping his anger. He spoke to all, but his eyes never left those of MacLean, and MacLean's did not waver. "We meet the Whigs at dawn. I invite Mr. MacLean to stand wi' me in the battle, and we shall see where the cowardice, if any, be."

It was a dead-gray dawn that Tuesday morning. The deadness and chill of a graveyard lay on the bristling frost which hugged the limbs and the grass and made even the rich green of the bay trees gray and grisly and cold. Campbell's vanguard swung down the road to Moore's Creek, with the whole army in support. They were not cold. They had been marching an hour, and the numbness had left their fingers and their blood coursed hot and free. But they were glum—seventy-five hand-picked men to flush and flay the enemy. It was their job to smash the Whig front lines, making the way clear for the riflemen to charge in and complete the slaughter. No matter how brave, one cannot contemplate splitting his first skull without dark thought.

A full mile back in the darkness the whole column had stopped its soft padding in the sand, and each captain had addressed his company. John Scalpie Campbell had said:

"I wi' not waste time telling Hielanders what tae do in battle. Ye hae the instinct in y'r blood and bones. All I say tae ye is follow me. Gin I fa', then charge o'er my body and keep going. Wherever a Whig shows his head, split it!"

The line had surged as though lashed. It had been too dark for one man to see the face of another. There was another mile to march. In that mile black night became dark gray, and the Highland column was like a great dim shadow moving on the road. Big dark Scots, big bright Scots drove grimly, each with his picture in his mind, a Whig going down with a gritty whack.

Duncan knew the bridge, a plank span, high in the middle, ten paces across. The vanguard would go across it like a spearhead and mushroom into the Whigs up the slope.

He had a cold, retching feeling. He was not afraid. His belly just quivered. He couldn't help it. He saw Whigs lurking in the swamp shadows at the left. But they weren't Whigs. They were trees. He whispered the company's battle cry: "King George and Broadswords!" No good. He whispered the ancient cry of the Stuarts: *"Creag-an-sgairbh!"* That was better.

He had the impulse for horseplay, to tangle Sandy MacCallum on his left with his broadsword, and to bump Laughlan Bethune, in front, with the butt of his rifle. Anything. Anything but this damnable glum, cold silence, with Whig eyes peering out of the dark behind every tree. It gave him the jerks.

There was a shuffling behind him, and he turned to look. Mary's brother, Malcolm MacLeod, tall and gawky and half crazed with excitement. He shouldered his way into the line. Those before and behind cursed him under their breaths. Duncan, too, swore. Braving a reprimand, he went back.

"Get out and get back," he whispered, thumbing down the road.

"I winna!" Malcolm shrilled.

"Ye can't stay here!"

"I wi'!"

"Listen, Malcolm," Duncan protested. "I told Mary—"

"T' hell wi' ye! I know my duty. Leave me be!"

A sergeant tugged at Duncan's arm, and Scalpie Campbell looked back. He flung the sergeant's arm aside and then gave up and took his place in line. An officer, walking fast, came up from behind, brushed against him and passed on. It was Colonel Donald MacLeod. He went to Captain Campbell, and they saluted. MacLeod took the left, Campbell the right, and they marched together.

Something gallant was in it. Duncan remembered last night. MacLeod had said: "We wi' see where the cowardice, if any, be." And now, there he was, out front, sharing the danger with Scalpie Campbell. Duncan's grinding belly came still. He shoved forward eagerly. If they'd let him, he wanted to march with 'em. His will to fight flamed alive.

"Halt!" was the hushed command.

Two hundred paces ahead was the bridge. They could see the timbers faintly. The dark blotches beyond were the trees on the slope. The yawning caverns on the left were black shadows in the swamp. The silence fairly screamed its hidden menace. The breathing of the men sounded like wind. But there were no fires, no Whigs, nothing but darkness and cold and the dim white light of frost.

MacLeod and Campbell crept up the road, and the company, forgetting instructions, crept behind them. Duncan took down his rifle and dribbled powder into the pan. Others did likewise. He wanted to shoot the damned thing, according to orders, and drop it.

The officers stopped and peered in the dark. They hissed softly for silence. If Whigs hid in the brush, they were as quiet as the frost. There was no sound. The colonel and the captain crept forward again. Whigs or no Whigs, it took guts to invite bullets like that.

Then Scalpie straightened and laughed softly. "See?" he pointed. "There's their trench just beyond the bridge. Not a soul in it. They've gone!"

"Sh-h-h-h-h!" Colonel MacLeod was cautious. "Take care!"

They were at the bridge now, and Scalpie stopped and swore roundly. "They stripped the planks off!" He stepped on one of the naked, peeled-pine stringers and fell back with new oaths. "It's the slickest damned log I ever—"

But now he was giving attention to getting over. He stuck his broadsword point into the log and braced his steps against it. MacLeod did likewise. They warned the men behind them that the logs were slippery with soap and tallow. They could smell it now themselves. It would be slow getting over, but the Whigs had fled.

MacLeod and Campbell stepped off on the far side, and the head of the line marched up on the stringers to pick its way across. Everybody suddenly tensed. A figure dimly moved beyond the trench to call out:

"Hey, you-all! Who comes thar?"

"A friend!" answered Colonel MacLeod.

"A friend o' whose?"

"A friend of King George!"

Scalpie Campbell screamed like a preying animal: "King George and Broadswords! Highlanders, charge!"

Back in the pines a battery of bagpipes shrieked. The Highlanders yelled. The darkness thundered with the sudden tumult. The soldiers rushed for the bridge. They threw down their rifles without firing. They brandished their broadswords, but only to creep across the stringers. Duncan shoved and trampled frantically until he felt the timber under his feet.

Little points of light flashed up there in the woods. They were like fireflies. There were no lightning bugs in February, he remembered. It was a hell of a job walking this footlog. You stuck in your sword, braced your foot against it, and took another step and balanced while you pulled out your sword and stuck it in for another step.

Colonel Donald MacLeod was across, still near the bridge, but Scalpie Campbell was running up the slope, yelling like the devil. Everybody was yelling. Everybody was pushing and shoving. The bagpipes split your ears. The little specks of light came and went. It was a slow job, getting over. Damned Whig trick, greasing the stringers. He had a sudden throttling sense of alarm.

Something was wrong! It wasn't right! Something in his brain shrieked a warning. If they didn't yell so, and the bagpipes didn't scream so, and if those behind didn't push so, you could hear yourself think. But he hadn't time to think. He had to get over. Wrong or right, this was the first job.

Some of them couldn't hold their places and fell headlong into the freezing water. Duncan laughed, high, like a horse's whinny. They splashed like rafting logs. Some of them screamed when they went under. No wonder. That water was cold enough to blister you. Duncan laughed again and shut his mouth. His laugh sounded crazy.

Colonel MacLeod was walking around the head of the bridge like a dazed man, waving his arm. What was the matter up ahead? Any countryman could walk a footlog. What was Colonel MacLeod's trouble? He fell over, and got up and waved his sword, and damned if he didn't fall again.

"God damn it, Laughlan," Duncan shouted, half laughing, "don't jostle me like that!" Then he whooped. Laughlan Bethune teetered desperately and shot to the water, head down. Then Duncan was teetering, too, dancing and waving his arms, trying to stay upright, but Laughlan had knocked him off balance. Both heels slipped in the goo, and he went down standing up.

Duncan shrieked. His kilt ballooned, and the water rose under it like a knife circling his belly. His knees bent and his head went under. He stood straight and the water was under his chin. He yelled. He laughed. A pack o' loons, couldn't walk a footlog!

"Goddlemighty!" he protested, dodging. Half of them were slipping off. A clumsy fellow fell on him and knocked him under again.

He came up and the fellow stared straight in his face—dead. The churning water rolled the man over, and his arm crumpled and struck Duncan on the cheek.

Duncan stared, breathless, and another dead one fell and knocked him under. He dived out of the way and came up with a dead man across his shoulder. He fought to shed the limp thing. It was John MacArthur.

It had all happened in a moment. Duncan gripped himself. He was cold. Freezing cold. Cold inside. Colder than the water. He must hold himself. It was not true: this deluge of the dead and dying was not truth. No more than if a horrendous dragon drew across the hill breathing fire and smoke. He had gone crazy. He must get back his senses.

There was a little twinkle of lights back in the trees. He looked. There they were. Still flashing. Scalpie Campbell, tragically alone, was going toward them. Toward the upper yellow gash on the hillside. Charging toward the crackle of the winking lights. He was like a man running on air—long, slow, high-kneed strides, waving his sword, calling his men. No one followed him. And in the same slow motion he dived to the ground. He struggled up to his arms' length and then sprawled out, still.

Duncan strained to cry out. He could not. It was like a dream. His voice was a thin squeak. Nevertheless he lunged out to go to Scalpie. The icy water pushed against him. He could not rush. The mud on the bottom was deep ooze, and his feet slipped and tangled with roots. He lifted them to swim, and his overthrown arm went across a man's body. Kenneth Murchison moaned and sank under Duncan's pressure.

Duncan sprang back and caught Murchison and lifted him back to the surface. "Ken! Ken!" he cried. Murchison was bleeding at the throat. The blood spurted into the water and made it red. Duncan pushed on to the bank. He laid the clansman on the grass. He stood ready to spring, his arms out like a runner, ready to dash to Scalpie's aid or to spring back and rescue the drowning wounded. The field up the slope still was bare. Not a soul stirred upon it. Near the bridge Highlanders lay prostrate or writhed on the ground. Others struggled to get across the slippery string-ers. Back of them the angry Scots pushed blindly and roared for those ahead to make way. But the two lines of men moved like snails. Some fell off. Some were shot off. Those who got across started running for the Whig breastworks and fell.

The water churned and clotted with the dead and the living. Duncan let the unhurt rescue the hurt and turned toward Scalpie. A tall soldier on the bridge teetered over him—a gangling, awkward fellow. He screamed and plunged. Malcolm, Mary's brother. He struck the water in a clear spot and went out of sight without another sound.

Duncan dived from the bank, grasped his clothing and stood up. Even so, strain on tiptoe as he would, he could not bring Malcolm's head to the surface. He plowed under blindly. He came up the opposite slope and laid him on the grass. Malcolm was dead. Undoubtedly. Duncan shook him and called him. But the bullet wound on his breast told too grim a tale. Duncan looked at his face, but his thought was not of Malcolm, but of Mary.

Up on the road the packed Highlanders crowded and raged. They did not yet understand the delay.

"Ye canna cross the bridge!" Duncan yelled to them. "Ye canna cross the bridge! Ye maun wade the creek!"

But it was like shouting in a storm. They couldn't hear him. Their own Gaelic roars smothered his voice. He barely could hear himself. He knew the way. He waved to them to follow. He struck for the water again. Nobody even saw him. Nobody came. He glanced toward Malcolm's body to mark it in his mind and plunged into the creek.

The dawn was still gray. What had seemed to him to be hours was not yet five minutes.

Duncan, waist-deep in the current, jerked and stopped. A thunderous explosion wiped out the crackle and roar of the conflict. He felt the con-cussion and quivered still.

Shrieks of pain came from the road. The whole cluster of Highlanders flew apart as though it, too, had exploded. It was the cannon. The Whigs had opened on the trapped men with grapeshot. The rifles had been mur-der, but the cannon was massacre. The fallen Scots screamed and twisted.

but they were alone. The others had sprung to the roadside and lay on their bellies in the grass.

Except one man. Duncan recognized him. His name was Far-earst Campbell, Farquard's cousin. He was not even in the advance guard, but had run up from behind. When the massed Scots leaped to the grass, they made way for him. He sprang upon the soapy logs, waving his sword. He ran all the way over, miraculously, like a winged man in the air. He called in a loud cry: "Scalpie!" There was a sob in his voice, a great, deep sob. "Scalpie!"

Duncan could see the bullets come through him, bursting tatters from the back of his jacket.

He ran halfway up the slope before he fell. His last sound was a strangled: "Scalpie!"

Duncan continued to stand still, for even before Far-earst had fully fallen, the Whigs charged, yelling, down the hill. He sank in the water up to his nose and watched. They came orderly enough, for Whigs, running in a good line, firing as they came and stopping to reload as the second line came in front. Alexander Lillington ran at their head, shouting like a madman. A detachment carried planks. Before the Scots had recovered from the cannon blast, the Whigs were on the bridge, relaying the floor. Some of the Highlanders, leaderless but unafraid, raced to them with swords, but fell on the way.

Duncan stood in the water, looking up the road, and moaned: "Oh!" Again and again "Oh!" As far back as he could see, the Scots were bursting from the line and running for the bushes, a mad rout. Nowhere did the line make a stand. The Whigs had broken across the creek higher up and had struck them on the flank. Nothing—nothing whatever—of Mac-Donald's proud Highland army was left. Not even the wagons, for all the horses, too, tore through the woods. Disgrace and shame had burst upon the clansmen.

As eager as he had been to stand beside Scalpie Campbell, the whole quick battle had ended with Duncan barely more than a spectator. He hadn't fired a shot. Few Scots had. They had marched into the trap to stand and be slaughtered helplessly.

The victorious Whigs raced across the bridge over his head, and Duncan turned and, pushing the half-floating corpses out of his way, slowly worked downstream until the bushes hid him. There was Malcolm. Even worse, there was Mary to face—to tell. He stood over the body and stared. He was numb. As numb as Malcolm. The Whigs might have seen him if they had looked. But they weren't looking for individuals. Up ahead they were taking the Highlanders by squads and companies. If they took him he wouldn't care. He wouldn't care if they did not. He had no feeling but an overwhelming numbness in his body and in his soul.

He took Malcolm in his arms, like a baby, and started home. The body seemed without weight. The morning had opened gray. And now it still was gray, gray with frost and death and defeat. His sodden clothes dripped cold water. So did Malcolm's.

He skirted the creek underbrush, moving downstream, away from the shouts and the shots to the right. Presently, moving as he was, he would be out of the area of action. The ground huckleberry bushes scraped their stiff branches against his shins, and the brier thorns raked his legs, but he did not notice.

The turmoil and the shouting raged nearer. The sound of a galloping horse drew his way. Duncan stepped into the shelter of small pines and looked. The horse, with three men astride it and one running behind, holding to its tail, burst through a slough, with the outdistanced Whigs running down the opposite hill, shooting and yelling. They gave up the chase and turned back. The horse, with its wagon harness flapping and rattling, charged on by, Colonel Cotten swinging desperately to its tail. Thus escaped what was left of Cotten's command.

Duncan turned into the pine forest, away from the little bushes which scraped and scratched him. But by now the yelling and the shooting were far to his right, and he needed the open ground. He was stumbling. The body suddenly was unbearably heavy.

Nevertheless he staggered on through the trees. He saw three empty turpentine barrels ahead, and they somehow gave him new heart. They were familiar. Something he always had recognized as helpful. They were screened from the conflict by the trees. He took his unwieldy burden to them. He laid the body on the brown carpet of pine straw and stood up to gasp and look.

In a minute a man burst through the trees and stared wildly about. He wore the tartan of the MacLeods, the same tartan that covered Malcolm.

"Alexander!" Duncan called in a loud whisper.

Colonel MacLeod, Anne MacDonald's husband, swung around, snatching at his dagger.

"Na! Na!" Duncan called. "I wi' not harm ye."

Alexander, his eyes flashing consternation, peered back through the trees. He strode over to Duncan, panting, too much out of breath to speak. He had taken a long run for a man more than fifty years old. His eyes fell on the body, and he looked at Duncan.

"Malcolm MacLeod—y'r cousin!"

"The first I knew," Alexander shouted, "the Whigs charged out of the bushes upon us, and my men—" He waved his arms. "Not a shot!"

Duncan said: "They got Scalpie Campbell!"

"What happened to Donald MacLeod? Did ye hear?"

"Dead. I saw him fa'."

"I'm headin' f'r the coast. Wi' ye go?"

Duncan's mind leaped at the idea. He could go to the coast—join Cornwallis, go to Nova Scotia, become a soldier in the British Army, march in strange places. He could escape the torment of facing Tom Brown and old Tom Hadley. He could escape the jibes and the sneers. But there was Mary. She would be alone. Flora had set her adrift, and her brother was dead.

"Na," Duncan said. "I wi' go home f'r what may betide."

Alexander MacLeod nodded. It was no time to argue. Each man for himself as he saw fit. He said: "Tell Anne and Flora that Allan and Alexander are unhurt, but captured. I dinna ken what may be done wi' 'em. Tell Anne she shall hear frae me the first opportunity."

This gave Duncan a flash of anger, for in some way not yet reasoned out he blamed Flora MacDonald for the disaster. He had taken her counsel, and this had happened.

There were new shouts beyond the sand ridge. Duncan and Alexander dashed for a pine thicket. They lay and peered out while a party of Whigs, gay and triumphant, marched rapidly by. They paused to see the strange sight of the water-soaked Malcolm on the straw, but they did not touch him.

When the Whigs had gone, they stood up. They paused, as if thinking what to say. They had no words. Not even thought. Only an overwhelming, nauseous sense of calamity.

"Weel," Alexander said, "I bid ye farewell." He turned toward the swamp. Duncan saluted in silence. He thought of Malcolm. He could not leave the body in the open. On account of the wolves. He could not bear it forty miles home. It was too heavy. The turpentine barrels would serve.

Fifteen minutes later he stood up, satisfied. The barrels, end to end, wedged between small trees, their heads, except the end two, bashed out, made a piny woods cairn that even wolves could not violate. Thus Malcolm could lie safely until he could return with the cart. Without looking back, Duncan struck out through the brush.

ORISKANY

by WALTER D. EDMONDS

THE MEN MADE an uneasy, sprawling mass throughout the little settlement. On the edge of the knoll the fort had been built on, Nicholas Herkimer straddled his old white horse, leaning his hands heavily on the somnolent withers.

He was using his deep voice to good effect, now giving orders in English to an officer, locating the muster ground of each company, now checking the list of supplies that trundled past in carts drawn either by oxen or by horses, now hailing in Low German some neighbor or acquaintance.

When Gil preceded the Palatine company into the village, he saw the general in the same position, in his worn blue campaign coat, warm enough in the stifling heat to keep the sweat steadily rolling down his cheeks. He was listening to the bombastic voice of Colonel Cox.

"All right, colonel," he said finally. "If you want to push ahead to-night, you can. But don't go beyond Staring's Brook. And don't go until your whole regiment's here, either. Leyp's and Dievendorf's companies haven't showed up yet."

Cox, flushed with heat and drink, said loudly that they were wasting time, he'd undertake to lick the Tories with his own company, and he could look out for his company, too, without being told.

"Those are orders," Herkimer said, tartly, for once. "I make Colonel Weston witness, if you don't like them."

The commandant of the Dayton garrison nodded brusquely, met the embattled colonel's eye with a Yankee gleam in his own, and said, "I've noticed them already."

"Where's Bellinger's regiment?" asked Gil.

"Beyond Doc's house," replied a delighted farmer from Snydersbush. "Cox had to haul his tail down that time." He grinned. "He used to hunt around and raise hell with young Johnson, and now he thinks he's drawn title to being a gentleman."

But Gil noticed what the Snyders man had not, that several of the

From: *Drums Along The Mohawk*. By permission of Little, Brown & Company and the Atlantic Monthly Press.

other officers were looking after Cox with sympathetic eyes. Like him they rode good horses, with English-made saddles and polished riding boots. In their company, Herkimer's faded outfit, horse and coat, looked like a shabby imitation. No doubt they thought him one.

George Weaver greeted him. "You're only just in time, Gil. How's Lana? We ain't seen her in a month, now."

"She's fine," said Gil. "How's Emma?"

"Just the same. She's been considering going down to visit Lana to get a quilting pattern off her. She said she might go down while I was away."

"That's fine," said Gil.

Finding the company mustered took him back more clearly than ever to the time before his house was burnt. Reall, with his gun clean for once, was there; and Jeams MacNod, looking a little pallid at the thought of war; and Clem Coppernol.

Gil said, "I thought you were over sixty."

The white-haired Dutchman said, "Too old? By Jesus, a Dutchman ain't ever too old to take a pot at the British."

Weaver said, "We're to camp along the road to-night, right here. We've got to wait for Fisscher's Mohawk company, and Campbell's Minutemen."

"I thought they'd have to stay, with Brant around here."

"Brant's cut back west again," said Weaver. "He's at Stanwix now."

A man gaped. He said, "That Indian can move through the woods faster than you get the news of him."

"He'd better look out where he shows his head," said Reall in a boisterous voice, raising his gun and aiming at a cabbage in the doctor's garden.

George Weaver smacked the barrel down, roaring:—

"Do you want to kill somebody?"

That evening it looked as if the drought might break. Slate-colored clouds with traveling veils of white lifted their heads over the southern hills. There was a distant rumble of thunder, but no rain came. Fires broke out beside the ox carts. Eatables were unloaded. Pork and bacon frying made an odor through the village. Men sat together, grumbling because they had been kept out of decent beds—men like Fred Kast who couldn't see the sense of walking east seven miles one day to walk back seven miles the next, merely for the sake of sleeping in a blanket on the ground.

"I ain't complaining of your company," he explained. "It's just the idea."

"You ought to have brought your bed along," a man said.

"Yes, with Katy in it," said Christian Reall.

Kast laughed.

"I thought of that, and then I thought I couldn't find no room in it, with all you ground pigs trying too."

George Weaver looked down the slope of ground to the river, where Peter Tygert's house was. Herkimer was staying there. Few noticed the late arrival of the Mohawk regiment until they saw Colonel Frederick Fisscher, dapper and dandy for all his gray hair, go cantering down to Tygert's.

"Well, they got here," Weaver said. "I'm going to bed."

He rolled over in his blanket. Reall said, "You'd better pull your feet out of the road, though."

Demooth came round at breakfast time, wearing the homespun coat he used around the farm. The men were pleased to see him. They had got sick of the handsomely outfitted officers of the other regiments. It made them feel too much like the plain bush Germans the others claimed they were.

"All present?" he said to Weaver.

"Yes. There's nobody missing."

"That's fine." His dark face, lean, alert, quick-eyed, looked them over.

"Boys," he said, "Herkimer was going to put us in front. But the way feeling is, he had to let Cox go up ahead. Bellinger's regiment and Klock's are going to be the main guard. Fisscher's so tired he'll just naturally have to come behind. You can fall in when you hear them cheering Herkimer off from the fort. When he goes by, you just drop in behind him. I've got to send Cox off now, but I'll join you up the road."

"Yes, captain," said George.

They both grinned.

It took them all one day to get to Staring's Brook. Ten miles. The companies straggled along the road, taking it easy in the heat. Up ahead, Cox lead the Canajoharie men, festering all the time in his wounded vanity. Then, after a long gap, came Herkimer, musing on the old white horse who picked his footing with such caution. With Herkimer rode half a dozen officers, Colonels Fisscher, Veeder, Klock, and Campbell, and Paymaster Isaac Paris, talking volubly on how a campaign of this sort should be conducted, making a bright patch of blue coats, like out-of-season gentians in the woods; and then the German Flats regiment and the Palatine, perhaps five hundred men. Then another gap, and the long line of ox carts jolting on the road, making their painful crawl, beasts and drivers choking in their own dust, stung by horse and deer flies. And after another gap, the Mohawk regiment, taking its ease along the way.

The total force of the army was eight hundred men. The number weighed heavily on Herkimer's mind that morning. He knew that St. Leger had four hundred regulars, that he had six hundred Tories, men just as good or better than his own straggling militia, and in addition almost a thousand Indians.

At Fort Stanwix, Gansevoort had seven hundred men under arms, but Gansevoort couldn't be expected to send them all out. His duty was to hold the fort. But if it were put up to him in time, he might be willing to spare a couple of hundred of them for a diversion.

The advance guard crossed Staring's Brook early in the afternoon. It took three hours for the train of carts and wagons and the rear guard to arrive. The army pitched camp wherever they could find room along the road, a scattering, unorganized mess of men, nearly two miles long. The fires were like glowworms in the big timber—the men lying beside them, talking softly, hugging close to get in the smoke, cursing the flies, and wondering how things were going at home.

In the morning camp was broken at ten and the troops set out at a good pace. A little before noon, Gil and Weaver, marching side by side along the road, came out in Deerfield, on their own land.

It was incredible how quickly the land had become overgrown, as if the mere fact that men had moved away had emboldened the weeds. The burnt acres on Gil's place already had a scrub of blueberries, and tall clumps of fireweed were flourishing among the charred stumps where corn by now should be beginning to tassel out. The houses were no more. Only the black lines of dead coals marked the squared outlines where the walls had stood.

"It don't do any good to look at it, Gil."

Weaver turned his face towards the alder bottom, through which, deep-rutted by the army carts that had passed that way last fall, the road headed straight to the river.

In the ford, a mile away, Cox's regiment was stirring up the mud.

"Thank God the water's low," said Captain Demooth. "All these wagons going through at once are going to cut the bottom out of the river."

The passage of two hundred men had softened the bottom. By the time Klock's and Bellinger's regiments had waded over, the mud was getting pulpy.

Klock and Bellinger halted their companies on the bank and ordered them to stack arms and take their pants off. But with the way the mosquitoes were taking hold, the men preferred wet leggins and shoes to bites, and raucously refused.

They had to wait an hour before the horns of the first yoke of oxen appeared at the bend of the Kingsroad. The animals came on, snuffing the corduroy and planting each hoof as if they wished the things to grow there. When they reached the riverbank, they came down willingly enough, then stopped and drank.

The teamster swung his bull whip on them, but they refused to stir. Behind the tailboard yoke after yoke was halted, until the train filled all the alder swamp, a dozing mass of beasts, with switching tails. Other teamsters came forward and applied their lashes to the first yoke. The cracking of the whips banged like musketry. There was no room to bring another yoke around the first cart. The whole army was held up by a pair of lousy steers.

Even Colonel Fisscher had time to overtake them. He came storming and swearing along the edge of the road on his bay horse and stared and said loud enough for all the men to hear, "You'd think they were a couple of brigadier generals to look at them."

The men looked up. This militia business, with its high-toned colonels all over the lot, was new to them. They couldn't think what to say. But Bellinger had also heard him. He jumped off his horse and waded into the ford.

"Just what did you say, Fisscher?"

"I said they were like brigadiers, the way they take their time."

"Perhaps they wanted to see whether you'd catch up," said Bellinger.

The Palatine and German Flats outfits guffawed. But the teamster, who was embittered by the whole concern, turned the situation off. "It's got me beat," he said, helplessly. "The buggers don't even want to move their bowels."

Fisscher splashed his horse through the water to find Colonel Cox.

"Can't you do anything?" Bellinger asked the teamster.

"I've licked them. I've twisted their tails. I bit the off one by the ear. It's got me beat."

Old Coppernol crossed the ford. He said, "I've cut me an ox gad. If you bush twerps will make two lines and look like fences, these critters might mind a sensible man."

People laughed. But Demooth called to Bellinger, "Clem knows oxen. Let him try."

Clem said, "You see, these animals have got intelligence. They wasn't born for Baptists and they have to be convinced. Besides, they're kind of bored with all the colonels around."

"Meaning me?"

Clem looked at Bellinger.

"Hell, no. You ain't even a brigadier's nephew. You only married his niece."

In the laughter, Bellinger said good-humoredly, "All right, Clem. Try a hand."

The men waded into the ford and formed two lines, like fences for a lane, but Clem Coppernol acted as if he didn't see them. He talked to the oxen, patted them behind their horns, and then he walked the length of the ford and back, between the lines of men. He said to the oxen, "If an old man like me can do it, you two God A'mightys ought to."

Then he pricked the off ox with the stick and said, "Hup."

The oxen, miraculously, blew their breaths out, lowered their heads, and lifted their knobbed knees. The cart creaked, sank into the mud, but did not stop. The beasts had got to work again.

Clem bawled, "The others will come now, but don't let one get stuck. If it starts to stop, lay hold of the spokes and pull like God A'mighty."

To the admiring teamster he said tolerantly, "You can fetch my muskit for me. Somebody's got to show these twerps the way."

He went ahead as unconcernedly as the slow brown beasts, talking to them happily, as if for the first time since the muster he had found something he could do.

That night the head of the straggling column got as far as the Oriskany Creek. Colonel Cox picked his camp site on the eastern bank, opposite the little hamlet of Oneida huts. But the huts were empty, and Joe Boleo explained that the Oneidas had cleared out the same day the British Indians left Oswego.

Along the road the rest of the army bivouacked as they had the night before, wherever there was room. It was nearly dark when Demooth's company were finally fed and ready to lie down in their smudges. But as they sat on the ground, quietly in the dark, with the firelight streaking the boles of the trees, and a white mist creeping towards them from the river flats, a man floundered down the line, calling over and over, "Captain Mark Demooth. Captain Mark Demooth."

"This way," Demooth answered for himself. "What is it?"

"Herkimer wants to see you in his tent."

"Who are you?"

"Adam Helmer. Do you know where Joe Boleo is?"

"Right here," said Joe. "Has Herkimer got any likker on him?"

Herkimer's tent was pitched in a natural clearing a little behind the Canajoharie militia. His old white horse, ghostly and gray in the mist, was grazing stodgily beside it. They could hear the steady crunching of his teeth, and the small tearing sound of the parting roots. There was no sentry. Nobody hailed them. Even the horse didn't trouble to prick his ears.

Joe pulled the flap open and asked, "What's bothering you, Honnikol?"

"Come in, Joe."

Seated on his blanket, the little German was thoughtfully smoking his pipe. "Sit down," he said when they had entered. "Spencer's bringing Skenandoa."

The low tent was rank with the tobacco, but none of them noticed that. Even Joe Boleo, when he saw the general's troubled face, forgot the liquor question.

"Those bug-tits been dripping again?" he asked.

"If you mean Cox and Fisscher and Paris," the general said quietly. "Yah." He pushed the tobacco down in the pipe bowl with a calloused thumb. "It ain't them bothers me."

But they could tell by his voice that the officers were getting under his skin.

"It ain't them," he said. "Spencer says Skenandoa thinks that Butler has moved out of camp and that he's waiting for us." He cocked his head towards the west and for a minute all four men were so still that the flowing of Oriskany Creek on its rift in the mist was audible in the tent. And queer mingling sounds came with it: the clink of a halter link on a tied horse; the raised voice of a distant man; the hooting of a small owl back in the hemlocks; the grumble of a frog by the waterside.

"Spencer's bringing Skenandoa." Herkimer stopped again. "That must be them outside."

The two Indians had come quietly. Turning, the four white men saw Spencer's blacksmith hand pull back the flap. Then the old chief of the Oneidas stepped in. He bent his head with dignity. He was wrapped around in his blanket, and he scarcely seemed to crease it as he squatted down in the door, so that they saw his dark-skinned wrinkled face, and the red head covering against the fire on the ground.

Spencer said above him. "Skenandoa's young men have come back."

Herkimer said nothing. After a minute more, Skenandoa nodded his head. "They say Butler and Brant have moved the Indians down the road from the camp. They are doing it now. The white men are coming along soon."

Herkimer thanked him quietly.

"That's all?"

"Yes."

"Have you Oneidas made up your minds?"

The chief seemed to have withdrawn inside his own old thoughts. When he replied, his voice was low. "The Mohawks and the Senecas have sent threats. Mr. Kirkland is my good friend. Some of us will go."

"Thanks."

The two Indians departed, almost as quietly as they had come.

"You see," said Herkimer. "It's what we would expect. But these military gentlemen, they want to ride right through, banging on drums. Cox says it is disgraceful we ain't got trumpets!"

"What do you want us to do, Honnikol?"

"I've been thinking, all day. I think if we could get Gansevoort to send out men against their camp, eh?"

Demooth nodded.

"You, Joe, and you, Adam, you know these woods. Do you think you could get into the fort? With the Indians coming this way, you could go round and get inside?"

Helmer laughed.

"Sure," he said offhand.

"I can't let Bellinger or Klock go. Mark, will you? You're the only other officer that knows these woods and Indians."

"What'll we tell him?" Demooth asked.

"Send out men if he can, and fire three cannon to let us know." He got up and walked to the door. "It's misty. You'll have good cover." The pipe smoke mingled with the mist. "You better get going now."

In the morning, Herkimer sent out a call for all commanding officers to come to his tent. While the men were cooking breakfast they arrived. They made a knot of uniforms, bright, light-hearted, against the dark hemlock boughs. Cox with his bellicose flushed face and staring eyes; Bellinger, raw-boned, simple, honest, looking worried; Klock, stodgy, chewing snuff and still smelling faintly of manure and already sweating; Campbell's gray face freshly shaved; Fisscher, dapper and dandy in his tailor-made coat and new cocked hat; and the black-coated, clerkly, calculating Mr. Paris. Behind them assorted captains and majors waited, watching.

Cox had the first word, as he always did.

"Well, Herkimer. Going to give us marching orders?"

"Pretty soon."

"Why not now? The sooner we get going, the sooner we'll have Sillinger making tracks for home."

"Listen, the Oneidas told me last night that Brant and Butler have got the Indians somewhere up the road. They moved down after dark. Johnson's troops ought to be there by now."

"Fine," Cox said boisterously. "We can lick the Tories and then we can tend to the regulars. Like eggs and bacon for breakfast."

Herkimer looked thoughtfully from face to face, looking for support, perhaps, or perhaps just looking for what was there. Only Bellinger was attentive—and maybe Klock.

"We won't break camp for a while," Herkimer said. "I've sent Demooth and two men up to the fort. They'll send a party out and shoot off three cannon when they do. We'll move when we hear the guns."

For a moment no one said a word. But they all looked at Herkimer in the sunshine, while the morning birds cheeped in the surrounding trees.

"You mean we've got to sit here on our arses?" demanded Cox.

"If you like to wait like that," said Herkimer. "I do not mind."

"Personally," said Fisscher, "I'm getting sick of waiting."

Herkimer said nothing.

"It's a good idea," Bellinger said loyally.

"You getting scared too?" said Paris.

Herkimer held up his hand with the pipe in it.

"There's no sense fighting among ourselves."

"What's the matter? We'll outnumber them. The whites. We can handle the Indians on the side."

"You've never seen an Indian ambush," said Herkimer.

"Oh, my God," cried Cox, "this isn't 1757! Can't you get that through your thick German head?"

Rumor had gone down the road that the gentry were having words. The men abandoned their fires to hear the fun. Many of them left their guns behind. They pushed off the road, surrounding the clearing, till the little German seated before his tent was the focal point of over a hundred pairs of eyes.

Gil Martin, coming with the rest, listened among strangers. For over an hour the silly fatuous remarks went on. Some said you could not hear a cannon that far; some said that the three men would surely get captured; some said that probably they'd never gone to the fort at all. That was Paris's voice.

Herkimer sat in their midst with the voices flinging back and forth above his head; his shirt was still unbuttoned, showing his stained woolen undershirt. Now and then he took his pipe from his lips to answer some remark that had a rudiment of sense behind it; but the rest of the time he kept his head turned to the west, listening. Apparently he was unheeding; but the men close to him could see his cheeks flexing from time to time and the slow even reddening of his skin.

It was Cox who finally touched the match.

"By Jesus Christ," he shouted in his roaring voice, "it's plain enough. Either he's scared, or else he's got interest with the British. I didn't bring my regiment this far to set and knit like girls." He looked round with his staring eyes. "Who's coming along?"

Fisscher cried, "I am."

Suddenly all the officers were shouting; and the men, following their voices, filled the woods with shouts.

It seemed to Gil that nobody was looking at Herkimer but himself. He saw the old man sitting there, his face pained, his eyes worried. He saw him knock the pipe out on his hand, blow out his breath, and lift his head.

"Listen to me, you damned fools." He used German. He was getting on his feet and yanking his coat over his arms. But his voice was enough to stop them. "Listen," he went on in English. "You don't know what you're doing, you Fisscher, Cox, the bunch of you. But if you want to fight so bad, by God Almighty, I'll take you to it."

He climbed aboard the old white horse and sat there, looking down on them for a change.

"God knows what's going to happen. But I'll tell you one thing," he said bitterly. "The ones that have been yelling so much here will be the first to pull foot if we get jumped."

For a moment they gaped up at him.

"*Vorwaerts!*" he shouted, and put the horse toward the creek. Some of them were still standing there when he splashed through and waited on the other side. Then the officers were running to their companies, yelling, "Fall in. Fall in."

The men went scrambling through the brush to find their guns and blankets.

"March! March!" the word was in all the woods where the abandoned breakfast fires still sent up their stems of smoke among the tree trunks. Up ahead at the ford, a drummer gave the double tap of the flam. It was like the first nervous beating of a drummer partridge. It was too early for such a sound, but there it was.

Then the whips began their rapid fire along the wagon train. The cartwheels screeched in starting. The still heat in the woods was overflowed with shouts, stamping hoofs, the rattle and slam of carts along the corduroy, the treading feet. The dust rose over the column. All at once it was jerking, getting started, moving.

At the head of the army, Cox moved his big horse beside Herkimer's. His face was triumphant, almost good-humored once more, because he had planted his will on the column. He felt half sorry for the little German farmer. But he would help the little bugger out.

The rough road went nearly straight along the level ground of the Mohawk Valley's edge, following the course of the low hill. Now and then it dipped down sharply to get over a brook. But the bottom was solidly corduroyed. The wagons didn't get stuck. They had even moved up a little on the marching men.

Blue jays squawked and fluttered off, cool spots of angry blue against the leaves. Squirrels, chattering, raced from limb to limb. A porcupine took hold of a tree and climbed it halfway, and turned his head to see the thronging, jumbled mass that heaved and started, checked, and went again along the narrow road.

The men marched in two lines, one for either rut, their rifles on their shoulders, their hats in their hands. When they came to a brook, the thirsty fell out and drank. Nobody stopped them. When they were through they wiped their mouths and looked up, startled, to see their company replaced by another. They got out of the way of other thirsty men and floundered in the bushes to catch up. There was no room left on the road to pass.

Even George Herkimer's company of rangers, who were supposed to act as scouts, would stop at a spring. And when they went ahead they crashed in the undergrowth like wild cattle. There was nobody to stop them. There were no tracks. The woods were dusty. Branches, whipping on hot faces, stung like salt. The heat grew. Not a breath of air in the branches anywhere, not a cloud in the bits of sky high overhead, nothing but leaves, nothing in all the woods but their own uproarious, bursting, unstemmable progress on the narrow road.

Gil, pushed on from behind, pushing on George Weaver just ahead of him, heard the birds singing in the dark swamp ahead. The ground fell steeply to a quiet flowing brook with a cool moss bottom. He felt his own step quicken with the instinct to drink and cool himself. Looking over George Weaver's thick round shoulders, he had a glimpse of the road turning into a causeway of logs across the stream; of George Herkimer's rangers crowding down on the crossing to make it dry-shod; of the Canajoharie regiment floundering in the swamp and drinking face down by the brook; of Cox turning his red sweaty face to Herkimer and bawling, "Where did you say Butler was?"; of the two banks, precipitous and thickly clothed with a young stand of hemlocks, so soft and cool and damp and dark that it made one wish to lie down there and rest. Now he felt the ground falling under his feet, and the resistless push at his back thrusting him out on the causeway. They had passed half of Cox's regiment and were plugging up the other side. The stamp of Klock's regiment came down the bank at their backs. Behind in the woods the jangle and rattle of the carts, the steady cracking of whips, and little futile *rattle-tats* of Fisscher's drummers. All in the moment: "I meant to get a drink of water," Reall's voice was saying at his shoulder. "So did I," said Gil. "My God," said Weaver, "what was that?"

At the top of the hemlocks a little stab of orange was mushroomed out by a black coil of smoke. They heard the crack. Cox's voice, caught short in another remark, lifted beyond reason. His big body swayed suddenly against his horse's neck. The horse reared, screamed, and, as Cox slid sack-like off his back, crashed completely over.

A shrill silver whistle sounded. Three short blasts. The young hemlocks disgorged a solid mass of fire that made a single impact on the ear. Gil felt George Weaver slam against his chest, knocking him sidewise on top of Reall. A horse screamed again and went leaping into the scrub. As he got up, Gil saw the beast fall over on his head. It was Herkimer's old white horse, galvanized into senseless vigor. He felt his arm caught and Bellinger was shouting, "Give me a hand with the old man." The old man was sitting on the causeway, holding onto his knee with both hands. His face was gray and shining and his lips moved in it.

But the voice was lost.

Gil stood before him with his back to the slope and stared down into the ravine. The militia were milling along the brook, flung down along the bank, like sticks thrown up by a freshet, kneeling, lying on their bellies, resting their rifles on the bellies of dead men. They were oddly silent. But the air around them was swept by the dull endless crash of muskets and a weird high swell of yelling from the woods.

Then beyond them he saw the Indians in the trees, adder-like, streaked with vermilion, and black, and white. From the head of the rise the first shearing of the air, as if a hand had swung an enormous scythe. He saw the green coats on men firing at him; but he bent down and grasped the general by the knees and heaved him on up the bank while Bellinger lugged him by the armpits.

The colonel was swearing in a strange way. He wiped his mouth on his sleeve and said, "By God, Fisscher has pulled foot!"

East of the causeway, where the rear guard had been, a dwindling tide of yells and firing fled backward into the woods. They dumped the general down behind a log and fell beside him. Gil put his rifle over the log and pulled the trigger on the first green coat that filled the sights. The butt bucked against his cheek. He yanked the rifle back and tilted his powder flask to the muzzle. He saw the man he had fired at lean forward slowly in the bushes, buckle at the hips, and thump face down. He felt his insides retract, and suddenly had a queer realization that they had just returned to their proper places; and he thought with wonder at himself, "That's the first shot I've fired."

"Peter."

"Yes, Honnikol."

"It looks as if the Indians was mostly chasing after Fisscher. You'd better try and fetch the boys up here."

The little German's voice was calm.

☆

☆   ☆

THERE WAS NO SENSE at first in any of it. The opening volley had been fired at ten o'clock. For the next half hour the militia lay where they had dropped, shooting up against the bank whenever they saw a flash. Their line extended roughly along the road, beginning with the disrupted welter of the wagon train, and ending at the west, just over the rise of ground, where a mixed group of Canajoharie men, and Demooth's company of the German Flats regiment, and what was left of Herkimer's rangers, made a spearhead by hugging the dirt with their bellies and doing nothing to draw attention to themselves. If the Indians had stayed put or if Fisscher had not run away, the entire army would have been destroyed.

But the Indians could not resist the temptation of chasing the terrified Fisscher. More than half of them had followed his men as far as Oriskany Creek before they gave over the attempt. And a large proportion of the rest, seeing easy scalps ready for the taking, started sneaking down out of the timber. When, at last, Bellinger began to rally the men and get them up the slope, the Indians made no attempt to follow them, for they had discovered that killing horses was an intoxicating business.

The ascent of the slope was the first orderly movement of the battle. It also revealed the initial mistake of the British side. Their flanks made no connection with the Indians, and they had to retire from the edge of the ravine to the bigger timber. It gave the Americans a foothold. They pushed to right and left along the ravine and forward with their centre, until their line made a semicircle backed on the ravine.

No single company remained intact. It was impossible to give intelligent orders, or, if that had been possible, to get them carried out. The men took to trees and fired at the flashes in front of them. And this new disposition of the battle, which remained in force till nearly eleven, was the salvation of the militia. They began to see that they could hold their own. Also it was borne in on them that to go backward across the valley would be sheer destruction.

The general, by his own orders, had been carried still farther up the slope until he could sit on the level ground under a beech tree, and see out through the tall timber. His saddle had been brought up for him to sit on, and Dr. Petry sent for. While the doctor was binding up his shattered knee, Herkimer worked with his tinder box to get a light for his pipe. Then, finally established, he looked the battle over and gave his second order of the day.

"Have the boys get two behind each tree. One hold his fire and get the Indian when he comes in."

It was an axiomatic precaution that none of the militia would have thought of for themselves. Gil, moved up behind a fallen tree, heard a crash of feet behind him, turned his head to see a black-bearded, heavy-shouldered man plunge up to him carrying an Indian spear in one hand and a musket in the other.

"You got a good place here," said the man.

He drove the butt of the spear into the ground.

"It may come handy."

"Where'd you get it?"

"Off an Indian." He turned his head. "Back there. They're scalping the dead ones. There's one of the bastards now."

He pushed his gun across the log and fired.

"Christ! I missed him. You'd better do the long shots, Bub. You've got a rifle there. I ain't a hand at this stuff."

Gil had found a loophole in the roots. He poked his gun through and waited for a sign. While he waited he said, "My name's Martin."

"Gardinier," said the bearded man. "Captain in Fisscher's regiment. Don't ask me why. We didn't have the sense to run when he did. There's fifty of us left, but I don't know where they are. Old Herkimer told me to get up in front. He said he wanted to see us run away next time."

Gardinier cursed. Gil saw a shoulder, naked, and glistening with sweat, stick out on the side of a tree. He pressed the trigger, easily. The Indian yelped. They didn't see him, but they saw the underbrush thresh madly.

"Pretty, pretty," said Gardinier. "We ought to make a partnership. You take my musket and I'll load for you. Jesus, you ain't a Mason, are you?"

"No, said Gil.

"You ought to be." He touched Gil's shoulder with the rifle barrel. "Here's your rifle, Bub."

Gil caught a spot of red over a low-lying bough. A headdress. It was a pot shot, but he let it go. The Indian whooped and the next moment he was coming in long buck jumps straight for the log. He was a thin fellow, dark-skinned like a Seneca, and stark naked except for the paint on face and chest.

Gil felt his inside tighten and rolled over to see what had become of Gardinier. But the heavy Frenchman was grinning, showing white teeth through his beard.

He had set down his musket and taken the spear. The Indian bounded high to clear the log and Gardinier braced the spear under him as he came down. The hatchet spun out of the Indian's hand. A human surprise re-formed his painted face. The spear went in through his lower abdomen and just broke the skin between his shoulders. He screamed once. But the Frenchman lifted him, spear and all, and shoved him back over the log.

"Hell," he said. "No sense in wasting powder."

Gil turned back to face the woods. The Indian, with the spear still sticking out of him, was trying to crawl under some cover. The odd thing was that he wasn't bleeding. But he kept falling down against the spear, as if his wrists had lost their strength.

"For God's sake shoot him."

The Frenchman stuck his head over the log.

"Jesus!" he remarked. He made no motion.

The Indian heaved himself up. He half turned toward the log. Then his mouth opened, and, as if a well had been tapped by the spear, and all this time had been necessary for the blood to find its level, it poured through the open mouth, down the painted chest, turning the front of his body wet and red.

Gil yelled, jumped up, and fired straight down into the pouring face. The Indian jerked back and flopped, raising the needles with his hands.

Gardinier said, "You hadn't ought to have done that. Wasting ball that way."

"For God's sake kill the next one, then."

"All right, all right. You don't need to get mad." But after a moment, he muttered, "I wish to God I'd pulled that spear out first, though. It was a handy tool."

All a man could see was the section of woods in front of him. The woods were dark with a green gloom, made by the high tops of the hemlocks, through which the sun came feebly. The heat was stifling. There was no movement of air. Only the bullets ripped passionate sounds out of the heat.

The ravine behind the militia had long since quieted with the death of the last horse. But now and then a solitary war whoop lifted in the trees to right or left; and the answering shot was like a period marking off the time.

In the American line, out of the disruption, figures began to grow into command that had no bearing on their rank. A man who shot better than his neighbors began to give orders. Jacob Sammons on the left began the first outward movement by taking twenty men in a quick charge against the Indian flank and halting them on a low knoll of beach trees. They started a cross fire against the white troops in front, and the militia in the centre, finding the woods cleared for a space, moved forward. Gil went with them. Gardinier stood up and scouted.

"There's a first-class maple up in front," he said.

They took it in a rush. Then they had a breathing space in which they could look back. They were surprised to find that this new view disclosed men lying on the intervening ground.

Back at the edge of the ravine, old Herkimer was still smoking his pipe. He had taken his hat off and his grizzled head showed plainly from where Gil and Gardinier had taken stand.

Gardinier laughed out loud.

"Look at the old pup," he said. "I wish Fisscher was here."

Both of them realized that they had one man they could depend on, though there was nothing one man could for them. But it was a feeling all the same.

The lull did not endure.

In the woods ahead they heard a whistle shrilling. The firing had stopped, except for sporadic outbursts way to right and left, where a few Indians still persisted.

Then Herkimer's voice came to them surprisingly loud.

"Get out your hatchets, boys. They're going to try bayonets."

To Gil it seemed as though the fight had begun all over again. Lying behind a tree was one thing. Standing up in the open was something he had not thought of.

But Gardinier suddenly found something he could understand. He heaved his great bulk up and asked, "What you got, Bub?" When Gil merely stared, "Hatchet or bagnet, son?"

Gil reached for the hatchet at his belt with stiff fingers.

"All right. You give them one shot with your rifle. I've got a bagnet." He was fixing it to the muzzle of his army musket. He wheeled back and roared, "Come on."

He seemed surprised when some of his own company came round the trees behind.

Gil saw them coming. They all saw them, in the green gloom under the trees which covered their faces with a pale shine. They were like water coming toward the militia, flowing round the tree trunks, bending down the brush, an uneven line that formed in places and broke with the shape of the ground and formed.

There was a moment of silence on both sides as the militia rose up confronting them. It was almost as if the militia were surprised. Herkimer's warning had suggested to them that regular troops were going to attack. Instead they saw only the green coats they knew belonged to

Johnson's company of Tories, and men in hunting shirts and homespun like themselves.

As the line came nearer, they saw that some of these men were the Scotch from Johnstown who had fled with Sir John. They weren't Sillinger's army at all. They were the men who had passed threats of gutting the valley wide open. For a moment the militia could hardly believe what they were seeing.

Then it seemed as if the senseless glut of war would overflow. Men fired and flung their muskets down and went for each other with their hands. The American flanks turned in, leaving the Indians where they were. The woods filled suddenly with men swaying together, clubbing rifle barrels, swinging hatchets, yelling like the Indians themselves. There were no shots. Even the yelling stopped after the first joining of the lines, and men began to go down.

The immediate silence of the woods was broken afresh. Gil, jostled and flung forward, saw a face in front of him met by a musket stock. The face seemed to burst. He swung his hatchet feebly against the arm that clubbed the musket and felt the axe ripped from his fingers. The man he had struck cried out, a small clear sound as if enunciated in a great stillness. Then Gil's ears cleared and he heard a man crying and he stepped on a body and felt it wince under his boot. The wince threw him, and he hit the dirt with his knees, and at the same time a gun exploded in front of him and he thought his whole arm had been torn away.

The boughs of the hemlocks heeled away from him, and the back of his head struck the ground and a man walked over him, three steps, down the length of his body, and he felt sick and then he forgot entirely everything but the fact that he was dying.

He did not feel any more. He was lying on the ground. It seemed to him that every needle leaf and twig on the ground stood up with painful clearness beyond any plausible dimension. A little way off someone kept yelling, "For God's sake, oh, for God's sake." He thought that if he could look he could see what the sound was, but he could not look.

Then the forest darkened. There was a blinding flash. He felt a man's hands taking hold of his shoulders. He felt himself moving backward while his legs trailed behind him. He was jerked up and put on his feet, and he knew that it was raining. He thought, "The drought's broken."

Peal after peal of thunder shook the hemlocks. The rain fell directly down, hissing on the dry ground, and raising mist in the trees. There was no sound left but the pouring rain and the continuous devastating thunder. You couldn't see when you opened your eyes. Only the tree trunks rising close to you, shining black with wet and the falling rain and the distortion of the lightning glares that lit up crooked alleys in the woods and shut them off again.

He felt himself being shaken, and a voice was saying, "Can you walk, Bub?"

He tried to walk, but his feet were overcome with a preposterous weariness.

"Put them down, Bub, put them down. Flat on your feet and stand up. Have a drink; you're all right."

He opened his eyes again and saw the beard of Gardinier matted with rain, and the wild white teeth and staring eyes of the Frenchman.

"Brandy makes the world go round," said the Frenchman. "It makes the girl handy, it makes for boys and girls, Bub. It'll fix you. Hell, you ain't only creased in one arm, and me, I've lost an ear."

The side of his face was streaming blood into his collar.

"They've quit, Bub. They're all to hell and gone. We've licked the pus clean out of them. Come on. Doc will fix you."

He sat Gil down on a mound, and then Dr. Petry's big fleshy face, muttering, looking enraged and tired, bent down. The Doc was splashing alcohol of some sort on his arm. He was being bandaged. The stinging revived him, and he looked up and saw just above him old Herkimer, white in the face now, but still puffing at his pipe, which he held in his mouth inverted against the rain.

"They'll come back," Herkimer was saying. "They're bound to. But we'll rest while it rains."

A little way off a man was eating on a log. The rest were standing, lying on the ground, steaming in the rain. Everyone looked tired, a little sick, and ugly, as if there had been a tremendous drunk a while before.

Nobody was keeping watch. They merely stood there in the rain.

The rain passed as suddenly as it had broken. The men got up and kicked other men to get up, and picked up their rifles. They drew the priming and reprimed, or loaded entirely fresh.

Gill got to his feet shakily, surprised to find his rifle still in his hand. It seemed a long time since the rain. The woods had changed so that he did not know where west lay, or east, or any direction.

Then he saw that Herkimer had moved the position so that the militia were in the centre of the level ground between the first ravine and a smaller, shallower watercourse. Any new attack would have to take them on a narrow flank, or directly up the new slope on top of which their line was formed.

The first shots came scatteringly. The Indians were firing from long range. They seemed to have lost their taste for war. They were being very careful now. Everybody was being careful. The militia stood their ground, but kept to cover.

In a line running north and south through the new position, a broken mass of men lay on the ground, like an uneven windrow of some preposterous corn. They seemed almost equally made up of militia and the green-coated troops that had come through the hemlocks. They lay in queer positions, on their arms, grasping knife or hatchet or musket, the purpose still on the blank face like an overlying plaster; or else they lay on their backs, their empty hands flung out as if to catch the rain.

The militia stepped over this line impersonally. There was an Indian transfixed to a tree by a bayonet, waist high, with his legs dangling lifelessly against the ground. But he kept his eyes open and the eyes seemed to Gill to turn as he went by.

A little way along a face struck him as familiar. He looked at it again. The possessor of the face had fallen with his chin over a log so that the face was tilted up. Gil looked at it curiously before he recognized it for Christian Reall's face. He had been scalped. The top of his head looked flat and red; and the circumcision of the crown had allowed the muscles to give way so that his cheeks hung down in jowls, tugging his eyes open and showing enormous bloody underlids.

The two armies merely sniped at each other for an hour. Then the second attack by the enemy developed from the southwest along the level ground. At first the militia mistook them for reënforcements from the fort. The direction they came from and the fact that they had pinned up their hat brims to look like the tricorn hats of Continental soldiers were deceptive.

The militia broke cover, cheering, and rushed forward to shake hands, and the enemy let them come. There was no firing. It was only at the last moment that the sun came through the wet trees, dazzling all the ground and showing the bright green of the approaching company.

Gil was not in the direct contact of the two companies. From where he stood he seemed divorced from the whole proceeding.

But another company of green coats was coming round the first in his direction, with the same quiet march, and the same bright glitter on their advanced bayonets.

He became aware of the instinct to run away. It suddenly occurred to him that he was hungry. Not merely hungry as one is at supper or breakfast; but a persisting, all-consuming gnawing in his intestines that moved and hurt. He felt that it was not worth staying for. He was too tired. And the oncoming men looked tired. And it seemed to take forever for them to make a contact. But they came like people who couldn't stop themselves, while he himself could not make his feet move to carry him away.

They made less noise. The rainstorm which had broken the drought had not had power to take the dryness from their throats. They seemed to strike each other with preposterous slow weary blows, which they were too slow to dodge, and they fell down under them preposterously.

It couldn't last.

Gil found himself standing alone in the militia. There were a few men near him, but there was no one whose face he recognized. They kept looking at each other as if they would have liked to speak.

On the flank, the firing continued where the Indians still skirmished. But that, too, broke off except for stray shots, the last survivors of all the holocaust of firing.

The Indians were calling in the woods. A high barbaric word, over and over. "Oonah, Oonah, Oonah." Suddenly a man shouted, "They've pulled foot!"

At first they thought another thunderstorm had started. Then they realized that what they had heard, with such surprising force, had been three successive cannon shots.

The messengers had reached the fort, and the garrison was making a diversion.

A deliberate understanding gradually dawned on all their faces. They leaned on their rifles and looked around. The woods were empty, but for themselves, for their dead, and for the enemy dead. The living enemy had run away.

Those that could walk began a retrograde movement to the knoll on which Herkimer was sitting under his tree. The old man was looking at them; his black eyes, yet ardent, passing feverishly from face to face, and then turning slowly to the lines of dead.

One of the officers spoke fatuously, "Do we go on to the fort now,

Honnikol?" He paused, swallowed, and said, as if to excuse himself, "We know they know we're here."

The little German swung his eyes to the speaker. The eyes filled and he put his hand over them.

Peter Bellinger and Peter Tygert came up to him and touched his shoulder. They said to the officer, "We can't move forward."

They picked Herkimer up by the arms.

"I can't walk, boys." He swallowed his tears noisily. "There's still Sillinger up there. With the British regulars there ain't enough of us. I think we'd better go home."

He asked first that the live men be assembled and counted. It was a slow business, getting them to their feet and lining them up under the trees. The earth was still steaming from the rain. There was a sick smell of blood from the ravine.

The naming of men took too long. The officers went along the wavering lines, cutting notches in sticks for every ten men. They figured that after Fisscher pulled foot with the Mohawk company there had been about six hundred and fifty concerned in the ambush and battle. Out of them about two hundred were judged able to walk. There were forty more who were not dead. How many had been killed and how many taken prisoner no one could say.

Stretchers were made of coats and poles, and the worst wounded were piled onto them. Those who were not acting as bearers dully reprimed or loaded their guns. They started east.

It seemed a long way to the ravine where the battle had started. It seemed a long time, longer than they could remember, since they had seen it last. It was sunset by the time they reached Oriskany Creek.

From there men were sent ahead to order boats rowed up the Mohawk, to meet the wounded at the ford. The whole army lay down when they reached the ford. They lay in the darkness, along the edge of the sluggish river, until the boats came up. They were apathetic.

Only when the boats arrived did they get onto their feet and help put the wounded men in. Several of them afterwards remembered Herkimer's face in the light of the fire. He had stopped smoking, though the pipe was still fast in his teeth. He wasn't saying anything. He sat still, holding onto his knee.

At the time, they had just stood around watching him being loaded aboard the boat and laid out in the bottom. Then they had been told to march through the ford, and along the road. They went wearily, too exhausted to talk, even to think. And tired as they were, they were forced to do the same march they had taken three days to make on the way up.

They did not look at the terrified white faces of the people when they came to the settlement. They were too exhausted to see. The word had already gone down the river. People were expecting the appearance of the enemy.

It was a calamity. The army had looked so big going west that nobody had thought they would not get through to the fort. Now they were back; they looked licked, and they acted licked, and they had not even met the regulars. It was pointless to think that the enemy had left the scene of battle before they had.

An officer, some said afterwards that it was Major Clyde, yelled from the foot of the fort stockade that they were dismissed. They were to go home and try to rest while they could. They should expect another summons very soon.

But the men did not stop to listen to him. Ever since they had come out of the woods at Schuyler they had been dropping from the ranks. The instinct to get home was irresistible. They weren't an army any more, and they knew it better than anyone could have told them.

BENNINGTON

by Bruce Lancaster

The sun broke through ragged clouds a little before noon and beat on the column as mercilessly as yesterday's rain. The stiff men and the unfed horses moved on through a steaming countryside of wide fields and woodland, halted, moved, halted again. The air was heavy, still, like a summer Sunday in Dresden, Ahrens thought. In the village of Cambridge they met Colonel Skene, who had ridden in from Baum's column with a string of captured horses and carts and with the news that Baum was doing well and had only a small force of rebels before him, rebels who did not dare attack.

From: *The Guns of Burgoyne.* Copyright 1939. Frederick A. Stokes Co.

Ahrens plodded along the miry road on a bony sorrel farm horse, hoping that it wouldn't be necessary to force his gunteams. The animals looked worse and worse as the day wore on. They had not been fed since they left the camp by Fort Miller, for there had been no forage in the camp in the woods. If he could only find *something* for them.

The column had halted again. Ahrens looked ahead down a gentle slope to a mill by a narrow bridge where Skene and Breymann talked with a knot of men by the mill door. He turned to Spangenberg, who bestrode a short, clay-colored horse, his heels nearly dragging on the ground. "I'm going to ride ahead. There may be a ford by the bridge. If there is, I'll signal; then have the drivers lead out to water."

He trotted his sorrel along the resting column, noting how the heat was telling on the heavy grenadiers. He found a ford close by the mill, rode back into the road to signal Spangenberg. Then he cursed under his breath. Breymann and Skene had remounted by the mill and he could hear the heavy Colonel's saddle creak as he settled himself, heard him wheeze as he snarled to an aide: "The command is forward!"

"Oh, the devil!" growled Ahrens. "A dozen halts in three miles and then when we get near water—'The command is forward.' How does he expect the horses to keep up?" Then he recognized a grenadier officer with whom he had once talked by the lake at Skenesboro. "Lieutenant Zweig—any news?"

The big man looked up. "Hello." His face was sweat-streaked and haggard. "News? Isn't any."

"Then why so short a halt? I wanted to water my horses."

Zweig shrugged. "There were four men from Baum's column at the mill, here. No two of them told the same story. A Tory captain said Baum was cut off—surrounded. A dragoon said he was in danger. An Englishman said he was doing very nicely, though all the Indians had run away. A lieutenant from Specht's regiment said there had been no fighting and no sign of rebels, beyond a scattering few who ran away into the woods."

"Wide range of choice," commented Ahrens. "What were the men doing at the mill?"

"That's what I can't understand. *Something* has happened. They were separated from their units. That doesn't happen unless there's a reason. Skene believed the Englishman—thinks the rebels may have attacked and been driven off. So the column is moving on." The grenadiers started off across the bridge, useless swords knocking against their legs.

Ahrens rode back to Spangenberg and the guns, told him Zweig's report. "Odd, damned odd," he concluded. "Those men were stragglers."

"But Baum can't be more than four miles away, unless the maps are wrong," objected Spangenberg. "So far, they've been right. This is Owl Kill, the mill is San Coick and that must be the Hoosic off there. Now, if there had been trouble, we'd have heard firing. It's peaceful as a convent garden."

Ahrens looked dubious. "Can't tell by that. A ridge or a line of hills *can* blanket sound. The range outside Dresden was like that. A quarter of a mile to the southeast you couldn't hear a shot. Wonder if—Well, Skene thinks everything is satisfactory."

"Isn't that enough? He knows the country and the people."

"But he's always talking about Tories swarming to join us. How many have you seen? A few hundred came to Skenesboro, and most of them deserted as soon as they were given a meal and a musket. Skene believes what he wants to."

The guns rumbled slowly along, hooves rang on the bridge across Owl Kill, timbers shook hissing dust into the smooth water below. Spangenberg leaned from his saddle, peered down into the cool depths of the kill. "Now if there aren't fish in that water, I'll, I'll—" He wagged his head. "I'll guarantee to reconcile Breymann and Baum."

Ahrens smiled. "I'll hold you to that. Wonder how Baum *is* doing—and the dragoon Heinz. Particularly the dragoon Heinz."

At that very moment the dragoon Heinz stood near the end of a long line of blue and yellow that sheltered itself behind a loose breastwork of logs and earth and fired his musket down a steep slope covered with sparse timber. It was very easy. You fired, then dropped your piece, reloaded, primed, raised it to your shoulder till it was almost on a level with your collar-bone, then you pulled the trigger and did it all over again. You always waited until the little three-pounder in the middle of the line had slammed, because the concussion made you wince, but otherwise, the whole thing was very easy.

As he raised his carbine he saw the slope was swarming with farmers. That's what they were, farmers. All except the huge man in blue and buff who kept calling to them. What were farmers doing in a battle? They might get hurt. He closed his eyes, squeezed the trigger again, blinked rapidly and dropped the butt to the ground to reload. The farmers were behind trees, they were creeping among piles of rocks. There was a dreadful sound of firing somewhere behind him, more firing down the hill, but the slope was so steep that he couldn't see the base where the Tories and the British sharpshooters had been stationed. His lieutenant kept screaming commands. Foolish. *Heinz* knew how to load, take time from the man at his left, fire. No need to shout at *him!* The farmers were coming closer. Something thudded close to Heinz and the man beside him slipped quietly to the ground, knees bent, head sagging forward. Heinz wondered why he didn't get up. The crashing muskets, the shouting, the clouds of smoke made him a little dizzy. Then he realized that he was shouting too, that the farmers—who were very close now—were shouting. The farmers had rifles, muskets. They were attacking *dragoons,* shooting at them. Country-people! Something buzzed viciously past Heinz' cheek. Why, they were shooting at him, at Heinz, the dragoon!

The firing died away for an instant. Heinz looked around. The lieutenant was no longer shouting foolish orders. Instead, he was lying on his back, arms over his head, mouth open as though stretching after a long sleep. And the sergeant, that hard man from Bremen—he was rolling back and forth slowly, clutching at his belly while black blood spouted from between his fingers. Beyond him were two dragoons, three dragoons, a dozen, on their faces, their backs, lying quietly, writhing. Klipfel, whom he had first seen among the hot rocks of Mount Defiance, pawed the ground with hands and elbows, dragging useless legs behind him and staring through bulging, sightless eyes.

Heinz' mouth quivered. His throat grew dry, and it was hard to swallow. His hands seemed absurdly light, and when he moved them they flew up to his face like feathers. Then a quiet voice behind him said: "Close up, close up!" Heinz grinned nervously, his wide mouth twitching. He sidestepped to the left until he closed with another dragoon. "Quite right, Captain," he thought. "Good idea, closing up." Odd. The Captain's voice had been so low, almost gentle all day. In camp and on the march he roared like a crazed bull. Why was it?

Muskets blazed again. There were shirtsleeved farmers inside the breastworks. Heinz couldn't understand it. They should have been frightened away. Out of the corner of his eye he saw a yellow-haired man in a smock kneel behind a rock far down the line and take aim at him, at Heinz! Heinz chuckled. That showed how stupid these farmers were. Taking all that time just to aim! Red suddenly crawled down the blond man's temple, his head jerked back. Slowly he crumpled over the rock. It was a lesson, Heinz told himself. Taking all that time to aim! He raised his own piece slowly. When it was nearly level with his shoulder, he fired. Much simpler. He fumbled in his cartridge box. Empty! He turned to the man on his left. There was no man on his left. Nor on his right. Nothing but swarming country-people and that big man in blue and buff and a handful of dragoons running down the hill. Heinz dropped his heavy carbine. With a start he realized that he had been running, that he was among a knot of dragoons, all running headlong down the hill, boots clumping and spurs rattling among hidden stones and mad things hissing in the air about them.

Then he found himself scrambling over a rail fence to join a stout man who stood on a rock and yelled: "To me, dragoons, to me!" as he waved his sword over his head. Others joined Heinz in his rush and he was shocked to find that the stout man was his colonel, the dreaded man Baum. Heinz found himself in a solid knot of nearly thirty dragoons rallying about the Colonel, who yelled that they should throw away their carbines, draw their sabers and cut their way out. Steel flashed about him and the knot moved on, Heinz stumping docilely along with them. Then more shirtsleeved men appeared. The Colonel yelled again: "They have no bayonets! At 'em with the saber!" Muskets blazed and the Colonel doubled up suddenly with a dreadful noise in his throat. The dragoons left him sprawled on the ground and Heinz ran with them.

It was nearly dark. Heinz found himself alone in a field. He was aware of a hideous din far away down the road along which he had marched with his fellows the day the Colonel had ordered them to climb the steep hill and throw up earthworks. Why, that was only yesterday. Building breastworks in the rain, a wet camp, more rain and then the sun and the fields around the hill full of farmers in smocks and shirtsleeves.

He stopped and shook his head. He couldn't understand it. The dragoons had fired and fired, but still the country-people had come on, while more and more dragoons pitched headlong over their carbines. Why didn't the farmers fall, too? And where were the other men, the English sharpshooters, the grenadiers, the Tories, the Indians? He shook his head again. It was too much for him. Dragoons! Their own colonel had said that they were the finest troops in the army, and there they lay, huddled over their carbines or dragging useless legs after them like Klipfel, shot by farmers who were so stupid that they aimed their shots. Why, they didn't even have uniforms!

His throat felt parched, his eyes ached violently. Water! Where could he find water? His own gallon canteen that had cut so cruelly into his shoulder on the march, was empty, pierced by a bullet. Some farmer had shot a hole in it and now it was useless. But there must be water nearby.

Perhaps if he had a long drink, a drenching drink of clear, cold water, he could understand about dragoons huddled over silent carbines. There *must* be water! Why, in soil like this— He dug the toe of his crippling boot into the ground. Then he made little grunting noises, squatted to look at the dent. He prodded the loose earth with his finger. Ah, this was loam, this was *earth!* He clucked to himself, picked up a handful, kneaded it in his palms. "Now here," he thought, "here I should plant wheat, good wheat!"

He lifted his head with a jerk. A tall man in gray smock and black knee-breeches was covering him with a wicked-looking rifle. The English words fell uncomprehended on his ears, but he understood the muzzle. "Hands up, Dutchy!" Two other men, one smocked and the other shirt-sleeved, came into the field from a belt of trees. They were both tall and lean like his captor and spoke in slow, measured sentences. One of them leaned his musket against a tree, took the dragoon sword from the farmer Heinz, the sword he had found such a trouble to keep bright, felt of his pockets. Again slow voices spoke: "Come on, Dutchy!"

Heinz brightened. They talked so like the English. He dropped his hands, thought of words he had heard when on guard at Headquarters. He grinned. "Ja, ja! I—gome!" Then his eyes fell on an English canteen slung about the shoulders of the shortest of the men. The word—the word he had heard the English general use so often. Ah—almost like German. "A—a trink!" The men looked startled. Then the eldest spoke. "Dutchy allows he'd admire a pull at your canteen, Bije."

Blessed water slid down Heinz' throat like silk. He handed the canteen back, bowed awkwardly. The men handled their rifles, looked up at the darkening sky. "Cap'n Blake'll be waitin' us. 'Tain't suitable to keep him tarryin'. Come along, Dutchy!"

Ahrens shifted uncomfortably in his backwoods saddle, wishing that an easier-gaited horse had been sent back for him. Then he grinned as he saw Spangenberg hitching up his long legs to keep his heels free of the ground. It was a mercy that he was mounted at all, now that the weather had turned so hot. Skene's carts had helped, too, although they only just offset that ammunition cart which he had had to abandon a mile back with its axle broken and a squad working at it. It would catch up in the course of time and then he would really have a surplus of vehicles. Horses, though—they looked about finished. Nothing but grazing and rest would bring them back into condition. He called to Spangenberg: "When we reach Baum, I'm going to talk to Breymann about cutting out these horses and leaving them to graze. No sense in knocking them to pieces."

"Good idea." Spangenberg nodded. "Only Breymann hates his men so much that he'll probably make us all drill in the dark till we drop. How much farther to Baum, do you think?"

"No telling. I'm taking a bearing over my horse's ears. Keep your eyes ahead of you and you'll see Baum before too long."

The road twisted ahead of them, bearing due east along a stream that must be the Walloomsac. Far ahead Ahrens could see the dark mass of the advance guard, some three companies of light infantry, then a knot of horsemen, Breymann and Skene riding at their head. Rising ground hid the rest of the light infantry, but he knew that they were in the blind space between Breymann's staff and the head of the grenadier column that stretched straight along in front of him. He shook his head. "Lord, how they drag! Long sleep tonight is what they need. Spangenberg, I'll bet you're right. Breymann will give everyone two hours of stiff drill when we get in tonight, just to show he's still master. He'll—" His arm shot out, caught Spangenberg by a bony shoulder. "Look, look!"

A rocky hill on the left of the road, nearly opposite the advance guard, was suddenly swarming with drab figures, with light-stepping men who ran easily, carrying long rifles. Spangenberg stared. "But—but they aren't uniformed! They're just farmers, peasants. Shouldn't be allowed muskets. What are they doing?"

"Farmers be damned! Look like the Hubbardton men to me. They're rebels, rebel militia! Don't you see, don't you see? *They're between us and Baum!* God above, what's happened? Look, they're taking cover behind that rail fence on the crest." He swung in his saddle, roared: "Prepare for action!" He smiled grimly as the men stripped tompions from muzzles, loosened the covers of the tumbrils, cleared rammer-staffs and worms, shifted their coiled drag-ropes from waist to shoulder. His recruits moved as deftly as the oldest soldier.

"Better stand by the second piece, Spangenberg. What? What's that?"

A long arm pointed to the hill whose low-running occupants were now sunk behind the rail fence, muskets bristling toward the road. "Sorry to take your rebels away from you," said Spangenberg. "Those are Tories, the Loyalists that Skene has been promising us. Look—there he goes to meet them." A single horseman had broken away from the staff group and was urging his mount across the fields. There was a dead hush along the halted column. Faint but clear Skene's voice ripped the still air. "Are you King George's men?"

"There!" said Spangenberg triumphantly. "Tories. See—Skene waves to them. He's—Lord *God!*"

Smoke suddenly billowed from the rails with a splintering crash. Skene's horse reared, lashed out viciously with its forefeet, then pitched sideways in a sprawl of waving legs and curved neck. The rider rolled clear, scrambled to his feet and ran back to the column. Spangenberg spun his mount about, galloped to the second piece. There was shouting up ahead, Breymann's bitter voice blurring all other sounds. The column moved on.

"We don't reply?" fretted Ahrens. Then he stood in his stirrups. The light infantry left the road, formed into line and started slowly up the slope, company after company. The rail fence still blazed. Here and there blue-coated men spun, doubled up, dropped, white-clad legs stumbled, tripped, but still the dark lines went on. A distant voice roared: "One volley, then at 'em with the bayonet!" The blue lines halted, dressed, fired, then broke into a clumsy trot, steel slanting before them. Ahrens pounded the pommel of his saddle. "They're closing, they're closing!" he shouted. "Ten yards more and they'll be among 'em with steel!"

The fence blazed again, more blue coats tossed heavily to the ground. Like a cloud of wild-fowl, the drab figures rose, scattered and sifted away through the thin woods beyond the fence. Ahrens cursed. Like Hubbardton. Ran before there could be any real action. He was now abreast of the slope down which the light infantry were trotting. An excited young ensign shouted to him: "They've black fellows with 'em! Saw 'em myself, two, three of 'em, black as the pit! Why didn't they wait? They're not soldiers!" He moved on down the road at a double, his men clumping after him.

Ahrens looked back up the slope. A few blue and white patches showed starkly in the lush grass. The ground back of the rail fence was bare. Beyond the woods he could see rebels emerging from the trees, moving at their light, quick pace. From the north another group moved easily along, joining the men from the fence and seeming to flow along toward some still higher ground to the left of the road.

Trees were denser now. Occasional shots cracked from under low boughs. A grenadier a few ranks ahead of the guns stumbled, fell heavily, his brass helmet rolling crazily into the long grass. Ahrens ducked his head as something snarled in the air above him. Then he saw four lean men loping away across the fields parallel to the road.

Another hill, more figures in smocks and shirts by another fence, among gray rocks. More lines of blue and white moving heavily on them.

Smoke and fire from the crest, blue and white on the grass, then brass shining in the green as the grenadiers swung out to support the light infantry. Another shout of, "To the bayonet! Give 'em steel!" Another covey of drab men rising from the ground, melting away like ghosts just before the heavy-stepping men could lunge among them with the bayonet.

The columns re-formed, went on, leaving another trail of still shapes in the grass. The grenadiers returning to the road cursed and raved, calling the Yankees cowards.

"Cowards?" thought Ahrens. "Why should they wait to be butchered?" He called back to Spangenberg: "If they stand long enough to let us come into action, try to get a shot on the uprights of the fences. Strip the whole line bare."

The thin man nodded, then shouted: "Bad soldiers, the rebels. They should have waited after that last volley and received our charge. Read any authority you like. They'll all say the same thing."

"Without bayonets? I've not seen a rebel yet with a bayoneted musket."

"They *should* have bayonets." Spangenberg was severe. "And see!" He pointed to a high fringe of woods that overhung the road. "They're firing on the column. The fields must be full of 'em. I'd planned to look at a couple of brooks back there as soon as we made camp. May have to wait till tomorrow."

"Tomorrow?" Ahrens laughed shortly. "I've only seen two or three rebels fall yet. And these are only scattered groups, come from God knows where. How'd you like to see a thousand, shooting like that? And what *can* have happened to Baum?"

He watched the grenadiers ahead, saw their lagging pace, wondered how, even if fresh, they could manage to come to grips with the rebels where their magnificent discipline and training with the bayonet would count. Even if fresh—and some of the men ahead were staggering.

Rifles and muskets cracked from time to time on the high ground to the left, isolated shots which occasionally left a light infantryman or grenadier sprawled beside the road, or kneeling in the mud clutching arm or knee and swearing through white lips.

Musketry crashed somewhere up ahead, crashed and rolled in heavy volleys. Ahrens felt a tingling along his spine, an empty feeling in his stomach, moisture in his palms. He felt as though he were riding into a gathering storm. The rebels must have halted, and in force. Hooves drummed along the road and Skene rode down the column on a fresh horse, face crimson.

"God damn it, Lieutenant, why aren't your guns ready? They're needed!" Skene's voice blared like a trumpet.

"In order for action, sir," Ahrens snapped.

"Then why in hell don't you bring them on?" the Englishman snarled.

"Is that an order?"

"From Colonel Breymann. The whole column will be engaged in a minute. Now, move, move!"

Ahrens' right hand stabbed the air with short jerks. He heard the quickened beat of hooves behind him as he set spurs to his horse. The grenadiers were already running, slanting off in long lines into the wide sweep of open fields at the left. At the edge of the road, Ahrens tossed his reins to a driver, ran over the slippery grass to the knot of men who stood behind Breymann. As he ran he saw that there were sloping woods at the distant edge of the field, woods which suddenly flamed hideously in a ripping crash. Light infantry and grenadiers in long lines marched steadily but sluggishly toward the trees, halting every now and then to dress their ranks. The air was full of hissing, wailing noises.

Breymann glanced over his shoulder, snapped: "Bring your guns into action! I want solid-shot among those trees at the left—see, by those piles of rocks. The rebels are trying to work around to that flank." He swung his head to the front again. There were more whining noises in the air. Breymann drew his sword. Without looking around he said through set lips: "I shall personally cut down any officer who flinches."

Ahrens ran back toward the guns, spread his arms wide. The cannoneers unlimbered the pieces, hooked on their drag-ropes and slowly trundled the guns over the bumpy ground. "First piece here!" he shouted. "Second at twenty paces to the left!" Something hot flicked past his face. He hoped the men didn't notice the start he gave. He covered himself by crying: "Hurry up those ammunition carts! Drive right onto the field!"

The first round crashed among the trees. A swarm of men in gray and brown scattered, loped away out of sight. The gunners cheered. Ahrens ordered three more rounds. The men seemed to be working the pieces coolly enough. The guns thudded and flashed. A mass of men in column loomed among the trees, began flowing out into the open, heading toward the open flank of Barner's light infantry. Ahrens sprang forward, pushed away the two gunners who stood by the trail. He seized the handspike in his powerful hands, swung the trail until the brass muzzle bore full on the Yankees. Then the trail thudded on the ground.

"Fire, bombardier!" yelled Ahrens. The linstock fell on the vent. The gun roared and rocked in a welter of smoke. When it cleared, Ahrens saw shattered forms on the grass, the rest of the column plunging back into the cover of the woods while Barner's men, undisturbed, loosed a volley at the shifting lines in front of them.

More rebels appeared, working round on the left. The two pieces were slewed around and again the drab men fell back; sifted away like wraiths. "Not getting away quite scot-free," muttered Ahrens grimly. Aloud he shouted: "Less water on the swab, first piece. Damp is all you need."

The musketry died away. Ahrens realized with a start that he felt very weak, that his hands were shaking. There was a stir in the distant woods and he felt fearfully conspicuous, standing there back of his gun. He turned his head, wondering if there were some more sheltered place for the pieces. Then the musketry swelled to a sudden roar. He saw that the lines were no longer advancing, that the light infantry and the grenadiers were standing their ground, firing into the woods. Some Jaegers slipped up on the left of the light infantry, began firing.

Ahrens started violently, mouth suddenly dry, eyes hot. Something whacked the ground at his side. "Was it my imagination, or did that shot come from the left rear?" He tried to think coolly, precisely, to cover up the feeling of near-nausea that flooded him. A bullet rapped sharply on the axle of the first piece. By Spangenberg's gun a cannoneer collapsed over the hot breech, another suddenly clapped hands to his head and ran jerkily in short circles, then pitched to the ground. Ahrens' heart pounded, his throat felt actually shriveled. The fire *was* from the left and rear. Masses of men, not mere straggling trickles, were filtering through the trees just out of range. He screamed a command. His voice sounded thin, reedy to him. The men sprang to the drag-ropes and the piece bumped away to the left, Spangenberg's leading it at twenty paces.

There was no need to indicate the target. The trails thudded to the ground, the guns banged. Men leaped to the muzzles with rammers. Again there were hot hissings in the air. The bombardier of Spangenberg's piece staggered back, tripped over a rock, fell heavily, his linstock flying in the air. Another gunner snatched it up, again the piece slammed. Spangenberg waved his long arms, raved at his men.

There was a flat slam from the woods. Spangenberg turned a wild face to Ahrens, shouted: "Look!" Brass gleamed among the trees, there was another crash. Two solid-shot sang through the air, ploughed at the ground at the left of the Jaegers. "They've brought guns of their own!" Spangenberg's voice cracked.

Ahrens bellowed: "Drag-ropes! We'll take 'em in the flank!" The volume of his voice startled him. He still felt weak and a little dizzy. The clamps of the drag-ropes snapped crisply, the pieces rocked ahead over the matted grass. "There! By that rock, Sergeant Pertz. That'll take 'em." Then his shout pealed over the ground. "Spangenberg! *Those are Bache's guns!* Where in hell did the Yankees get 'em? Where in hell is Baum? Sergeant Pertz! How many rounds left?"

"Only two cartridges, sir. Plenty of ball."

"Two only? Good God! Send a man back at the double to hurry up that ammunition cart. They must have mended the axle by now. Hurry!"

A cannoneer started for the road, running desperately. A snarling voice whipped through the air. "Bring that man back!"

Ahrens swore under his breath. "After more ammunition, Colonel."

"Send that skulker back to his piece! Keep your men at their posts till the carts come up!"

"But, Colonel—"

Breymann screamed: "Are you trying to argue with *me?* Shut your mouth and give us more fire on the left!" He waved his arms, then screamed again: "Hell and death! Hold those men firm!"

A thin trickle of infantry began to flow back across the field, then the wavering lines sagged, broke and plunged heavily in the direction of the road. Yells echoed among the trees, the rebels broke cover and moved forward cautiously, firing as they came. Ahrens ran back to the limbers, shouting. One horse, then another slumped down in its harness. The rebel guns slammed again, furrowed the earth by the waiting teams. He cried above the din: "Cut those dead horses loose! Move on with what are left! My God, we'll lose the guns!" A driver toppled from his saddle, another leaped to the ground, ran off down the road. Muskets and rifles cracked nearer and nearer. Ahrens shouted again: "Cannoneers on the drag-ropes! Pieces to the rear by hand! Lieutenant Spangenberg! Bring 'em off!"

He sprang into the saddle of the lead horse, but even as he leaped, there was a dull smack. The horse tossed its head in the air, screamed, then lunged forward, collapsed in a kicking tangle. Ahrens cleared himself from the stirrups, unhooked the traces with frantic hands, shouting to the drivers to help, but found that he was calling to empty saddles. Then a torrent of staring infantrymen engulfed him, carried him away down the road. He fought his way clear, struggled back to the field, where he saw two pieces moving slowly along, cannoneers straining at the drag-ropes as though on parade. Beyond them a knot of grenadiers stood firm, exchanging shots with the rebels as they fell back, step by step. Breymann had rallied a mass of light infantry and some grenadiers and was moving off the field with them. The rebels, lacking bayonets, did not dare close on the remnants of the force, but hung in clouds on the flanks, firing.

Ahrens battled his way to his piece through a crowd of staring men who wanted only to get away from that distant belt of trees at the top of the slope which had spit death at them. He seized a trailing drag-rope and heaved with his men. The air about them was stinging and sharp with flying lead. The rebels had marked their prize. The man on the next rope threw out his hands and lunged forward, his face a streaming mask of red. There was a curse and Rentner went down, clutching at his shoulder, then struggled to his feet. He had not let go of his drag-rope. Sergeant Pertz sprang into the air, spun and thudded to the ground.

There were shouts close behind. A hard voice called in English: "Clean out the gunners! Swing your butts if you've no more shot!" The rolling wheels checked, stopped, the carriage was buried under a swarm of sweating men in homespun. A musket-butt fell with a sickening whack on the head of the man beside Ahrens. He went down like a log, lay heavily, arms twitching. Ahrens seized a rammer staff from the ground, turned to face the men who swarmed over the piece. He felt a queer exaltation, a high, cold rage at these country-men who dared lay hands on his piece. Above the dreadful tumult he yelled: "Abandon the piece! Rally on the road! Do you hear me, Spangenberg?" Then he slammed viciously with the metal end of the rammer. It was struck from his hands by the heavy down-swing of a rifle. A short, broad-shouldered man sprang at him, weaponless, shouting: "I've got an officer! I've got an officer!" Ahrens grappled him. Their bodies locked. Slowly Ahrens swung the man's feet off the ground, tightened his grip about the barrel-like chest, pitched him headlong into the oncoming mass.

He fell back, brushing against two Jaegers who trotted doggedly along, shoulder to shoulder. He saw the second piece engulfed in a silent flood of rebels. He shouted again: "Spangenberg! Abandon your piece! The men are to rally in the road! It's an order!" Even as he spoke the thin man wrenched a musket from the hands of a gray-haired Yankee, leaped astride the trail of his gun, swinging in wide sweeps. The rebels fell back, then a powerful man, sleeves torn off at the elbow, rushed at him, parried his swing with a strong guard. A butt whirled in the air, cracked against Spangenberg's head. Ahrens saw long arms fly up in the air, saw white legs sag at the knees as Spangenberg slipped heavily down on the trail of the piece he would not abandon. "Spangenberg!" Ahrens yelled again. But the long form was still and two Yankees were lifting it clear of the trail with a sort of rough reverence.

Then he found himself near the edge of the road, a choking sensation in his breast. He wanted to stop each grenadier who jostled past him, explain that he was too late to save Spangenberg, that he *had* shouted to him to abandon his piece. He stumbled on blindly, seeing with every beat of his pulse the dread sag of those long white legs, the helpless clutch in the air as the Yankee swung his musket. What would his men think of him, of Kurt Ahrens? Lost his pieces, lost his horses and lost the tall man with the sad eyes! He could never face them again. Pertz was dead and Slagle and Heim and the tall man who loved clean rocks and the running water was dead, dead across the trail of his gun.

It was dark on the road whose wooded sides occasionally blazed stabs of flame into the fugitive mass. Jostled by Jaegers and light infantrymen, Ahrens swept on with the ruck. Then in the darkness a voice spoke: "Now we're all right. Here's Lieutenant Ahrens." "Where? Where do you see him?" "Where is he?" The questions popped in the night. To his amazement Ahrens heard himself saying crisply: "That you, Rentner, Meister? Who's that beyond, Meyer? Good. How many in all? Eight? Got your carbines? Fall back with me to the rear of the column."

They drew out of the press, formed and worked their way to the rear. Meyer, the oldest soldier, explained: "We tried to wait for you on the road, but got carried along. Then Rentner made us pick up all the cartridge boxes that were thrown away and we've got a few rounds apiece."

"Good!" said Ahrens mechanically. "Now fall in here at the end of the column. There'll be no more coming now."

The pursuit was not close. Random shots cracked out from the gloom, occasionally men staggered and fell, but there was no concerted effort to round up the broken, nearly defenseless mass. Waves of panic swept over the retreat. Ahrens saw unwounded grenadiers scream with terror and break into the woods where merciless branches caught their trailing swords, knocked off their tall helmets, ripped at their heavy packs until swift-moving rebels nonchalantly disarmed them and took them to the rear. Unwounded men suddenly turned, knelt in the mud, arms raised in supplication and waited for the stealthy advance that would engulf them. The rest staggered on, heads down and shoulders hunched as though they were breasting a heavy rain.

From time to time Ahrens faced his men about, ordered a volley fired into the crackling woods from which fire still spurted in rare jets. The blackness deepened and the column swayed on, a limping figure bringing up the rear where Breymann, last of his command, his temper sharpened by a flesh wound in the leg, cursed Ahrens and his gunners for not having more ammunition. The dark woods on either side of the road still rustled as silent shapes flitted between the trees, keeping pace with the column. Then little by little the ghostly forms dropped behind and the stillness of night fell over the road through the trees.

Captain Thaddeus Blake leaned on his long rifle and looked at the three men lounging by the wide elm. Their prisoner, the dragoon Heinz, sat awkwardly on the ground, resting his back against the great bole of the tree. "So you boys are resolved to return to your farms?" the Captain asked, drawing a bony hand over the stubble of his lean jaws. He frowned, turned toward the tallest of the three, who wore Heinz' broad saber. "You, Ephraim Hicks, you don't see your way clear to tarrying a little?"

Hicks held his powder-horn to his ear, shook it. "No, Cap'n, I 'lows to how I don't. Powder don't even rattle in the horn and they ain't any more this side Bennington. 'Sides, *I* got to git the hay in. Might set in to rain 'most any time. The woman'll be lookin' for me. Parlin and Joslin, they aim to move, too."

Both men nodded slowly. "Best be movin'," said Joslin, squinting up at the darkening sky.

Blake shook his head. "You were very late at the rendezvous. I sent Nehemiah Sherwood and his squad off with their prisoners as General Stark ordered. Had you come earlier, your man could have gone with them. It is out of the question for me to remain longer. I have my school, my sermons to consider. Tomorrow is the Sabbath."

Parlin drew a long knife, began slowly to whittle a dry stick which he had picked up. "Best be movin', as 'Bije says," he remarked. The blade rolled thin shavings from the stick.

Blake sighed. "Well, boys, something must be done. I consider that it would be most unfitting to release the man. He might do us considerable harm. These mercenary troops, you know. Now, I propose that one of you escort him to Bennington. I hold that it would be quite proper for you to draw lots. Of course, it is after sundown and the Sabbath has technically begun, but as an ordained minister I authorize you to overlook that point this once. It is not like drawing in a game of chance."

Heinz spread his tired legs in their gigantic boots and fanned himself with his heavy hat. The conversation was far beyond the fragmentary English he had picked up in his service. Dully he wondered where these strange men might take him, and if there would be food for him. He felt dreadfully empty.

Parlin shifted the rifle to the crook of his left arm, snapped shut the blade of his knife and threw away his bit of wood. "Now, Cap'n." He spoke respectfully but firmly. "Johnny Stark called us boys out to fight Dutchies. We've fit two lots of 'em and them as could has gone home. So we're goin' home, too, like the Dutchies. Johnny Stark ain't no king to keep me fiddlin' round these woods while my hay spoils. *I* ain't got time to trail clear to Bennington." His companions nodded in silence.

Blake's eyes fell on Heinz, who stared uncomprehendingly at his captors. "I repeat that I feel it would be *most* unwise to release him," he observed.

Joslin plucked a long blade of grass and chewed at its white, pulpy stem. "You ain't partial to freein' him, Cap'n. We ain't partial to totin' him over the trail to Bennington, not none of us." He picked another spear of grass, eyed the root reflectively. "He ain't worth a hay-crop. Maybe we better shoot him."

Thaddeus Blake gravely considered the thought. "I can foresee no reasonable objection to such a course," he said at length. Then he slung his piece under his arm and moved lightly off through the woods.

Joslin threw away his spear of grass. "Might take a bite, first," he said. He began gathering dry twigs. Hicks got out flint and steel. Parlin dug into his deep haversack. "I'm plum worried 'bout my hay. Been on my mind. Spoilt my aim twice today. Shot at a gunner and only hit him on one shoulder. 'Twa'n't more 'n a hundred yards. I'd have let Johnny Stark holler like a hoot-owl if I hadn't heard 'bout that McCrae girl. Made me downright uneasy. Ain't been a mean redskin in these parts nigh on ten year."

Hicks eyed him. "That dried venison looks prime, Ez. Go good with the cornbread. Yes, I talked to my woman. She 'lowed I'd better go. Story didn't seem to set easy on her mind. What you think, Bije?"

Joslin dumped a heap of crackling twigs on the bare ground. "I been bundlin' with neighbor Brigham's girl nigh two year come hayin'. Any Injun that wants her scalp had better talk to me. I'm peaceable-natured, but I'm kind o' partial to that girl. What a tone she can get from a spinnin'-wheel!" He sighed.

A small fire snapped and glowed in the dusk under the great elm. Heinz drew up his knees and squatted on his haunches like a clumsy bear, nose quivering as the venison on the ramrods hissed and sizzled. Hicks shook the hot meat from his rod. "'Bout done." He sniffed. "Prime, prime!" Then his eye caught Heinz' hungry stare, which seemed to stab out from under his battered hat. His knife neatly divided the chunk of meat. Half he tossed to Heinz. "Have some, Dutchy," he said. Parlin and Joslin nodded approvingly. "That were kindly in you, Eeph," said Parlin. He went on in food-muffled tones: "Too bad we got to shoot him. Don't look like a bad Dutchy."

The sense of the words was lost on Heinz, who was tearing at his venison. He pointed at the blackened lump of meat and mumbled: "Gut! Gut!"

His captors laughed and repeated: "Goot! Goot!" Heinz beamed and gnawed away.

Between bites Joslin said, "Wonder what he does at home? Hey, Dutchy, what you do at home, huh? Work—what work, huh?"

Heinz' face twisted in an exquisite agony of thought. Then he grinned. "Ach! Vork! Me? I vos—I vos Bauer!" He made vague motions of digging and reaping.

Hicks looked up. "Bower, bower? Look—look at him! He means he worked a piece of land. Like this, Dutchy? Farm, huh?" With his knife he mowed tall grasses close by the fire's edge.

The dragoon nodded frantically. "Ja, ja! Pfarm, pfarm!" He swept his arms as though they held an invisible scythe.

"Damned if he *ain't* a farmer!" said Hicks. " 'Pears like he don't hold a scythe the same as we do. Snathe too close to his body. I'd admire to see them thick legs of his followin' a furrow in my north forty, I would I vum!" He plunged his rammer into the soft ground to cleanse it of venison grease. "Well, who's goin' to do him in? I ain't. I got to move. Joe Bagby's ailin' and can't help me with this lot of hay. You boys draw lots." He rose slowly.

Parlin picked two spears of grass and palmed them expertly. Joslin drew the shorter blade. "Looks like your chore, Ez," he said. "I'll go 'long the trail a piece with Eeph." Parlin sighed and looked at the priming of his rifle, then at Heinz, who still gnawed at his last fragment in deep unconcern and content.

Hicks started along the trail, then stopped short. His voice boomed through the clearing. "Hey, Dutchy! You like farm? Goot, huh?" He waved his arms like a man pitching hay. "Goot? You like, huh?"

Heinz looked up, nodding and grinning. "Ja, gut! Pfarm iss gut!"

Parlin changed the priming of his rifle. Hicks slouched over to the dying fire. "Stand up, Dutchy!" he said.

Heinz struggled to his feet, long spurs rasping against the jutting roots of the elm. He stretched himself, repeating: "Stand op! Stand op!"

With quick hands Hicks slapped the dragoon's arms and chest. Then he nodded. "You'll do. The woman'll feed you when we get in. Hay needs tendin' bad." He turned on his heel and started off. Heinz stared after him, mouth open. Parlin rammed a fresh charge into his piece, sighing. From the darkness Hicks' voice called: "Ain't you comin', Dutchy?"

"Ja! Ja! I gome, gome! To der pfarm!" The heavy dragoon boots clumped and crashed in the wake of Hicks' light tread. Parlin grinned and drew the charge from his piece.

BATTLE OF COWPENS

by JAMES BOYD

THE MONTH WHICH FOLLOWED brought no change except that the air turned colder, the nights came sooner, carried a sharper hint of coming winter. Disconsolate, they hugged their fire or stared across the fields of scarlet clay and tawny broom-straw to the cold blue hills beyond. Men so naked, so listless as they, thought Johnny, could not stand much; the first hard freeze would fix them forever where they stood. If that were so, they had not long to wait; December was here.

Up the company street he saw the men gathering by the rail fence to watch a stranger pass. He joined them. A cold white sun foreboded snow, the distant hills looked blue and hard. Hoofs rang on the red, frost-crusted road. In column of fours a troop of dragoons was posting up the valley. By Zooks, they were something like soldiers: nodding plumes curled above their brass helmets, their polished scabbards swung; in the lead, a short, powerful man, in buff and blue, leaned forward on his mud-caked horse and kicked it eagerly along.

As he passed along the old rail fence, he looked at the men's rags and frowned; he looked at their faces and smiled. Pulling up at the whipping-post before headquarters, he swung down, chafed his gloves together smartly, strode in the door.

In all Johnny Fraser's life of adventure there had been no change greater than that between the first month he spent in camp and the month which followed it. The door of headquarters had no sooner closed on the short, broad general in buff and blue than things began to happen. Long wagon trains came rolling from the north, strings of horses on rope halters followed, and a drove of cattle. The crowd along the fence cheered the lowing herd to the last heifer. "Meat!" they shouted and danced grotesquely in their blankets. Rifles were issued, woolen caps, shoes, hunting shirts; they began to look like something, now, when they fell in for drill. Early and late they paraded under arms; they performed the manual by the hour, did foot drill by the months, it seemed, and practice marches by the year.

One night they heard the ring of marching columns on the frozen ground; they woke next morning to see the long straight tent-rows of the Continentals.

"It looks mighty bad," Bill confided to Johnny as he stroked his new-shaved chin. "That Delaware regiment is the one they call the Blue Hen's Chickens."

"That's a curious name," said Johnny.

"The Blue Hen," Bill went on, "bein' the name of a game cock. They tell me they send them boys 'round wherever they's liable to be a fight."

"Well," said Johnny, "I'd as soon be killed fightin' as drillin'."

Bill gazed wistfully down at the herd of stock beyond the horse lines. "I know," he said, "but after a fellow's et fire-cake for a year, he kind o' despises to have anything come between him and them nice fat steers."

Before Christmas they left the fat beeves behind them and marched away. Standing at ease along the road, Johnny's company taunted the main column with pleasant indecencies as they marched by and disappeared among the rolling hills to the East. Their own force, a thousand strong, wheeled into column and took the straight road to South Carolina. The leather caps of Colonel William Washington's light horse showed at their head; then came the blue coats of Maryland Continentals; then the tan shirts of North Carolina militia; the scarlet facings of the Virginians were in the rear.

At the first halt the blacksmith from Blue's Crossing hobbled back from the leading company. "Look here, son," he said to Johnny, "I

joined with the idea that this was to be a shootin' war; if it's to be a
walkin' war, I'm goin' home." A big-boned hand fell on the blacksmith's
shoulder, the long brown face, stern but fatherly and infinitely worn,
of Daniel Morgan, their commander, peered down at him.

"Listen, brother," he said. "I'll make a trade with you. You do all
the marching they is to be done and I'll guarantee you get all the shootin'
they is to be done." A ghost of a smile just touched his tired mouth and
vanished. "You'd better take my offer," he said. "Because you ain't a-goin'
home." The blacksmith made an attempt at a salute.

"All right, Captain," he said, and hobbled back to his company.

The blacksmith did not have long to wait; they passed the South
Carolina line, turned westerly, and crossing a broad river, camped on a
hill. Below them stretched wide meadows, sparsely scattered with pine
trees; behind, the distant river circled half around them. They waited
while the cavalry patrols clinked off through the forest.

The drums roused them in the chill January dawn; far off to the
southward they heard a faint, clear note.

"Them's the Kent bugles," the veterans said. "Here comes the British!"
They swallowed their tea and biscuit, put out their fires and fell in.
Wheeling into column, the North Carolina brigade marched down to the
lower shoulder of the hill. They wheeled again and halted, their long
front stretching clear across the slope. Ahead of them a line of buckskin
skirmishers in single file moved out, took cover behind scattered trees
and lay down in the grass. To their rear, up the hill, stood the straight,
stiff ranks of the dark blue Continentals.

Johnny's company, standing at ease in the chill dawn, fingered their
rifles and whispered. Their Captain, a veteran of the Carolina Line
with a hawklike peak to his high shoulders and sabre-cut across his hawklike face, advanced to the center of the company and held up his hand.
The men fell silent; he struggled for utterance, coughed, blew his nose
and blushed till his weather-beaten, hollow cheeks turned crimson.

"Well, boys!" he mumbled huskily, "here we are!" He beamed on
them with ironic benignity. His voice gained confidence. "They's a river
behind us with picquets along the bank to shoot the man that tries to
cross it and the British is about to come at us in front. Tarleton is leadin'
'em; he killed all the men that surrendered to him at the Waxhaws——"
he paused, the broad scar on his face crinkled in an ugly, friendly grin—
"So let every man do his duty!" The men looked at the ground awkwardly and chuckled. The Captain's voice turned sharp. "Two volleys,"

he said, "and then re-form behind the Continentals." He hesitated, pulled bashfully at his bony fingers. "Boys," he said, "I've fought the British four times and never really whipped 'em. Stick by me!" There was a moment's pause.

"Doggone your sneakin' hide, Bill!" said a voice from the rear rank. "The Cap'n means you!" The tension broke in a burst of laughter.

Patches of scarlet glinted through the distant pines. English bugles sounded close at hand, the head of the scarlet column came in view. They marched straight on past the American front, their white breeches flashed rhythmically, their bayonets winked in unison; their precision was unreal, incredible; it was hard for Johnny to think of them as men, their column was a unit, a monstrous toy, red and white and shining, which was being drawn across the scene.

In the cold still air he could hear the words of command passing down their line; the column wheeled together, together their pipe-clayed cross belts flashed in view; their steady-moving legs showed white, then dark, white—dark, in the wan winter sunlight. Behind them Johnny saw two brass cannon gallop to a gentle rise, wheel smartly and unlimber. He saw the green jackets of Tarleton's dragoons.

Now they had come so close that Johnny could make out the epauletted company officers marching in front of the rigid scarlet wall.

"Shoot for the epaulette-men when I give the word!" the Captain called out. "But don't any man fire till I do!"

Ahead of them, the skirmish line, crouching low behind their trees, opened a scattering fire on the enemy. A few gaps showed in the red line, closed up again. The British regiments came on. To right and left the skirmishers ran for cover.

"Ready the North Carolina Brigade!" he heard an officer shout behind them. "Take aim!" the Captain said. Johnny Fraser saw a small toy figure of an epaulette-man through his sights. "Now fire!" A crash and a cloud of smoke enveloped him. Through the blaze he saw long, broken fragments of the red line coming on. "Load your pieces, you scoundrels!" the Captain cried. "Now take aim!" Their volley crashed again. The clearing smoke showed scarlet fragments, fragments so close that Johnny could see the faces of the soldiers, pale and haggard as they halted wavering in the blast, or, turning to run, stumbled over the crimson windrows on the ground. The British were stopped; not a man moved forward. Yes, there was one; one little epaulette-man, a slender, pink-faced baby, carrying his big sword as stiffly as on parade, marched steadily up the hill.

Galloping up to the wavering line, a British field officer pointed him out with his gold-laced hat.

"Now then, Seventy-first!" Johnny could hear his voice, "support the little gentleman!"

"One more volley!" his captain shouted. "Just one!" They fired hastily, broke ranks and fell back under cover of the smoke.

Retreating around the flank of the Continentals, Johnny stopped to look behind him; the red line, newly formed and steady, came on again. He ran his eye along it. The little gentleman was gone.

Below him, to the rear, the hunting shirts were falling in again. He joined them; in column they marched off to the right flank and halted. He saw the British reserves running at the double quick; the blue line and the red were firing at close range; a troop of cavalry passed him, swinging their sabres and cheering.

"Charge!" the word came back; the hunting shirts were running down hill.

They had no bayonets, but they fired from the hip as they hit the British flank, then clubbed their rifles. A red-faced man with staring eyes thrust a long bayonet at Johnny, Johnny cracked the rifle butt against his mouth and felt the bones cave in: still staring at him, the man slid gently down between his knees.

Now his same old arm was bleeding again; the pain, the blood, the smoke, the stench of sweating men were sickening him. He raised his face to the sky for air; above the crowding heads he saw the troop of cavalry, he heard their hoofs and saw their long sabres thrusting and hacking through the mêlée. Then suddenly, a forest of hands was raised high in air; down the long line, a thousand British voices called for quarter.

GUILFORD COURTHOUSE

by INGLIS FLETCHER

DAVID CAUGHT AT MARY'S ARM. "What is that?" he whispered.

At the bottom of the hill, drifting across the valley, lay three puffs of smoke, like small cumulus clouds. A moment later, the sound reached them, the dull boom of cannon. Cannon! They had opened fire with cannon. The surprise of Greene's three-pounders, hidden in a clump of bushes, had halted Tarleton's dragoons. They checked, wheeled and scattered. Colonel Lee's cavalry took advantage of the confusion. They charged, cutting down Tarleton's troops and officers. Then they disappeared up the road, both pursuers and the pursued.

Mary looked in the opposite direction. More troops were coming, marching to the staccato beat of drums. She heard the wild skirl of pipes. The Highlanders! It was the Black Watch, the fighting 71st, advancing toward the open field. She had seen them many times in London on parade. But not like this, marching at double quick, kilts swirling, pipes skirling—not piping parade now, but piping men to battle. A solid rank they came, row on row, spreading out into battle line. How splendid they were! How brave! "Oh, Scots, do you not know that behind the fences men are waiting to kill?" Her teeth clamped down on her lips to keep from screaming the words aloud. It was too late. In a few moments rifle fire would strike them down! "God in Heaven, defend the Right," she prayed, tears rolling unheeded down her white cheeks.

Across the field other troops were running forward to close the broken ranks.

"They're mobbing the Queen's Guard," Grieves told her, pointing to a position to the west. Field pieces rumbled up; trotting horses reared and plunged; soldiers made way; guns were unlimbered, charges rammed; there was the sudden flash of a fusee. Then came the answering fire to Green's three-pounders.

The British column advanced with fixed bayonets along the split rail fence. Mary could not see the Americans, only a few puffs of smoke from the trees that told of the presence of hidden sharpshooters. The High-

From: *Raleigh's Eden*. Copyright 1940. Used by special permission of the publishers, The Bobbs-Merrill Company.

landers still advanced in formation. Mary realized that they did not know that Lawson's Virginians lay concealed along the zigzag fence.

Suddenly, they knew. The sharp fire of rifles—men falling, screaming and cursing. The front line of the British lay on the ground—one out of every ten wounded or dying. The rest took to cover, behind trees, bushes, stones. Bent over, they ran, dodging the deadly fire that came from behind the fence. Officers shouted, rallying them. Then they charged the fence, sweeping forward. Havoc—dreadful, tragic havoc before her eyes.

Grieves called out, "The Americans are giving way. God damn them all for yellow-livered cowards." He seized his musket and ran through the leafless trees down the hill.

David sprang to his feet and started to follow. Mary caught at his arm. "Stay here, David, don't leave me," she cried.

The boy tore himself loose from her grasp and ran down the hill toward the road, Mary after him calling to him to wait.

The roar of cannon came with startling regularity now. Mary saw David through the trees, far below. He was running at full speed. She stumbled after him, the skirt of her habit unhooked, catching on brambles and thorns, delaying her. At the bottom of the hill, she stopped for breath and leaned against the trunk of a pine tree. David had gone, she knew not where, caught in the wild hysteria of battle.

Then she saw him. Two soldiers held the struggling boy by the arms, keeping him back. She hurried forward. At the turn of the road she came to the big hospital tent. Dr. Armitage stood in front, directing stretcher-bearers. He was bareheaded, his white hair flying. "The British are rallying," she heard him cry. Mary pressed her face against the rough bark of the tree to shut out the sight of men charging with fixed bayonets.

Armitage, turning around, saw her. "God in Heaven, Mary, what are you doing here? Get back! Get back! Have you lost your senses?"

His voice calmed her. She walked across the open space. "I've come to help," she said quietly.

Armitage nodded. "There'll be work aplenty. The field is already black with British dead. As long as you're here, you may as well be of some use."

"Where are the Carolinians and Lawson's Virginians?" she asked.

He was sweeping the open country with his glass. "I can't see their position; they are in the woods behind that knoll," he said briefly. Then he turned to the south. "God! Look down the road! More British! The Welsh Fusiliers—the Guards. Look, Mary, take the glass, it's Cornwallis—Cornwallis himself."

Mary took the glasses. She saw a soldierly man on a big horse. There was the man who had put fear and terror into the hearts of the Carolinians. He was riding in advance of the Guards, indifferent of danger, a target for any sniper behind tree or fence. He was close enough for her to see his proudly held head, his strong aquiline nose.

"He is not without courage," Armitage said grudgingly. "The officer with him is Webster. He is a splendid officer, Mary. I don't know how our men can hold out against such troops as these!"

"God defend the Right." Mary did not know whether or not she spoke the words aloud. Beyond the hospital tent she saw David. He was standing still, white and bewildered. When he saw her he ran to her and caught her hand, but his eyes shone with wild excitement.

"It's a battle, Aunt Mary, a real battle," he cried.

Armitage saw him. "God's death! You here, David?"

The awful ear-splitting skirl of pipes! Would it never stop? The Black Watch advanced—the sturdy, grim-faced men running, their plaid skirts flying, waving from side to side. A snatch of song came from the smoke-covered field:

"March, March, Ettrick and Teviotdale,
    Why the deil dinna ye march forward in order?"

The words of the old rallying song of the Scots were blurred under the boom of mortars. When the roar stopped the song rose again.

"March, march, Eskdale and Liddesdale,
    All the Blue Bonnets are bound for the border."

The shrill pipes—the steady roll of drums. "Stop! stop! stop!" Mary cried out in agony.

Armitage turned, quickly, his glasses falling on the strap. He grasped her shoulder, shaking her violently. "Quiet, quiet, woman!" he said sternly.

Mary pulled herself together.

David was tired of watching. "If I only had Black Douglas and my grandfather's lance, I would go into battle."

"David, don't say such things," she cried.

She saw Lawson galloping up. He shouted to Armitage. "Send out the stretcher-bearers to the left flank under a white flag. Have them bring in the wounded—British and Americans, all of them." He scarcely paused to give the orders. Nor did he seem to see Mary. He turned his horse and galloped back to the line. She saw him riding up and down at the head of his men, shouting encouragement. Armitage caught at her elbow.

"Look! Lawson's men are breaking. They have thrown down their rifles! They are running—running—God! Don't they do anything but run?"

The Maryland militia gave way first. Eaton's men, then Butler's. They broke under the savage charge of the 71st. Bayonets gleamed in the light; drums beat, funeral drums, not drums of war. No longer able to bear the shrill lament of the pipes, Mary went into the tent. Her people were running. "God of Battles, save them." Her lips moved soundlessly. Soldiers were running past the hospital station, choking the road in their mad rush. Fear-stricken men with glazed, staring eyes; boys with drawn, white faces, livid with anguish and horror. She saw Lawson on his foam-flecked horse, riding along the road, shouting above the tumult, "Rally, rally and charge—turn and charge!" But they did not hear him. They kept on running away. They were already beaten men, and the battle scarce begun.

Bloody and fierce was the battle that raged all about them. Colonel Washington's cavalry came up. They charged once, but they too were caught in the panic of fear. What was happening? Were all men in all the world running? Was Greene's army falling to pieces before they were tried and tempered by fire? Mother of Mercy! Were these strong, free men, who fought to protect their land?

Suddenly she was conscious of a new sound. It seemed to flow through her body, beat against her ears. It came out of the earth, vibrating through the air. Men were marching—the steady unfaltering pulsation of marching feet. Armitage heard it, too. He swung around, facing the west. Mary followed his fixed gaze.

Along the western road, horsemen galloped—a long line of men coming forward at double quick.

"The Back Country men have come at last," Armitage shouted, his voice high. "They are coming again, just as they did at King's Mountain." Tears ran down his shrunken cheeks. "Thank God!" he whispered. "I thought they would come."

Mary stood at the tent door, her hands held tightly together. The fleeing soldiers hesitated, half turned. What were the words they heard to give them courage? Kneeling men caught up rifles. An order rang out, sharp, staccato. It passed down rank after rank of soldiers, growing in volume. *Stand and defend, men, stand and defend!* They caught up the cry. . . .

Mary heard a voice above the roar of battle and the mad skirling of Highland pipes. Was it Adam's voice carrying above the shouts and cries? The wavering lines stiffened. More men turned, caught up their rifles. Then she saw him. He was riding a great bay horse, his naked sword in his hand. He rode at a gallop down the line.

"Stand and defend!" he shouted, over and over. "God damn you for cowards!"

Words of courage passed from lip to lip down the breaking line, behind hedge fences and into woods and swamps. A new battle cry that filled the hearts of defeated men with new courage. *"Stand and Defend!"* The lines turned, hesitated, then stood as if suddenly reinvigorated.

The British column wavered. A moment before Americans had been running, now they were spreading fanwise across the battle field. The rifle fire was sharp, steady. What had happened? The British did not know, but the Carolinians and the Virginians knew. The men of the Back Country had come! Marching swiftly—the rugged, hawk-eyed men advanced. Behind every beardless, frightened boy a strong man stood. Bronzed woodsmen stood shoulder to shoulder with unseasoned boys, giving them the strength of the far-flung forests, of the deep rivers. Sturdy, weather-beaten men, with steady eyes, trained to the cunning of Indian fighting.

Greene galloped down the road, rallying his troops. Lawson whirled among his men, his chestnut horse in a white lather. He took up the cry of the Back Country men—*"Freemen . . . stand and defend!"*

Mary ran through the bushes to the edge of the road and waited. Presently he came in sight.

"Adam, Adam Rutledge," she screamed, her voice high and shrill.

Adam pulled up his horse with a jerk. "Mary," he cried. He jumped to the ground, catching both her hands. "What are you doing here? Get out quickly! God knows what's going to happen."

David found her then and she pushed him forward. "Here's David," she said. There was so little time for them.

Adam and David looked into each other's eyes a moment. "Go back to the tent, David. It is not safe here." Adam spoke gently.

"I will ride with you into battle," the boy said.

"No, no, stay with me, David," Mary cried shrilly. "Don't let him go, Adam, he is so young, so young."

Adam looked at the boy. "You are tall, my boy. Can you use a musket?"

A dull red came to David's cheeks, his lips quivered. "As well as any," he answered.

Adam signaled to Herk. "Give him your horse, Herk. Find another on the battlefield for yourself. David shall ride with me today." The boy swung into the saddle without touching a stirrup, his face alive with excitement.

Mary stood alone by the roadside. They did not turn to wave farewell or speak a last word to her before they rode forward into battle. She moved wearily to the dressing tent. Stretcher-bearers were coming in, carrying groaning, cursing men. She threw her cap over a bush and rolled back the cuffs of her riding habit. Bandages and packets of lint lay on a long table outside the tent—packets of lint waiting to be unrolled. Dully she carried them into the tent, stripped the covers from a box and laid out the shining steel instruments on a fresh piece of cotton cloth. After a time, she forgot father and son—even the battle ceased to exist.

Wounded men were placed in front of her. Faces passed in the line of her vision—bodies of men, broken, drowned in their own blood and the blood of their enemies. Lint, staunching wounds; bright red blood of youth; grey figures passing in quick succession; the swift sharp orders of surgeons; stretcher-bearers moving rapidly, laying down one burden, taking up another. . . .

"Get out into the air, Mary Warden." A sharp order—Armitage with sleeves rolled back, his hands and arms red to the elbow with blood. "Get out into the air!"

She walked to the opening of the tent. The roar of cannon broke on her ears. Before her, lines of men straggled by, enveloped in grey smoke. The glint of gold and red—blue—faded buff. The strong, heavy odor of powder choked her. Clouds of smoke obscured the field. Leaden clouds overhead were heavy with rain.

Greene rode up the road below the dressing station. His corpulent figure had shrunk, his cheeks sagged, hanging loosely. His dark, agonized eyes looked across the field. Lawson galloped up, his right arm hanging limply at his side.

"I have to report, sir, the Virginian line broke. My men are in complete disorder."

Greene turned to an orderly. "My compliments to Colonel Rutledge. Tell him to throw his Back Country men behind the Virginians," he shouted over his shoulder. "Go to the dressing tent and get your arm fixed up, Lawson, then return to your men. If we must retreat, let it be in good order." There was discouragement in his voice as he rode off.

Lawson swung from his saddle. He swayed, grasping his horse's mane for support. Mary ran to him and led him to the tent. Blood was streaming from a saber cut over his eye, dripping from the corners of his mouth. He wiped it away impatiently with the back of his hand.

"Webster of the Highlanders is dead," he mumbled. "I saw him fall from his horse, and Stuart of the Queen's Own. Gallant officers, both of them. God damn all War!" He talked between set teeth while Armitage worked on the shattered arm.

Greene rode up to the dressing tent. The Doctor went out but came back in a moment. "The General wants to see you, Mary," he said.

Mary went out. Greene sat on his tall horse, scribbling a line on a piece of paper. "In case we have to retreat, give this to Tarleton or Cornwallis. I have asked for your protection and safe conduct to Edenton." He handed the paper to her. "I'm sorry, more sorry than I can ever say, about your husband, Mrs. Warden. If he had been brought to me, it might have been different." He stopped abruptly. Messengers were riding toward him. Captain Blount saluted.

"Our men are retreating in good order, General. They are no longer running but are making a stand all along the three battle lines. When they are forced to give way, they give way slowly. The British loss is heavier than ours, I think."

Mary went back to her work, washing blood-caked wounds, preparing broken bodies for the swift, keen knife of the surgeon. She laid her hand gently on the smooth forehead of young boys. Enemies, wounded and dying, came under the quiet touch of her fingers.

A young Highlander of the Black Watch held tight to her hand, while Armitage cut away the flesh of his thigh to remove a bullet. The lad's sandy hair fell over his white face. Mary pushed it back from his fast glazing eyes.

"Take the pin from my plaid, lassie," the boy whispered. Mary undid the great silver pin set with a Cairngorm and Scotch pebbles. "Wear it for a lad who died far from Glen Orchy."

Hot tears came to her eyes. "You will get well," she said, smoothing his hair.

He shook his head feebly. "I ha' seen the Doctor look at ye. There was death in his look, lassie."

She knelt beside him.

"Dinna forget, Mither, dinna forget . . ." he said clearly. His fingers loosened.

She closed his eyes, laid her cheek against his. So young—so very young.

The stream of wounded men brought to the station seemed unending. Men, fainting from loss of blood, leaned against the trees or lay on the ground waiting. There was no room inside. Mary worked on mechanically, her hands moving rapidly, binding, washing wounds, making preparations for the surgeons. Adam, where was he? What was happening out on the dark and bloody field? Someone brought her a cup of hot rum. She drank eagerly. The scalding liquid brought warmth to her cold body. Then she looked up. She saw it was Colonel Lawson.

"Drink it all, every drop!"

"But your arm! You must be careful."

"They have bound it up. Mary, listen. We are going to lose the battle. In a little while Cornwallis' men will be here."

Mary clung to him. "But the Back Country men—I thought they had turned the tide."

"They did, but they could not hold forever. They have given us the chance to retreat in good order. Already our men are moving swiftly toward Reedy Ford, but Cornwallis has thrown in the second battalion of Guards near Guilford Courthouse. The Hessians and the Black Watch have recovered. Tarleton, damn him, has managed to keep his dragoons intact. Cornwallis will win this battle, but I think it will break his army to pieces." He took her hand. "You will be quite safe, Mary. You have Greene's paper?"

"Yes, I have it." She hesitated a moment, then said, "Have you seen Adam Rutledge?"

Lawson shook his head. "Not since noon. He was in command of the right wing across the field from my men. He is probably throwing his men in to protect the ford and cover the retreat. I must go, Mary. Good-by and God bless you for a brave woman. I will never forget you."

He rode off into the night, lost in the heavy shadows. As she watched him go, she had the feeling that she would never see him again. A great weariness came over her. It had begun to rain. Night hid the dark and bloody ground. The sound of pipes came from the field—a dirge, piping a last call to dead men, a lament to brave warriors dead on foreign soil.

YORKTOWN

by HERMAN MANN

SIX YEARS HAVING ELAPSED since our revolutionary *Epoch,* four years and ten months since our ever memorable *Independence*—Columbia's Daughter treads the field of *Mars!* And though she might, like Flora, have graced the damask rose, and have continued, peradventure, in the contemplation and unmolested enjoyment of her rural and sylvan scenes; yet, for a season, she chose the sheathless cutlass, and the martial plume. She is a nymph, scarcely past her teens!—Think—females, think—but do not resolve till you shall have heard the sequel.

We have already found, that she did not engage in this perhaps unprecedented achievement, without the precaution of reflection and pathetic debates on the cause. And this renders her more excusable than many soldiers, who rush, like the horse, to the battle, before they establish their proper *ultimatum,* which is derived only from a thorough investigation of the principles of the contention. Happy for us, that a dessimination of this knowledge is oftener the effect of a confederated Republic, than of the jurisdiction of an unlimited monarch. But neither a delirium, nor love in distraction, has driven her precipitate to this direful extremity. In cool blood, yet with firm attachment, we now see blended in her, the peerlessness of enterprise, the deportment, ardor and heroism of the veteran, with the milder graces, vigor and bloom of her secreted, softer sex.

On the tenth day in the morning, at reveille-beat, the company to which she belonged, with some others, had orders to parade and march. They drew four days provision; which, with her large sack of clothes and martial apparatus, would have been a burthen too much for females, accustomed only to delicate labor. She left some of her clothes, performed the march, and use soon became a second nature.

As the infantry belonged to the rangers, a great part of their business was scouting; which they followed in places most likely for success. In this duty she continued till they arrived at Haerlim; where they continued a few days, and then proceeded in like manner to White Plains. Here they, in their turn, kept the lines, and had a number of small skirmishes; but nothing uncommon occurred in these places.

On July 3d, she experienced in a greater degree, what she had before mostly known by anticipation. Captain Webb's company being on a scout in the morning, and headed by Ensign Town, came up with a

From: *The Female Review.*

party of Dutch cavalry from Gen. Delancie's core then in Morsena. They were armed with carabines, or fusees, and broad swords. The action commenced on their side. The Americans withstood two fires before they had orders to retaliate. The ground was then warmly disputed for considerable time. At length, the infantry was obliged to give way: but they were quickly reinforced by a detachment led on by Col. Sproat, a valiant officer of the second Massachusetts regiment. They were then too much for the enemy, although a large number had landed from boats for their assistance. The ground they had gained was then measured back with precipitance, even to a considerable distance within their own lines; where the action terminated.

The Americans having retired to their encampment, our fair Soldier, with some others, came near losing her life by drinking cold water. She says, she underwent more with the fatigue and heat of the day, than by fear of being killed; although her left-hand man was shot dead the second fire, and her ears and eyes were continually tormented with the expiring agonies and horrid scenes of many others struggling in their blood. She recollects but three on her side, who were killed, John Beeby, James Battles and Noble Sperin. She escaped with two shots through her coat, and one through her cap.

Perhaps, by this time, some may be ready to tax her with extreme obduracy, and, without mercy, to announce her void of all delicacy of sentiment and feeling. And really, had this been her customary plight in her kitchen at home, she might not have passed for an agreeable companion: for she was perfectly besmeared with gunpowder. But if we reflect, that this was not the effect of indolence or sluttishness, but for ought we know, of the most endearing attachment to her country; it ought, at least, to awaken the gratitude of those, who may remain too callous to this great philanthropic passion. It behooves every one to consider, that war, though to the highest degree destructive and horrid, is effectually calculated to rouze up many tender and sympathetic passions. If the principles of humanity and benevolence are ever to be *forced* into exertion, war, which should be the last resource, must have the desired effect. And this renders it, at best, but a necessary evil; and the promoters of it are the subjects of the greatest aspersion. Let us be free from all other evils, to which dire necessity does not prompt, and we may excuse, even a *female* for taking arms in defence of all that is dear and lovely.—She, doubtless, once thought she could never look on the *battle-array*. She now says, no pen can describe her feelings experienced in the commencement of an engagement, the sole object of which is, to open the sluices of human blood. The unfeigned tear of humanity has more than once started into her eyes in the rehearsal of such a scene as I have just described.

From this time till Autumn, nothing unusual in war happened to her. Indeed, it may be said, everything she did in this situation was *singular;* much of which might afford amusement and moral inferences. But the limits prescribed to these MEMOIRS will not admit the detail of minute circumstances.

In August, the Marquis de la Fayette had been dispatched from the main army to contemplate the operations of Lord Cornwallis's army in Virginia. After a multiplicity of military manœuvres between them, his Lordship selected York-Town and Gloucester Point as the most conspicuous and advantageous posts for the seat of military operations.— York-Town lies on the river of the same name, which empties into the Chesapeake. It forms a capacious harbor, admitting ships of great burthen. Gloucester Point being on the opposite side, and projecting so far into the river, that the distance being but about a mile, they entirely command the navigation of it. Thither Cornwallis with 7000 excellent troops repaired; strongly fortified the places, and made other good arrangements.

About the last of August, Count de Grasse arrived with a powerful French fleet in the Chesapeake, and blockaded York-Town by water. Soon after, Admiral Graves with a fleet appeared off the capes of Virginia. The French immediately slipped their cables, turned out of their anchorage ground, and an action succeeded; and though both sides sustained considerable loss, it was not decisive.

The Generals, Washington and Rochambeau had previously moved their main armies to the Southward: and when they heard of the French Admiral's arrival in the Chesapeake, they made the most rapid marches till they arrived at the head of the Elk. Within an hour after their arrival, they received an express from de Grasse, with the joyful intelligence of his arrival and situation. The combined armies embarked on board the vessels which the French Admiral had previously prepared to transport them down the Chesapeake; and by the 25th of September they landed at Williamsburgh. The American and French Chief Commanders had reached Williamsburgh by excessive travelling eleven days sooner. They immediately proceeded to visit the Admiral on board the *Ville de Paris.* A council being called, and their plan of co-operation settled, they returned; and all the Americans and allied troops soon formed a junction at Williamsburgh. Fayette had previously been joined by 3000 under the Marquis de St. Simon: The whole regular force thus collected, amounted to nearly 12,000 men, exclusive of the Virginia militia, which were called to service, and commanded by governor Nelson. Preparations were then made with great dispatch for putting the army in a situation to move on to York-Town.

It is almost needless to mention the hardships, that common soldiers must have undergone in so long and rapid a march. The deficiency of clothing, particularly of shoes, but most of all, the scanty and wretched quality of provisions, augmented their sufferings. Our heroine sustained her march from some part of New-York with good heart, and without faltering, till the day on which she landed with the troops at Williamsburgh. She was then much indisposed; which was not the only time she had experienced the inconveniences of the concealment of her sex. She puked for several hours without much intermission; which she imputed chiefly to the rolling of the vessel. With the rest, she here drew good provision and spirits: and by the next day, she was revived; and the lustre and august manœuvring of the army seemed to perfect a cure beyond the reach of medicine.

On the morning of the 28th of September, after parade and review, general orders were read to the armies; wherein his Excellency, Gen. Washington, emphatically enjoined—"If the enemy should be tempted to meet the army on its march, the General particularly enjoins the troops to place their principal reliance on the *bayonet,* that they may prove the *vanity of the boast, which the British make of their peculiar prowess in deciding battles by that weapon.*" After this, the American and French Chief Commanders personally addressed their armies. Our blooming *soldier,* always attentive to understand every new manœuvre and eventful scene, happened to stand so near his Excellency Gen. Washington, that she heard distinctly what he said. He spoke with firm articulation and winning gestures: but his aspect and solemn mode of utterance affectingly bespoke the great weight, that rested on his mind. The common soldiers were before mostly ignorant of the expedition, upon which they were going. Being now informed by general orders and the affectionate addresses of their leaders, every countenance, even of many who had discovered a mutinizing spirit, wore an agreeable aspect, and a mutual harmony and reverential acquiescence in the injunctions of their commanders were reciprocated through the whole.

The Phalanx composed the advanced guards, and was mostly commanded by de la Fayette. Our heroine was one of these; and by reason of the absence of a non-commissioned officer, she was appointed to supply his place. Just before the setting of the sun, Col. Scammell, being officer of the day, brought word for the army to halt two miles from York-Town. The officers and soldiers were strictly enjoined to lie on their arms all night.

Such language (strange to say) was perfectly familiar to our fair soldier. It did not even excite in her a tremor: although it was a prelude to imminent danger. She had been used to keep her martial apparatus bright and in the best order; as they were often prematurely wanted. Anticipating no greater danger than she had often actually experienced, although she foreboded a great event, she acquiesced in the mandates of her officers with a calmness, that might have surprised an unexperienced soldier.

Next morning, after roll-call, their equipments again reviewed, they went through the quick motions of loading and firing blank cartridges by the motion of the sword. They formed in close column, displayed to the right and left, and formed again. The grand division then displayed, formed by platoon, when they were ordered to march in the best order. The next day, Col. Scammell, approaching the enemy's works, was mortally wounded and taken prisoner by a party of horse in ambuscade. York-Town was this day strongly invested by the allied armies. Their lines being formed, the French extending from the river above the town to a morass, where they were met by the Americans on the right, their hard fatigues begun. They continued more than a week laborious, sustaining a very heavy cannonade from the besieged. This business came near proving too much for a *female* in her teens. Being naturally ambitious, it was mortification too severe for her to be outdone. Many apparently able-bodied men complained, they were unfit for duty, and were relieved. Among others, she affected pleasure in giving them the mortifying consolation—that, although she believed their *fever* was settled upon them, she hoped it would prove nothing worse than the *cannon* or *gun-powder fever*.

The fifth night, she was one of a party, who was ordered to work on a battery; the completion of which had been prevented by a too intense rain of bombs. Before morning, she was almost ready to yield to the horrors of despair. Her hands were so blistered, that she could scarcely open or shut them; and it was nearly twenty-four hours since she had taken much nourishment. But she resolved to persevere as long as nature would make her efforts; which she effected almost beyond credibility.

On the ninth, the American intrenchments being completed, a severe cannonade and bombardment commenced by them on the right, and continued all night without intermission. Next morning, the French opened their redoubts and batteries on the left; and a tremendous roar of cannon and mortars continued that day without ceasing.—Our Heroine had never before seen either of the main armies together. Being thus brought into view of them, and led on to a general engagement, doubtless excited in her sensations and emotions different from what she had before experienced. And I should need the pathos of a Homer, and the polished numbers of a Hume or Pope, to do justice to her feelings, or to exceed the reality of this scenery.—The ground actually trembled for miles by the tremendous cannonade, which was incessantly maintained by both sides day and night. Notwithstanding it was not so horribly destructive as is generally the consequence of an open field action; yet, the contemplation of two immense armies, headed by the most illustrious leaders, each strenuously contending for victory, must have afforded ideas peculiarly shocking and august. The nights exhibited scenes, to the highest degree, solemn and awfully sublime. Perpetual sheets of fire and smoke belched, as from a volcano, and towered to the clouds. And whilst the eye was dazzled at this, the ear was satiated and stunned by the tremendous explosion of artillery and the screaming of their shot.

I shall here notice a heroic deed of this gallantress; which, while it deserves the applause of every patriot and veteran, must chill the blood of the tender and sensible female.

Two bastion redoubts of the enemy having advanced two hundred yards on the left, which checked the progress of the combined forces, it was proposed to reduce them by storm. To inspire emulation in the troops, the reduction of one was committed to the Americans, and the other to the French. A select corps was chosen. The command of the infantry was given to Fayette, with permission to manage as he pleased. He therefore ordered them to remember *Cherry-Valley* and *New-London Quarters,* and to retaliate accordingly, by putting them to the sword, after having carried the redoubts. Our Heroine was one of these! At dark, they marched to the assault with unloaded arms, but with fixed bayonets; and with unexampled bravery, attacking on all sides at once, after some time of violent resistance, were complete victors of the redoubts. There were two women in the one attacked by the Americans, and when our fair soldier entered, the *third* was unknown. After entering, the carnage was shocking for a few minutes. She, standing near one of the women, heard her pronounce *yankee,* which was no sooner articulated, than she saw a bayonet plunged into her breast, and the crimson, vital liquid, that gushed from the incision, prevented her further utterance! After this, they cried and begged so on their knees for quarters, that the humanity of the Americans overcame all resentment, and they spared all, who ceased to resist; for which they were afterwards applauded by their humane officers. Before they left the fort, one clapped her on the shoulder, and said—*"Friend, fear not; you are only disfigured behind."* She took no apparent notice of what he said, till an opportunity presented: when, happy for her, she found it no worse! The lapelle of her coat dangled by string; which must have been the effect of a broad sword, or of a very close shot.

Was not this enterprise, alone, in a *female,* worth the attainment of *liberty?* Yet, where is the fair one, who could again hazard it! Methinks I see the crimson cheek of the female turning pallid, her vigorous limbs relaxing and tottering in the rehearsal of this eventful scene. Yet, let no one imagine I have painted it to the life. The fact is simply narrated; and the proper coloring is left for those peculiar inmates of the female benevolent and heroic breasts.—I hasten to drop the scene.

The French commanders, whose services demand the gratitude of every American, led on their troops with a heroic bravery, scarcely to be excelled. And whilst de Grasse displayed much valor, and was doing great execution with his Armada, the Americans, headed by the ever dear and unrivalled Washington, redoubled their activity and resolution. Nothing, thus, but inevitable ruin, or an entire surrender, awaited Cornwallis: And on the 19th of October, after three weeks severe storm, an armistice having taken place for twenty-four hours, he was glad to accept the terms of capitulation.—He was not permitted to march out with colors flying—an honor that had been refused to Gen. Lincoln the preceding winter, when he, with all the American garrison, was captured in Charleston, South Carolina. Lincoln was now appointed to receive his sword and the submission of the royal army precisely in the mode his own had been conducted.

The marching out of such an immense army, as prisoners of war, must have been a scene the most solemn and important. The magnanimity which was discovered in Gen. Washington upon this occasion, was inexpressibly peculiar. Tears trickled from his eyes during the most of the scene. And a view of him in these moments must have forced a tear of reverential gratitude from the most obdurate. He thought of his COUNTRY!—Remember the PATRIOT—remember the PHILANTHROPIST!

Thus, was the grand pillar of war, at length, broken down, and an ample foundation laid for the establishment of the so much celebrated, and wished for *palladium* of peace. We certainly owe this event, at least, in a great measure, to our generous auxiliaries. Had they not lent us their powerful and timely aid, America, for any thing we can tell, might have still clanked her chain under a monarchical and despotic sway. Must not a remembrance of their LEADERS, particularly of Fayette, start the tear of gratitude, and of filial and sympathetic attachment? He generously and nobly made Columbia's Cause his own. Unhappy man! Happy perhaps he might have continued, had not his philanthropic designs been baffled in his exertions to put them in execution in his native country. Disappointed in these, his warmest wishes, behold him dragging out a more useful intended existence in a loathsome dungeon! O wretched, inhuman return for philanthropy—the best services of man!

> See vegetable nature all conspire
> To make man blest, his ultimate desire:
> Yet, mark how erring to great NATURE's plan,
> That man, made wise, should be unjust to man!

Whilst our blood can never cease to thrill with indignation for his sufferings, may our gratitude and reverence never cool towards this illustrious, but distressed, nobleman. May a reciprocity of friendship and affection conciliate and cement us more strongly with France, our once helpful and now sister republic. We solicit England to shake hands with Columbia, her natural offspring. Let the banners of war be forever furled, the sword of contention sheathed in its proper place; and may she always forget to prove inimical to her established CAUSE. May philanthropy become as extensive as the nations of the earth: Men shall then quit their fallacious pursuits, retire to their respective and proper occupations, and learn humility and propriety of conduct. Then shall mutual harmony, peace and prosperity pervade the world.

I shall leave our fair Soldier, or as she was frequently called, the *blooming boy,* in winter quarters not far from West-Point and the banks of the Hudson, or North River, in what were called the York huts. She arrived at this place in December, much debilitated and dispirited by hard marches and fatigues. She was destitute of shoes, as were most of the soldiers during the march; excepting raw hides, which they cut into straps and fastened about their feet. It was not uncommon to track them by the bleeding of their feet on the snow and ice. And it appeared, their officers fared not much better; although they used their greatest efforts to soothe, animate and encourage the soldiers, principally with the prospects of peace, and the great honor they should gain by persevering to the end.

Just before their arrival, one of her company having been severely chastised for stealing poultry, importuned her to desert with him and two others. But she not only disdainfully refused, but used all the eloquence, of which she was mistress, to dissuade them from so presumptive an attempt. Having hazarded one desperate presumption herself, she chose to take her lot in the present and future ills; though, peradventure, her sex might in some measure, have justified her breach of contract. The arguments she enforced were—that, it would not only be an evidence of disloyalty to their country, a token of cowardice, a breach of civil obligation, but the greatest jeopardy of their lives. As female eloquence is generally irresistible, they here yielded to its energy: although they were insensible, that it was articulated through *female* organs.

Having repaired the huts, in which business she froze her feet to that degree, that she lost all her toe-nails, the soldiers were culled, in order that all who had not had the small pox might be inoculated. The soldiers, who were to be inoculated, paraded; when our Heroine, for the first time, shewed an aversion to it. Determined to hazard taking this malignant distemper unaware, she would even have falsified the truth of her having had it, sooner than have gone to the hospital; where the pride and glory of her sex, the source of the *blooming boy,* might have been disclosed.

She did duty, sometimes as a common soldier, and sometimes as a sergeant; which was mostly on the lines, patrolling, collecting fuel, etc. As the winter was very intense, the snow the most of the time deep, I shall leave it for the considerate to imagine the unusual hardships of a female in this situation. She went cheerful to her tasks, and was never found loitering when sent on duty or enterprise.

THE WAR OF 1812
1812-1814

THE WAR OF 1812
1812-1814

Democracies are traditionally reluctant about going to war—even in order to protect their possessions against aggression. It is perhaps unkind to point out that Thomas Jefferson, who believed so profoundly in democracy, was a prime offender in the neglect of our military establishment. That excellent beginning which had been made in instituting the Continental Army never developed further. The army was suffered to lapse and decay, and what remained of it found itself top-heavy with incompetents. The high command, at the outset of our second war with England, was in the control of superannuated Revolutionary War veterans, brandy swilling toss-pots, egocentrics in glittering uniforms, and a horde of common grafters.

More by good luck than by good management the lean-jawed frontiersman and the city-bred, holiday soldier muddled through. But at terrible cost. Americans can find little satisfaction in the horrible massacre at Fort Mims or the shameful surrender of Detroit by regular army officers, brave, but pompous and hopelessly out-of-date. The American Army's ignominious defeat at Bladensburg is sad reading, but an eloquent testimonial to the fact that lack of discipline cannot be replaced by enthusiastic élan.

Ironically enough, it was not until after the Peace of Ghent that Andrew Jackson led his motley regiments to a rousing series of victories culminating before New Orleans. The destruction of Pakenham's Peninsular veterans is a bright strand in a sombre pattern, but historians of the Army of the United States can take small satisfaction from the land exploits of the War of 1812. Fortunately for us, Great Britain was weary of war.

MASSACRE AT FORT MIMS

by JAMES STREET

THOMAS HAD FORMED THE HABIT of calling his bone-handled pistols "Clotho" and "Atropos," two of the goddesses of fate who drew out the threads of men's lives. He slept with his pistols beside his bed in his tiny, stuffy room at Fort Mims.

Frequently, during the hot nights, he woke up, always feeling first for his weapons, for he feared that the day of reckoning was coming at the fort. And he had no faith in Major Dan'l Beasley. . . .

Major Beasley was drunk again today, even a bit drunker than usual. His teeth felt like they were wearing sweaters and his temper was much sharper than his wits. He was hot, too. Hot and sweaty and dusty. The chair on which he sat in his little headquarters at Fort Mims was wet with the sweat that oozed from his flesh. It was a horsehide chair. No wonder it was hot. Horsehide was always hot. Even these damned addle-pated, mule-headed, dirty-nosed folks in the Tensaw district should have known that horsehide was hot. A horsehide chair was all right in the winter time but was no good in the summer time. A man sweated right through his breeches and on to the hide. And when the hide got wet it stank.

The major drank his grog and then stretched out his arms on the table so his aide would know that he wanted another drink. The table was wet where his arm touched it. Damme, this was a fine command for a first-class soldier, sweating his life away, nursing children, nursing sick cows.

He wondered how Sam Dabney's wife was doing. Perhaps he had better go see about her. Sam Dabney was a big man in the territory. He could repay favors. Dabney would be grateful to him if he saw to all of Mrs. Dabney's needs. Perhaps Dabney could get him a command in Jackson's army, or in New Orleans. New Orleans—that was a place for a soldier. There was shade in New Orleans—nice, cool shade—and women to sit in the shade with a man.

It made him ill to look at Mrs. Dabney. He had seen her the night before. She wasn't a fitting sight. And that damned Thomas seemed to resent his presence. The Negro resented him, too. Of course he had been a little drunk when he called, but Donna Dabney had seen drunk men before.

He had gone over to tell her about the excitement of the day. Two Creek warriors had sent word to relatives within the fort that an attack was imminent. The Creeks had walked boldly up to Beasley and had warned him. The major had laughed. A negro slave belonging to John Randon had reported that he had seen twenty Red Sticks in the brush. Beasley had had him tied up and flogged for alarming the garrison. John Fletcher's slave made the same report and Beasley would have flogged him but Fletcher objected. The major had ordered Fletcher and his family to leave the fort. Mrs. Dabney had listened to his story without replying. Thomas had scowled at him. The little lawyer had walked with him back to headquarters and had requested that he bring no more alarming reports to Donna. He had said that she couldn't live more than two or three days and that she was entitled to a peaceful deathbed.

Beasley drank his grog at one gulp and ran his tongue around his parched lips. It was hard on Dabney having his wife down here while he was up there at Madison. Beasley wished he were at Madison. Maybe it was cooler there and he had heard that it was much cleaner. There was a stench at Mims' that even liquor could not hide. Some of the settlers went outside the fort to attend to their needs, but others just squatted on the ground. The cattle! Beasley did nothing about it, however. He ordered the gate left open and if the settlers had any modesty they could go through it and find privacy in the woods. Thomas had criticized him for leaving the gate open—but, what the hell!—he couldn't be ordering his guard to open the gate every time a settler wanted to get outside to get water or to get rid of it.

The well within the fort wasn't large enough for the people's needs and it was easier to let them go out to the lake or river than to dig new wells. The Indians were not going to attack. They might strike at Dabney at Madison, but they would never bother him. Hell, Sam Mims was an Indian. He had a hundred half-breed women in the fort. Some of them were cousins of the warriors in Red Eagle's army. Red Eagle wouldn't fight. After all, Red Eagle had only one drop of Indian blood in his veins. He wouldn't dare attack Dan Beasley, who was half Creek. The Red

Sticks would rebel rather than fight against their own kith for a leader who was almost white.

Beasley saw Jasper come out of the big house and walk through the gate, heading toward the lake for cool water. He saw the slave return, walking rapidly, and watched him into the big house. A few minutes later Thomas and Jasper presented themselves and the lawyer said, "Major, Jasper here was just down to the lake. He saw some Indians."

"He's crazy with the heat," sneered Beasley.

"It seems to me," bridled Thomas, "that we should at least shut the gate."

The major laughed as though Thomas had told a very funny joke. "I started to shut it this morning but sand has washed against it and now it's propped open. I'll get some men to dig the sand away when the sun goes down and it gets cool." He glanced at Jasper. "Where do you think you saw those red 'uns?"

"Jasper saw them hiding in the gulley."

"You're lying. I whipped a slave yesterday for lying. You wouldn't know a Creek Red Stick if you saw one."

"Jasper knows Indians," the slave answered politely.

Major Beasley struggled to his feet, his face red with rage. "He's impudent! I have a cure for impudent slaves. Tie him up, men!"

Thomas stepped quickly to the door. He reached behind him and parted his coat tails and pulled out Clotho and Atropos. "The first man who touches that Negro will get a ball in his belly."

Beasley's mouth flew open and the soldiers stepped back. They were afraid of Thomas. They were afraid of him without guns, but when the little lawyer held pistols in his hands they were terrified.

Struggling to maintain his poise, Beasley thundered, "This is insubordination. I can have you court-martialed."

Thomas did not lower his pistols. "You know even less about law, Beasley, than you know about defending women and children. This is mutiny. I'm guilty as hell. You have the right to court-martial me this minute and then line me up against the wall and shoot me. I'm going back to the big house. If you want me, come after me. Jasper and I are going to walk across the yard with our backs to you. If you decide to shoot me, for God's sake shoot me in the back of the head. And then go look up a preacher and get right with God. Sam Dabney might hear what you've done and he'd twist your head off. So if you want to kill me, be damned sure you're ready to die yourself. Good day, gentlemen. Come on, Jasper."

Thomas put his pistols back, turned around and walked away from the men. The soldiers looked at one another and then at their commander, but Beasley glanced away.

The major was playing cards when Jim Cornells returned from a scouting expedition up the river. He halted at the gate and shouted to the major, "Better get ready. The red 'uns are coming."

Beasley struggled to his feet and went to the look-out.

"Jim," he said, "are you loony, too? Good old Jim. Are you drunk?"

The scout did not laugh. "Pull yourself together, Beasley. Hell's a-coming."

"You just saw some red cattle," Beasley mocked, "and thought they were Indians."

"Those cattle are going to give you a hell of a kick before night."

Beasley ordered the scout's arrest. "I'll have you flogged," he thundered.

The soldiers around the gate agreed with the major. Cornells covered them with his rifle. "You're all drunk! You drunken bunch of sons of bitches! I'll stay here and fight if you want me to, but if you don't want me, I'm getting out of here."

The soldiers jeered him away.

Red Eagle stood in the ravine and watched a courier ride out of the fort. Peter McQueen watched him and so did Josiah Francis, a minor prophet.

Peter McQueen grinned. "The time has come."

"Nay," cautioned Red Eagle. "Let us wait until the cool of the evening." He watched the fort hoping to see the women and children march out. He had delayed the attack for days. He had sent warnings to the fort. His one thousand Red Sticks were mad for blood.

The drums rolled in Fort Mims, calling the people to dinner. It was exactly high noon. Josiah Francis crawled to the ledge of the ravine and faced the warriors. "Strike. Strike for The Open Door." The redskin force surged forward, taking Red Eagle with it. The braves were within thirty yards of the fort before a look-out saw them.

"Injuns!" the look-out screamed and fired into the ranks.

Beasley overturned his black coffee when he jumped to his feet and ran toward the gate. "Close the gate! Sound the alarm! Man the block-houses!" He stumbled over his own feet as he ran. But he ran toward the enemy. Let that be said for Major Dan Beasley. He didn't even have a gun. He had only a sword, a sword that had been given him by the Territory of Mississippi. He didn't withdraw the sword. Dan Beasley was a good man with the rifle. He was a heller with a dirk, and a first-class fighting man with a tomahawk. But a sword and a sash! God's jaw bone! He never thought of his sword. He ran to the gate and tried to close it. He was alone there. Women and children were pouring out of the houses, shrieking and getting in one another's way. Drums rolled and the soldiers tried to assemble. The look-outs had to prime their guns.

Beasley put his great shoulders to the gate and shoved it, but it wouldn't budge. Sand was piled more than a foot around its base. He had his shoulder against the gate when a Red Stick cut him down, burying his tomahawk in his head. Fifty bullets ripped into his body. An Indian scalped him quickly, raised the bloody trophy and screamed his war-cry. A prophet, dressed entirely in feathers, rushed up and snatched the scalp away. Dixon Bailey hurried to the gate, shoved his pistol into the prophet's belly and blew him into the arms of Aba Inki. Bailey fell, his body slashed with knives.

Thomas ran out of the big house, his guns blazing. Jasper was right behind him, loading while Thomas fired. A handful of soldiers opened fire and the Indians fell back. Thomas kept advancing to the gate, cursing and shooting. He walked with a waddle, his little pot-belly shaking from side to side and his bald spot gleaming in the sun. The sun burned his tender skin and that irritated him. He had forgotten his hat. He hated to have the sun beam on his head. He hated sweat and dirt and blood. Hosey Thomas liked cool shade and good rum and good comrades. He loved a pistol and was the kind of man to handle one. He was awkward with a rifle but a pistol was small and pudgy and was a part of him. He blew down the barrel each time he finished shooting and then calmly handed the empty pistol back to Jasper and accepted a primed one.

The Indians retreated about fifty yards and went into council. The Americans scattered them with a withering but disorganized fire. The Red Sticks ran back to the woods and reassembled. Thomas stood by the gate, covering it to give the soldiers time to rally. He could see Red Eagle standing in the center of the Indians, gesticulating as he talked.

"I won't do it," the Eagle was shouting. "I'll not kill women and children. That is not war. Heed Tecumseh. One of our prophets was killed. He died as any mortal man. You have been told by false leaders that the white man's bullets can't kill any of our prophets. Maybe Aba Inki is displeased with us."

The death of the prophet who fell under the pistol of Dixon Bailey was responsible for the Red Sticks' hesitation. They could have carried the fort easily, but a prophet had fallen and they had gone into council to discuss it. It might be an ill omen.

Seekaboo, fearing that Red Eagle would persuade the Indians to retire, sprang to his feet and yelled to the warriors. "The prophet who died wasn't a true prophet. I'm a true prophet. The bullets did not touch me."

"You were safe behind the bodies of the men," Red Eagle said. "Do as you will, but the Red Eagle will not lead you into that fort." He turned and walked away, praying that his men would follow him—but he walked alone. A few miles from the fort he met his half brother, David Tate, and told him what had happened.

"They'll attack again," Tate predicted. "And the white men will blame you. Because you are the accepted leader of the Creeks and the spokesman of the nation, you'll be blamed. Because you are mostly white, the white men will call you a renegade, a butcher, a savage."

"Before man, I'll take the blame," said Red Eagle sadly. "But before God, I'm innocent."

Back at the fort the soldiers milled around the yard and did not man their posts. They thought they had driven the Indians away. Thomas implored them, threatened them. The women and children gathered around the soldiers and praised them as heroes. They had defeated the Creeks with only a few shots.

While the Indians hesitated, Seekaboo, Peter McQueen and two Negroes slipped around to the boatyard. They hid there, tied rags to their arrows, set fire to the rags and shot the blazing arrows at the Mims' smoke-house. A tiny flame appeared and McQueen ran back to his men calling, "Follow me! The fort's on fire! The great prophet will bless you."

The Red Sticks surged forward again in a long column that flanked the fort. Thomas measured their line with his eye. He estimated their number at eight hundred. He fired both his guns and fell back. Old Clotho was hot and smoking. He loaded and fired again, cocking his left eye as he fired. "Belch, madam!" he muttered, and held Atropos up and blew into the barrel. "Spit, you old hags! This day you and I are going to get a bellyful of killing Indians. *Advokaten und Soldaten sind des Teufels Spielkameraden!* . . . Lawyers and soldiers are the devil's playmates!" Thomas smiled to himself as he repeated it. He wished he could sing. He picked off two more Indians and then tried to hum, "Over the Hills and Far Away." He laughed at his own efforts. He remembered the motto of his family and quoted it reverently. *"Dare fatis vela*—Sail where fate directs." Hosea Cincinnatus Thomas laughed again. At Harvard, his Latin and Greek had been the pride of his instructors. Now he gladly would trade all of his knowledge for just one cannon. Or for Sam Dabney.

The soldiers fired one volley as the Indians swarmed through the gate and over the walls, cutting down the few defenders who guarded the walls. They cleared the look-outs. The Mississippians were herded like cattle in the yard, and the Creeks butchered them as cattle are butchered. They rounded up their prey. Some of the Americans thought the Creeks were going to take them prisoners.

Seekaboo ran through the Indians, snatched a child from among the prisoners and severed its head with his scalping knife. The white people froze in horror. The prophet held the child's head by its hair, brandished his knife and shouted, "Kill!" He snatched for another child but before he could wield his knife Thomas shot the child through the head. Thomas couldn't get a bead on Seekaboo.

The Red Sticks hesitated for a minute. There were a few wild shots from the defenders and then the massacre began. . . .

The Creeks ripped and tore at the whites, clawing open their throats, hacking them. They smeared their own bodies with blood. The sun went behind a cloud as though to blot out the scene of horror.

The whites fought as best they could. Husbands ran to their wives and children, and stood before them, shooting down the Red Sticks until they themselves were overwhelmed. Many men shot their own families. One man cut his baby's throat. His wife went stark mad at the sight and he killed her, hurled his knife into the charging Creeks and died with twenty wounds in his body.

Thomas retreated to the big house, loaded a pistol carefully—it was not one of his two favorites—and handed it to Jasper. He put his hand on the Negro's shoulder. "Go to your mistress. She's already unconscious. The red 'uns mustn't take her. If they get to her room and she's still alive, shoot her."

Thomas was glad he was on the porch of the big house. It was cooler there and his vision was better. He watched the Indians dash around the yard chasing the children. It reminded him of a game he had often played with his kinsman, little Sam Houston. He used to chase Sam and tag him and then Sam would chase him. By God, Sam must be quite a man by now! Thomas picked the Indians off as they ran, shooting for their bellies. It was like shooting rabbits and deer. He always aimed just a fraction in front of his man. Damme! He didn't shoot the man; the man ran into the bullet. The Indians were killing themselves. Thomas removed his long black coat, folded it and laid it on the porch. Then he wiped his face with his big handkerchief and returned his handkerchief to his pocket. He talked to his guns as he killed—"Oh, you handmaidens of hell. Smoke, damn you! Pour out your spleen! *You* are the bloody sluts who make all men equal." He recited snatches of poetry to himself, verse after verse of Homer.

About fifty soldiers formed a band and rushed the Creeks. The Indians hacked them to bits. There were not many cries, only an occasional war-whoop, or a scream from a mother as she saw her children die. A few of the children shrieked, but most of them just whimpered. They didn't whimper for mercy, but for their mothers. If their mothers were with them the Indians could not bother them. Their mothers would protect them. Their mothers had always protected them against goblins and sickness.

Shellie MacLeod stood by a window in the big house and watched the carnage. When Jasper entered the house and left Thomas alone, she calmly went to the front porch and took up the task of loading the pistols. She saw many Indians whom she knew. There was Sanota, a handsome brave who used to cut willow whistles for her. His parents had been killed by the whites and he had been adopted by Mrs. Vicey McGirth. Merciful God! Shellie thought, Mrs. McGirth was in the fort.

Thomas looked at the child and smiled as she handed him his pistol. He started to speak but changed his mind, leaned against the door to steady his aim and shot Indians until he retched at the sight of blood.

Flames from the smoke-house spread and the Red Sticks lighted other torches and kindled other fires. About sixty persons took refuge in the loom-house. The Creeks set it on fire and as the Mississippians ran out, the Indians grabbed them, slit their throats and ripped off their scalps.

A score gathered in the Steadham house near the big house, but the Indians battered the door down and killed them. Others gathered in the Randon house and were roasted alive. There were few shots. The soldiers were hopelessly scattered and fired occasionally. Most of them, however, used their guns as clubs. But the Creeks swarmed over their own dead, ripping and tearing the flesh of their comrades to get over them and reach the whites. A few women picked up guns and fired. Some used tomahawks and others used knives, slashing awkwardly as though they were cutting food. The children fought too, biting and kicking and clawing. Thomas kept blazing away, but his shots scarcely could be heard above the crackling roar of the flames that swept through the tents of the Volunteers and ate toward the big house.

The Indians used their knives and tomahawks. It was easy to kill with a tomahawk. The Creeks wrestled their victims to the ground, held them with one knee and shattered their skulls with one blow. Then they cut gashes in the scalps, inserted their fingers and ripped the scalps off.

A mile away at Pierce's Mill, Lieutenant Montgomery and a small company saw the smoke rising from the fort and heard the tumult. Perhaps the Creeks would strike there next. Lieutenant Montgomery assembled his men. Eagerly the Mississippi Volunteers fell into line. The lieutenant was going to take them over to Mims'. There was going to be a fight, boys! The lieutenant was going to lead them. Maybe they would die, too, but they would take some red hides with them. "Forward march!" the lieutenant commanded and marched his men away toward the river, abandoning his post. They marched in the opposite direction from Mims'. The lieutenant did not give them a chance to collect red hides, but he saved their own and his. He was a very cautious lieutenant.

Shellie saw Mrs. McGirth run from the kitchen, a log structure back of the big house. She was shouting in Creek. Sanota heard her and ran to her. He put his arm around her and led her and her children to safety. "I knew you were here," he said. "That is why I came. I came to save you, to repay a debt."

"Don't go back there!" Mrs. McGirth pleaded.

"I am a Creek Red Stick," the boy said. "I have done my duty to you and now I will avenge the death of my people."

Hester, a lithe slave wench, dashed from the kitchen and made a break for the gate. A Creek shot her in the side and leaped at her, his tomahawk raised. Thomas shot him in the belly with two slugs. The Red Stick dropped his tomahawk and ran around in circles for a few seconds, holding his entrails in his hands. Hester clasped her hand over her wound and kept running. She reached the Alabama River and found a big barge. She climbed aboard, poled the barge into the river and, while blood gushed from her side, she piloted the clumsy craft across the stream, a feat that would have given a strong man cause to boast. Once on the other side, the Negress ran through the woods toward Fort Easely to give the alarm to General Claiborne.

Peggy Bailey snatched a butcher knife from the table in the kitchen and ran across the yard, waving the blade and screaming. She cut down a warrior who sought to stop her and outran two others who gave chase. Reaching the big river, she turned and hurled her knife at her pursuers, then dived into the stream and swam across.

Two Spanish soldiers, deserters from Pensacola, threw down their guns and knelt by the well, imploring mercy from God and from the Indians. A big Red Stick put his arm under their chins, snapped their necks and tore off their scalps. A boy child ran by. An Indian reached out, grabbed him by the leg and battered his brains out against the well. He wiped the blood and brains off his hand when he completed the scalping and looked up. Thomas shot him through the neck.

Jasper came from Donna's room to see how the fight was going and Thomas spoke over his shoulder to the Negro. "Cut a hole in the north wall and let Shellie out. Maybe she can get to Madison. Maybe we can hold this house unless the fire gets us."

Jasper did as he was told and Shellie slipped through the opening, flattened herself against the wall and looked around. Then she dived for a stump and began working her way toward the river. Once in the water, she swam rapidly to the other side.

The Creeks stormed the Dyer cabin and then turned to the big house. There were eight men there, fourteen women and two children. The Americans beat back the first assault and the Creeks retired to the gate and waited. They could afford to wait. The flames were leaping from the kitchen and were licking toward the big house.

Inside her room, Donna coughed fitfully and Jasper closed the windows and door to keep out the smoke. He wondered if she were unconscious, if she could feel pain. Blood formed on her lips when she coughed and a look of agony spread over her face. Jasper turned his face away. He couldn't look at her. But maybe she would want to speak. He must lean over her and watch her, so if she spoke he could hear her. Massa Sam might ask him about that. The smoke became so thick in the room that even he coughed. He prayed that the Lord would take her before the Indians attacked again.

"Lord," he begged, "take her."

It was right that he should pray to the Lord. She believed in the Lord and so did Massa Sam. He was a good Lord and a stout Lord. Then why didn't He take her? Maybe He was a stubborn Lord, or maybe He wasn't any Lord at all, but just another weak tobie. Jasper would take no chances. He prayed to Sam's Lord, but held his own tobie in his hand as he prayed. If Sam's Lord wouldn't hear him, the Big Tobie of the Congo would.

He saw the convulsion pass over Donna and he put the lobe of his ear near her mouth. Her breath was moist. He could feel her breath.

Back near the gate, the Indians amused themselves by cleaning the scalps they had taken. They milled around the yard, seeking wounded, and when they found a wounded person they clubbed him. Seekaboo watched the flames leap from the kitchen to the big house, and then commanded his warriors to advance. Thomas and the other men fired from the windows until the flames ate into the parlor where they had barricaded themselves. Thomas looked down his pistol barrel and blew into it and said calmly, "It's no use. Run!"

The Mississippians dashed out of the house and scattered. Mrs. Mims and three of her sons, David, Alexander and Joseph, got away. Sam Smith got away, too. The Indians took Mrs. Susan Hatterway and Elizabeth Randon as prisoners.

Thomas backed against the door that led to Donna's room and was crouching there when the Indians leaped into the parlor. He discharged both his pistols, then gripped their barrels and used them as clubs. A tomahawk crunched to the base of his skull, and Hosea Cincinnatus Thomas, Harvard *magna cum laude,* pitched on his face. The Creeks riddled his body with bullets and hacked it with knives. Seekaboo took his scalp, mumbling disapproval of the bald spot. The prophet took Clotho, too. Peter McQueen took Atropos.

Jasper heard the Indians try the door. Maybe they wouldn't know that Donna and he were in there. He breathed lightly, scarcely drawing in his breath and exhaling it quickly. The smoke hurt his lungs. The smoke was pouring in. It smelled like pine pitch and was black. The smoke also brought an odor of grease—burnt flesh!

The slave stood by Donna's bed and looked at her. She could not live more than a few hours. His first impulse was to lift her up and jump through the window and run for the gate. He knew if they were captured, they both would be scalped. Massa Sam would never forgive him if he allowed her to be scalped. However, there always was a chance that he might get away. He stooped over to lift her and a spasm of coughing passed through her body. The Indians lunged against the door, shrieking for one more scalp.

Jasper clearly heard an Indian shout, "Sam Dabney's wife is in there. Her scalp's worth almost as much as his."

Jasper felt his way to the mantel and ran his hand along it until he found the conch shell. He put it into his jacket. He pushed it around to his back so it would not press against him when he lifted her. Then he reached for the pistol Thomas had given him, watched a convulsion shake Donna for a second, pressed the pistol to her side, covered it with a pillow to muffle the sound, and jerked the trigger. He threw the pistol under the bed and lifted Donna, covering the wound with his right arm. He held her mouth close to his ear and could not feel her breath. He was standing there in the smoke when the Creeks broke in.

"There she is!" cried one of the Indians.

"She's dead," said Jasper calmly.

"We'll see," said the Indian. "It may be a trick."

"She's dead," Jasper repeated. "Massa Sam Dabney's wife died of the lung fever. Look at her mouth. See the blood there. She got to coughing when the smoke came in and then she died. Jasper's going to take her away. Let me through, Red Sticks."

The Creeks stepped back and bowed their heads. They would not touch a body that had died of the lung fever. They were rather weary of blood, anyway. Here in the presence of one that Aba Inki had taken they felt ashamed, and they were awed. There was nothing awesome about the bodies they had hacked and scalped. A man can understand his own work. A man can understand death when he causes it, but when Aba Inki kills, death becomes a mystery.

The slave walked out of the burning house and across the yard, stepping over some bodies, stumbling over others. He walked through the gate without seeing the body of Dan Beasley. Down to the river he went, and laid Donna on the bank. He went to the boatyard and collected lumber, nails and an ax and took them to the river. He found a canoe and put Donna and the supplies aboard and paddled across the Alabama.

Seekaboo and Peter McQueen ordered the Creeks to collect their dead, about one hundred and ten of them. Fifty more were dying of wounds. It was five o'clock when the Indians marched away and left Mims' in flames. The flames leveled the buildings and danced over the bodies of several hundred American dead. The Creeks did not count the persons they had slain. History would never know the toll. Some of the survivors said that about fifteen white persons got away. Others said that at least thirty-five survived. Some insisted that the Indians took a few whites and about three-score Negroes as slaves. But there was no record. The survivors scattered. The bodies could not be counted, for as soon as the Indians left, great packs of wild dogs and a few wolves raided the fort and dragged some bodies away and fought over them.

Twelve miles from Mims' the Red Eagle sat under a tree and planned

his next move. The whites would really fight now. They would pour
into the Creek country. Sam Dabney would come, Big Sam whose rifle
roared like thunder and whose arms struck like the lightning. Andy
Jackson might come, Old Jacksa Chula Harjo, Old Mad Jackson, as the
Indians called him. The Red Eagle was ashamed of what his people had
done. Ay, they would call him a renegade, the Red Eagle whose blood
was purer than almost any man between the Ohio and the Gulf. In his
veins was the blood of old Lachlan McGillivray, the wealthy Scotchman
who made his fortune in the new land and returned to Scotland to die
in peace, leaving behind his son, Alexander. The Red Eagle was Alexander McGillivray's nephew. He had good French and good Scotch
and good Spanish blood in him, and his only Creek blood was a small
strain of the godlike Clan of the Wind. Ay, the whites would put a
price on his head and hunt him down. But he would fight back. He
would raise a good army and train it. He would take British gold and
buy supplies. In his heart he knew what his Indian rabble had done
at Mims', but he would accept responsibility for its behavior. He was
the Red Eagle, the leader, and a brave leader always accepts responsibility
for the conduct of his men. He got slowly to his feet and walked away,
thinking of many things and hoping that Sam Dabney's wife had died
before the Creeks reached her.

Jasper finished the coffin by the light of the moon and put Donna
into it. Massa Sam would never know how she had died. He would
tell the Massa that she hadn't suffered, that she had just punied a bit
and then died.

He heard men digging across the river where the fort had been. He
could see the finger of smoke spiraling up. He thought he heard voices
several times. The sound of his ax, as he cut two strong saplings, startled
him. He lay the saplings upon the ground, braced them, and tied the
coffin across them. He wished he had a wagon, a light Jersey wagon.
It hurt him to think that Donna's body would bounce in the box as
the saplings were dragged over the rough road and across the wilderness where there was no road at all. He got in his canoe and crossed
the river and went to Pierce's Mill where he thought he could steal a
horse from the garrison. The mill was deserted. Jasper cut back near
the boatyard and found the horses tied there. He selected the strongest
and led him away. Swimming the horse across the river, he backed him
between the saplings. He lashed the saplings to the saddle and picked up
the ax and stuck it in his belt. He felt in his jacket to make sure the

conch shell was safe. He would give it to Sam and would tell him, "She asked me to fetch it to you. That's all she said when she was dying." It would be a good lie. His Big Tobie would approve of such a good lie. Even Massa Sam's Lord would sanction such a lie.

Jasper took the horse's reins and they moved north toward Locha Poka, the horse dragging the saplings upon which rested the coffin. He would bury her under the Big Tree beside her baby. No one would ever see the body and no one would ever know that he had killed his mistress. Massa Sam wouldn't be at Locha Poka. He would be off fighting the red 'uns. If any of the slaves or Choctaws at Locha Poka demanded to see the body he would tell them that the lung fever was inside the coffin and that if he opened it, the fever would climb out and get them. No, nobody would see the body. Her body might be dust before they reached Locha Poka. Massa Sam didn't like dust. He was a funny man. Jasper wondered if Sam would get another woman. Would she be good to Jasper?

He would get the old spade that Massa Sam had fetched from Georgia and dig Mis' Donna's grave. He would put out a few flowers and have the grave ready for Massa Sam's return from killing red 'uns. He would get a stone to put there. That would please Massa Sam.

BLADENSBURG

by JOHN JENNINGS

IF CAPTAIN CREED MEANT to discipline Peter for his mistake he was not given the opportunity, for on the following day Lieutenant-Colonel Laval arrived, with the rest of the squadron from Carlyle. Also arrived, in the afternoon, a troop of Maryland Dragoons. Everyone was far too busy to think of past errors.

On the twenty-first came word that Commodore Barney had blown up his flotilla and was retreating overland toward Upper Marlborough with his sailors and marines and such artillery as he had been able to

From: *Call the New World.* Copyright 1941 by the author. The Macmillan Company.

rescue, hard pressed by a large force of the enemy. All the mounted troops in Marlborough were despatched to cover the sailors' retreat, and all supplies were sent under convoy of a regiment of militia into Washington itself. Peter, before departing with his troop, made certain that Sam accompanied the train.

That day proved one of anticipation and ultimate disappointment. Barney retreated rapidly, the enemy following close behind with an overwhelming column. Colonel Laval rode southwest upon the La Plata road, to guard against any diversion by the enemy through Piscataway or Brandywine. Captain Creed and A Troop were assigned to the actual task of covering the sailors' march, riding the road between Barney's rear guard and the British advanced parties. To Peter it seemed that much could be done to slow the British advance. The road was narrow and frequently passed between high wooded banks. With the advantage of mobility on their side it would have been easy to deliver a series of swift attacks upon the advanced parties, which would have had the desired cumulative effect of hampering their movements and retarding their progress considerably. Captain Creed, however, was content to be more than prudent. He held his position steadily between the retreating sailors and the advancing English, and so long as the one did not attempt to overtake the other he was content to let matters rest.

They lay that night at Upper Marlborough, while the enemy camped at Nottingham, some twelve miles south. General Winder, they learned then, lay with such of the army as he had been able to gather, some two thousand five hundred men, at a place called the Woodyard, a few miles north. In the morning came orders to join the rest of the army at the Woodyard, where they lay for some time in idleness, it being still uncertain whether the enemy would move from Nottingham, in the direction of Marlborough, or west through Piscataway, toward the capital. About noon word came that the British had taken the road to Marlborough, and the order was passed for the army to move to Long Old Fields, eight miles to the west. That night the British lay at Upper Marlborough.

At dawn on the twenty-third the troops, refreshed by a night's rest, were turned out and stood to arms, in readiness to march. No orders came, however, and presently word was passed to rest. The men stacked arms, took off their coats, for the heat already was severe, and gathered in little knots to talk and pass away the time. Rumors flew thick and fast. The British, fearing a trap, had turned about and were returning to their boats— The British were moving north from Marlborough

toward Baltimore, and presently the army would move to catch them
in the rear— The British were moving westward on the capital, and the
army would meet them here in Long Old Fields, and give battle— The
President was coming out to review the troops before the battle. The men
were refreshed and rested. Courage that had oozed away in the heat
of the day before returned twofold, and they were full of fight and
fire. The morale was high, and talk turned time and again to the various
ways in which they would celebrate their victory when the enemy had
been put to rout.

Peter, looking and listening, was not so sanguine. He had seen the
enemy on the march and in action, and he reflected that they moved
with clocklike precision and maintained the strictest discipline. The
army gathered here before him, for all its color and bombast, was little
more than an armed mob. Not more than eight hundred were regulars,
and of those more than half were raw recruits. Not one in ten, of all
the army, had ever smelled powder burning, save in target practice, or
stood to face cold steel; while the men they had to stand against were
veterans of Waterloo and the Peninsular Campaigns.

About mid-morning the order was passed again for the men to
stand to arms, and for an hour they were held at attention in the blazing
sun, waiting, nobody seemed to know for what. They made a splendid
spectacle standing in long ranks; flags waving, the vari-colored uniforms
of the militia battalions and independent companies showing brightly
in contrast to one another, and the sun gleaming on their arms and
accoutrements. But after an hour they began to wilt. Skulls, slowly cooking beneath clumsy leather-topped shakos and heavy, beplumed, brass
helmets, began to feel the strain. Here and there men fainted in the
sultry heat, and were carried back among the shadow of the woods by
their comrades and laid among the cool leaves.

At last, however, the moment for which they had been waiting arrived. An open barouche, drawn by a team of prancing bays, turned from
the road and entered the field. In the back sat a tall spare man with an
aristocratic, nervous face, dressed in a black coat with a high white stock.

At the end of the field, where those who were closest had a full view
of him, a cheer went up, as the waiting men recognized the President.
As the carriage swept down the field the cheer grew and swelled to a
thunderous roar. Mr. Madison raised his hat and acknowledged the ova-
tion gravely. Beside him, resplendent in a uniform highly decked with
gold braid, smugly smiling as though he believed the cheers were as
much for him as for the President, sat the man largely responsible for

the situation—General Jack Armstrong, the Secretary of War. Beside the carriage, mounted on his magnificent gray, rode the same serious, pinch-faced Colonel Monroe, whom Peter had encountered at Aquasco. Not until that moment did Peter realize, with a start of surprise, that he had been face to face with the Secretary of State.

General Winder and his staff rode out to meet the President's carriage. Words of greeting were exchanged, and there were handshakes all around, after which staff and carriage took up a position at the side of the field. The men stiffened. Orders crackled along the line. A band struck up a brazen march, and the long lines moved slowly out to pass, a trifle raggedly but none the less spiritedly, in review, sending a cloud of dust drifting across the reviewing party.

When the review was ended the troops were drawn up in a hollow square about the President's carriage, and he rose to address them.

"Gentlemen!" he shouted, and his voice barely carried to the outermost ranks. "The enemy—is at—our gates! Never before—has our—national life—been so seriously threatened! The fate—of our nation—in the next few days—lies—in your hands. I commend it to your keeping—knowing that—you will defend it—with your lives!"

The men cheered wildly as he sat down, tossing helmets and shakos high in the air. The bays pranced with rolling eyes. A way was opened through the close packed ranks, and the carriage rolled through and swept from the field.

It was midday when the ceremony was over, and the men broke ranks and fell upon their rations like a pack of famished wolves. They were scarcely half finished when a despatch rider on a lathered horse burst from the road at top speed and slithered to a halt beside the field table that had been set up for General Winder and the staff. A thrill of expectancy ran through the field, and spoons and knives hung in mid-air. A tense hush settled over all. Then, as though a bomb had burst in their midst, the officers grouped about the table scattered and ran in all directions. Hurried commands were shouted. Unfinished rations were gulped or dumped upon the ground and forgotten. Packs were resumed. There was an instant's wild confusion, as the men of the various commands sought out their positions. As swiftly as the confusion came order as the men fell into place. Word passed down the lines: "The British have left Marlborough, and are moving this way."

For perhaps a quarter of an hour they stood to arms, waiting once more. Then, at length, the General and his staff mounted and rode out across the field to the road to turn, not toward Marlborough, but toward

Washington. Hoarse commands rippled along the line. Two thousand rifles moved as one, slanting up across two thousand shoulders. Five hundred sabers rattled from their scabbards and flashed in the sun. The long lines moved out into column of fours, traversed the field and turned into the road behind the staff. A band began to play—"Yankee Doodle"— and a thousand voices took up the song and shouted it defiantly at the sun. Dust rose in choking clouds, but nobody noticed it. Peter, riding at the rear of the column, tied his handkerchief about his face, and settled his helmet grimly about his ears.

At four in the afternoon they were still marching, creeping along at snail's pace, with frequent halts to rest the men. Only a few were singing now, far up near the head of the column. The band was silent, only the drums tapping out the regular measured beat of the step. The dust still rolled in blinding clouds and the men marched silent, tight lipped, red eyed. In the rear Peter was beginning to have trouble with stragglers. Sergeant Dove was cursing under his breath.

At six they were still marching, even more slowly, as the men began to feel the effects of exhaustion. There was no more singing. Even the drums were silent. No one tried to keep step. The dust, which still rose in billowing masses, filled the air with tiny particles that coated the throat and the nose and the eyes and the tongue. The men muttered rebellious curses under their breath, and Peter was having to threaten stragglers with the flat of his saber. At eight, in the long shadowed twilight, they came out on Capitol Heights, in view of the city, and a thin cheer went up. At their feet the road dropped away, twisting and winding down the slope to the long bridge that crossed the Eastern Branch. And at the far end of the bridge, in the open fields to the right of the road, were visible the white tops of many tents: their camp.

On the very edge of darkness, they swung down off the hills and across the bridge. Under their dragging tread the long wooden structure groaned and trembled. As quickly as they turned in from the road they were dismissed, and Peter, among the last to come in, found that many had simply turned aside and dropped where they stood.

Lying, literally, under arms, too exhausted to eat, most of them, the defenders of Washington slept.

☆

☆   ☆

Not all the army lay in the open. The supply wagons had gone forward early that morning. Some had gone on into the city, others had taken the northern route to Bladensburg. But some had found their way to the appointed place, and about half the army enjoyed shelter. The light dragoons' equipment, having come directly up from Marlborough and being among the first to arrive, had a choice location along the river bank. Peter found himself sharing a tent with Smith again.

There was a fire burning before the tent, built of what looked suspiciously like the butts of rails torn from a neighboring fence. A kettle simmered over the flame, sending out a savory aroma, all the more pronounced because of the summer dusk and their keen appetites. Inside the tent Sam was puttering around.

"Hello, Sam!" Peter called as they approached.

Sam stuck his head out.

"Bless me, MistaPetah!" he said. "I begin to think you all ain' comin'."

"What you got in the pot, Sam?" Smith asked.

"Mist' Smith, suh," Sam told him, "that a hen-chicken."

Peter looked at him severely.

"Where'd you get that chicken?" he demanded.

The negro gulped.

"MistaPetah, suh," he said plaintively, "they was jes' a-lyin' oveh yondeh, behime de gin'erl's tent, an' Ah knowed 'at good-fer-nuttin' black niggah de gin'erl's got done stoled 'em f'um somebuddy. So Ah jes' figgers Ah'll tak' 'em an' give 'em back to dey ownah."

Smith looked down at the ground, avoiding Peter's glance. Peter felt laughter welling up inside him, but tried to look grim.

"Then how does it happen they're in the pot?" he said.

Sam gulped again.

"Well, suh, MistaPetah," he whined, "you see, it like dis. Ah take an' Ah look an' Ah look. Ah looks undeh de bridge, an' Ah looks up in de woods, an' Ah looks down by de Naby Yahd. But Ah cain' fin' nobuddy whut own 'em hen-chickens. So Ah thinks, 'ey ain' but one thing tuh do wif hen-chickens whut yo cain' fin' de owneh, an' 'at's jes' kill 'em an' pick 'em an' put they in de pot, 'caze if yo jes' leaves 'em lay dey's some rat gointer git 'em, or udder dey jes' rots away!"

"You think they'd spoil if we didn't eat 'em?" Peter asked.

The squat darky rolled his eyes.

"Lawd, yes, MistaPetah, suh!" he declared with deadly earnestness. "Shorest thing 'ey is!"

"All right, Sam," Peter grinned. "I guess we better eat 'em, then."

He started to turn away, but swung back abruptly.

"But one thing, Sam," he said sternly. "You said there was a 'hen-chicken' in the pot. And now you say it's 'hen-chickens.' How many are there in there?"

Sam looked embarrassed.

"Good lan'!" he said. "Did Ah say 'hen-chicken'? If Ah ain' de forgettinest man! MistaPetah, they's fo' hen-chickens in 'at pot."

Smith whooped with laughter, and Peter unable longer to contain himself joined in.

Their merriment was interrupted by the approach of several riders, who pulled up at the edge of the circle of firelight.

"Hello, there!" called a voice. "Is there room to bed down these men on the other side of your camp?"

Peter looking up caught a flash of red and gold in the ruddy light, and recognized Lieutenant Cargill of the Alexandria Hussars.

"There's space between us and Tilghman's," he said.

"Thanks!" said Cargill. "The old man's gone off to Woodward's to rest in comfort. God knows what's become of our wagons."

"Bed your men down over there," Peter told him, "and join us. We've room for three or four if you care to bunk in here."

"Thanks," was the answer. "We'll do that. Back in a minute!"

He turned away and led his men off down the long row of tents to the open space that lay between the Light Dragoons and Tilghman's Maryland Cavalry. A few minutes later he returned shouldering blanket roll and saddlebags, and leading three other young men, resplendently uniformed and similarly burdened.

"This was decent of you, old chap!" he said as he swung into the firelight. "The men are all put down for the night, and I—"

He stopped speaking abruptly as Peter turned to greet him.

"Hullo!" he said. "I didn't recognize you before."

"Sorry," Peter smiled. "I thought you did. Don't feel obliged to stay if you don't want to, but the invitation still stands."

"I didn't mean that." Cargill was confused. He looked down at his uniform. "I guess it was an easy mistake to make. Anyway it's happened four times since. I just couldn't see you through the fire, and you rather took me by surprise."

He presented his companions.

"Mr. Surratt, Mr. Byrd, Lieutenant Tripp, all of Alexandria."

None could have been more than nineteen and all were obviously flattered and delighted at being invited to hob-nob with an officer of the regular army. Peter realized with a start that in their eyes he must seem a seasoned, hard-bitten old campaigner. He shook hands gravely all around and presented Smith. The latter cocked an amused eye at Peter.

"Well, gentlemen," he said, "when you're ready, our host here has a chicken dinner."

"Chicken!" exclaimed Surratt.

"He's stuffing us!" said Byrd.

"The devil he is!" said Tripp, who had looked in the pot.

Cargill dropped his blanket roll and, dipping a hand into his saddle-bags, pulled out a narrow flask.

"At least," he said, "we can provide something. Shall we drink a toast to our commander, General Winder, and damnation to the British?"

There were whoops of agreement from the other three, and Tripp promptly produced a flask of his own, in case Cargill's should prove insufficient. Cups were filled, and they drank standing with solemn ceremony. Peter, catching Smith's cocked eye across the rim of his cup, came near to choking, but controlled himself with an effort.

The supper was delicious. In addition to chicken there were corn and sweet potatoes, which Sam had neglected to mention in his account, and concerning which Peter thought it best not to interrogate him. The four young Virginians kept up a cheerful stream of conversation.

"This is the life!" exclaimed Byrd. "Good food and good friends around a campfire, and a clear sky overhead!"

"Yes, sir!" Tripp agreed. "And a good horse to ride into action!"

"I wish we'd see some action," Surratt said. "I'm getting tired of riding on patrol."

"We'll have some action before long," said Cargill. "I heard Colonel Monroe tell the Captain he thought there'd be a battle tomorrow."

"If you ask me," Surratt replied, "the British are afraid. They say they don't number more than four thousand, and we've got thirty-five hundred here and forty-five hundred more at Bladensburg. That includes cavalry and artillery which they don't have."

"I hear they have some black troops with them," Tripp said.

"The damned scoundrels!" Surratt exploded. "Father says they've been trying to stir up the niggers to rebellion down around Norfolk."

"It don't amount," said Byrd. "They've run some off from the plantations they've burned. They ran off Uncle Henry's when they burned Kinsale. But the niggers won't rise. They know what's good for 'em."

"Do you think they'll fight, sir?" Cargill asked Peter.

"The British?" Peter asked. "No doubt about it."

"Tomorrow?" Tripp and Surratt asked in unison.

Peter nodded.

"Whoo-eee!" they yelled.

"Ten to one they run at the first fire," Byrd said.

"I hope not," said Surratt. "I've got to get the plume from an officer's shako. I promised Amy."

Smith and Peter listened with amazement. They talked of war as though it were a sport, like riding to hounds, or a pretty play upon a stage. It did not seem to occur to them that men must die tomorrow. Nothing was further from their minds than that they themselves might fall with a bullet through their bowels or a bayonet in their throat. It gave Peter a cold feeling in the pit of his stomach to realize how great a part of all the army assembled before Washington that night must be having the same thoughts.

Tripp produced a handful of segars from his saddlebags and passed them around. They lighted up and lay back at their ease about the fire, while Sam cleaned up. The mild aroma of the segars reminded Peter of a day, less than a month since, though it seemed longer, on the Baltimore Pike. It made him think of Doña Carlota. For a moment he thought of riding in to the Indian Queen to see if she were still in Washington and to pay his respects if she were. But he rubbed his hand across his jaw and reflected that he was hardly presentable. In the last few days he hadn't had much opportunity to shave. He was grimy from a week in the saddle. Moreover, the hour was late, and there was undoubtedly a hard day before them. He sighed. It would have been fun though. He remembered the soft pressure of her fingers in his, as she had said good-by, and the faint scent of her as she had leaned close to him on the bench.

The approach of two men in uniform on the other side of the fire, the one tall and lean, the other short and stout, with a jolly, ruddy face, broke in upon his reflections.

"Hello, boys!" said the tall one.

Cargill sprang to his feet.

"Father!" he cried.

"Hello, Tom," said the man. "I heard you were over this way. Everything all right?"

"Everything's fine, Father. Hello, Mr. Mason! Father, I want you to meet these gentlemen. Mr. Brooke and Mr. Smith, of the Light Dragoons. My father, Major Cargill, of Minor's brigade, and Mr. Mason, of Georgetown."

Peter and Smith shook hands with the two older men.

"I'm glad to see you're in such good hands," said the Major. "You're sure you've everything you need, Tom?"

"Everything, Father, thank you," said Cargill.

"That's fine," the Major said. "Thank you, gentlemen, for taking such good care of these boys." He looked around at the four Virginians. "You lads better turn in soon."

He turned on his heel with a curt "good night" and disappeared in the darkness with the smaller man trotting along behind. Peter was amused. The younger men might play at war, but their parents meant to see they weren't uncomfortable at it!

"That's Joshua Mason," Cargill was saying. "Used to be secretary at the legation in London, before the war, and will be again, I guess, when it's all over."

"He has a daughter," said Surratt dreamily from where he lay on the other side of the fire.

"A frosty beauty!" Tripp exclaimed sleepily, "cool as a London fog, and haughty as a dowager!"

"If you fellows plan to do any fighting tomorrow," Peter said, "you'd better turn in."

"I reckon so."

They struggled stiffly to their feet, gathering up their blanket rolls, and started toward the tent, dumping them down within wherever there was room. Tripp's roll was more than twice the thickness of the others' and he seemed little inclined to open it.

"Aren't you going to use that blanket?" Surratt demanded as he spread his on the ground.

"I'm not cold," said Tripp.

"I should think you'd be afraid of foundering your horse with all that load," said Cargill.

"What've you got in there anyway?" Surrat asked.

Tripp flushed.

"Nothing!" he said elaborately.

"Let's have a look!" Byrd exclaimed.

He and Surratt pounced on Tripp, while Cargill pulled away the straps about the blanket roll, and Smith and Peter looked on. The blanket unrolled with a rush and a shower of clothing fell out. There was a dress shirt with a white ruffle and high stock, a dress coat, knee breeches, silk stockings, and dancing pumps.

The three Virginians sat up laughing. Tripp was ruffled.

"Ho—Ho! My God, what's all that for?" Cargill demanded, when he could get his breath.

Trip was sulky.

"You fellows can laugh," he said, "but when this fight is over and the British are on the run, there'll be a ball at the White House, and I'll be prepared!"

"Gosh!" said Surratt. "I wish I'd thought of that!"

"I put mine in a trunk in the wagon," Cargill said contemptuously. "What's the sense of carrying all that stuff around with you?"

"Where's the wagon now?" Tripp retorted.

Cargill's face fell.

"We'll find it right enough, when this is over," he said.

"After the ball is over," Tripp taunted.

Peter rolled himself in his blankets and buried his face in his pillow to keep from laughing aloud. The thing was fantastic, weird as a dream, and yet it was all happening!

He must have dozed then, for the next he knew he was awakened by a chorus of exclamations outside the tent flap.

"A magnificent illumination!" said Cargill's voice.

"This is really war!" he heard Tripp reply.

He opened his eyes. The tent was suffused with a ruddy glow which seemed to rise and fall and shimmer on the wall. From a distance came the dull steady roar and crackle of flames. He thrust his head out through the door. There it seemed as though the whole river were afire. Bright yellow flames showed between the rows of tents, and towering orange tongues licked at the sky.

Cargill turned toward him, his face clear in the fierce light.

"They're burning the bridge," he said.

Peter grunted.

"You fellows better turn in again," he said, "if you want to be in on things tomorrow."

They came trooping back into the tent like a pack of abashed schoolboys.

"What's it mean, sir?" Surratt asked. "Why are they burning it?"

"It means, my lad," said Peter feeling very fatherly, "that unless the enemy has his boats with him he must march around through Bladensburg to get at the city. And, mark my words, we too will march to Bladensburg at dawn."

The words proved prophetic. The bugles blasted them from their beds before the dawn was more than a misty gray dream in the east. In the grizzly light the charred pilings of the bridge looked like a row of black, hunchbacked sentinels stretching out into the river. A pall of smoky mist still hung low over the water, obscuring the far bank.

The young Virginians protested at the call to arms at such unseemly hours. Smith and Peter routed them out unmercifully.

"Roll out, roll out!" they called. "This is war, too!"

And the boys came creeping out with heavy lidded eyes, still thick with slumber; haggard and weary from lack of sleep. An hour later they were on their way northward, moving at snail's pace along the road to Bladensburg.

It was nine o'clock, and the sun had not yet gained its full strength, when they came up with the rest of the army. It lay in a strong position, across a little peninsula of rising ground, and facing directly toward the village of Bladensburg on the far side of the river. The right was covered by a deep ravine, and by thick woods that spewed up out of it. On the left was a swamp and a large scattering orchard. The center, behind a first outer fringe of willows along the river, was composed of open fields, crossed at intervals by fences of heavy rails, and climbing, gradually at first, and then more sharply to the woods which crowned the heights. The road from Marlborough, by which the enemy must approach, followed the opposite bank of the river, well up on the hillside, and dipped down into the village to join the Baltimore-Washington Pike. From that point it ran straight down the slope across a narrow bridge and a strip of swampy ground, past the row of willows, and then climbed straight up, through the center of the American position, to the woods at the crest of the hill, whence it bore away southwestward toward the city.

There was some confusion in the allocation of position to the various bodies of troops, a situation not lessened by the arrival of the army from the south. Companies and battalions marched and countermarched back and forth across the face of the hill, while batteries of artillery tried out first this position and then that. In the road at the foot of the hill a little knot of officers crowded around the commanders of the two Maryland brigades, the ranking officers present. General Smith looked hopelessly bewildered, while General Stansbury looked angry, and most of the active directing seemed to be done by Colonel Monroe and by a civilian in a pearl-gray coat, whom Cargill pointed out to Peter as a Mr. Francis Key, of Georgetown.

It was Colonel Monroe who directed the cavalry, to the extreme left, where they would be screened to some extent by the orchard and ready for a sally by the flank. Once in that position there was nothing to do but watch and wait. Captain Creed dismounted the troop and flung himself down in the shade of a spreading tree, where he was soon snoring stertorously. Sergeant Dove strolled up and down before the ranks, cursing the men in a low monotone, trying to whip up some evidence of fighting spirit. Smith and Peter sat beneath a tree and watched the movements of the hillside above.

It was an interesting sight. The bulk of the troops were militia, sullen faced, in blue coats and white cross belts. But there was a generous scattering of volunteers, splendid in gaudy and somewhat ridiculous uniforms, with heavy, be-plumed helmets and shakos. Peter noticed many haggard, weary faces, and he learned that most of Stansbury's brigade and a large part of Sterett's had been kept marching and countermarching, shifting position, most of the night through a confusion of orders.

It was half-past ten before the lines were finally drawn, and even then small bodies of men were kept shifting. In the row of willows, covering the river and the bridge, a battalion of riflemen was posted. At the head of the first gradual rise was the first line, its left on the swamp behind the cavalry, and its right resting on the ravine. Halfway up the steeper slope the second line was posted behind a fence, with the bulk of the artillery just in front. Near the top of the hill Barney's sailors, with their heavy guns, were concentrated around the road, while the third line and the reserve were sheltered in the woods. In front of the first line, posted so that they covered the bridge approach at point-blank range, were two batteries of Baltimore artillery.

It was hot, high noon before General Winder came up. He made some few changes in the dispositions of the first and second lines, which to Peter appeared to weaken rather than strengthen their position. Even as his commands were being carried out the bugles blared. A mutter of excitement passed down the lines.

"Here they come!"

The troopers, scattered about on the ground beneath the orchard trees, scurried to their feet and mounted. From atop his horse Peter could look out over the trees, dropping away before him, to Bladensburg and the slope of the hill beyond. Behind the village, past a scattering of farm buildings on the hill, where the road broke from the woods, he could see the British column emerging, a solid, compact red worm that stretched out long and ever longer, following the undulations of the roadway, moving with steady, relentless precision to the muffled tap of the drum, down toward the village. Evidently they, too, judging from the number of stragglers who dropped out and fell away to the rear, were oppressed by the heat of the day.

As they came within range, the riflemen in the willows along the river opened a scattered fire upon them, and the artillery on the hill loosed a few rounds of grape. Almost immediately they broke into open order in the fields flanking the road, while some sheltered themselves behind the farm buildings. In extended order they moved forward swiftly into the village, where they seemed to halt momentarily. Then Peter could see them advancing in short rushes down through the town, toward the lower edge, where they again formed their solid ranks and resumed their steady march down toward the bridgehead.

The rifle fire from the willows swelled as they moved onto the bridge. In the road the artillery, laid at point-blank range, belched out a withering blast of grape that tore great gaps in their line. The horses of the cavalry in the orchard danced and snorted. Peter saw the gaps fill relentlessly and the column came on. The recoil of the first discharge had disturbed the aim of the guns, and the green militiamen were too hurried to relay them carefully.

As the first British divisions gained the near bank they poured down off the road to their left, deployed and plunged with the bayonet into the willows. From the village a flight of Congreve rockets roared overhead, emitting a train of sparks and bursting with terrific detonations far up the hillside. Their only effect was to demoralize the men and frighten the horses. As the enemy plunged into the willows on the one side the riflemen scurried out on the other and ran for the shelter of the first line. Behind them the enemy's light troops charged in a ragged line. A concentrated fire from the Baltimore regiments checked them and drove them back. The first line then advanced and was in turn checked by British fire from the thicket, driven to shelter behind a fence, and for some time exchanged a hot fire with the enemy. In the road, the Baltimore artillery, seeing its position growing uncomfortably hot, limbered up and dashed to new positions in front of the second line. In the meantime the British second divisions were pouring across the bridge and deploying to their right, advancing up the hill, driving a wedge between the American left wing and the center, threatening to flank the first line.

From the orchard Peter watched the whole movement almost with detachment. As the British wedge began to lengthen, however, thrusting into the American lines, this feeling gave way to one of impatience. Now was the moment for cavalry. A charge by the mounted troops upon that thin British spearhead might hurl it back upon the bridge, giving the left wing time to come in and drive the British across. His horse, nervous in the constant crash of battle, danced over near to Captain Creed. Glancing up Peter caught the Captain's eye. The man looked unhappy.

Another flight of rockets screamed overhead, lower and more accurately directed this time, aimed evidently to demoralize the second line, about which it burst with a terrific roar. Peter's horse skittered sidewise the length of the line, away from the Captain. A rider on a lathered horse dashed up out of the welter of confusion on the right and saluted. He put his lips close to Peter's ear and shouted.

"General Stansbury's orders sir. Cavalry to advance at the charge!"

Peter nodded.

"Cavalry to advance at the charge," he repeated.

The man was gone instantly in a swirl of dust. Peter looked around. As the nearest cavalry officer to the right of the line it was natural that the rider should give him the order to relay. He wheeled and galloped toward the Captain. There was a tightening in the lines. Creed looked up as he approached. His eyes were yellow and the corners of his mouth twitched. Peter leaned over and bellowed the command to him. He looked stunned.

"At the charge!" he screamed, and then appeared to take a grip on himself. His eye swept the field before him swiftly. "Look there!" he shouted. "That battery!"

One of the batteries of Baltimore artillery was being hard pressed. Red coats mingled already with the blue of the militia in the mêlée around the guns.

"Get your platoon in there, Lieutenant," Creed shouted. "Save those guns!"

Peter needed no second invitation; he wheeled his horse and signalled his men forward at the charge. The rest of the cavalry would be close behind. Even as he was turning Captain Creed rode toward Colonel Laval to relay the order.

The fury of Peter's charge carried him straight to the heart of the mêlée about the guns. He hacked at the redcoats that appeared about him, dodging a bayonet thrust here, parrying another there, lunging at a red-clad throat in the next instant. Behind him a horse screamed as a bayonet ripped its vitals. But the platoon hammered its way through, clearing, by sheer surprise, the ground about the guns. The artillerymen, freed of the brunt of the attack, limbered up and fell back, and Peter's platoon, fighting doggedly, covered them as they went. One minute, two, three, they hammered and slashed and fought, until it came to Peter that something was wrong. Where was the cavalry that should be so close behind?

He looked about and saw where it was in one swift glance. The force of his charge had carried him through the tip of the British spearhead. Behind them the gap had closed again, and the red lines were already far up the hill, a solid column, unbreakable, between him and the left wing. And on the other side was the cavalry, drawing off!

Nor were they alone. Cut from the center by the red wedge of the British, threatened in front and on the flank, the entire left wing was following the example set by the cavalry. Even as he looked the retreat became a rout. Some of the companies held their formation, and drew from the field in order. But many had flung away their arms and were streaming off in confusion, northwestward, across the swampy ground. For an instant Peter was bewildered. Then as plainly as if he had heard the command, he knew that this was Creed's doing. The Captain must have reversed the order and relayed the command to withdraw, and with that had gone the day. It was too late to rally the left.

It was too late, too, for Peter to rejoin his command. The greatest strength of the British lay between himself and the retreating cavalry. Below, the first line which had stood so long, flanked to left and right, and in danger of encirclement, broke and fell back upon the second line. In the face of the retreat the artillery scattered along the line limbered up and dashed for the road. The second line fired one wavering volley, then broke in panic-stricken flight as a burst of rockets crashed among them. Peter, mindful of his orders, stuck doggedly to the guns. Come what may, he meant to carry out that command.

All about him now men were running, flying, flinging their muskets aside and scampering like rabbits for the shelter of the woods, while the red tide rolled up the hill behind them. Peter saw one youngster, hatless and dishevelled, the brilliant uniform of which he had yesterday been so proud, torn now and fouled with blood, running, stumbling toward the hilltop with terror in his eyes and tears streaking his boyish face.

"You didn't know war was like this!" he thought grimly.

He wondered fleetingly about his friends of the night before, Cargill and Tripp and Surratt and Byrd, and what their thoughts were now.

He escorted his guns on up the hill, covering the retreat; up past the position where Barney's sailors still held their ground gallantly around their heavy eighteen pounders. In the shelter of the woods, with the guns rolling on their way, two sweat-soaked, dust-streaked, red-faced riders barred their way.

An authoritative voice demanded: "What troops are those?"

Peter recognized General Winder.

"First platoon, A Troop, Light Dragoons, sir," he replied. "Lieutenant Brooke commanding."

"What the devil are you doing here?" Winder roared. "Where's the rest of the cavalry? Why didn't they charge when ordered? Eh? Answer me that?"

"Sir," said Peter, "I was ordered to go to the relief of the artillery, and charged believing the rest would follow. When next I looked the entire left wing was in retreat."

"Hmph! At least you follow orders," Winder snorted. "Great God! I ordered Stansbury to advance and he retires. I send him a second order to advance, and he refuses. I send him a third order and demand an explanation. He sends back word that he is responsible for the disobedience and will answer for it when required! My God!"

Stansbury! Peter thought. At least Stansbury had the guts to assume the blame for the failure of his command. He hoped when the whole dirty business came out the blame would fall where it rightly belonged.

"Well, we can do nothing more here." The General continued to think aloud. "Undoubtedly Stansbury will rally his men and fall down on the city from the north. Possibly we may yet make a stand. Bring your men, Lieutenant. I'll need you."

He whirled his horse away and set out at a gallop. Peter threw the platoon in behind and followed. Along the way they passed the bedraggled army. The artillery whirled rapidly toward the city. Here and there a company or even a battalion of infantry moved with some semblance of order, but for the most part the men stumbled on at will. Most of them did not even look up as they galloped past.

At the outskirts of the city they came upon Minor's Virginia brigade, held there in reserve and so unaware of the extent of the rout. General Winder drew up in a cloud of dust before Colonel Minor.

"Hold your position here, Colonel," he barked, "and try to rally the army behind you as they retreat through you. Prepare to make a stand unless you receive orders from me to the contrary."

He looked around at Peter.

"Here, you, Lieutenant," he commanded. "Take your men through the city. Look for General Stansbury coming down from the north. If you find him, tell him my orders are to come here and prepare to make a stand. When you've done that report to me at the Capitol Building."

Peter saluted and whirled away. He led his men at a gallop across the

city to the outskirts of Georgetown and back again. All was quiet. Here
and there a householder moved belongings out in wagons, but apparently only as a safeguard. Evidently, as yet, word of the rout at Bladensburg had not seeped into the city, for there was no sign of that panic
which was presently to come. As they clattered through the streets pass-
ersby hurled questions after him, but he paid no heed. There was no
sign of Stansbury. Nor was there any indication that he was coming this
way. Peter rode back to the Capitol and there found General Winder in
conference with Colonel Monroe and General Armstrong, the Secretary
of War.

"Well?" said Winder, as Peter appeared, "what news of Stansbury,
Lieutenant?"

"None, sir," Peter replied.

"No sign of him at all?"

"No, sir," said Peter.

The General's shoulders sagged.

"Well, that's the end," said Armstrong hopelessly.

Winder was silent.

"Well, General?" said Monroe.

"Good God, Colonel!" Winder's head snapped up. "We can't make a
stand with those men out there. More than half of them are completely
demoralized. At least half have thrown away their arms. To try to make
a stand with them would subject what is left of the army to certain
annihilation!"

"Very well," said Monroe. "Draw your men off through the city to
Tenleytown Heights. The enemy will undoubtedly stop to plunder. That
may give you an opportunity to rally there."

He spoke without hope.

"General Armstrong and I will notify the President," he added.

He turned away. Winder turned to Peter.

"Lieutenant," he said, "detach a man to Colonel Minor with orders to
fall back to Tenleytown Heights. You take the rest of your men and find
General Stansbury. He will be somewhere north of the city, between
Bladensburg and Montgomery Courthouse. My compliments to him and
tell him to rally at Tenleytown."

Peter sent Dove and a trooper with the message to Minor, while he
himself rode northwestward through the city. It was instantly apparent
that news of the rout had spread quickly into the city. Already the first
stragglers from the army were filtering in. Where all had before been
calm and quiet everything now was in an uproar of confusion. Women

tossed bedding and household goods from the windows of houses, while men below piled them into wagons. Many who could not find vehicular conveyance were carrying off their most prized possessions on their backs. Already there was a growing stream of foot traffic in the direction of Georgetown and the Potomac bridges. Near the Mall, Peter came upon the supply train from the camp by the bridge, plodding unobtrusively in the general direction of Georgetown. Driving one of the sutler's wagons, big as life, was Sam. Peter paused long enough to order him to drive through to Tenleytown and await him there.

"Yas, suh, MistaPetah!" said Sam. "Is dey comin' sho' nuff?"

"Sure enough, Sam," Peter told him.

The negro rolled his eyes until the whites showed all around and cracked his whip. Peter rode on. At the corner of Ninth and Pennsylvania Avenue, not far from the Indian Queen Tavern, someone called his name. He looked around and saw, standing on the corner, Don Ramon de Olivares. Doña Carlota was clinging to his arm, and Doña Elvira loomed sullenly in the background.

He halted his command and rode toward them.

"Señor Brooke!" Don Ramon and Carlota cried in unison, and Carlota added, "Is it true, señor, that the English are coming?"

"I am afraid it is, señorita," he replied. He looked at Don Ramon. "What are you doing here?" he demanded.

Don Ramon shrugged.

"I am looking for a way out of this accursed city," he replied, "but there seem to be no conveyances."

A sudden thought came to Peter.

"Wait!" he said.

With four men he rode back toward the Mall and overtook the supply train. Finding Sam and his wagon he cut him from the line.

"Hey!" shouted the sutler in the next wagon. "That's my rig. I jest hired it out to the army!"

Peter flung him a coin.

"Well, hire it out to me, now," he replied. "You'll find it safe at the Fountain Inn in Baltimore, if the British don't get it first."

"Now looky here, Cap'n," the man began, but Peter cut him short.

"Shut up!" he said. "Here, take this stuff in your wagon."

Ten minutes later he was back at the corner where the Olivares waited. Two troopers loaded their baggage in the back of the wagon, while Peter told Sam how to get to Baltimore by a roundabout route. There he was to take the Olivares where they wished to go, deliver team and wagon to the Fountain Inn, and wait Peter's orders at his cousin's house. Peter himself helped Doña Carlota up onto the rough seat, and was rewarded by a dazzling smile. He cut short their thanks with a curt wave of the hand.

"Sorry!" he said. "I must be off. You'll be all right now. Sam will have you in Baltimore tomorrow."

After that he rode on past the White House, where things were being loaded hastily into wagons and driven away. On the other side of the President's mansion he turned into the northern road that led out to join the Frederick Pike. Somewhere along this road, he felt certain, he would come upon Stansbury and the missing left wing. As they passed through the outskirts of the city an old lady stood on her porch and shook her fist after them.

"Cowards!" she screamed. "Cowards! Running away! Why don't you stand and fight like men?"

They were halfway to Montgomery Courthouse before they came finally on Stansbury's column, or what was left of it after wholesale desertions. The light dragoons brought up the rear, and Peter ordered his men to take their places as he passed. At the head of the line he found Stansbury, the very picture of gloomy despond.

"General Winder's compliments, sir," he reported. "He requests that you and your command rendezvous with the rest of the army at Tenleytown Heights at once."

Stansbury made no reply. He halted the column by the side of the road, turned them about and started them back along the road by which they had come. Peter dropped back and fell in beside Captain Creed at the head of A Troop. Lieutenant Smith was bringing up in the rear. As Peter fell in beside him Creed spoke flatly, as if he did not expect to be believed.

"The order was countermanded," he said.

Peter glanced at him sharply. He seemed to see him through a haze of red. All the resentment that had welled up within him at the sight of the cavalry retreating from the field of Bladensburg came back upon him with redoubled force, and the surge of his anger seemed to have the power to set him down hard in his saddle.

"Captain Creed," he said coldly, making no effort to lower his voice, "you are a God-damned liar! I hope that some day I may have the honor and pleasure of filling your fat guts with lead!"

Creed's eyes bulged, but he gave no other sign that he had heard. Behind them a titter ran through the ranks. The Captain was not popular with the troop. Peter waited a moment for a reply. When none came he reined his horse aside and galloped to the rear, where he joined Smith.

Night found them still far from Tenleytown. For a long time, almost since they had turned back, they had seen the great columns of smoke that rose against the sky ahead. Now, as the darkness closed in upon them, the smoke gave way to a bright, angry glow that spread along the horizon and brightened the southern sky. As they marched into Tenleytown, about midnight, they found the place lighted, as if it were day, by the great red tongues of flame that leapt skyward from the city below. Far off on Capitol Hill the burning shell of the Capitol Building was limned against the brighter blaze of the Navy Yard behind. Several other government buildings scattered through the lower section of the city, the Library, the Treasury, the State and Navy Buildings and the White House, also burned fiercely, and there was some private property ablaze. Off in the northeast section an entire block of houses added their flames to the ghastly beauty of the scene.

Toward one in the morning a terrific thunderstorm broke, loosing torrents of rain upon the stricken city. Although it checked the flames to some extent it did nothing to add to the comfort of the already miserable army huddled on the heights. It had no power to disturb Peter's rest, however. For him there was no rest that night. Throughout the hours of darkness he was kept busy, carrying despatches, rounding up stragglers, running the errands of Winder and his staff. And when morning came there was renewed activity.

All that day the army hung on Tenleytown Heights, while the British carried on their work of destruction. Smoke rolled in clouds from the city below, but neither general nor soldiers showed any disposition to interfere. Throughout the day, too, the army kept growing as belated detachments of militia poured in from outlying regions and shamed stragglers crept back to their commands. By early afternoon, however, when a force sufficient to have accomplished something was collected and a semblance of military order was restored, the sudden bursting of a hurricane, swooping out of the sultry heat of the day without warning, once again scattered the troops before it like chaff in the wind. By its fury houses were unroofed and trees laid flat and men hurled to the ground. Peter, lying for shelter behind a wall, saw an outhouse not far distant lifted from its foundations and hurled against the side of a barn, while the old beldame who occupied it at the moment screamed blue murder. After it had come to rest against the barn wall she stayed where she was until the wind had abated, when she opened the door and climbed out, none the worse for her experience save for shocked and injured dignity and a few bruises.

With the wind came a terrific downpour of rain which effectually extinguished such fires as still burned, though not before they had done their damage. At least, the storm put an end to the British program of destruction, for it scattered them as effectually as it had the Americans. It was night before the two armies were reassembled in their respective camps, the Americans at Tenleytown and the British on Capitol Hill. Looking down through the pitchy dark the Americans could see the fires of the British dotting the farther hillside with bright pin points of light. Every now and again these points of light would flare up and gleam more brightly as a wakeful sentry dumped an armload of wood upon them.

That night Peter rolled into his blankets in a state of exhaustion and slept the sleep of the dead. But in the gray light of a murky dawn he was awakened, even before the bugles had sounded the reveille, by the cry of a watchful picket:

"They've gone! The British have gone! They left their fires burning and pulled out in the night!"

BATTLE OF NEW ORLEANS

by MEREDITH NICHOLSON

"YOU'LL EAT YOUR CHRISTMAS DINNER in New Orleans!" Cochrane, the British Admiral, had boasted to the men of his fleet.

On the twenty-third of December it seemed possible that he would keep his promise. The British controlled Lake Borgne, but between it and New Orleans lay a diversity of bayous, cypress swamps, dikes and ditches not pleasing to a lord admiral of the sea. Sailors and redcoats poled their way in barges through Bayou Bienview and camped on Villere's plantation. Young Major Villere, escaping under a fusillade of British musketballs, galloped into the city and gave warning of the enemy's approach.

At the Royal Street house Jackson received the news calmly; issued

From: *The Cavalier of Tennessee.* Copyright 1928. Used by special permission of the publishers, The Bobbs-Merrill Company.

orders swiftly. Commodore Patterson with the schooners *Carolina* and *Louisiana* was ordered down the river. Coffee was in motion with his mounted riflemen who, cheerful souls, had brought along their hunting knives and hatchets. Batteries of artillery rumbled to the front; the Orleans Rifle Company, the Mississippi Dragoons, companies of regulars, battalions of the free negroes Jackson had urged into the service and a band of Choctaws in war paint were flung forward to arrest the invader.

Contemptuous reports of the American forces were borne back to the British commanders by the withdrawing pickets. It was near the end of the day and no offensive was expected from the oddly assorted battalions of Americans visible on the New Orleans road.

Jackson, worn with his day's labors, flung himself on a couch and slept half an hour while Fowler replaced the orderly at the door and received reports. Waking refreshed, the commander ate a few spoonfuls of rice as he listened to Fowler's recital of the disposition of the troops.

"The enemy are camped on Villere's plantation. They'll hardly strike until they have reinforcements from their fleet."

"Patterson's on the way down the river? Good. Is Livingston here?"

"Yes; and he reports the Louisiana militia in fine spirits and anxious to show their patriotism. Your orders are all executed. Governor Claiborne remains in town with General Carroll's troops to guard against a flank movement."

"Get the staff together and we'll ride down to the front. If things look right we'll stir 'em up a little tonight."

The shadows of the winter twilight gathered upon the plain. Jackson gazed across the British bivouac, brilliantly lighted by their camp-fires; sent a messenger to signal Patterson on the *Carolina* to begin firing when he got in position.

The British, not expecting an attack, thought the American schooner a trading ship and were aware of their error only when the cannon began booming. The camp-fires were at once extinguished but the sudden assault, followed at once by vigorous pressure by the American line, shook the morale of the invaders and they were slow in forming to resist the attack. For two hours and a half the battle raged in the dark. Bayonets on the British side and hunting-knives in the hands of the Kentuckians and Tennesseans were plied fiercely as the battle lines clashed and clinched. This hand to hand fighting in the dark, against a foe of uncertain numbers, with black and red faces to contend with and wild white men in caps made of the skins of wild beasts was not like warfare in Europe! To add to the din and confusion the little *Carolina* belched hot shot at intervals and now and again the terrified redcoats heard the shrill high voice of the American commander shouting orders, cheering on his men.

A smothering fog drifted up from the sea and Jackson decided to risk no more that night. Not so formidable, those British! He would wait for a chance to clean them up in daylight!

"This is only a little Christmas fandango," he remarked to Coffee. "They've got to hurry if they hand Louisiana to their king for a Christmas present!"

"We've picked up seventy-four prisoners," Reid reported. "They thought they'd march right into town but this night attack's chilled 'em. There'll hardly be another move till the big chief arrives—General Sir Edward Pakenham. His men say he'll make short work of us—he's brother-in-law to the Duke of Wellington."

"Let 'em send the duke!" said Jackson with a sardonic grin. "We'll take him home to Nashville in a basket!"

In the gray dawn of Christmas morning the American pickets reported that the night had been marked by great activity in the British camp. The enemy had pushed forward their artillery and additional infantry. Within a few hours lusty cheering announced that Pakenham had arrived to take command.

Coffee feinted at intervals with detachments of cavalry and the *Carolina,* hanging along the west bank of the river, dropped a shot into the enemy's camp occasionally.

"Keep 'em worried," were Jackson's orders. "We need time to establish our lines."

The city and the neighboring plantations were ransacked for picks and spades and with furious energy the Americans began building entrenchments. Not for nothing had the commander established military law! All the horses, oxen and mules in the region were hauling timbers and cotton bales to strengthen the breastworks. Soft-handed citizens accepted without grumbling the rough labor assigned them. Mutinous mutterings were silenced as Jackson rode the lines, scolding, praising, exacting every ounce of strength the hard-driven laborers could bring to their task. He had established headquarters in a planter's house close to the breastworks, and partaking sparingly of his rice ration and sleeping not at all, he strengthened and lengthened his line.

The insolence of the *Carolina* having at last become insufferable, Pakenham planted his heaviest ordnance on the levee and for half an hour the little vessel gallantly responded to the British cannon. Set on fire by a hot ball that landed near her powder chests the commander gave orders to abandon ship. The crew fired a final broadside and left her only a few minutes before she blew up with a mighty explosion.

The *Louisiana* got away to the western side of the river and Jackson turned his spy-glass upon the enemy's land forces.

Posted on the levee, the sick man from the Hermitage summarized recent history with satisfaction. Pakenham might be a great strategist by European standards, but he had dallied three days in the presence of an enemy greatly inferior on land and sea when he might have eaten his Christmas pudding in New Orleans if he had made a determined offensive.

"By the Eternal! He'll never get there!" Jackson declared, and turned to find Jean Lafitte beside him. A modest gentleman, the pirate of Barataria! He merely wished to announce that his men, among them skilled artillerists, had been assigned to service in keeping with their talents and that they would give a good account of themselves.

"My frien's of Barataria know not the wor' fear! They know onl-ee to fight and die!" he declared. "In what way can I serve you, Generale Jacksone?"

Jackson, pleased with his zeal, gave him a message to carry with all speed to Commodore Patterson across the river. The British were already advancing in two magnificent columns as if on parade. One line moved along the river, the other skirted the fringes of a cypress swamp. Ignorant of the extent of the American entrenchments, the British veterans marched to within six hundred yards of the American lines only to falter and retreat before a devastating fire.

Pakenham, (knighted for valor at Salamanca over yonder in Spain!) watched with amazement and mortification the repulse of the best troops in the British Army by American backwoodsmen. Through his glass he had caught a glimpse the day before of the American commander, who wasn't a general at all—only a frontier farmer and a sick man at that! Pestiferous fellows, those Tennessee riflemen; every time one fired there was a redcoat the less. A poor yarn this adventure would make for the drawing-rooms when he got back to London! To echoing cheers from the American lines he withdrew bewilderedly, to confer with Cochrane, the admiral.

Neither Sir Edward nor the admiral understood the ways of the Americans. They were constantly abroad on terrifying errands. Most annoying were the movements of Tom Hinds, a young and handsome Mississippian who, abroad on reconnaisance duty, swept with a company of dragoons close to British batteries, delivered a deadly musket fire and galloped away in safety. Even more fearsome were Coffee's Tennesseans in their homespun, prowling about at night, a terror to pickets, stragglers and reconnoitering parties.

More guns must be brought from the ships and dragged through that thrice damned network of swamps and bayous! To add to the general joylessness, it rained frequently. The British seamen were vastly annoyed by the queer reptiles that snapped at their legs. At dusk the breeze wafted across the plain the mocking strains of a band attached to Planche's Orleans battalion playing the *Marseillaise!*

"Let all the bands play," Jackson ordered. "Music will be soothing to Sir Edward's feelings!"

He surveyed the wrecked British batteries grimly. He had won the day but the greater struggle was yet to come. Ammunition was not reaching his lines as he expected, and he held Governor Claiborne responsible.

"Send me powder and ball or by the Eternal! I'll cut off your head and ram it into a cannon!"

This clearly was no way to address a governor. Harassed by a thousand annoyances and tormented by pain, it was well that the commander's vituperative gifts afforded outlet for his emotions. Kentucky's long delayed phalanx arrived at New Orleans half clad and without arms. Jackson swore brilliantly, but ordered the city's shops and warehouses raided for equipment. He was giving personal attention to every detail of his defenses, guarding against every imaginable peril. He had established three successive lines of defense in case the first shouldn't hold. While the British were at their elaborate preparations the sick lord of the Hermitage had three thousand men strengthening his lines even though they had already survived massed infantry assaults and the thumping of cannon. The cotton bales used in the embrasures of some of the batteries failed to resist and Jackson replaced them with Delta mud, which, he had noted, sucked up cannon balls.

One o'clock in the morning. Fowler touched the commander's shoulder as he lay asleep in his uniform in the plantation house.

"What day is this?" Jackson demanded, at once on his feet buckling on his sword.

"The eighth of January. The enemy are preparing to attack. Butler has issued orders to all officers to be ready."

"Call Reid and come with me; we'll ride our lines. I want to see John Coffee."

He wanted to see John Coffee! Comforting, indeed, on a murky morning, with a big job on hand, to have old Coffee within reach; fearless John Coffee, a military genius in his own right, but loved as a friend and neighbor. There was a moral stimulus to be got just from hearing the old fellow's gruff voice and feeling the touch of his hand. And Coffee, of course, was over there, where he had been told to be, at the edge of the cypress swamp with his men of the Cumberland. Many of them had slept on logs to lift them out of the slime.

As the day broke grudgingly a shotted rocket from the British lines hissed through the mists and fell into the river.

"The scoundrels have got to shoot better than that," Jackson commented to his staff as they watched the zigzag course of the fiery missile.

Pickets, falling back through the fog, announced the British advance. Out of the hovering mists they came, like an army with banners seen in a dream. A cannon boomed as an American gunner caught sight of them; then the fog curtained them again. The air was clearing and the Americans saw the approaching enemy—a magnificent pageant under the flags of their hard-won victories in the Old World.

Back of the center of his lines, unattended for the moment, Jackson saw them, knew that his great hour had come. In his breast pocket was Rachel's last letter, and he thrust in his hand to touch it. He would not have Rachel ashamed of what he should do this day!

"Take your time, men," he was saying as he walked along his lines swinging his cane. "Be sure the squirrel's on your side of the tree before you shoot!"

The earth trembled as the American batteries thundered. Gaps in the solid British lines were quickly closed only to be ripped open again by murderous grape and cannister. In mighty diapasons the cannon roared and in interludes the rifles of the frontiersmen caught up the strain with the rippling roll of a thousand drums. Damned good shots, those Baratarians! Jackson sent his compliments to Jean Lafitte. The British batteries, helpless to support the three thousand infantry that charged the American breastworks, fell back, confused, appalled by the pitiless hail of iron and lead that beat upon their faces. Gibbs, in immediate command of the movement, sought in vain to check the panic.

"Bring up the reserves!" Pakenham ordered, urging his horse through his broken staggering army. His men regained confidence as General Keane flung in a regiment of Highlanders. Brave Scots! Two hundred perished in the raking fire of a single American cannon.

Pakenham in a frantic effort to rally his men rode to the head of his legion. Shot in the arm, he kept on. Falling a moment later he died without knowing the extent of the catastrophe that had befallen his army.

Eight o'clock. The smoke cleared and the mounting sun revealed a trail of death on the miry plain. They lay in windrows—two thousand valiant Britons—as if cut down by some monstrous scythe. Only on the west bank of the river had the invaders won any advantage and this availed nothing as against the crushing defeat of the main army on the Chalmette plain.

Gazing across the blood-drenched field Jackson raised his hand in salute.

"Brave fellows!" he exclaimed brokenly. "There are many of their wounded lying among the dead. Order the men to stop cheering and send our doctors over the field."

Quills were flying the next morning in the commander's headquarters; couriers groomed their horses for hard riding. Washington, Knoxville and Nashville must know the news. Sam Dale, a Mississippian, endeared to the commander by his feats of daring, was chosen to bear the news to the president. Coffee picked the other messengers from his Tennesseans— intrepid youngsters proud of the chance to carry the great news home to the neighbors. Jackson had Livingston, Reid and Fowler at work while he was still issuing orders to guard against a renewal of hostilities. Rachel must know from him the victory and he wrote her, first of all, to say that the British were whipped and that he himself was well.

"I hope, my dear love, that you may join me here soon, but not until all is safe. The city is joyfully celebrating the triumph, but I remain on the field. My men have been bringing in a queer lot of odds and ends from the battle-field—the instruments of the Scotch Highlander's band, General Pakenham's chapeau, General Keane's trumpet and sword. The British threw away their guns as they ran and our men have been collecting them. You will gather from this the completeness of the rout. My best love to our dear boy. Be careful of yourself. Amid all these moving scenes you fill my heart. I am eager to be at the Hermitage again, but while my country needs me we must sacrifice our own happiness and peace."

He was busy with his report to President Madison when his orderly handed him a paper. Incredible! Only six Americans killed and seven wounded. The British loss of more than two thousand included the lieutenant-general commanding, two major-generals, eight colonels, six majors, eighteen captains and fifty-four lieutenants. On the west side of the river the American casualties were one killed and five wounded against the enemy's loss of one hundred and twenty killed and wounded.

"God was with us!" exclaimed Jackson reverently.

"A committee of citizens to see you, General," reported Fowler.

"Thank them and say I'll not be ready for entertainment till I've finished my business here. When I go into the city I'll march with the men who won the victory. We'll not do any bragging till we know the enemy's satisfied. If they want more punishment we must be ready to give it to 'em."

But with their most distinguished officers killed and the rain-splashed plain one vast grave, the British were already creeping back through the swamps to their ships, sending the conqueror a quite unnecessary request that he care for the wounded they were leaving behind.

THE MEXICAN WAR
1846-1848

THE MEXICAN WAR
1846-1848

Lessons learned by the United States in the War of 1812 were conned by the nation with greater attention than appears on the surface. The United States Military Academy, founded in 1802 and then directed with skill and efficiency, made possible the creation of a small corps of officers distinguished for zeal in study and dependability in the field. The talents of the Academy graduates in the 1820's, 1830's and early 1840's were directed mainly toward engineering, artillery, and to frontier duty, but the necessity of discipline and the methods whereby it might be obtained had become cardinal points in the creed of the gentlemen from West Point.

When this war commenced the Army of the United States was small indeed but it had become highly efficient. Although based upon the best European models it retained sufficient flexibility to meet and to overcome local problems.

Thus it came about that when diplomatic difficulties with Mexico were translated into a state of war, our Army for once was ready. Officers and men from the South, (it must not be forgotten that Southerners have always given themselves more readily to the profession of arms than those of any other region) were anxious for field service.

The result was a series of brilliant campaigns which might serve as models for wars to be fought as soldiers would elect to fight them.

As never before militia and volunteers became absorbed rapidly into the disciplined framework of the Regular Army. The resultant forces, few in numbers but deadly in efficiency, sliced through hordes of hapless Mexicans, as at Palo Alto, Cherubusco, and at the bloody battle of Resaca de la Palma.

The excerpt from THE ADVENTURES OF DAVY CROCKETT serves quite as much to represent a typical American folk hero as to depict the heroic defense of the Alamo.

The accurate description of Sam Houston at San Jacinto depicts the cold, devastating rage of the Texans. In this earlier war against Mexico, their fury carried them, rebellious and undisciplined, victoriously against enemies they considered to be the murderers of their people.

THE ALAMO

I write this on the nineteenth of February, 1836, at San Antonio. We are all in high spirits, though we are rather short of provisions, for men who have appetites that could digest any thing but oppression; but no matter, we have a prospect of soon getting our bellies full of fighting, and that is victuals and drink to a true patriot any day. We had a little sort of convivial party last evening: just about a dozen of us set to work, most patriotically, to see whether we could not get rid of that curse of the land, whisky, and we made considerable progress; but my poor friend, Thimblerig, got sewed up just about as tight as the eyelet-hole in a lady's corset, and a little tighter too, I reckon; for when he went to bed he called for a boot-jack, which was brought to him, and he bent down on his hands and knees, and very gravely pulled off his hat with it, for the darned critter was so thoroughly swiped that he didn't know his head from his heels. But this wasn't all the folly he committed: he pulled off his coat and laid it on the bed, and then hung himself over the back of a chair; and I wish I may be shot if he didn't go to sleep in that position. Seeing the poor fellow completely used up, I carried him to bed, though he did belong to the Temperance society; and he knew nothing about what had occurred until I told him the next morning. The Bee hunter didn't join us in this blow-out. Indeed, he will seldom drink more than just enough to prevent his being called a total abstinence man. But then he is the most jovial fellow for a water drinker I ever did see.

This morning I saw a caravan of about fifty mules passing by Bexar, and bound for Santa Fé. They were loaded with different articles to such a degree that it was astonishing how they could travel at all, and they were nearly worn out by their labours. They were without bridle or halter, and yet proceeded with perfect regularity in a single line; and the owners of the caravan rode their mustangs with their enormous spurs, weighing at least a pound a piece, with rowels an inch and a half in length, and lever bits of the harshest description, able to break the jaws of their animals under a very gentle pressure. The men were dressed

From: *The Adventures of Davy Crockett:* Edited by John W. Thomason, Jr. Copyright 1934. Charles Scribner's Sons.

in the costume of Mexicans. Colonel Travis sent out a guard to see that they were not laden with munitions of war for the enemy. I went out with the party. The poor mules were bending under a burden of more than three hundred pounds, without including the panniers, which were bound so tight as almost to stop the breath of the poor animal. Each of the sorrowful line came up, spontaneously, in turn to have his girth unbound and his load removed. They seemed scarcely able to keep upon their feet, and as they successively obtained relief, one after another heaved a long and deep sigh, which it was painful to hear, because it proved that the poor brutes had been worked beyond their strength. What a world of misery man inflicts upon the rest of creation in his brief passage through life!

Finding that the caravan contained nothing intended for the enemy, we assisted the owners to replace the heavy burdens on the backs of the patient but dejected mules, and allowed them to pursue their weary and lonely way. For full two hours we could see them slowly winding along the narrow path, a faint line that ran like a thread through the extended prairie; and finally they were whittled down to the little end of nothing in the distance, and were blotted out from the horizon.

The caravan had no sooner disappeared than one of the hunters, who had been absent several days, came in. He was one of those gentlemen who don't pride themselves much upon their costume, and reminded me of a covey who came into a tavern in New York when I was last in that city. He was dressed in five jackets, all of which failed to conceal his raggedness, and as he bolted in, he exclaimed,

"Worse than I look, by—. But no matter, I've let myself for fourteen dollars a month, and find my own prog and lodging."

"To do what?" demanded the barkeeper.

"To stand at the corner for a paper-mill sign—'cash for rags'—that's all. I'm about to enter upon the stationery business, you see." He tossed off his grog, and bustled out to begin his day's work.

But to return to the hunter. He stated that he had met some Indians on the banks of the Rio Frio, who informed him that Santa Anna, with a large force, had already crossed the Neuces, and might be expected to arrive before San Antonio in a few days. We immediately set about preparing to give him a warm reception, for we are all well aware, if our little band is overwhelmed by numbers, there is little mercy to be expected from the cowardly Mexicans—it is war to the knife.

I jocosely asked the ragged hunter, who was a smart, active young fellow, of the steamboat and alligator breed, whether he was a rhinoceros

or a hyena, as he was so eager for a fight with the invaders. "Neither
the one, nor t'other, Colonel," says he, "but a whole menagerie in myself.
I'm shaggy as a bear, wolfish about the head, active as a cougar, and can
grin like a hyena, until the bark will curl off a gum log. There's a
sprinkling of all sorts in me, from the lion down to the skunk; and before
the war is over you'll pronounce me an entire zoological institute, or I
miss a figure in my calculation. I promise to swallow Santa Anna without
gagging, if you will only skewer back his ears, and grease his head a
little."

He told me that he was one in the fatal expedition fitted out from
New Orleans, in November last, to join the contemplated attack upon
Tampico by Mehia and Peraza. They were, in all, about one hundred
and thirty men, who embarked as emigrants to Texas; and the terms
agreed upon were, that it was optional whether the party took up arms
in defence of Texas, or not, on landing. They were at full liberty to
act as they pleased. But the truth was, Tampico was their destination,
and an attack on that city the covert design, which was not made known
before land was in sight. The emigrants were landed, some fifty, who
doubtless had a previous understanding, joined the standard of General
Mehia, and the following day a formidable fort surrendered without an
attack.

The whole party were now tendered arms and ammunition, which
even those who had been decoyed accepted; and, the line being formed,
they commenced the attack upon the city. The hunter continued: "On
the 15th of November our little army, consisting of one hundred and
fifty men, marched into Tampico, garrisoned by two thousand Mexicans,
who were drawn up in battle array in the public square of the city. We
charged them at the point of the bayonet, and although they so greatly
outnumbered us, *in two minutes* we completely routed them; and they
fled, taking refuge on the house tops, from which they poured a destructive fire upon our gallant little band. We fought them until daylight,
when we found our number decreased to fifty or sixty broken down and
disheartened men. Without ammunition, and deserted by the officers,
twenty-eight immediately surrendered. But a few of us cut our way
through, and fortunately escaped to the mouth of the river, where we
got on board a vessel and sailed for Texas.

"The twenty-eight prisoners wished to be considered as prisoners of
war; they made known the manner in which they had been deceived,
but they were tried by a court-martial of Mexican soldiers, and con-

demned to be shot on the 14th day of December, 1835, which sentence was carried into execution."

After receiving this account from my new friend, the old pirate and the Indian hunter came up, and they went off to liquor together, and I went to see a wild Mexican hog, which one of the hunters had brought in. These animals have become scarce, which circumstance is not to be deplored, for their flesh is of little value; and there will still be hogs enough left in Mexico, from all I can learn, even though these should be extirpated.

February 22. The Mexicans, about sixteen hundred strong, with their President Santa Anna at their head, aided by Generals Almonte, Cos, Sesma, and Castrillon, are within two leagues of Bexar. General Cos, it seems, has already forgot his parole of honour, and is come back to retrieve the credit he lost in this place in December last. If he is captured a second time, I don't think he can have the impudence to ask to go at large again without giving better bail than on the former occasion. Some of the scouts came in, and brought reports that Santa Anna has been endeavoring to excite the Indians to hostilities against the Texians, but so far without effect. The Cumanches, in particular, entertain such hatred for the Mexicans, and at the same time hold them in such contempt, that they would rather turn their tomahawks against them, and drive them from the land, than lend a helping hand. We are up and doing, and as lively as Dutch cheese in the dog-days. The two hunters that I have already introduced to the reader left the town, this afternoon, for the purpose of reconnoitring.

February 23. Early this morning the enemy came in sight, marching in regular order, and displaying their strength to the greatest advantage, in order to strike us with terror. But that was no go; they'll find that they have to do with men who will never lay down their arms as long as they can stand on their legs. We held a short council of war, and, finding that we should be completely surrounded, and overwhelmed by numbers, if we remained in the town, we concluded to withdraw to the fortress of Alamo, and defend it to the last extremity. We accordingly filed off, in good order, having some days before placed all the surplus provisions, arms, and ammunition in the fortress. We have had a large national flag made; it is composed of thirteen stripes, red and white, alternately, on a blue ground with a large white star, of five points, in the centre, and between the points the letters Texas. As soon as all our little band, about one hundred and fifty in number, had entered and secured the fortress in the best possible manner, we set about raising our flag on the battlements; on which occasion there was no one more active than my young friend, the Bee hunter. He had been all along sprightly, cheerful, and spirited, but now, notwithstanding the control that he usually maintained over himself, it was with difficulty that he kept his enthusiasm within bounds. As soon as we commenced raising the flag he burst forth, in a clear, full tone of voice, that made the blood tingle in the veins of all who heard him:—

> "Up with your banner, Freedom,
>   Thy champions cling to thee;
> They'll follow where'er you lead 'em,
>   To death, or victory;—
> Up with your banner, Freedom.
>
> Tyrants and slaves are rushing
>   To tread thee in the dust;
> Their blood will soon be gushing,
>   And stain our knives with rust;—
> But not thy banner, Freedom.
>
> While stars and stripes are flying,
>   Our blood we'll freely shed;
> No groan will 'scape the dying,
>   Seeing thee o'er his head;—
> Up with your banner, Freedom."

This song was followed by three cheers from all within the fortress, and the drums and trumpets commenced playing. The enemy marched into Bexar, and took possession of the town, a blood-red flag flying at their head, to indicate that we need not expect quarter if we should fall into their clutches. In the afternoon a messenger was sent from the enemy to Colonel Travis, demanding an unconditional and absolute surrender of the garrison, threatening to put every man to the sword in case of refusal. The only answer he received was a cannon shot, so the messenger left us with a flea in his ear, and the Mexicans commenced firing grenades at us, but without doing any mischief. At night Colonel Travis sent an express to Colonel Fanning, at Goliad, about three or four days' march from this place, to let him know that we are besieged. The old pirate volunteered to go on this expedition, and accordingly left the fort after nightfall.

February 24. Very early this morning the enemy commenced a new battery on the banks of the river, about three hundred and fifty yards from the fort, and by afternoon they amused themselves by firing at us from that quarter. Our Indian scout came in this evening, and with him a reinforcement of thirty men from Gonzales, who are just in the nick of time to reap a harvest of glory; but there is some prospect of sweating blood before we gather it in. An accident happened to my friend Thimblerig this afternoon. He was intent on his eternal game of thimbles, in a somewhat exposed position, while the enemy were bombarding us from the new redoubt. A three ounce ball glanced from the parapet and struck him on the breast, inflicting a painful but not dangerous wound. I extracted the ball, which was of lead, and recommended to him to drill a hole through it, and carry it for a watch seal. "No," he replied, with energy, "may I be shot six times if I do; that would be making a bauble for an idle boast. No, Colonel, lead is getting scarce, and I'll lend it out at compound interest.—Curse the thimbles!" he muttered, and went his way, and I saw no more of him that evening.

February 25. The firing commenced early this morning, but the Mexicans are poor engineers, for we haven't lost a single man, and our outworks have sustained no injury. Our sharpshooters have brought down a considerable number of stragglers at a long shot. I got up before the peep of day, hearing an occasional discharge of a rifle just over the place where I was sleeping, and I was somewhat amazed to see Thimblerig mounted alone on the battlement, no one being on duty at the time but the sentries. "What are you doing there?" says I. "Paying my debts," says he, "interest and all." "And how do you make out?" says I. "I've nearly got through," says he; "stop a moment, Colonel, and I'll close the account." He clapped his rifle to his shoulder, and blazed away, then jumped down from his perch, and said, "That account's settled; them chaps will let me play out my game in quiet next time." I looked over the wall, and saw four Mexicans lying dead on the plain. I asked him to explain what he meant by paying his debts, and he told me that he had run the grape shot into four rifle balls, and that he had taken an early stand to have a chance of picking off stragglers. "Now, Colonel, let's go take our bitters," said he; and so we did. The enemy have been busy during the night, and have thrown up two batteries on the opposite side of the river. The battalion of Matamoras is posted there, and cavalry occupy the hills to the east and on the road to Gonzales. They are determined to surround us, and cut us off from reinforcement, or the possibility of escape by a sortie.—Well, there's one thing they cannot prevent· we'll still go ahead, and sell our lives at a high price.

February 26. Colonel Bowie has been taken sick from over exertion and exposure. He did not leave his bed to-day until twelve o'clock. He is worth a dozen common men in a situation like ours. The Bee hunter keeps the whole garrison in good heart with his songs and his jests, and his daring and determined spirit. He is about the quickest on the trigger, and the best rifle shot we have in the fort. I have already seen him bring down eleven of the enemy, and at such a distance that we all thought it would be waste of ammunition to attempt it. His gun is first-rate, quite equal to my Betsey, though she has not quite as many trinkets about her. This day a small party sallied out of the fort for wood and water, and had a slight skirmish with three times their number from the division under General Sesma. The Bee hunter headed them, and beat the enemy off, after killing three. On opening his Bible at night, of which he always reads a portion before going to rest, he found a musket ball in the middle of it. "See here, Colonel," said he, "how they have treated the valued present of my dear little Kate of Nacogdoches." "It has saved your life," said I. "True," replied he, more seriously than usual, "and I am not the first sinner whose life has been saved by this book." He prepared for bed, and before retiring he prayed, and returned thanks for his providential escape; and I heard the name of Catherine mingled in his prayer.

February 27. The cannonading began early this morning, and ten bombs were thrown into the fort, but fortunately exploded without doing any mischief. Provisions are becoming scarce, and the enemy are endeavouring to cut off our water. If they attempt to stop our grog in that manner, let them look out, for we shall become too wrathy for our shirts to hold us. We are not prepared to submit to an excise of that nature, and they'll find it out. This discovery has created considerable excitement in the fort.

February 28. Last night our hunters brought in some corn and hogs, and had a brush with a scout from the enemy beyond gun-shot of the fort. They put the scout to flight, and got in without injury. They bring accounts that the settlers are flying in all quarters, in dismay, leaving their possessions to the mercy of the ruthless invader, who is literally engaged in a war of extermination, more brutal than the untutored savage of the desert could be guilty of. Slaughter is indiscriminate, sparing neither sex, age, nor condition. Buildings have been burnt down, farms laid waste, and Santa Anna appears determined to verify his threat, and convert the blooming paradise into a howling wilderness. For just one fair crack at that rascal, even at a hundred yards distance, I would bargain to break my Betsey, and never pull trigger again. My name's not Crockett if I wouldn't get glory enough to appease my stomach for the remainder of my life. The scouts report that a settler, by the name of Johnson, flying with his wife and three little children, when they reached the Colorado, left his family on the shore, and waded into the river to see whether it would be safe to ford with his wagon. When about the middle of the river he was seized by an alligator, and, after a struggle, was dragged under the water, and perished. The helpless woman and her babes were discovered, gazing in agony on the spot, by other fugitives who happily passed that way, and relieved them. Those who fight the battles experience but a small part of the privation, suffering and anguish that follow in the train of ruthless war. The cannonading continued, at intervals, throughout the day, and all hands were kept up to their work. The enemy, somewhat imboldened, draws nigher to the fort. So much the better.—There was a move in General Sesma's division toward evening.

February 29. Before daybreak we saw General Sesma leave his camp with a large body of cavalry and infantry, and move off in the direction of Goliad. We think that he must have received news of Colonel Fanning's coming to our relief. We are all in high spirits at the prospect of being able to give the rascals a fair shake on the plain. This business of being shut up makes a man wolfish.—I had a little sport this morning before breakfast. The enemy had planted a piece of ordnance within gun-shot of the fort during the night, and the first thing in the morning they commenced a brisk cannonade, point-blank, against the spot where I was snoring. I turned out pretty smart, and mounted the rampart. The gun was charged again, a fellow stepped forth to touch her off, but before he could apply the match I let him have it, and he keeled over. A second stepped up, snatched the match from the hand of the dying man, but Thimblerig, who had followed me, handed me his rifle, and the next instant the Mexican was stretched on the earth beside the first. A third came up to the cannon, my companion handed me another gun, and I fixed him off in like manner. A fourth, then a fifth, seized the match, who both met with the same fate, and then the whole party gave it up as a bad job, and hurried off to the camp, leaving the cannon ready charged where they had planted it. I came down, took my bitters, and went to breakfast. Thimblerig told me that the place from which I had been firing was one of the snuggest stands in the whole fort, for he never failed picking off two or three stragglers before breakfast, when perched up there. And I recollect, now, having seen him there, ever since he was wounded, the first thing in the morning, and the last at night,—and at times, thoughtlessly playing at his eternal game.

March 1. The enemy's forces have been increasing in numbers daily, notwithstanding they have already lost about three hundred men in the several assaults they have made upon us. I neglected to mention in the proper place, that when the enemy came in sight we had but three bushels of corn in the garrison, but have since found eighty bushels in a deserted house. Colonel Bowie's illness still continues, but he manages to crawl from his bed every day, that his comrades may see him. His presence alone is a tower of strength.—The enemy becomes more daring as his numbers increase.

March 2. This day the delegates meet in general convention, at the town of Washington, to frame our Declaration of Independence. That the sacred instrument may never be trampled on by the children of those who have freely shed their blood to establish it, is the sincere wish of David Crockett. Universal independence is an almighty idea, far too extensive for some brains to comprehend. It is a beautiful seed that germinates rapidly, and brings forth a large and vigorous tree, but like the deadly Upas, we sometimes find the smaller plants wither and die in its shades. Its blooming branches spread far and wide, offering a perch of safety to all alike, but even among its protecting branches we find the eagle, the kite, and the owl preying upon the helpless dove and sparrow. Beneath its shade myriads congregate in goodly fellowship, but the lamb and the fawn find but frail security from the lion and the jackal, though the tree of independence waves over them. Some imagine independence to be a natural charter, to exercise without restraint, and to their fullest extent, all the energies, both physical and mental, with which they have been endowed; and for their individual aggrandizement alone, without regard to the rights of others, provided they extend to all the same privilege and freedom of action. Such independence is the worst of tyranny.

March 3. We have given over all hopes of receiving assistance from Goliad or Refugio. Colonel Travis harangued the garrison, and concluded by exhorting them, in case the enemy should carry the fort, to fight to the last gasp, and render their victory even more serious to them than to us. This was followed by three cheers.

March 4. Shells have been falling into the fort like hail during the day, but without effect. About dusk in the evening, we observed a man running toward the fort, pursued by about half a dozen Mexican cavalry. The Bee hunter immediately knew him to be the old pirate who had gone to Goliad, and, calling to the two hunters, he sallied out of the fort to the relief of the old man, who was hard pressed. I followed close after. Before we reached the spot the Mexicans were close on the heels of the old man, who stopped suddenly, turned short upon his pursuers, discharged his rifle, and one of the enemy fell from his horse. The chase was renewed, but finding that he would be overtaken and cut to pieces, he now turned again, and, to the amazement of the enemy, became the assailant in his turn. He clubbed his gun, and dashed among them like a wounded tiger, and they fled like sparrows. By this time we reached the spot, and, in the ardour of the moment, followed some distance before we saw that our retreat to the fort was cut off by another detachment of cavalry. Nothing was to be done but to fight our way through. We were all of the same mind. "Go ahead!" cried I, and they shouted, "Go ahead, Colonel!" We dashed among them, and a bloody conflict ensued. They were about twenty in number, and they stood their ground. After the fight had continued about five minutes, a detachment was seen issuing from the fort to our relief, and the Mexicans scampered off, leaving eight of their comrades dead upon the field. But we did not escape unscathed, for both the pirate and the Bee hunter were mortally wounded, and I received a sabre cut across the forehead. The old man died, without speaking, as soon as we entered the fort. We bore my young friend to his bed, dressed his wounds, and I watched beside him. He lay, without complaint or manifesting pain, until about midnight, when he spoke, and I asked him if he wanted any thing. "Nothing," he replied, but drew a sigh that seemed to rend his heart, as he added, "Poor Kate of Nacogdoches!" His eyes were filled with tears, as he continued, "Her words were prophetic, Colonel"; and then he sang in a low voice that resembled the sweet notes of his own devoted Kate,

"But toom cam' the saddle, all bluidy to see,
And hame cam' the steed, but hame never cam' he."

He spoke no more, and, a few minutes after died. Poor Kate, who will tell this to thee!

March 5. Pop, pop, pop! Bom, bom, bom! throughout the day.—No time for memorandums now.—Go ahead!—Liberty and independence forever!

[*Here ends Colonel Crockett's manuscript.*]

SAN JACINTO

by CLARK VENABLE

THE WINGS OF THE WIND would have been none too swift to suit Summers, Abel and Buell on their ride to Gonzales, but when they reached there it was to learn that the hard ride had been in vain. Houston, with a ragamuffin, untrained, undisciplined and poorly armed force totaling a little over three hundred, was preparing to evacuate Gonzales and fall back to the Colorado. He had already dispatched a messenger to Fannin ordering him to abandon the defense of Goliad and retreat to Victoria on the Guadalupe. Word had reached Houston that Santa Anna was moving eastward with a strong force of infantry, horse and artillery. No one knew his exact whereabouts. He might strike at any hour, and Houston was wise enough to know that the pitiable army of Texans, however thirsty for the blood of the butcher of the Alamo, would be trampled under by the first charge of Santa Anna's dragoons. The Texans were poorly equipped and there was no supporting artillery.

Gonzales was a town of tears and panic. Thirty-two men from the small town had perished in the Alamo. Wives were weeping and wringing their hands; fatherless children were groping for an understanding of what had befallen them; and every rifle in the ragged army was challenging Houston to stand and fight.

This was the condition when Summers, Jeff and Abel reached there. That night they became three more miserable units in a crestfallen handful of men, who, representing the army of Texas, filled their mouths with bitter oaths as Houston ordered the retreat. They had but two wagons and two yoke of oxen for transporting supplies and ammunition. The man who came without provisions in his saddlebags or in a cotton sack stood an excellent chance to go hungry.

Santa Anna, drunk with the blood of his victory at the Alamo, had publicly announced that he would burn every American house in Texas. To rob him of this satisfaction, Houston appointed "Deaf" Smith and Summers as the leaders of a small rear guard who were to burn everything in the wake of the retreating army. All night long the army of Texas moved eastward, their trail marked by the flaming walls and roofs

From: *All The Brave Rifles*. Copyright 1929. The Reilly and Lee Company.

of homes that had seen joy and sorrow, want and plenty, privation and the bright flame of zeal.

Four days and nights the army moved eastward, their progress greatly delayed by the necessity of riding wide on both flanks to warn and bring in unprotected families. Santa Anna's code did not exempt the defenseless.

On the fourth day they reached the Colorado, crossed over and went into camp. Two days thereafter the rear guard scouts reported that a strong Mexican force under General Sesma was moving forward toward the river crossing. Houston at once began preparations to ambush them. The spirit of the men arose, but their enthusiasm was short-lived. The Mexicans, learning of the ambush, pitched camp on the opposite side of the river to await reinforcements. The chance for ambush gone, Houston began to make plans for recrossing the river and engaging the enemy in open battle.

While these plans were being pushed to completion, two reports came to him that quenched the fire of his ardor and threw his command into uproar. The convention at Washington, hearing of his retreat, had moved the seat of government to Harrisburg. This move, on the part of the leaders, threw all of east Texas into unreasoning panic. If both the government and army were fleeing before Santa Anna, the people reasoned, then it was high time for the citizen to take flight.

But it was the second report that staggered Houston. A rider came from Goliad, spurring frantically into camp and shouting out that Fannin's entire command at Goliad had been captured and massacred to the man.

That night Houston did not sleep, and his men sat around their small camp fires, retelling again and again the story the rider had brought from Goliad. First the Alamo, now Goliad. What manner of beast was this Santa Anna? Was it his rule to give no quarter? What would happen to this motley crowd if they chanced to fall in his path? Doubtless Sesma, across the river, was awaiting his arrival. Here was their chance to even the score! They would cross the river in the morning and give the Mexicans a taste of their own medicine. An eye for an eye. Blood for blood.

So they talked throughout the night. But Houston had been doing some clear thinking. He decided to fall back to the Brazos and by such continued retreat lure the enemy further and further away from their base. Perhaps Santa Anna might even divide his forces in his zeal to lay waste all Texas. At any rate, it was the one clear chance. To stand here would be to add another massacre to the blood red record of Santa Anna's advance.

When dawn came, Houston, red-eyed from lack of sleep but with his powerful shoulders squared to meet the blast of anger which he knew he was about to provoke, stalked before his paraded army and told them of his plan to strike camp and retreat to the Brazos.

The storm broke. What had been a mob of untrained men now became a mob in open rebellion. They shouted curses and swore they would not retreat another step.

"Look at him!" Abel growled to Summers. "He run out of Tennessee once and now he's fixin' to run clean out of Texas." He turned and shouted loud enough to be heard above the angry growls of the others. "Boys!" he called, "I stick right here. I come to fight, not to run. If I'd a-knowed the army was goin' to run plumb back to the Brazos I could a-stayed there and saved myself a lot of steps. I motion we stick right here and give 'em lead when they try to cross the river."

There was a shout of approval. Abel was voicing the will of every man present—save one. That one was the towering giant who stood so calmly before them, drawing his colored sash a little tighter about his middle and shifting his big hat to a more determined angle.

His voice rose above the others like the roar of a bull above the drone of bees. He offered no explanation; made no effort to tell them what he expected them to do. He told them what they were *going to do!* Only a few short, sharp sentences. Then he stood there, seeming to have the ability to look into the eyes of every man in the command.

The growling ceased. Silently, in little groups, the men turned away and began to make ready for further retreat. Even Abel was silenced, and Summers knew that he had met a will stronger than his own.

2

The retreat to the Brazos was a way of sorrow. The spring rains began. Water fell in sheets. Creeks became rivers; the prairies were turned into bogs. The wagons and oxen were no sooner extricated from one mud hole than they forthwith mired down in another.

The countryside was in shambles. Every house had been abandoned, the owners fleeing eastward ahead of the retreating army. Beside the road was to be found bedding, trunks, kitchen ware, pieces of household furniture—all cast from over-loaded wagons by frantic settlers who had tried to save all and were now willing to cast all aside in an effort to save their lives. Many of the wagons and ox carts preceding the army were driven by women. Their husbands were in the army behind, or had perished at the Alamo or at Goliad. And many a man in Houston's army, coming in sight of his own home, saw that the door swung wide open and that all he had worked to gain—cattle, hogs, chickens, and the house itself—must be left in the path of the pursuing enemy, while somewhere ahead of the army his wife and children were goading weary oxen into still greater effort. Under such conditions, it took a brave man to stay behind with the army. Fortunately, many of them knew the quality of courage possessed by their women who, somewhere ahead, were plodding through the dark nights, and the lowering days, their long bull whips cracking over the backs of lagging oxen while their lips spoke courage and crooned melodies to frightened, crying children.

The army that trailed these refugees was sullen and angry. The man who rode at their head had once seen a star rising and had made prophecy. His speeches had been phrased in words of fire. Now, it seemed, the rains had quenched his fire; the sodden prairies sucked at his feet until he no longer walked like a giant.

Perhaps he was lost. Perhaps the clouds had blotted out the star.

3

Summers was not of the bravest when it came to the question of Carolin's safety, and his worry changed to fear when word reached the army that the citizens of San Felipe were fleeing the town. He at once called Jeff and Abel into conference. They were solemn and depressed. Summers knew their distress was as great as his own.

"You can't stay with us any longer, Jeff," he began. "You must ride ahead and take Carolin up to Washington. I would say to Harrisburg, but Santa Anna is south of us and I'm afraid he is aiming at the new seat of government. To go there might be jumping out of the kettle into the fire."

"I'm glad you think I should go," Jeff answered. "I've been worried to death about her. Of course I hate to leave, but I can't stand to see her there alone when everyone is moving out."

"Old Sam says he's going' to make a stand at the Brazos," Abel offered.

"He said the same at the Colorado," Summers answered dourly. "I've about lost faith in his standing ability. Besides, that would leave Carolin within gunshot of the battle and we can't expect Santa Anna to respect women. It's time to act! Abel will go with you——"

"Now, Will!" Abel protested. "I've bin keepin' my powder dry in all this rain fer shootin', not fer runnin'. I figger to——"

"This is no time for argument, Abel!" Summers' voice was crisp. "If there is going to be any shooting, which I doubt, you'll get your share of it. I want you to go back with Jeff. Go out to the farm and get the wagon and the oxen, load up as much of Carolin's stuff as you can haul and take the road to Washington. Stay with Jeff until you get them to Washington. Then you can come back and join us—if Houston makes a stand. If you get word that he has fallen back beyond the Brazos, then light out for Nacogdoches. In that case, I'll join you along the road. I don't propose to stay with him a step beyond the Brazos."

"Let me git this straight, Will. If Old Sam crosses the Brazos I'm to stay with Jeff till you ketch up. That'll mean we're headed out of Texas."

"Yes. We can't make a stand alone—and I'm tired of running."

"It's kinda like desertin', ain't it?" Abel asked.

"I don't care what it's like!" Summers retorted "Some of us must go. Either you go, or I will."

"You might do better than me," Abel suggested.

Lacking logic with which to meet this argument, Summers resorted to flattery.

"It's a question of the best man for the job, Abel. I don't know of any man who can get more miles out of a yoke of oxen than you can. Buck and Bell will sulk on me. You can keep the wheels rolling."

"I'm tolerable handy with a prod," Abel admitted. "Do you want me to take any of our stuff?"

"No. If we retreat beyond the river I'm through with Texas. Save all the space for Carolin."

"And Aunt Chloe," Abel added, grinning. "She'll take up a right smart room."

4

When Houston came in sight of San Felipe he immediately announced his intention of moving north along the river to Groce's Ferry. Mutiny at once flamed up. Many of the men considered it another ruse for continuing the retreat. Houston had declared that he would not retreat beyond the Brazos, but had said nothing about retreating northward. It was a trick. A cowardly trick. The leaders pointed out that here was the place to make the stand. When Houston turned a deaf ear to this plan, a hundred and fifty men refused to follow him further.

One group elected to remain at the San Felipe crossing while a second group moved down to Fort Bend.

Houston was a commander without authority to enforce command. With set lips he ignored the rebellion and marched northward. Even in retreat he had a quality of leadership that made men follow. Five hundred growling, cursing, but still loyal men followed him to Groce's and went into camp.

The downpour of rain continued. The camp at Groce's became first a quagmire, then a lake. The men were continually moving to higher ground until at last the camp became a small island surrounded by the coffee colored backwater from the swollen river.

Houston, deaf to all complaints and favoring himself least of all, sternly went about the business of drilling his men and trying to whip them into an organization responsive to command. But his men had come to fight, not to spend hours drilling on a small island cut off from the world. Somewhere beyond the turgid water of the river their wives and children were fleeing east, north, south—anywhere but westward. It was a sorry time for drilling.

The rains never ceased. The clouds never broke. Gloom settled over the army. What man could see a star when even the sun was held in thrall by the darkest clouds that had ever lowered over Texas?

Every report that reached the army increased the gloom. Word came that Santa Anna was at the crossing at San Felipe, only to find the town in flames. Again the fleeing citizens had robbed him of one of his chief delights. With pillage denied him, he turned south to make a thrust at Harrisburg. He was tired of chasing a jack-rabbit that hadn't the nerve to stand and fight. He would raze Harrisburg and stamp out the rebel leaders.

Houston smiled as the army growled and clamoured for pursuit. It was all working out just as he had planned. Santa Anna had grown contemptuous. Next he would become careless. He was working farther and farther away from his base and his forces were now divided and widely separated.

The hour had struck. Houston went before his army with a new gleam in his eye. Now they would see Old Sam in action. The hare would become the hound. But, wisely, he gave them no word of his plans. There were too many men deserting for him to trust such a precious message to tongues that might to-morrow find expression in some place where eager ears would carry the news to Santa Anna.

Keeping his plans to himself, he spent two days in crossing the swollen river, making use of a steamboat which he commandeered for that purpose.

The crossing of the river filled Summers with misgivings. Houston offered the army no explanation of the move; gave no hint of his purpose. Many of the men thought it was the beginning of another long retreat, but there was something about the quiet force with which Houston now moved that caused Summers to believe that this silent, wilful man was preparing to draw the sword. If so, Abel would be left out. If word of the move reached Washington, Abel and Jeff would consider it evidence of flight and would at once set out for Nacogdoches.

While Summers was debating in his mind whether to remain with the army or, as he had promised, leave it and rejoin Abel and Jeff at Washington, Houston ordered him to report as orderly. An hour after Summers reported, Houston started the march eastward toward Donohue's. It was at this place that the road forked, one road continuing eastward to the Trinity and thence north to Nacogdoches, the right hand road turning south to Harrisburg.

Summers, now acting as orderly, decided to remain with the army until they reached Donohue's. There, where the road forked, Old Sam would be forced to disclose his plan. Then the army would know whether they were in for a fight or a foot race.

Two pieces of artillery, six pounders, sent as a gift by the citizens of Cincinnati, Ohio, reached the army just as they had completed the crossing of the Brazos. The men promptly christened them "The Twin Sisters." Now at last Old Sam had his artillery, the soldiers said among themselves, and if he lacked the courage to use them and did not follow the road to Harrisburg someone was going to get shot in the back.

As the army came within sight of the fork of the road at Donohue's, Wharton, who had brought the six pounders from Velasco, rode up to Houston and said:

"Sir, these men are in no mood for further retreat. All the rifles of this command are eager for a fight."

Houston pressed his lips the tighter, gave his sash a determined hitch and answered not a word.

"They are ready to mutiny," Wharton warned.

Houston rode on in silence. Summers, who rode immediately behind, was one who could understand and appreciate the force of silence.

"If you take the fork to the Trinity," Wharton continued, "some of these men who have followed you so long will turn their rifles on *you,* sir."

Houston gave him a look of eloquent contempt. Summers, seeing this look, knew that a tall man was riding at the head of the army. But Wharton was not yet satisfied.

"These men have a right to know your plans," he continued. "They want to know where you are going."

"Toward glory—glory enough for them all," Houston answered.

At that moment the advance guard reached the forks of the road. Without a moment's hesitation they swung south. Houston's eyes twinkled as he shot a quick glance at Wharton.

"There is your answer, sir," he said. "Perhaps the men will now save their powder for Mexicans—who deserve it more than I do."

A wild shouting went up as the ranks realized that at last the retreat had become an advance. Maybe Old Sam had been right after all, they reasoned.

Summers did not join in the shouting, although he was as eager as any for combat. He had a score to settle as great as any of the others. If only Abel were here he could find heart for the shouting. But in all probability word would reach Washington that Houston was retreating to the Trinity. In that case, Abel and Jeff would start back along the road to Nacogdoches.

For the next two days Summers kept his eyes to the rear, hoping for the sight of a big-boned chestnut galloping along under a slouching, bearded rider.

5

In the meanwhile, Santa Anna was having a glorious time. He had burned Harrisburg. Then, confident that Houston was retreating toward the Trinity, he marched to New Washington and began amusing himself by setting fire to the homes of American colonists and making forays on their live stock. While he was thus employed one of his scouts brought the news that a force of Texans had appeared at Lynch's Ferry and were preparing to march against the town.

Santa Anna was happy to learn that at least a few Texans had deserted the jack-rabbit and had come to offer him more cups of blood like those which had been drunk at the Alamo and at Goliad.

In high spirits he set fire to the town and moved northward to trap the small band of foolish men who, his scouts declared, had crossed Buffalo Bayou and established a camp in a grove of trees near the junction of the bayou with the San Jacinto.

Reaching the prairie that extended in front of the position held by the Texans, he ordered a halt near the southern edge of this open ground and pitched camp with his back to a wide marsh which extended to San Jacinto Bay. Having established his position, he sent forward a single piece of artillery, supported by a detachment of cavalry and infantry, to force the Texans from the woods into the open prairie where more fun could be had during the slaughter.

He had sent his men forward to rout out rabbits and they met a bear. From the cover of the woods the "Twin Sisters" greeted the advancing Mexicans. Unappreciative of the salutation and somewhat surprised thereby, the Mexicans retreated.

Santa Anna now lost his lust for battle. He had but one piece of artillery. The enemy had two. He began looking anxiously for the arrival of reinforcements under General Cos. He began to wonder, too, as night came on, if he could have fallen into error in his guess that the jack-rabbit was retreating beyond the Trinity. The Napoleon of the West, as he chose to call himself, began to have faint stirrings of misgiving.

6

Houston had reached his position by marching night and day. Again and again he had rolled up his sleeves to lend his strength to that of his staggering men as they sweated and grunted at the mud-clogged wheels of wagons and guns. He had won in his race to reach Lynch's Ferry ahead of Santa Anna and thus cut off the dictator's only chance of escape. Now the Mexicans were trapped, but Houston's exhausted men were too tired to spring the trap. They had to content themselves with repulsing Santa Anna's feeble thrust. This, however, so enheartened them that strength returned and they chafed under the restraint of Houston's inactivity.

Night closed down with the leaders and the men clamouring for a night attack. Houston counseled only with himself. He knew that the men needed rest and food. The hot fever of their excitement was not strength. Even when warned that Santa Anna might at any moment be reinforced by the arrival of Cos, Houston shook his head and held his tongue.

Morning came and the men at once began preparations for battle. Hours passed and still Houston made no move. The men again began their growling. Sure enough, the old fool had waited too long. Cos had arrived. Now it would be just like him to order a retreat.

Summers thought he saw the trick Houston was planning. He felt sure it was the commander's plan to remain inactive until the enemy was lulled into a feeling of security. Then he would strike quickly.

So thinking, Summers made his way through the camp, openly championing the delay. There was no man reckless enough to accuse this tall, powerful Tennessean of lacking courage. They had seen too much of his strength on the long march, and many of them had seen him in action at Bexar. They listened to him, even though their patience was short.

Houston's position in the grove of trees was well concealed from the eyes of the enemy, while he could observe all that went on in their camp. Near two o'clock in the afternoon the Texans saw that the Mexicans were beginning to fortify their position. Houston at once sent for "Deaf" Smith.

"Smith," he said when the squat, burly man entered the tent, "I am picking you for a job I would not trust to another. There is just one way out of this pocket—Vince's Bridge. Select some man to go with you, take axes and ride to Vince's Creek and destroy that bridge."

Smith's eyes lit up. "That's our only way of escape, General."

"*We* will have no need for escape," Houston answered dryly.

Smith beamed. "It looks like a fight at last."

"It is. The future of Texas will be decided here before sundown. You'd better hurry back if you want to get in the fight. Take one other man to help you."

"I'll take that man Summers, who has been actin' as your orderly," Smith replied. "He's got the only horse that can keep up with me on the way there or back. Go slow, General. I've rid a long ways to miss out on this."

7

At three o'clock Houston ordered his officers to parade their commands. The right wing was under Colonel Millard, the center under Colonel Burleson, the left wing under Colonel Sherman. The "Twin Sisters" occupied the position on the right of the center, and the mounted men, under Lamar, ranged on the extreme right flank.

When they were formed, Houston mounted his mud-splashed white horse and rode down the length of his ragged and dirty command. His blanket was gone from his shoulders, lost somewhere on the line of march, and the incessant rains had faded the bright colors in his sash. It was nothing more than a soiled, tattered band. His sabre hung suspended from buckskin thongs and his fawn-colored trousers were stuffed into boots that bore the caked mud of many a muddy mile. But they had carried a giant from seclusion to this field of decision and glory.

"Forward!" rang out his sharp, incisive command.

On the left the clear notes of a fife struck up the tune, "Come to the Bower I Have Shaded for You." The "Twin Sisters" rolled forward, bumping and rumbling. There was the quick step of hurrying feet and the clatter of hoofs as the impatient cavalry swung into the advance.

"Hold your fire until you can pick your man!" Houston shouted as he rode down the line. "Hold your fire!"

Just as the cavalry unit under Lamar swung out from behind the trees masking their advance, "Deaf" Smith and Summers came dashing up to join them. Their horses were a welter of foam and mud. Smith was yelling like an Indian.

"The Bridge is down! The Bridge is down! You've got to lick 'em!"

Summers, spurring along the line, echoed the shout, "The Bridge is down! The Bridge is down! Remember the Alamo! Remember Goliad!"

All along the advancing line the cry was taken up. "Remember the Alamo! Remember Goliad!"

The attack had come at the very hour when the Mexicans had least suspected it. Many of them, including General Santa Anna, were taking an afternoon siesta. A considerable number of Mexican cavalry were leading their horses to water. Surprised by the suddenness of the attack, they rushed to their feeble fortifications and fired aimlessly at the advancing line. Several Texans, forgetting Houston's order, opened in reply.

Houston wheeled in his saddle. "Hold your fire, God damn you! I told you to hold your fire!"

Summers could hold his fire but could not control the fire of vengeance within him. He sank his spurs into his tired horse and like a man made mad by torturing memories rode full at the enemy position. Infantry and horse quickly closed the gap and when almost upon the Mexicans the Texans opened fire. It was a volley at point blank range. The Mexicans fell like grain before the sickle. No time for reloading now. The Texans clubbed their muskets and skulls were smashed like nuts under a heavy hammer. It was grim, close work.

"Remember the Alamo! Remember Goliad!" Between the swings of their clubbed rifles the men found time to keep up the cry.

All along the line the dazed Mexicans cast aside their guns, fell to their knees and cried out: "Me no Alamo! Me no Goliad!"

Crack! went their skulls with a sound like the splintering of seasoned pine. That would silence their lying tongues!

Summers was riding up and down the line, his rifle swinging in great arcs as he beat down all in his path. He was remembering the Alamo. He was adding to the red toll which Bullard and Crockett had taken before the weight of numbers bore them down.

Hard Cash, nostrils dilated and red with the strain of the hard ride to Vince's Bridge, caught the spirit of his master's vengeance. He became the coal black mount of Death.

A small group of Mexican soldiers and officers were attempting to rally on a small knoll a few yards back of the advance position. Summers saw them, as did a score of Lamar's horse, and with the unity of purpose that comes to men in moments of high action, they swung their horses into line and swept over the knoll as frightened cattle would beat down an ant hill.

Directly in Summer's path one man, in the uniform of a Mexican officer, realizing that nothing could stop that charge, fired wildly with his pistol and took to his heels. Summers swung wide to pursue him. The man cast one frightened look backward. Then it was that Summers recognized him. It was Gant, the betrayer of Sally, the plotter, the schemer, the philanderer, and now a renegade in the uniform of a Mexican officer, running like a rabbit to escape death under the heels of a thundering black Nemesis.

A riderless horse, with bridle reins flying, came galloping across the field at an angle that would intersect Gant's line of flight. Gant had one hope left—that he could catch the reins of that horse.

Summers' rifle had been empty since that first charge, and there was now no time for reloading. As he drove his spurs into Hard Cash's flanks a hundred memories flashed through his mind. Before him, in the flesh it seemed, stood lovely Sally Ransome, her eyes wide with wonderment and dismay.

Summers sank deep his spurs and grasped his rifle by the very end of the long barrel. If only Jeff were here in his place! If only Jeff could see what was about to take place at the end of the long trail.

Gant, running and stumbling, threw up his hands to catch the reins of the riderless horse. They closed upon them and the horse, brought to a sudden stop, swung around in a wide half circle.

That moment a tornado of vengeance struck. Summers' rifle, swinging in a great arc, descended on Gant's head like the hammer of angered Thor. There was a splintering crash, a flinging upward and outward of arms as Gant's fingers released their hold on the bridle reins. Like a reed he went down under the pounding hoofs of Hard Cash.

Summers cast one backward look as he swung to rejoin the unit that had swept over the knoll and were turning to seek further opposition. The outstretched form in the tall grass lay very, very still. The riderless horse, again free, galloped away.

Now, within ten minutes from the beginning of the attack, all the Mexicans left alive were in wild, frantic flight. They sought escape over the prairie, and they ran back into the marsh where, bogged down to their waists, they made easy targets for the Texans who seemed never to tire of that vengeful chant, "Remember the Alamo! Remember Goliad!"

Lamar's cavalry unit rode pellmell through the camp and then took up the individual pursuit of those seeking escape across the prairie toward the crossing where once had stood Vince's Bridge.

Houston, shot in the ankle and with his horse down, was being carried from the field. But not for a second did the fighting and the slaughter cease.

The battle had begun at sundown. Before the color had faded from the western sky the grass and flowers of the prairie were drinking freshets of blood. Vince's Creek ran red as the western sky. Eight hundred dead and wounded Mexicans had paid for blood with blood.

But Santa Anna had lost all appetite for it. The butcher of the Alamo, his heart turned from stone to a tremulous, pulsing thing that hammered like the heart of a frightened hare, was crawling through the tall grass seeking escape. Belly down in the wet grass, "the Napoleon of the West" crawled from his Waterloo toward Vince's Bridge.

All night long galloping horsemen sought for him. The skies were clear now. Every man could see the bright star of independence rising. But not until Santa Anna was captured would it become a star of the first magnitude.

Over the prairies Summers ranged, in company with others from Lamar's command, urging their spent horses to still greater efforts. Lying in the tall grass, Santa Anna could hear the clippety-clop, clippety-clop of hoofs that would glory in riding him down.

From a camp fire under the trees on the banks of Buffalo Bayou came the clear, soft notes of a single fife, playing over and over the one tune known by the fifer, "Come to the Bower I Have Shaded for You."

Santa Anna heard the hated, alien tongues that were lifted in triumphant chorus. He heard, too, the ranging hoof beats of the horses of the more energetic Texans who would join voices in a still louder chorus could they but come upon the butcher of the Alamo.

Under a tree, where a camp fire burned brightly, Old Sam Houston, child of destiny, sat nursing a wounded ankle and listening with grim satisfaction to the acclaim of those who were now willing to admit that he had led them to a field where there was glory enough for all.

BUENA VISTA

by George C. Furber

It is not the size of the person alone that makes the efficient soldier; neither does it always happen in the field that those regiments composed, as the remark is, "of the finest looking men," who move "like clock work," in every drill and evolution to the spot, distinguish themselves in action above the others. Sometimes it is the reverse of this with whole regiments, and often so with individual soldiers, who, good for nothing at drill, or in camp, or in fatigue parties, are yet the very d—v—l for fighting.

Elgin A. Mullins, of company I. of the 1st Mississippi rifle regiment, was an instance of this. Mullins was a little fellow, a very little fellow; so short was he that when he made his application at Vicksburg for admission to the ranks of the company from Holly Springs, under the command of the gallant Captain J. H. Taylor, he was refused, solely on account of his diminutive stature, and perhaps the looks of his "phiz," which was by no means handsome; but the captain, seeing in it the indications of a determined spirit, and fearless disposition, evaded the military restriction by receiving Mullins as a fifer, and so in that capacity he was mustered into the service;—but a fife had always been Mullins' aversion, he had never tried to blow one himself, and his limited knowledge of music did not enable him to distinguish one note or tune from another. However, when the instrument was handed over to him he made some vigorous efforts to extract music of some sort from it, to the great amusement of the company; entirely failing therein, he threw it down, and applied to Captain Taylor for a rifle and accoutrements, and was accordingly furnished with one, which to load he had to place with the butt of it from him before the muzzle could be sufficiently depressed to enable

From: *Fighting On One's Own Hook.*

him to insert the cartridge. So Mullins went to the war, on the muster roll a fifer, but any thing but that elsewhere. During the whole campaign he never again touched a fife, though he was extremely fond of the name of a musician, and it was of much advantage to him, for being neither that, nor marshaled in the ranks, he moved in a sort of independent manner,—going and coming pretty much as he chose. A perfect stranger to fear, completely reckless of consequences, he would go alone out of camp for beef, stroll off further, run more risks, and bring in more beef than any other one chose to do. Several little skirmishes he got into with rancheros and guerrillas, but his rifle was good—though held low, its aim was sure. At the battle of Monterey he was in his element, for rapidly back and forth behind walls, and houses, and in the open streets, amid the thunders of the battle, did "little Mullins," as he was called, coolly load, and as coolly, and every time with effect, fire upon the enemy on the house tops, and behind the barricades;—storms of grape and canister swept continually by and around him, but touched him not. If his eye caught a good view of a Mexican through the smoke, that chap was sure to hear from his rifle. He noticed not what troops he was amid, for part of the time he was with his own regiment, then in the 1st Tennessee, and then in the 1st Ohio. The little Mississippian, known by his rifle, was in all ranks occasionally, but mostly by himself, and in the latter way was he, when after fort Tannerio was taken, the commanding officer advanced toward General Twiggs, drawing his sword to deliver it, Mullins was near, covered with sweat, and blackened by the smoke of gunpowder, he was resting, breathing hard with his previous exertions. In no manner had the conflict slackened in front, or on the right of them as they thus stood—the cannon shot and shells from the other forts were turned upon the captured, and were striking around, while the discharges of small arms were incessant. A dim, blue, hazy smoke hung above the captured fortress, in, and before which, so many lay dead, dying, or freely bleeding. Mullins casting his eye toward the officer as he was thus drawing his sword, thought that he was about to attack General Twiggs, and without the least reflection, leveling his rifle, at the instantaneous crack, down dropped the Mexican with the sword in his hand. Twiggs was furious, and forgetting his station, he ran toward the little fifer with his drawn sword lifted, and anger flashing from his eyes, looking more enraged on account of his having white mustachios, and Mullins, on his approach, for the first time, "turned tail," and ran as fast as his duck legs could carry him, looking behind him, and up to the sword gleaming over the head of the infuriated general, who had overtaken him with the same ratio of speed that a war horse would run down a pony. The blow descending on the little fifer's head was, however, diverted by the second thought of the general, to a severe slap with the broad side, instead of the edge, across the shoulders of the culprit, followed by others with all the force of the general's brawny arm, accompanied by a storm of curses at "the little rascal," who danced around, more concerned, however, at having the general thus upon him, than at the blows. This castigation, which was given directly under the full fire of fort Diablo, was only stopped by the running up of the other officers of Twiggs' staff, who interfered, and the little fifer cleared out; the general composing himself, returned. The Mexican was dead, and the only effect on the other Mexican officers was a quiet smile at seeing *el general Americano* running so furiously after his little soldier. They were conducted off, and in less than ten minutes Mullins was with some scattered men of the Baltimore battalion;—he fought the whole time, and though so exposed, came out without a mark, save the one left by the sword of General Twiggs.

At Buena Vista, Mullins was present. When the regiment marched from Saltillo in the morning for the field, and the sudden peals of cannon reverberating along the mountains informed them that the bloody conflict was already commenced, the march was hastened, and in the quickest step they hastened along. Mullins' legs were worked to great disadvantage in conveying their owner fast enough, loaded as he was with the rifle, and full supplies of ammunition, together with his knapsack. He puffed and blowed, trotted and walked by turns, as eager as any; he was fretted and angry because he could not keep up. He swore he would have a horse before night, that he would fight like a gentleman, and so grumbling, cursing, trotting and puffing, the little fifer kept in the rear of his company.

As the regiment arrived at the battle field, it went immediately into action, advancing against the heavy body of the Mexican army which had driven in the left of the American line. Mullins, as the regiment halted, and formed in line of battle, forgot his short legs, and delivered his fire for several successive volleys with effect. The regiment, however, were obliged to fall back, and then were charged upon by a body of Mexican lancers, who were repulsed by the rifle balls alone, which emptied the saddles of many, and the loose horses bounded in terror over the field. Again did the little fifer long for a horse as he saw these thus loose, but there was no time then to endeavor to get one. United with the 3d Indianians, the regiment again successfully withstood a heavy attack of the Mexican column, and Mullins' rifle rang clear as any at their approach; but a lull in the storm of battle took place at the appearance of a flag of truce from the Mexican general. During the temporary cessation of the firing, the wearied soldiers threw themselves on the ground and endeavored to assuage the sufferings of their companions. A Mexican horse richly caparisoned, came bounding over the field. Upon seeing him, the fifer, unable to resist the temptation, started after him, and getting near to him, attracted his attention by his soothing voice. The horse stopped, turned round, threw higher his head, and examined Mullins as he silently approached, but not satisfied with his appearance, the animal turned with a loud snort, and rapidly ran off farther, and toward the Mexicans who were at the foot of the mountain. Within the reach of their fire did Mullins pursue, unmindful of them, and as much engaged, in these terrible moments of suspense to thousands, in endeavoring to catch the horse, as though he and the animal were in a quiet pasture at home. No thought of the instantaneous renewal of the battle crossed his mind. Luckily for him, the horse starting onward again, ran around over the scene of the late conflict down between the stations of the American troops; becoming more gentle towards his pursuer, and soothed by the latter's continual coaxing as he came near, the horse finally stopped in a ravine, and allowed Mullins to secure him. Once mounted, he found two fine pistols in the holsters, both loaded; exulting in his prize, he came up out of the ravine, looking for his regiment, but the battle had recommenced in all its fury. Far over the plain and the mountains on either hand his vision extended, the former here and there obscured by clouds of rising dust and smoke; to his left was a long and imposing body of Mexican cavalry, already on the move; to his right, as he faced the gorge, or pass, where the heat of the fight was going on, was the hacienda of Buena Vista, and between him and that was a small body of American cavalry. His own regiment having shifted its position, toward this body of Arkansas cavalry he rode, was welcomed by them, and joined in the ranks, though he had but his rifle and pistols. The Mexican cavalry making a circuit, came down on the hacienda of Buena Vista like an avalanche. Nobly did the little band under Col. Yell meet the shock, and although the column in its impetuosity forced these out of the way and destroyed the gallant leader with many of his men, yet the destruction in their own ranks, forced the column after much loss, to divide—part to retreat, and part to continue on towards the mountain; upon those thus retreating the fire of the scattered bodies of Americans rapidly recruiting, was incessant, while the cavalry pursued, using their sabers with effect. With these our little fifer and his charger rapidly rode, but his long rifle was empty, nor could he there load it, his pistols were also discharged, and he was not skillful enough in cavalry exercises to be able then to reload them. It was more than he could do to hold his rifle and restrain his fiery horse. So on after the retreating column Mullins sped like the wind; the foremost rank of the pursuers was gained, and Mullins was in the "mêlée," but wholly inefficient where the blow of the saber was parried by the lance, and steel clashed with steel.

"Hold on, Mississippian, you will be killed," shouted an officer of May's dragoons, as Mullins was passing him, both going at the top of their speed. "G-d, I can't do it," was the reply, as Mullins dashed ahead, tugging with all his might at the reins, but the furious horse recognizing his companions, ran after them regardless of restraint, and singling out one that was ridden by a Mexican sergeant, pursued him with all the vigor with which his powerful limbs were endowed. The sergeant thus so rapidly pursued, though well armed, turned and doubled as he sped over the plain, but the horse of the fifer turned and doubled as the other did, and gained upon him at every leap;—Mullins now was rather anxious to be on foot again. He would not have cared, but been highly gratified, had he only a loaded pistol, a rifle, or a bayonet,—but as he rapidly neared, in spite of himself, the long keen lance that glistened in his vision, he felt it in imagination, already insinuating its cold surface through his liver, and again he gave a desperate pull at the reins, but the horse with a higher bound than before, still kept on. The Mexican plunged his long spurs in the side of his animal. With the swiftness of the wind, and far away from either of the contending armies, did the two speed on in their singular race. Nearer and nearer yet came Mullins to the dreaded lance, and again did he throw his strength on the reins, but to no purpose, and as bound after bound brought the head of his horse up near to the quarter of the other, the Mexican glancing behind for an instant, lowered his formidable weapon, as Mullins thought, to transfix him with its sharp point. A most vigorous jerk on one rein did he give the steed to pull him off from the other, but the advantage thus for an instant gained, was lost by the next bound bringing him full along side of his antagonist. The Mexican, frightened nearly out of his wits, raised his lance quickly, and handed it over to the other. Checking his horse, Mullins also slackened his speed, as his rider eagerly clutched the lance so unexpectedly presented to him, and after a few short bounds the two stopped. Our little fifer, out of breath with his race, demanded in broken Spanish the name of the other, "Francisco Alvases, señor," said the sergeant, who in turn then asked the name of his captor—"my name is fifer Mullins, of Captain

Taylor's company of the 1st Mississippi rifle regiment, at your service," pompously replied Mullins,—"*no entienda Engles,*" (I don't understand English,) said the other, wagging his head. "Well, come along then," said Mullins, "you can understand this," as he caught the other's horse by the reins, and his own then satisfied, willing to walk, he led the prisoner triumphantly back to Colonel May, to whom he delivered him. When complimented by that officer amid the smiles of all in the ranks, who having discontinued the pursuit, had seen the race, and were now for a few moments at rest, he replied that he was only anxious the prisoner should know by whom he had been captured, "for," said he, "colonel, the d—d Mexican don't understand me." One of the men in the ranks who spoke Spanish was called out by the colonel, who was amused at the eagerness of the little Mississippian. To him the fifer spoke,—"Tell him," pointing to the prisoner,—"that my name is fifer Mullins, of Captain Taylor's company, 1st regiment of Mississippi rifles." This was translated to the prisoner, who acknowledged it by a polite bow. The fifer rode off satisfied, and the prisoner was sent to the rear. Mullins, however, had enough of fighting on horseback for that time, and getting to the hacienda he secured his horse, and on foot fought the remainder of the day, part of the time with the 2d Kentucky infantry, part by himself, until near the close of the action, he again joined his own company, swearing "by G—d, this thing of fighting on horseback, and loading one's gun going at full speed among the enemy, was not the thing it was 'cracked up to be.'"

INDIAN WARS

INDIAN WARS

So many wars were fought against the Indians of various tribes it is well-nigh impossible to tabulate them. For the most part they were composed of fierce, merciless skirmishes and deadly little sieges which killed people just as dead as any great crashing battle.

In these myriad half-forgotten conflicts the typical American soldier showed to best advantage. Such fighting gave latitude to his individualism, to his personal prowess, and to his basic pugnacity.

Sometimes the Army became over-confident or careless as at Wounded Knee and Little Bighorn, but in the main a mere handful of troops, aided by scouts, held at bay or drove off masses of crafty enemies.

If ever we have fought all-out battles, it was during these half-forgotten conflicts. Men, women and children, soldiers and civilians all served on the fighting front, all risked their scalps and lives.

That the course of Empire continued Westward was entirely due to the ingenuity, the adaptibility, and the rough-and-ready hardihood of the pioneers and the scattering of troops sent by a begrudging government to guard them.

THE NORTH CAROLINA FRONTIER

by WILLIAM GILMORE SIMMS

THERE ARE PROBABLY some old persons still living upon the upper dividing line between North and South Carolina, who still remember the form and features of the venerable Daniel Nelson. The old man was still living so late as 1817. At that period he removed to Mississippi, where, we believe, he died in less than three months after his change of residence. An old tree does not bear transplanting easily, and does not long survive it. Daniel Nelson came from Virginia when a youth. He was one of the first who settled on the southern borders of North Carolina, or, at least in that neighbourhood where he afterwards passed the greatest portion of his days.

At that time the country was not only a forest, but one thickly settled with Indians. It constituted the favourite hunting-grounds for several of their tribes. But this circumstance did not discourage young Nelson. He was then a stalwart youth, broad-chested, tall, with a fiery eye, and an almost equally fiery soul—certainly with a very fearless one. His companions, who were few in number, were like himself. The spirit of old Daniel Boone was a more common one than is supposed. Adventure gladdened and excited their hearts—danger only seemed to provoke their determination,—and mere hardship was something which their frames appeared to covet. It was as refreshing to them as drink. Having seen the country, and struck down some of its game,—tasted of its bear-meat and buffalo, its deer and turkey,—all, at that time, in the greatest abundance,— they returned for the one thing most needful to a brave forester in a new country,—a good, brisk, fearless wife, who, like the damsel in Scripture, would go whithersoever went the husband to whom her affections were surrendered. They had no fear, these bold young hunters, to make a home and rear an infant family in regions so remote from the secure walks of civilization. They had met and made an acquaintance and a sort of friendship with the Indians, and, in the superior vigour of their own frames, their greater courage, and better weapons, they perhaps had come

From: *The Wigwam and the Cabin.*

to form a too contemptuous estimate of the savage. But they were not beguiled by him into too much confidence. Their log houses were so constructed as to be fortresses upon occasion, and they lived not so far removed from one another, but that the leaguer of one would be sure, in twenty-four hours, to bring the others to his assistance. Besides, with a stock of bear-meat and venison always on hand, sufficient for a winter, either of these fortresses might, upon common calculations, be maintained for several weeks against any single band of the Indians, in the small numbers in which they were wont to range together in those neighbourhoods. In this way these bold pioneers took possession of the soil, and paved the way for still mightier generations. Though wandering, and somewhat averse to the tedious labours of the farm, they were still not wholly unmindful of its duties; and their open lands grew larger every season, and increasing comforts annually spoke for the increasing civilization of the settlers. Corn was in plenty in proportion to the bear-meat, and the squatters almost grew indifferent to those first apprehensions, which had made them watch the approaches of the most friendly Indian as if he had been an enemy. At the end of five years, in which they had suffered no hurt and but little annoyance of any sort from their wild neighbour, it would seem as if this confidence in the security of their situation was not without sufficient justification.

But just then, circumstances seemed to threaten an interruption of this goodly state of things. The Indians were becoming discontented. Other tribes, more frequently in contact with the larger settlements of the whites,—wronged by them in trade, or demoralized by drink,—complained of their sufferings and injuries, or, as is more probable, were greedy to obtain their treasures, in bulk, which they were permitted to see, but denied to enjoy, or only in limited quantity. Their appetites and complaints were transmitted, by inevitable sympathies, to their brethren of the interior, and our worthy settlers upon the Haw, were rendered anxious at signs which warned them of a change in the peaceful relations which had hitherto existed in all the intercourse between the differing races. We need not dwell upon or describe these signs, with which, from frequent narratives of like character, our people are already sufficiently familiar. They were easily understood by our little colony, and by none more quickly than Daniel Nelson. They rendered him anxious, it is true, but not apprehensive; and, like a good husband, while he strove not to frighten his wife by what he said, he deemed it necessary to prepare her mind for the worst that might occur. This task over, he felt somewhat relieved, though, when he took his little girl, now five years old, upon his

knee that evening, and looked upon his infant boy in the lap of his
mother, he felt his anxieties very much increase; and that very night he
resumed a practice which he had latterly abandoned, but which had been
adopted as a measure of strict precaution, from the very first establishment
of their little settlement. As soon as supper was over, he resumed his rifle,
thrust his *conteau de chasse* into his belt, and, taking his horn about his
neck, and calling up his trusty dog, Clinch, he proceeded to scour the
woods immediately around his habitation. This task, performed with the
stealthy caution of the hunter, occupied some time, and, as the night was
clear, a bright starlight, the weather moderate, and his own mood restless, he determined to strike through the forest to the settlement of Jacob
Ransom, about four miles off, in order to prompt him, and, through him,
others of the neighbourhood, to the continued exercise of a caution which
he now thought necessary. The rest of this night's adventure we propose
to let him tell in his own words, as he has been heard to relate it a thousand times in his old age, at a period of life when, with one foot in his
grave, to suppose him guilty of falsehood, or of telling that which he did
not himself fervently believe, would be, among all those who knew him,
to suppose the most impossible and extravagant thing in the world.

☆

☆   ☆

"WELL, MY FRIENDS," said the veteran, then seventy, drawing his figure
up to its fullest height, and extending his right arm, while his left still
grasped the muzzle of his ancient rifle, which he swayed from side to
side, the butt resting on the floor—"Well, my friends, seeing that the
night was cl'ar, and there was no wind, and feeling as how I didn't want
for sleep, I called to Clinch and took the path for Jake Ransom's. I knew
that Jake was a sleepy sort of chap, and if the redskins caught any body
napping, he'd, most likely, be the man. But I confess, 'twarn't so much
for his sake, as for the sake of all,—of my own as well as the rest;—for,
when I thought how soon, if we warn't all together in the business, I
might see, without being able to put in, the long yellow hair of Betsy and
the babies twirling on the thumbs of some painted devil of the tribe,—I
can't tell you how I felt, but it warn't like a human, though I shivered
mightily like one,—'twas wolfish, as if the hair was turned in and rubbing agin the very heart within me. I said my prayers, where I stood,
looking up at the stars, and thinking that, after all, all was in the hands
and the marcy of God. This sort o' thinking quieted me, and I went
ahead pretty free, for I knew the track jest as well by night as by day,

though I didn't go so quick, for I was all the time on the look-out for the enemy. Now, after we reached a place in the woods where there was a gully and a mighty bad crossing, there were two roads to get to Jake's—one by the hollows, and one jest across the hills. I don't know why, but I didn't give myself time to think, and struck right across the hill, though that was rather the longest way.

"Howsomedever, on I went, and Clinch pretty close behind me. The dog was a good dog, with a mighty keen nose to hunt, but jest then he didn't seem to have the notion for it. The hill was a sizeable one, a good stretch to foot, and I began to remember, after awhile, that I had been in the woods from blessed dawn; and that made me see how it was with poor Clinch, and why he didn't go for'ad; but I was more than half way, and wasn't guine to turn back till I had said my say to Jake. Well, when I got to the top of the hill, I stopped, and rubbed my eyes. I had cause to rub 'em, for what should I see at a distance but a great fire. At first I was afeard lest it was Jake's house, but I considered, the next moment, that he lived to the left, and this fire was cl'ar to the right, and it did seem to me as if 'twas more near to my own. Here was something to scare a body. But I couldn't stay there looking, and it warn't now a time to go to Jake's; so I turned off, and, though Clinch was mighty onwilling, I bolted on the road to the fire. I say road, but there was no road; but the trees warn't over-thick, and the land was too poor for undergrowth; so we got on pretty well, considering. But, what with the tire I had had, and the scare I felt, it seemed as if I didn't get for'ad a bit. There was the fire still burning as bright and almost as far off as ever. When I saw this I stopt and looked at Clinch, and he stopped and looked at me, but neither of us had any thing to say. Well, after a moment's thinking, it seemed as if I shouldn't be much of a man to give up when I had got so far, so I pushed on. We crossed more than one little hill, then down and through the hollow, and then up the hill again. At last we got upon a small mountain the Indians called Nolleehatchie, and then it seemed as if the fire had come to a stop, for it was now burning bright, on a little hill below me, and not two hundred yards in front. It was a regular camp fire, pretty big, and there was more than a dozen Indians sitting round it. 'Well,' says I to myself, 'it's come upon us mighty sudden, and what's to be done? Not a soul in the settlement knows it but myself, and nobody's on the watch. They'll be sculped, every human of them, in their very beds, or, moutbe, waken up in the blaze, to be shot with arrows as they run.' I was in a cold sweat to think of it. I didn't know what to think and what to do. I looked round to Clinch, and the strangest thing of all was to see him sitting quiet on his haunches, looking at me, and at the stars, and not at the fire jest before him. Now, Clinch was a famous fine hunting dog, and jest as good on an Indian trail as any other. He know'd my ways, and what I wanted, and would give tongue, or keep it still, jest as I axed him. It was sensible enough, jest then, that he shouldn't bark, but, dang it!—he didn't even seem to see. Now, there warn't a dog in all the settlement so quick and keen to show sense as Clinch, even when he didn't say a word;—and to see him looking as if he didn't know and didn't care what was a-going on, with his eyes sot in his head and glazed over with sleep, was, as I may say, very onnatural, jest at that time, in a dog of any onderstanding. So I looked at him, half angry, and when he saw me looking at him, he jest stretched himself off, put his nose on his legs, and went to sleep in 'arnest. I had half a mind to lay my knife-handle over his head, but I considered better of it, and though it did seem the strangest thing in the world that he shouldn't even try to get to the fire, for warm sake, yet I recollected that dog natur', like human natur', can't stand every thing, and he hadn't such good reason as I had, to know that the Indians were no longer friendly to us. Well, there I stood, a pretty considerable chance, looking, and wondering, and onbeknowing what to do. I was mighty beflustered. But at last I felt ashamed to be so oncertain, and then again it was a needcessity that we should know the worst one time or another, so I determined to push for'ad. I was no slouch of a hunter, as you may suppose; so, as I was nearing the camp, I begun sneaking; and, taking it sometimes on hands and knees, and sometimes flat to the ground, where there was neither tree nor bush to cover me, I went ahead, Clinch keeping close behind me, and not showing any notion of what I was after. It was a slow business, because it was a ticklish business; but I was a leetle too anxious to be altogether so careful as a good sneak ought to be, and I went on rather faster than I would advise any young man to go in a time of war, when the inimy is in the neighbourhood. Well, as I went, there was the fire, getting larger and larger every minute, and there were the Indians round it, getting plainer and plainer. There was so much smoke that there was no making out, at any distance, any but their figures, and these, every now and then, would be so wrapt in the smoke that not more than half of them could be seen at the same moment. At last I stopped, jest at a place where I thought I could make out all that I wanted. There was a sizeable rock before me, and I leaned my elbows on it to look. I reckon I warn't more than thirty yards from the fire. There were some bushes betwixt us, and what with the bushes and the smoke, it was several minutes before I could separate man from man, and see what they were all adoing, and when I did, it was only for a moment at a time, when a puff of smoke would wrap them all, and make it as difficult as ever. But when I did contrive to see clearly, the sight was one to worry me to the core, for, in the midst of the redskins, I could see a white one, and that white one a woman. There was no mistake. There were the Indians, some with their backs, and some with their faces to me; and there, a little a-one side, but still among them, was a woman. When the smoke blowed off, I could see her white face, bright like any star, shining out of the clouds, and looking so pale and ghastly that my blood cruddled in my veins to think lest she might be dead from fright. But it couldn't be so, for she was sitting up and looking about her. But the Indians were motionless. They jest sat or lay as when I first saw them —doing nothing—saying nothing, but jest as motionless as the stone under my elbow. I couldn't stand looking where I was, so I began creeping again, getting nigher and nigher, until it seemed to me as if I ought to be able to read every face. But what with the paint and smoke I couldn't make out a single Indian. Their figures seemed plain enough in their buffalo-skins and blankets, but their faces seemed always in the dark. But it wasn't so with the woman. I could make her out clearly. She was very young; I reckon not more than fifteen, and it seemed to me as if I knew her looks very well. She was very handsome, and her hair was loosed upon her back. My heart felt strange to see her. I was weak as any child. It seemed as if I could die for the gal, and yet I hadn't strength enough to raise my rifle to my shoulder. The weakness kept on me the more I looked; for every moment seemed to make the poor child more and more dear to me. But the strangest thing of all was to see how motionless was every Indian in the camp. Not a word was spoken—not a limb or finger stirred. There they sat, or lay, round about the fire, like so many effigies, looking at the gal, and she looking at them. I never was in such a fix of fear and weakness in my life. What was I to do? I had got so nigh that I could have stuck my knife, with a jerk, into the heart of any one of the party, yet I hadn't the soul to lift it; and before I knew where I was, I cried like a child. But my crying didn't make 'em look about 'em. It only brought my poor dog Clinch leaping upon me, and whining, as if he wanted to give me consolation. Hardly knowing what I did, I tried to set him upon the camp, but the poor fellow didn't seem to understand me; and in my desperation, for it was a sort of madness growing out of my scare, I jumped headlong for'ad, jest where I saw the party sitting, willing to lose my life rather than suffer from such a strange sort of misery.

☆

☆   ☆

"WILL YOU BELIEVE ME! there were no Indians, no young woman, no fire! I stood up in the very place where I had seen the blaze and the smoke, and there was nothing! I looked for'ad and about me—there was no sign of fire any where. Where I stood was covered with dry leaves, the same as the rest of the forest. I was stupefied. I was like a man roused out of sleep by a strange dream, and seeing nothing. All was dark and silent. The stars were overhead, but that was all the light I had. I was more scared than ever, and, as it's a good rule when a man feels that he can do nothing himself, to look to the great God who can do everything, I kneeled down and said my prayers—the second time that night that I had done the same thing, and the second time, I reckon, that I had ever done so in the woods. After that I felt stronger. I felt sure that this sign hadn't been shown to me for nothing; and while I was turning about, looking and thinking to turn on the back track for home, Clinch began to prick up his ears and waken up. I clapped him on his back, and got my knife ready. It might be a *painter* that stirred him, for he could scent that beast a great distance. But, as he showed no fright, only a sort of quickening, I knew there was nothing to fear. In a moment he started off, and went boldly ahead. I followed him, but hadn't gone twenty steps down the hill and into the hollow, when I heard something like a groan. This quickened me, and keeping up with the dog, he led me to the foot of the hollow, where was a sort of pond. Clinch ran right for it, and another groan set me in the same direction. When I got up to the dog, he was on the butt-end of an old tree that had fallen, I reckon, before my time, and was half buried in the water. I jumped on it, and walked a few steps for'ad, when, what should I see but a human, half across the log, with his legs hanging in the water, and his head down. I called Clinch back out of my way, and went to the spot. The groans were pretty constant. I stooped down and laid my hands upon the person, and, as I felt the hair, I knew it was an Indian. The head was clammy with blood, so that my fingers stuck, and when I attempted to turn it, to look at the face, the groan was deeper than ever; but 'twarn't a time to suck one's fingers. I took him up, clapped my shoulders to it, and, fixing my feet firmly on the old tree, which was rather slippery, I brought the poor fellow out without much trouble. Though tall, he was not heavy, and was only a boy of fourteen or fifteen. The wonder was how a lad like that should get into such a fix. Well, I brought him out and laid him on the dry leaves. His groans stopped, and I thought he was dead, but I felt his heart, and it was still warm, and I thought, though I couldn't be sure, there was a beat under my fingers. What to do was the next question. It was now pretty late in the night. I had been all day a-foot, and, though still willing to go, yet the thought of such a weight on my shoulders made me stagger. But 'twouldn't do to leave him where he was to perish. I thought, if so be I had a son in such a fix, what would I think of the stranger who should go home and wait till daylight to give him help! No, darn my splinters, said I—though I had just done my prayers—if I leave the lad— and, tightening my girth, I give my whole soul to it, and hoisted him on my shoulders. My cabin, I reckoned, was good three miles off. You can guess what trouble I had, and what a tire under my load, before I got home and laid the poor fellow down by the fire. I then called up Betsy, and we both set to work to see if we could stir up the life that was in him. She cut away his hair, and I washed the blood from his head, which was chopped to the bone, either with a knife or hatchet. It was a God's blessing it hadn't gone into his brain, for it was fairly enough aimed for it, jest above the ear. When we come to open his clothes, we found an- other wound in his side. This was done with a knife, and, I suppose, was pretty deep. He had lost blood enough, for all his clothes were stiff with it. We knew nothing much of doctoring, but we had some rum in the cabin, and after washing his wounds clean with it, and pouring some down his throat, he began to groan more freely, and by that we knew he was coming to a nateral feeling. We rubbed his body down with warm cloths, and after a little while, seeing that he made some signs, I give him water as much as he could drink. This seemed to do him good, and hav- ing done every thing that we thought could help him, we wrapped him up warmly before the fire, and I stretched myself off beside him. 'Twould be a long story to tell, step by step, how he got on. It's enough to say that he didn't die that bout. We got him on his legs in a short time, doing little or nothing for him more than we did at first. The lad was a good lad, though, at first, when he first came to his senses, he was mighty shy, wouldn't look steadily in our faces, and, I do believe, if he could have got out of the cabin, would have done so as soon as he could stagger. But he was too weak to try that, and, meanwhile, when he saw our kindness, he was softened. By little and little, he got to play with my little Lucy, who was not quite six years old; and, after a while, he seemed to be never better pleased than when they played together. The child, too, after her first fright, leaned to the lad, and was jest as willing to play with him as if he had been a cl'ar white like herself. He could say a few words of English from the beginning, and learn't quickly; but, though he talked tolerable free for an Indian, yet I could never get him to tell me how he was wounded, or by whom. His brow blackened when I spoke of it, and his lips would be shut together, as if he was ready to fight sooner than to speak. Well, I didn't push him to know, for I was pretty sure the head of the truth will be sure to come some time or other, if you once have it by the tail, provided you don't jerk it off by straining too hard upon it.

☆

☆　　　☆

"I SUPPOSE THE LAD had been with us a matter of six weeks, getting better every day, but so slowly that he had not, at the end of that time, been able to leave the picket. Meanwhile, our troubles with the Indians were increasing. As yet, there had been no bloodshed in our quarter, but we heard of murders and sculpings on every side, and we took for granted that we must have our turn. We made our preparations, repaired the pickets, laid in ammunition, and took turns for scouting nightly. At length, the signs of Indians got to be thick in our parts, though we could see none. Jake Ransom had come upon one of their camps after they had left it; and we had reason to apprehend every thing, inasmuch as the out-lyers didn't show themselves, as they used to do, but prowled about the cabins and went from place to place, only by night, or by close skulking in the thickets. One evening after this, I went out as usual to go the rounds, taking Clinch with me, but I hadn't got far from the gate, when the dog stopped and gave a low bark;—then I knew there was mischief, so I turned round quietly, without making any show of scare, and got back safely, though not a minute too soon. They trailed me to the gate the moment after I had got it fastened, and were pretty mad, I reckon, when they found their plan had failed for surprising me. But for the keen nose of poor Clinch, with all my skill in scouting,—and it was not small even in that early day,—they'd 'a had me, and all that was mine, before the sun could open his eyes to see what they were after. Finding they had failed in their ambush, they made the woods ring with the war-whoop, which was a sign that they were guine to give us a regular siege. At the sound of the whoop, we could see the eyes of the Indian boy brighten, and his ears prick up, jest like a hound's when he first gets scent of the deer, or hears the horn of the hunter. I looked closely at the lad, and was dub'ous what to do. He mout be only an enemy in the camp, and while I was fighting in front, he might be cutting the throats of my wife and children within. I did not tell you that I had picked up his bow and arrows near the little lake where I had found him, and his hunting-knife was sticking in his belt when I brought him home. Whether to take these away from him, was the question. Suppose I did, a billet of wood would answer pretty near as well. I thought the matter over while I watched him. Thought runs mighty quick in time of danger! Well, after turning it over on every side, I concluded 'twas better to trust him jest as if he had been a sure friend. I couldn't think, after all we had done for him, that he'd be false, so I said to him—'Lenatewá!'— 'twas so he called himself—'those are your people!' 'Yes!' he answered slowly, and lifting himself up as if he had been a lord—he was a stately-looking lad, and carried himself like the son of a Micco,* as he was—'Yes, they are the people of Lenatewá—must he go to them?' and he made the motion of going out. But I stopped him. I was not willing to lose the security which I had from his being a sort of prisoner. 'No,' said I; 'no, Lenatewá, not to-night. To-morrow will do. To-morrow you can tell them I am a friend, not an enemy, and they should not come to burn my wigwam.' 'Brother—friend!' said the lad, advancing with a sort of freedom and taking my hand. He then went to my wife, and did the same thing,—not regarding she was a woman,—'Brother—friend!' I watched him closely, watched his eye and his motions, and I said to Betsy, 'The lad is true; don't be afeard!' But we passed a weary night. Every now and then we could hear the whoop of the Indians. From the loop-holes we could see the light of three fires on different sides, by which we knew that they were prepared to cut off any help that might come to us from the rest of the settlement. But I didn't give in or despair. I worked at one thing or another all night, and though Lenatewá gave me no help, yet he sat quietly, or laid himself down before the fire, as if he had nothing in the world to do in the darkness. Next morning by day-light, I found him already dressed in the same bloody clothes which he had on when I found him. He had thrown aside all that I gave him, and though the hunting-shirt and leggins which he now wore, were very much stained with blood and dirt, he had fixed them about him with a good deal of care and neatness, as if preparing to see company. I must tell you that an Indian of good family always has a nateral sort of grace and dignity which I never saw in a white man. He was busily engaged

* A prince or chief.

looking through one of the loop-holes, and though I could distinguish nothing, yet it was cl'ar that he saw something to interest him mightily. I soon found out that, in spite of all my watchfulness, he had contrived to have some sort of correspondence and communication with those outside. This was a wonder to me then, for I did not recollect his bow and arrows. It seems that he had shot an arrow through one of the loop-holes, to the end of which he had fastened a tuft of his own hair. The effect of this was considerable, and to this it was owing that, for a few hours afterwards, we saw not an Indian. The arrow was shot at the very peep of day. What they were about, in the meantime, I can only guess, and the guess was only easy, after I had known all that was to happen. That they were in council what to do was cl'ar enough. I was not to know that the council was like to end in cutting some of their own throats instead of ours. But when we did see the enemy fairly, they came out of the woods in two parties, not actually separated, but not moving together. It seemed as if there was some strife among them. Their whole number could not be less than forty, and some eight or ten of these walked apart under the lead of a chief, a stout, dark-looking fellow, one-half of whose face was painted black as midnight, with a red circle round both his eyes. The other party was headed by an old white-headed chief, who couldn't ha' been less than sixty years—a pretty fellow, you may be sure, at his time of life, to be looking after sculps of women and children. While I was kneeling at my loop-hole looking at them, Lenatewá came to me, and touching me on the arm, pointed to the old chief, saying—'Micco Lenatewá Glucco,' by which I guessed he was the father or grandfather of the lad. 'Well,' I said, seeing that the best plan was to get their confidence and friendship if possible,—'Well, lad, go to your father and tell him what Daniel Nelson has done for you, and let's have peace. We can fight, boy, as you see; we have plenty of arms and provisions; and with this rifle, though you may not believe it, I could pick off your father, the king, and that other chief, who has so devilled himself up with paint.' 'Shoot!' said the lad quickly pointing to the chief of whom I had last spoken. 'Ah! he is your enemy then?' The lad nodded his head, and pointed to the wound on his temple, and that in his side. I now began to see the true state of the case. 'No,' said I; 'no, Lenatewá, I will shoot none. I am for peace. I would do good to the Indians, and be their friend. Go to your father and tell him so. Go, and make him be my friend.' The youth caught my hand, placed it on the top of his head, and exclaimed, 'Good!' I then attended him down to the gate, but, before he left the cabin, he stopped and put his hand on the head of little Lucy,—and I felt

glad, for it seemed to say, 'you shan't be hurt—not a hair of your head!'
I let him out, fastened up, and then hastened to the loop-hole.

☆

☆   ☆

"AND NOW CAME a sight to tarrify. As soon as the Indians saw the
young prince, they set up a general cry. I couldn't tell whether it was of
joy, or what. He went for'ad boldly, though he was still quite weak, and
the king at the head of his party advanced to meet him. The other and
smaller party, headed by the black chief, whom young Lenatewá had
told me to shoot, came forward also, but very slowly, and it seemed as
if they were doubtful whether to come or go. Their leader looked pretty
much beflustered. But they hadn't time for much study, for, after the
young prince had met his father, and a few words had passed between
them, I saw the finger of Lenatewá point to the black chief. At this, he
lifted up his clenched fists, and worked his body as if he was talking
angrily. Then, sudden, the warwhoop sounded from the king's party, and
the other troop of Indians began to run, the black chief at their head;
but he had not got twenty steps when a dozen arrows went into him,
and he tumbled for'a'ds, and grappled with the earth. It was all over
with him. His party was scattered on all sides, but were not pursued. It
seemed that all the arrows had been aimed at the one person, and when
he sprawled, there was an end to it: the whole affair was over in five
minutes.

☆

☆   ☆

"IT WAS A FORTUNATE affair for us. Lenatewá soon brought the old Micco
to terms of peace. For that matter, he had only consented to take up the
red stick because it was reported by the black chief—who was the uncle
of the young Micco, and had good reasons for getting him out of the
way—that he had been murdered by the whites. This driv' the old man
to desperation, and brought him down upon us. When he knew the
whole truth, and saw what friends we had been to his son, there was no
end to his thanks and promises. He swore to be my friend while the
sun shone, while the waters run, and while the mountains stood, and I
believe, if the good old man had been spared so long, he would have
been true to his oath. But, while he lived, he kept it, and so did his son
when he succeeded him as Micco Glucco. Year after year went by, and
though there was frequent war between the Indians and the whites, yet

Lenatewá kept it from our doors. He himself was at war several times with our people, but never with our settlement. He put his *totem* on our trees, and the Indians knew that they were sacred. But, after a space of eleven years, there was a change. The young prince seemed to have forgotten our friendship. We now never saw him among us, and, unfortunately, some of our young men—the young men of our own settlement—murdered three young warriors of the Ripparee tribe, who were found on horses stolen from us. I was very sorry when I heard it, and began to fear the consequences; and they came upon us when we least looked for it. I had every reason to think that Lenatewá would still keep the warfare from my little family, but I did not remember that he was the prince of a tribe only, and not of the nation. This was a national warfare, in which the whole Cherokee people were in arms. Many persons, living still, remember that terrible war, and how the Carolinians humbled them at last; but there's no telling how much blood was shed in that war, how many sculps taken, how much misery suffered by young and old, men, women, and children. Our settlement had become so large and scattered that we had to build a sizeable blockhouse, which we stored, and to which we could retreat whenever it was necessary. We took possession of it on hearing from our scouts that Indian trails had been seen, and there we put the women and children, under a strong guard. By day we tended our farms, and only went to our families at night. We had kept them in this fix for five weeks or thereabouts, and there was no attack. The Indian signs disappeared, and we all thought the storm had blown over, and began to hope and to believe that the old friendship of Lenatewá had saved us. With this thinking, we began to be less watchful. The men would stay all night at the farms, and sometimes, in the day, would carry with them the women, and sometimes some even the children. I cautioned them agin this, but they mocked me, and said I was gitting old and scary. I told them, 'Wait and see who'll scare first.' But, I confess, not seeing any Indians in all my scouting, I began to feel and think like the rest, and to grow careless. I let Betsy go now and then with me to the farm, though she kept it from me that she had gone there more than once with Lucy, without any man protector. Still, as it was only a short mile and a half from the block, and we could hear of no Indians, it did not seem so venturesome a thing. One day we heard of some very large b'ars among the thickets—a famous range for them, about four miles from the settlement; and a party of us, Simon Lorris, Hugh Darling, Jake Ransom, William Harkless, and myself, taking our dogs, set off on the hunt. We started the b'ar with a rush, and I got the first shot at a mighty big she b'ar, the largest I had ever seen—lamed the critter slightly, and dashed into the thickets after her! The others pushed, in another direction, after the rest, leaving me to finish my work as I could.

"I had two dogs with me, Clap and Claw, but they were young things, and couldn't be trusted much in a close brush with a b'ar. Old Clinch was dead, or he'd ha' made other guess-work with the varmint. But, hot after the b'ar, I didn't think of the quality of the dogs till I found myself in a fair wrestle with the brute. I don't brag, my friends, but that *was* a fight. I tell you my breath was clean gone, for the b'ar had me about the thin of my body, and I thought I was doubled up enough to be laid down without more handling. But my heart was strong when I thought of Betsy and the children, and I got my knife, with hard *jugging*—though I couldn't use my arm above my elbow—through the old critter's hide, and in among her ribs. That only seemed to make her hug closer, and I reckon I was clean gone, if it hadn't been that she blowed out before me. I had worked a pretty deep window in her waist, and then life run out plentiful. Her nose dropped agin my breast, and then her paws; and when the strain was gone, I fell down like a sick child, and she fell on top of me. But she warn't in a humour to do more mischief. She roughed me once or twice more with her paws, but that was only because she was at her last kick. There I lay a matter of half an hour, with the dead b'ar alongside o' me. I was almost as little able to move as she, and I vomited as if I had taken physic. When I come to myself and got up, there was no sound of the hunters. There I was with the two dogs and the b'ar, all alone, and the sun already long past the turn. My horse, which I had fastened outside of the thicket, had slipped his bridle, and, I reckoned, had either strayed off grazing, or had pushed back directly for the block. These things didn't make me feel much better. But, though my stomach didn't feel altogether right, and my ribs were as sore as if I had been sweating under a coating of hickory, I felt that there was no use and no time to stand there grunting. But I made out to skin and to cut up the b'ar, and a noble mountain of fat she made. I took the skin with me, and, covering the flesh with bark, I whistled off the dogs, after they had eat to fill, and pushed after my horse. I followed his track for some time, till I grew fairly tired. He had gone off in a scare and at a full gallop, and, instead of going home, had dashed down the lower side of the thicket, then gone aside, to round some of the hills, and thrown himself out of the track, it moutbe seven miles or more. When I found this, I saw there was no use to hunt him that day and afoot, and I had no more to do but turn about, and push as fast as I could for the block. But this was work enough. By this time the sun was pretty low, and there was now a good seven miles, work it how I could, before me. But I was getting over my b'ar-sickness, and though my legs felt weary enough, my stomach was better, and my heart braver; and, as I was in no hurry, having the whole night before me, and knowing the way by night as well as by light, I began to feel cheerful enough, all things considering. I pushed on slowly, stopping every now and then for rest, and recovering my strength this way. I had some parched meal and sugar in my pouch which I ate, and it helped me mightily. It was my only dinner that day. The evening got to be very still. I wondered I had seen and heard nothing of Jake Ransom and the rest, but I didn't feel at all oneasy about them, thinking that, like all other hunters, they would naterally follow the game to any distance. But, jest when I was thinking about them, I heard a gun, then another, and after that all got to be as quiet as ever. I looked to my own rifle and felt for my knife, and put forward a little more briskly. I suppose I had walked an hour after this, when it came on close dark, and I was still four good miles from the block. The night was cloudy, there were no stars, and the feeling in the air was damp and oncomfortable. I began to wish I was safe home, and felt queerish, almost as bad as I did when the b'ar was 'bracing me; but it warn't so much the body-sickness as the heart-sickness. I felt as if something was going wrong. Jest as this feeling was most worrisome, I stumbled over a human. My blood cruddled, when, feeling about, I put my hand on his head, and found the sculp was gone. Then I knew there was mischief. I couldn't make out who 'twas that was under me, but I reckoned 'was one of the hunters. There was nothing to be done but to push for'ad. I didn't feel any more tire. I felt ready for fight, and when I thought of our wives and children in the block, and what might become of them, I got wolfish, though the Lord only knows what I was minded to do. I can't say I had any raal sensible thoughts of what was to be done in the business. I didn't trust myself to think whether the Indians had been to the block yet or no; though ugly notions came across me when I remembered how we let the women and children go about to the farms. I was in a complete fever and agy. I scorched one time and shivered another, but I pushed on, for there was now no more feeling of tire in my limbs than if they were made of steel. By this time I had reached that long range of hills where I first saw that strange campfire, now eleven years gone, that turned out to be a deception, and it was nateral enough that the thing should come fresh into my mind, jest at that moment.

While I was thinking over the wonder, and asking myself, as I had done over and often before, what it possibly could mean, I reached the top of one of the hills, from which I could see, in daylight, the whole country for a matter of ten miles or more on every side. What was my surprise, do you reckon, when there, jest on the very same hill opposite where I had seen that apparition of a camp, I saw another, and this time it was a raal one. There was a rousing blaze, and though the woods and undergrowth were thicker on this than on the other side, from which I had seen it before, yet I could make out that there were several figures, and them Indians. It sort o' made me easier to see the enemy before, and then I could better tell what I had to do. I was to spy out the camp, see what the red-devils were thinking to do, and what they had already done. I was a little better scout and hunter this time than when I made the same sort o' search before, and I reckoned that I could get nigh enough to see all that was going on, without stirring up any dust among 'em. But I had to keep the dogs back. I couldn't tie 'em up, for they'd howl; so I stripped my hunting-shirt and put it down for one to guard, and I gave my cap and horn to another. I knew they'd never leave 'em, for I had l'arned 'em all that sort of business—to watch as well as to fetch and carry. I then said a sort of short running prayer, and took the trail. I had to work for'ad slowly. If I had gone on this time as I did in that first camp transaction, I'd ha' lost my sculp to a sartainty. Well, to shorten a long business, I tell you that I got nigh enough, without scare or surprise, to see all that I care to see, and a great deal more than I wished to see; and now, for the first time, I saw the meaning of that sight which I had, eleven years before, of the camp that come to nothing. I saw that first sight over again, the Indians round the fire, a young woman in the middle, and that young woman my own daughter, my child, my poor, dear Lucy!

☆
☆   ☆

"THAT WAS A SIGHT for a father. I can't tell you—and I won' try—how I felt. But I lay there, resting upon my hands and knees, jest as if I had been turned into stone with looking. I lay so for a good half hour, I reckon, without stirring a limb; and you could only tell that life was in me, by seeing the big drops that squeezed out of my eyes now and then, and by a sort of shivering that shook me as you sometimes see the canebrake shaking with the gust of the pond inside. I tried to pray to God for help, but I couldn't pray, and as for thinking, that was jest as impossible. But I could do nothing by looking, and, for that matter, it was pretty cla'r to me, as I stood, with no help—by myself—one rifle only and knife—I couldn't do much by moving. I could have lifted the gun, and in a twinkle, tumbled the best fellow in the gang, but what good was that guine to do me? I was never fond of blood-spilling, and if I could have been made sure of my daughter, I'd ha' been willing that the red devils should have had leave to live for ever. What was I to do? Go to the block? Who know'd if it warn't taken, with every soul in it? And where else was I to look for help? Nowhere, nowhere but to God! I groaned—I groaned so loud that I was dreadful 'feared that they'd hear me; but they were too busy among themselves, eating supper, and poor Lucy in the midst, not eating, but so pale, and looking so miserable—jest as I had seen her, when she was only a child—in the same fix, though 'twas only an appearance—eleven years ago! Well, at last, I turned off. As I couldn't say what to do, I was too miserable to look, and I went down to the bottom of the hill and rolled about on the ground, pulling the hair out of my head and groaning, as if that was to do me any good. Before I knew where I was, there was a hand on my shoulder. I jumped up to my feet, and flung my rifle over my head, meaning to bring the butt down upon the stranger—but his voice stopped me.

"'Brother,' said he, 'me Lenatewá!'

"The way he talked, his soft tones, made me know that the young prince meant to be friendly, and I gave him my hand; but the tears gushed out as I did so, and I cried out like a man struck in the very heart, while I pointed to the hill—'My child, my child!'

"'Be man!' said he, 'come!' pulling me away.

"'But, will you save her, Lenatewá?'

"He did not answer instantly, but led me to the little lake, and pointed to the old tree over which I had borne his lifeless body so many years ago. By that I knew he meant to tell me, he had not forgotten what I had done for him; and would do for me all he could. But this did not satisfy me. I must know how and when it was to be done, and what was his hope; for I could see from his caution, and leading me away from the camp, that he did not command the party, and had no power over them. He then asked me, if I had not seen the paint of the warriors in the camp. But I had seen nothing but the fix of my child. He then described the paint to me, which was his way of showing me that the party on the hill were his deadly enemies. The paint about their eyes was that of the great chief, his uncle, who had tried to murder him years ago, and who had been shot, in my sight, by the party of his father. The young chief, now in command of the band on the hill was the son of his uncle, and sworn to revenge the death of his father upon him, Lenatewá. This he made me onderstand in a few minutes. And he gave me farther to onderstand, that there was no way of getting my child from them onless by cunning. He had but two followers with him, and they were even then busy in making preparations. But of these preparations he either would not or could not give me any account; and I had to wait on him with all the patience I could muster; and no easy trial it was, for an Indian is the most cool and slow-moving creature in the world, unless he's actually fighting, and then he's about the quickest. After awhile, Lenatewá led me round the hill. We fetched a pretty smart reach, and before I knew where I was, he led me into a hollow that I had never seen before. Here, to my surprise, there were no less than twelve or fourteen horses fastened, that these red devils had stolen from the settlement that very day, and mine was among them. I did not know it till the young prince told me.

" 'Him soon move,' said he, pointing to one on the outside, which a close examination showed me to be my own—'Him soon move,'—and these words gave me a notion of his plan. But he did not allow me to have any hand in it—not jest then, at least. Bidding me keep a watch on the fire above, for the hollow in which we stood was at the foot of the very hill the Indians had made their camp on—though the stretch was a long one between—he pushed for'ad like a shadow, and so slily, so silently, that, though I thought myself a good deal of a scout before, I saw then that I warn't fit to hold a splinter to him. In a little time he had unhitched my horse, and quietly led him farther down the hollow, half round the hill, and then up the opposite hill. There was very little noise, the wind was from the camp, and, though they didn't show any alarm, I was never more scary in my life. I followed Lenatewá, and found where he had fastened my nag. He had placed him several hundred yards from the Indians, on his way to the block; and, where we now stood, owing to the bend of the hollow, the camp of the Indians was between us and where they had hitched the stolen horses. When I saw this, I began to guess something of his plan. Meantime, one after the other, his two followers came up, and made a long report to him in their own language. This done, he told me that three of my hunting companions had been sculped, the other, who was Hugh Darling, had got off cl'ar, though fired upon twice, and had alarmed the block, and that my daughter had been made prisoner at the farm to which she had gone without any company. This made me a little easier, and Lenatewá then told me what he meant to do. In course, I had to do something myself towards it. Off he went, with his two men, leaving me to myself. When I thought they had got pretty fairly round the hill, I started back for the camp, trying my best, you may be sure, to move as slily as Lenatewá. I got within twenty-five yards, I reckon, when I thought it better to lie by quietly and wait. I could see every head in the huddle, and my poor child among them, looking whiter than a sheet, beside their ugly painted skins. Well, I hadn't long to wait, when there was such an uproar among the stolen horses in the hollow on the opposite side of the hill—such a trampling, such a whinnying and whickering, you never heard the like. Now, you must know, that a stolen horse, to an Indian, is jest as precious as a sweetheart to a white man; and when the rumpus reached the camp, there was a rush of every man among them, for his critter. Every redskin, but one, went over the hill after the horses, and he jumped up with the rest, but didn't move off. He stood over poor Lucy with his tomahawk, shaking it above her head, as if guine to strike every minute. She, poor child—I could see her as plain as the fire-light, for she sat jest on one side of it—her hands were clasped together. She was praying, for she must have looked every minute to be knocked on the head. You may depend, I found it very hard to keep in. I was a'most biling over, the more when I saw the red devil making his flourishes, every now and then, close to the child's ears, with his bloody we'pon. But it was a need-cessity to keep in till the sounds died off pretty much, so as not to give them any scare this side, till they had dashed ahead pretty far 'pon the other. I don't know that I waited quite as long as I ought to, but I waited as long as my feelings would let me, and then I dropped the sight of my rifle as close as I could fix it on the breast of the Indian that had the keep-ing of my child. I took aim, but I felt I was a little tremorsome, and I stopped. I know'd I had but one shoot, and if I didn't onbutton him in that one, it would be a bad shoot for poor Lucy. I didn't fear to hit *her*, and I was pretty sure I'd hit him. But it must be a dead shot to good, for I know'd if I only hurt him, that he'd sink the tomahawk in her head with what strength he had left him. I brought myself to it again, and this time I felt strong. I could jest hear a little of the hubbub of men and horses afar off. I knew it was the time, and, resting the side of the muzzle against a tree, I give him the whole blessing of the bullet. I didn't stop to ask what luck, but run in, with a sort o' cry, to do the finishing with the knife. But the thing was done a'ready. The beast was on his back, and I only had to use the knife in cutting the vines that fastened the child to the sapling behind her. The brave gal didn't scream or faint. She could only say, 'Oh, my father!' and I could only say, 'Oh! my child!' And what a precious hug followed; but it was only for a minute. We had no time to waste in hugging. We pushed at once for the place where I had left the critter, and if the good old nag ever used his four shanks to any purpose, he did that night. I reckon it was a joyful surprise to poor Betsy when we broke into the block. She had given it out for sartin that she'd never see me or the child again, with a nateral sculp on our heads.

☆

☆   ☆

"THERE'S NO NEED to tell you the whole story of this war between our people and the redskins. It's enough that I tell you of what happened to us, and our share in it. Of the great affair, and all the fights and burnings, you'll find enough in the printed books and newspapers. What I tell you, though you can't find it in any books, is jest as true, for all that. Of our share in it, the worst has already been told you. The young chief, Oloschottee—for that was his name—the cousin and the enemy of Lenatewá, had command of the Indians that were to surprise our settlements; and though he didn't altogether do what he expected and intended, he worked us quite enough of mischief as it was. He soon put fire to all our farms to draw us out of the block, but finding that wouldn't do, he left us; for an Indian gets pretty soon tired of a long siege where there is neither rum nor blood to git drunk on. His force was too small to trouble us in the block, and so he drawed off his warriors, and we saw no more of him until the peace. That followed pretty soon after General Middleton gave the nation that licking at Echotee,—a licking, I reckon, that they'll remember long after my day. At that affair Lenatewá got an ugly bullet in his throat, and if it hadn't been for one of his men, he'd ha' got a bag'net in his breast. They made a narrow run with him, head foremost down the hill, with a whole swad of the mounted men from the low country at their heels. It was sometime after the peace before he got better of his hurt, though the Indians are naterally more skilful in cures than white men. By this time we had all gone home to our farms, and had planted and rebuilt, and begun to forget our troubles, when who should pop into our cabin one day, but Lenatewá. He had got quite well of his hurts. He was a monstrous fine-looking fellow, tall and handsome, and he was dressed in his very best. He wore pantaloons, like one of us, and his hunting shirt was a raaly fine blue, with a white fringe. He wore no paint, and was quite nice and neat with his person. We all received him as an old friend, and he stayed with us three days. Then he went, and was gone for a matter of two weeks, when he came back and stayed with us another three days. And so, off and on, he came to visit us, until Betsy said to me one day, 'Daniel, that Indian, Lenatewá, comes here after Lucy. Leave a woman to guess these things.' After she told me, I recollected that the young prince was quite watchful of Lucy, and would follow her out into the garden, and leave us, to walk with her. But then, again, I thought—'What if he is favourable to my daughter? The fellow's a good fellow; and a raal, noble-hearted Indian, that's sober, is jest as good, to my thinking, as any white man in the land.' But Betsy wouldn't hear to it. 'Her daughter never should marry a savage, and a heathen, and a redskin, while her head was hot:'—and while her head was so hot, what was I to do? All I could say was this only, 'Don't kick, Betsy, till you're spurred. 'Twill be time enough to give the young Chief his answer when he asks the question; and it won't do for us to treat him rudely, when we consider how much we owe him.' But she was of the mind that the boot was on the other leg,—that it was he and not us that owed the debt; and all that I could do couldn't keep her from showing the lad a sour face of it whenever he came. But he didn't seem much to mind this, since I was civil and kind to him. Lucy too, though her mother warned her against him, always treated him civilly as I told her; though she naterally would do so, for she couldn't so easily forget that dreadful night when she was a prisoner in the camp of the enemy, not knowing what to expect, with an Indian tomahawk over her head, and saved, in great part, by the cunning and courage of this same Lenatewá. The girl treated him kindly, and I was not sorry she did so. She walked and talked with him jest as if they had been brother and sister, and he was jest as polite to her as if he had been a born Frenchman.

"You may be sure, it was no pleasant sight to my wife to see them two go out to walk. 'Daniel Nelson,' said she, 'do you see and keep an eye on those people. There's no knowing what may happen. I do believe that Lucy has a liking for that redskin, and should they run!'—'Psho!' said I,—but that wouldn't do for her, and so she made me watch the young people sure enough. 'Twarn't a business that I was overfond of, you may reckon, but I was a rough man and didn't know much of woman natur'. I left the judgment of such things to my wife, and did pretty much what she told me. Whenever they went out to walk, I followed them, rifle in hand; but it was only to please Betsy, for if I had seen the lad running off with the girl, I'm pretty sure, I'd never ha' been the man to draw trigger upon him. As I said before, Lenatewá was jest as good a husband as she could have had. But, poor fellow, the affair was never to come to that. One day, after he had been with us almost a week, he spoke softly to Lucy, and she got up, got her bonnet and went out with him. I didn't see them when they started, for I happened to be in the upper story,—a place where we didn't so much live, but where we used to go for shelter and defence whenever any Indians came about us. 'Daniel,' said my wife, and I knew by the quickness and sharpness of her voice what 'twas she had to tell me. But jest then I was busy, and, moreover, I didn't altogether like the sort of business upon which she wanted me to go. The sneaking after an enimy, in raal warfare, is an onpleasant sort of thing enough but this sneaking after one that you think your friend is worse than running in a fair fight, and always gave me a sheepish feeling after it. Besides, I didn't fear Lenatewá, and I didn't fear my daughter. It's true, the girl treated him kindly and sweetly, but that was owing to the nateral sweetness of her temper, and because she felt how much sarvice he had been to her and all of us. So, instead of going out after them, I thought I'd given them a look through one of the loop-holes. Well, there they went, walking among the trees, not far from the picket, and no time out of sight. As I looked at them, I thought to myself, 'Wouldn't they make a handsome couple!' Both of them were tall and well made. As for Lucy, there wasn't, for figure, a finer set girl in all the settlement, and her face was a match for her figure. And then she was so easy in her motion, so graceful, and walked, or sate, or danced, —jest, for all the world, as if she was born only to do the particular thing she was doing. As for Lenatewá, he was a lad among a thousand. Now, a young Indian warrior, when he don't drink, is about the noblest-looking creature, as he carries himself in the woods, that God ever did make. So straight, so proud, so stately, always as if he was doing a great action—as if he knew the whole world was looking at him. Lenatewá was pretty much the handsomest and noblest Indian I had ever seen; and then, I know'd him to be raally so noble. As they walked together, their heads a little bent downward, and Lucy's pretty low, the thought flashed across me that, jest then, he was telling her all about his feelings; and perhaps, said I to myself, the girl thinks about it pretty much as I do. Moutbe now, she likes him better than any body she has ever seen, and what more nateral? Then I thought, if there is any picture in this life more sweet and beautiful than two young people jest beginning to feel love for one another, and walking together in the innocence of their hearts, under the shady trees—I've never seen it! I laid the rifle on my lap, and sat down on the floor and watched 'em through the loop until

I felt the water in my eyes. They walked backwards and for'ads, not a hundred yards off, and I could see all their motions, though I couldn't hear their words. An Indian don't use his hands much generally, but I could see that Lenatewá was using his—not a great deal, but as if he felt every word he was saying. Then I began to think, what was I to do, if so be he was raally offering to marry Lucy, and she willing! How was I to do? what was I to say?—how could I refuse him when I was willing? how could I say 'yes,' when Betsey said 'no!'

"Well, in the midst of this thinking, what should I hear but a loud cry from the child; then a loud yell—a regular war-whoop—sounded right in front, as if it came from Lenatewá himself. I looked up quickly, for, in thinking, I had lost sight of them, and was only looking at my rifle; I looked out, and there, in the twinkle of an eye, there was another sight. I saw my daughter flat upon the ground, lying like one dead, and Lenatewá staggering back as if he was mortally hurt; while, pressing fast upon him, was an Indian warrior, with his tomahawk uplifted, striking—once, twice, three times—hard and heavy, right upon the face and forehead of the young prince. From the black paint on his face, and the red ring about his eyes, and from his figure and the eagle feathers in his head, I soon guessed it was Oloschottee, and I then knew it was the old revenge for the killing of his father; for an Indian never forgets that sort of obligation. Of course, I didn't stand quiet to see an old friend, like Lenatewá, tumbled in that way, without warning, like a bullock; and there was my own daughter lying flat, and I wasn't to know that he hadn't struck her too. It was only one motion for me to draw sight upon the savage, and another to pull trigger; and I reckon he dropped jest as soon as the young Chief. I gave one whoop for all the world as if I was an Indian myself, and run out to the spot; but Lenatewá had got his discharge from further service. He warn't exactly dead, but his sense was swimming. He couldn't say much, and that warn't at all to the purpose. I could hear him, now and then, making a sort of singing noise, but that was soon swallowed up in a gurgle and a gasp, and it was all over. My bullet was quicker in its working than Oloschottee's hatchet; he was stone dead before I got to him. As for poor Lucy, she was not hurt, either by bullet or hatchet; but she had a hurt in the heart, whether from the scare she had, or because she had more feeling for the young prince than we reckoned, there's no telling. She warn't much given to smiling after that. But, whether she loved Lenatewá, we couldn't know, and I never was the man to ask her. It's sartin she never married, and she had about as many chances, and good ones, too, as any girl in our settlement. You've seen her—some among you—and warn't she a beauty—though I say it myself—the very flower of the forest!"

THE KENTUCKY FRONTIER

by ROBERT MONTGOMERY BIRD

THE MORNING-STAR, peeping into the hollow den of the wanderers, was yet bright on the horizon, when Roland was roused from his slumbers by Nathan, who had already risen and prepared a hasty meal, resembling in all respects that of the preceding evening. To this the soldier did better justice than to the other; for, although feeling sore and stiff in every limb, he experienced none of the feverish consequences Nathan had predicted, from his wounds; and his mind, invigorated by so many hours of rest, was more tranquil and cheerful. The confidence Nathan seemed to feel in the reasonableness and practicability of their enterprise, however wild and daring it might have seemed to others, was his own best assurance of its success; and hope thus enkindled, growing with his growing strength, it required no laborious effort to summon the spirits necessary to sustain him during the coming trials.

This change for the better was not unnoticed by Nathan, who exhorted him to eat freely, as a necessary prelude to the labors of the day; and the rude meal being quickly and satisfactorily despatched, and little Peter receiving his due share, the companions, without further delay, seized their arms and re-commenced their journey. Crossing the river at the buffalo-ford above, and exchanging the road to which it led for wilder and lonelier paths traced by smaller animals, they made their way through the forest, travelling with considerable speed, which was increased as the warmth of exercise gradually restored their native suppleness to the soldier's limbs.

And now it was that, as the opening of a glorious dawn, flinging sunshine and life over the whole wilderness, infused still brighter hopes into Roland's spirit, he began to divide his thoughts between his kins-

From: *Nick of the Woods.*

woman and his guide, bestowing more upon the latter than he had previously found time or inclination to do. His strange appearance, his stranger character, his sudden metamorphosis from a timid, and somewhat over-conscientious professor of the doctrines of peace and good-will, into a highly energetic and unremorseful, not to say, valiant, man of war, were all subjects to provoke the soldier's curiosity; which was still further increased when he pondered over the dismal story Nathan had so imperfectly told him on the past day.

Of those dreadful calamities which, in Nathan's own language, "had made him what he was," a houseless wanderer of the wilderness, the Virginian would have gladly known more; but his first allusion to the subject produced such evident disorder in Nathan's mind, as if the recollection were too harrowing to be borne, that the young man immediately repressed his inquiries, and diverted his guide's thoughts into another channel.

His imagination supplied the imperfect links in the story; he could well believe that the same hands which had shed the blood of every member of the poor borderer's family, might have struck the hatchet into the head of the resisting husband and father; and that the effects of that blow, with the desolation of heart and fortune which the heavier ones, struck at the same time, had entailed, might have driven him to the woods, an idle, and perhaps aimless wanderer.

How far these causes might have operated in leading Nathan into those late acts of blood which were at such variance with his faith and professions, it remained also for Roland to imagine; and, in truth, he imagined they had operated deeply and far; though nothing in Nathan's own admissions could be found to sanction any belief, save that they were the results partly of accident, and partly of sudden and irresistible impulse.

At all events, it was plain that his warlike feats, however they might at first have shocked his sense of propriety, now sat but lightly on his conscience; and, indeed, since his confession at the Piankeshaw camp, he ceased even to talk of them, perhaps resting upon that as an all-sufficient explanation and apology. It is certain, from that moment he bore himself more freely and boldly, entered no protest whatever against being called on to do his share of such fighting as might occur—a stipulation made with such anxious forethought, when he first consented to accompany the lost travellers—nor betrayed any tenderness of invective against the Indians, whom, having first spoke of them only as "evil-minded poor Shawnee creatures," he now designated, conformably to establish usage among his neighbors of the stations, as "thieves and dogs," "bloody villains, and rapscallions"; all which expressions he bestowed with as much ease and emphasis as if he had been accustomed to use them all his life.

With this singular friend and companion, Roland pursued his way through the wilderness, committing life, and the hopes that were dearer than life, to his sole guidance and protection; nor did any thing happen to shake his faith in either the zeal or ability of Nathan to conduct to a prosperous issue the cause he had so freely and disinterestedly espoused.

As they thridded the lonely forest-paths together, Nathan explained at length the circumstances upon which he founded his hopes of success in their project; and in doing so, convinced the soldier, not only that his sagacity was equal to the enterprise, but that his acquaintance with the wilderness was by no means confined to the region south of the Ohio; the northern countries, then wholly in the possession of the Indian tribes, appearing to be just as well known to him, the Miami country in particular, in which lay the village of the Black Vulture. How this knowledge had been obtained was not so evident; for although he averred he hunted the deer or trapped the beaver on either side of the river, as appeared to him most agreeable, it was hardly to be supposed he could carry on such operations in the heart of the Indian nation. But it was enough for Roland that the knowledge so essential to his own present plans was really possessed by his conductor, and he cared not to question how it had been arrived at; it was an augury of success, of which he felt the full influence.

The evening of that day found him upon the banks of the Kentucky, the wild and beautiful river from which the wilderness around derived its name; and the next morning, crossing it on a raft of logs speedily constructed by Nathan, he trod upon the soil of the north side, famous even then for its beauty and for the deeds of bloodshed, almost daily enacted among its scattered settlements, and destined, unhappily, to be rendered still more famous for a tragedy which that very day witnessed, far off among the barren ridges of the Licking, where sixty of the district's best and bravest sons fell the victims less of Indian subtlety than of their own unparalleled rashness. But of that bloody field the travellers were to hear thereafter; the vultures were winging their flight towards the fatal scene; but they alone could snuff, in that silent desert, the scent of the battle that vexed it.

Sleeping that night in the woods, the next day, being the fourth since they left the Piankeshaw camp, beheld the travellers upon the banks of the Ohio; which, seen for the first time in the glory of summer, its crystal waters wheeling placidly along amid hills and forests, even reflected in the bright mirror below, and with the air of virgin solitude which, through so many leagues of its course, it still presents, never fails to fill the beholder's mind with an enchanting sense of its loveliness.

Here a raft was again constructed; and the adventurers pushing boldly across, were soon upon the opposite shore. This feat accomplished, Nathan took the precaution to launch their frail float adrift in the current, that no tell-tale memorial of a white man's visit should remain to be read by returning warriors. The next moment ascending the bank of the river, he plunged with his companion into a maze of brake and forest, neither of them then dreaming that upon the very spot where they toiled through the tangled labyrinths, a few years should behold the magic spectacle of a fair city, the Queen of the West, uprisen with the suddenness, and almost the splendor, of the *Fata-Morgana,* though, happily, doomed to no such evanescent existence. Then handling their arms, like men who felt they were in a foeman's country, and knew that every further step was to be taken in peril, they resumed their journey, travelling with such speed and vigor (for Roland's strength had returned apace), that at the close of the day, they were, according to Nathan's account, scarce twenty miles distant from the Black Vulture's village, which they might easily reach the following day. On the following day, accordingly, they resumed their march, avoiding all paths, and stealing through the most unfrequented depths of the woods, proceeding with a caution which was every moment becoming more obviously necessary to the success of their enterprise.

Up to this period their journey had presented nothing of interest, being a mere succession of toil, privation, and occasional suffering, naturally enough to be expected in such an undertaking; but it was now about to be varied by an adventure of no little interest in itself, and, in its consequences, destined to exercise a powerful influence on the prospects of the travellers.

Laying their plans so as to reach the Indian village only about nightfall, and travelling but slowly, and with great circumspection, they had not at midday accomplished much more than half the distance; when they came to a halt in a little dell, extremely wild and sequestered, where Nathan proposed to rest a few hours and recruit their strength with a warm dinner—a luxury they had not enjoyed for the last two days, during which they had subsisted upon the corn and dried meat from the Indian wallets. Accident had a few moments before provided them materials for a more palatable meal. They had stumbled upon a deer that had just fallen under the attack of a catamount; which, easily driven from its yet warm and palpitating quarry, surrendered the feast to its unwelcome visitors.

An inspection of the carcass showed that the animal had been first struck by the bullet of some wandering Indian hunter, a discovery that somewhat concerned Nathan, until, after a more careful examination of the wound, which seemed neither severe nor mortal, he was convinced the poor beast had run many long miles, until, in fact, wholly exhausted before the panther had finished the work of the huntsman. This circumstance removing his uneasiness, he helped himself to the choicest portion of the animal, amputated a hind leg without stopping to flay it, and, clapping this upon his shoulder in a very businesslike way, left the remainder of the carcass to be despatched by the wildcat at her leisure.

The little dell, in which Nathan proposed to cook and enjoy his savory treasure, at ease and in safety, was enclosed by hills; of which the one by which they descended into it fell down in a rolling slope densely covered with trees; while the other, rocky, barren, and almost naked, rose precipitously up, a grim picture of solitude and desolation. A scanty brook, oozing along through the swampy bottom of the hollow, and supplied by a spring near its head, at which the two friends halted, to prepare their meal, ran meandering away, among alders and other swampy plants, to find exit into a larger vale that opened below, though hidden from the travellers by the winding of the rocky ridge before them.

In this lonely den, Nathan and Roland began straightway to disencumber themselves of arms and provisions, seeming well satisfied with its convenience. But not so little Peter; who, having faithfully accompanied them so far, now following humbly at his master's heels, and now, in periods of alarm or doubt, taking post in front, the leader of the party, uplifted his nose, and fell to snuffing about him in a way that soon attracted his master's notice. Smelling first around the spring and then giving a look both up and down the glen, as if to satisfy himself there was nothing wrong in either of those quarters, he finally began to ascend the rocky ridge, snuffing as he went, and ever and anon looking back to his master, and soliciting his attention by a wag of his tail.

"Truly, thee did once wag to me in vain!" said Nathan, snatching up his gun, and looking volumes of sagacious response at his brute ally, "but thee won't catch me napping again; though, truly, what thee can smell here, where is neither track of man nor print of beast, truly, Peter, I have no idea!"

With these words, he crept up the hill himself, following in little Peter's wake; and Roland, who also grasped his rifle, as Nathan had done, though without perhaps attaching the same importance to Peter's note of warning, thought fit to imitate his example.

In this manner cautiously crawling up, the two friends reached the crest of the hill; and peering over a precipice of fifty or more feet sheer descent, with which it suddenly dipped into a wild but beautiful little valley below, beheld a scene that, besides startling them somewhat out of their tranquillity, caused both to bless their good fortune they had not neglected the warning of their brute confederate.

The vale below, like that they had left, opened into a wider bottom land, the bed of a creek, which they could see shining among the trees that overshadowed the rich alluvion; and into this poured a rivulet that chattered along through the glen, at their feet, in which it had its sources. The hill on the other side of the little vale, which was of an oval figure, narrowest at its outlet, was rough and precipitous, like that on which they lay; but the two uniting above, bounded the head of the vale with a long, bushy, sweeping slope—a fragment of a natural amphitheatre—which was evidently of easy ascent, though abrupt and steep. The valley thus circumscribed, though broken, and here and there deeply furrowed by the watercourse, was nearly destitute of trees, except at its head, where a few young beeches flung their silver boughs and rich green foliage abroad over the grassy knolls, and patches of papaws drooped their loose leaves and swelling fruit over the stream.

It was in this part of the valley, at the distance of three or four hundred paces from them, that the eyes of the two adventurers, directed by the sound of voices, which they had heard the instant they reached the crest of the ridge, fell, first, upon the smoke of a huge fire curling merrily up into the air, and then upon the bodies of no less than five Indian warriors, all zealously and uproariously engaged in an amusement highly characteristic of their race. There was among them a white man, an unfortunate prisoner, as was seen at a glance, whom they had bound by the legs to a tree; around which the savages danced and leaped, yelling now with rage, now in merriment, but all the while belaboring the poor wretch with rods and switches, which, at every turn round the tree, they laid about his head and shoulders with uncommon energy and zest.

This was a species of diversion better relished, as it seemed, by the captors than their captive; who, infuriated by his pangs, and perhaps desiring, in the desperation of the moment, to provoke them to end his sufferings with the hatchet, retaliated with his fists, which were at liberty, striking fiercely at every opportunity, and once with such effect as to tumble one of the tormentors to the earth,—a catastrophe, however, that the others rewarded with roars of approving laughter, though without for a moment intermitting their own cruelties.

This spectacle, it may be well supposed, produced a strong effect upon the minds of the travellers, who, not without alarm on their own account at the discovery of such dangerous neighbors, could not view without emotion a fellow white man and countryman helpless in their hands, and enduring tortures perhaps preliminary to the more dreadful one of the stake. They looked one another in the face; the Virginian's eyes sparkled with a meaning which Nathan could not misunderstand; and clutching his rifle tighter in his hands, and eyeing the young man with an ominous stare, he muttered,—"Speak, friend,—thee is a man and a soldier—what does thee think, in the case made and provided?"

"We are but two men, and they five," replied Roland, firmly, though in the lowest voice; and then repeated, in the same energetic whisper,— "we are but two men, Nathan; but there is no kinswoman now to un- man me!"

Nathan took another peep at the savages, before speaking. Then looking upon the young man with an uneasy countenance, he said,— "We are but two men, as thee says, and they five; and, truly, to do what thee thinks of, in open day, is a thing not to be thought on by men that have soft places in their bosoms. Nevertheless, I think, according to thy own opinion, we being strong men that have the wind of the villains, and a good cause to help us, truly, we might snap the poor man they have captivated out of their hands, with considerable much of damage to them besides, the murdering rapscallions! But, friend," he added, seeing Roland give way to his eagerness,—"thee spoke of the fair maid, thy cousin—if thee fights this battle, truly, thee may never see her more."

"If I fall," said Roland,—but he was interrupted by Nathan:—

"It is not *that* thee is to think of. Truly, friend, thee may fight these savages, and thee may vanquish them; but unless thee believes in thy conscience thee can kill them every one—truly, friend, thee can hardly expect it?"

"And why should we? It is enough if we can rescue the prisoner."

"Friend, thee is mistaken. If thee attacks the villains, and but one of them escapes alive to the village, sounding the alarm, thee will never enter the same in search of the maid, thy kinswoman. Thee sees the case; thee must choose between the captive there and thy cousin!"

This was a view of the case, and, as Roland felt, a just one, well calculated to stagger his resolutions, if not entirely to abate his sympathy for the unknown sufferer. As his hopes of success in the enterprise for which he had already dared and endured so much, evidently depended upon his ability to approach the Indian village without awakening suspicion, it was undeniable that an attack upon the party in the vale, unless resulting in its complete destruction, must cause to be borne to the Black Vulture's town, and on the wings of the wind, the alarm of white men in the woods; and thus not only cut him off from it, but actually bring upon himself all the fighting men who might be remaining in the village. To attack the party, with the expectation of wholly destroying it, was, or seemed to be, an absurdity. But to desert a wretched prisoner whom he had it perhaps in his power to rescue from captivity, and from a fate still more dreadful, was a dereliction of duty, of honor, of common humanity, of which he could scarce persuade himself to be guilty.

He cast his eyes upon the glen, and once more looked upon the captive, who had sunk to the ground as if from exhaustion, and whom the savages, after beating him awhile longer, as if to force him again on his feet, that they might enjoy their amusement awhile longer, now fell to securing with thongs. As Roland looked, he remembered his own night of captivity, and hesitated no longer. Turning to Nathan, who had been earnestly reading the struggles of his mind, as revealed in his face, he said, and with unfaltering resolution,—"You say we can rescue that man—I was a prisoner, like him, bound too,—a helpless, hopeless captive,—three Indians to guard me, and but one friend to look upon me; yet did not that friend abandon me to my fate. God will protect my poor cousin, we must rescue him!"

"Thee is a man, every inch of thee!" said Nathan, with a look of uncommon satisfaction and fire; "thee shall have thy will, in the matter of these murdering Shawnee dogs; and it may be, it will be none the worse for thy kins-woman."

With that, he motioned Roland to creep with him beyond the crest of the hill, where they straightway held a hurried consultation of war to determine upon the plan of proceedings, in the prosecution of an adventure so wild and perilous.

The soldier, burning with fierce ardor, proposed that they should take post respectively, the one at the head, the other at the outlet of the vale, and creeping as nigh the enemy as they could, deliver their fire, and then rushing on, before the savages could recover from their surprise, do their best to finish the affair with their hatchets, a plan which, as he just said, offered the only prospect of cutting off the retreat of those who might survive the fire.

But Nathan had already schemed the matter otherwise; he had remarked the impossibility of approaching the enemy from below, the valley offering no concealment which would make an advance in that quarter practicable; whereas the bushes on the slope, where the two walls of the glen united, afforded the most inviting opportunity to creep on the foe without fear of detection.

"Truly," said he, "we will get us as nigh the assassin thieves as we can; and, truly, it may be our luck, each of us, to get a brace of them in range together, and so bang them beautiful!"—an idea that was manifestly highly agreeable to his imagination, from which he seemed to have utterly banished all those disgusts and painsgivings on the subject of fighting, which had formerly afflicted it; "or, perhaps, if we can do nothing better," he continued, "we may catch the vagabonds wandering from their guns, to pick up sticks for their fire; in which case, friend, truly, it may be our luck to help them to a second volley out of their own pieces; or, if the worst must come, truly, then, I do know of a device that may help the villains into our hands, even to their own undoing!"

With these words, having first examined his own and Roland's arms to see that all were in proper battle condition, and then directed little Peter to ensconce in a bush, wherein little Peter straightway bestowed himself, Bloody Nathan, with an alacrity of motion and ardor of look that indicated any thing rather than distate to the murderous work in hand, led the way along the ridge, until he had reached the place where it dipped down to the valley, covered with the bushes, through which he expected to advance to a desirable position undiscovered.

But a better auxiliary even than the bushes was soon discovered by the two friends. A deep gully, washed in the side of the hill by the rains, was here found running obliquely from its top to the bottom, affording a covered way by which, as they saw at a glance, they could approach within twenty or thirty yards of the foe entirely unseen; and, to add to its advantages, it was the bed of a little watercourse, whose murmurs, as it leaped from rock to rock, assured them they could as certainly approach unheard.

"Truly," muttered Nathan, with a grim chuckle, as he looked, first at the friendly ravine, and then at the savages below, "the Philistine rascals is in our hands, and we will smite them hip and thigh!"

With this inspiring assurance, he crept into the ravine; and Roland following, they were soon in possession of a post commanding, not only the spot occupied by the enemy, but the whole valley.

Peeping through the fringe of shrubs that rose, a verdant parapet, on the brink of the gully, they looked down upon the savage party, now less than forty paces from the muzzles of their guns, and wholly unaware of the fate preparing for them. The scene of diversion and torment was over; the prisoner, a man of powerful frame but squalid appearance, whose hat,—a thing of shreds and patches,—adorned the shorn pate of one of the Indians, while his coat, equally rusty and tattered, hung from the shoulders of a second, lay bound under a tree, but so nigh that they could mark the laborious heavings of his chest. Two of the Indians sat near him on the grass, keeping watch, their hatchets in their hands, their guns resting within reach against the trunk of a tree, overthrown by some hurricane of former years, and now mouldering away. A third was engaged with his tomahawk, lopping away the few dry boughs that remained on the trunk. Squatting at the fire, which the third was thus laboring to replenish with fuel, were the two remaining savages; who, holding their rifles in their own hands, divided their attention betwixt a shoulder of venison roasting on a stick in the fire, and the captive, whom they seemed to regard as destined to be sooner or later disposed of in a similar manner.

The position of the parties precluded the hope Nathan had ventured to entertain of getting them in a cluster, and so doing double execution with each bullet; but the disappointment neither chilled his ardor, nor embarrassed his plans. His scheme of attack had been framed to embrace all contingencies; and he wasted no further time in deliberation. A few whispered words conveyed his last instructions to the soldier; who, reflecting that he was fighting in the cause of humanity, remembering his own heavy wrongs, and marking the fiery eagerness that flamed from Nathan's visage, banished from his mind whatever disinclination he might have felt at beginning the fray in a mode so seemingly treacherous and ignoble. He laid his axe on the brink of the gully at his side, together with his foraging cap; and then, thrusting his rifle through the bushes, took aim at one of the savages at the fire, Nathan directing his piece against the other. Both of them presented the fairest marks, as they sat wholly unconscious of their danger, enjoying in imagination the tortures yet to be inflicted on the prisoner. But a noise in the gully,—the falling of a stone loosened by the soldier's foot, or a louder than usual splash of water,—suddenly roused them from their dreams; they started up, and turned their eyes towards the hill. "Now, friend!" whispered

Nathan; "if thee misses, thee loses thy maiden, and thy life into the bargain. Is thee ready?"

"Ready," was the reply.

"Right, then, through the dog's brain,—fire!"

The crash of the pieces, and the fall of the two victims, both marked by a fatal aim, and both pierced through the brain, were the first announcement of peril to their companions; who, springing up with yells of fear and astonishment, and snatching at their arms, looked wildly around them for the unseen foe. The prisoner also, astounded out of his despair, raised his head from the grass, and glared around. The wreaths of smoke curling over the bushes on the hillside betrayed the lurking-place of the assailants, and savages and prisoner turning together, they all beheld at once the spectacle of two human heads,—or, to speak more correctly, two human caps, for the heads were far below them,—rising in the smoke, and peering over the bushes, as if to mark the result of the volley. Loud, furious, and exulting were the screams of the Indians, as, with the speed of thought, seduced by a stratagem often practised among the wild heroes of the border, they raised and discharged their pieces against the imaginary foes so incautiously exposed to their vengeance. The caps fell, and with them the rifles that had been employed to raise them; and the voice of Nathan thundered through the glen, as he grasped his tomahawk and sprang from the ditch,—"Now, friend! up with thy axe, and do thy duty!"

With these words the two assailants at once leaped into view, and with a bold hurrah, and bolder hearts, rushed towards the fire, where lay the undischarged rifles of their first victims. The savages yelled also in reply, and two of them bounded forward to dispute the prize. The third, staggered into momentary inaction by the suddenness and amazement of the attack, rushed forward but a step; but a whoop of exultation was on his lips, as he raised the rifle which *he* had not yet discharged, full against the breast of Bloody Nathan.

But his triumph was short-lived; the blow, so fatal as it must have proved to the life of Nathan, was averted by an unexpected incident. The prisoner, near whom he stood, putting all his vigor into one tremendous effort, burst his bonds, and, with a yell ten times louder and fiercer than had been yet uttered, added himself to the combatants. With a furious cry of encouragement to his rescuers,—"Hurrah for Kentucky! —give it to 'em good!" he threw himself upon the savage, beat the gun from his hands, and grasping him in his brawny arms, hurled him to the earth, where, rolling over and over in mortal struggle, growling and whooping, and rending one another like wild beasts, the two, still locked in furious embrace suddenly tumbled down the banks of the brook, there high and steep, and were immediately lost to sight.

Before this catastrophe occurred, the other Indians and the assailants met at the fire; and each singling out his opponent, and thinking no more of the rifles, they met as men whose only business was to kill or to die. With his axe flourished over his head, Nathan rushed against the tallest and foremost enemy, who, as he advanced, swung his tomahawk, in the act of throwing it. Their weapons parted from their hands at the same moment, and with perhaps equal accuracy of aim; but, meeting with a crash in the air, they fell together to the earth, doing no harm to either. The Indian stooped to recover his weapon, but it was too late; the hand of Nathan was already upon his shoulder; a single effort of his vast strength sufficed to stretch the savage at his feet; and holding him down with knee and hand, Nathan snatched up the nearest axe. "If the life of thy tribe was in thy bosom," he cried, with a look of unrelenting fury, of hatred, deep and ineffaceable, "thee should die the dog's death, as thee does!" and with a blow furiously struck, and thrice repeated, he despatched the struggling savage as he lay.

He rose, brandishing the bloody hatchet, and looked for his companion. He found him upon the earth, lying upon the breast of his antagonist, whom it had been his good fortune to overmaster. Both had thrown their hatchets, and both without effect, Roland because skill was wanting, and the Shawnee because, in the act of throwing, he had stumbled over the body of one of his comrades, so as to disorder his aim, and even to deprive him of his footing. Before he could recover himself, Roland imitated Nathan's example, and threw himself upon the unlucky Indian,—a youth, as it appeared, whose strength, perhaps at no moment equal to his own, had been reduced by recent wounds,—and found that he had him entirely at his mercy. This circumstance, and the knowledge that the other Indians were now overpowered, softened the soldier's wrath; and when Nathan, rushing to assist him, cried aloud to him to move aside, that he might "knock the assassin knave's brains out," Roland replied by begging Nathan to spare his life. "I have disarmed him," he cried—"he resists no more—don't kill him."

"To the last man of his tribe!" cried Nathan, with unexampled ferocity; and, without another word, drove the hatchet into the wretch's brain.

The victors now leaping to their feet, looked round for the fifth savage and the prisoner; and directed by a horrible din under the bank of the stream, which was resounding with curses, groans, heavy blows, and the splashing of water, ran to the spot, where the last incident of battle was revealed to them in a spectacle as novel as it was shocking. The Indian lay on his back, suffocating in mire and water, while astride his body sat the late prisoner, covered from head to foot with mud and gore, furiously plying his fists, for he had no other weapons, about the head and face of his foe, his blows falling like sledge hammers or battering rams, with such strength and fury, that it seemed impossible any one of them could fail to crush the skull to atoms; and all the while garnishing them with a running accompaniment of oaths and maledictions little less emphatic and overwhelming. "You switches gentlemen, do you, you exflunctified, perditioned rascal? Arn't you got it, you nigger-in-law to old Sattan? you 'tarnal half-imp you? H'yar's for you, you dog, and thar's for you, dog's dog! H'yar's the way I pay you in a small change of sogdologers!"

And thus he cried, until Roland and Nathan, seizing him by the shoulders, dragged him by main force from the Indian, whom, as was found, when they came to examine the body afterwards, he had actually pommelled to death, the skull having been beaten in as with bludgeons. The victor sprang upon his feet, and roared his triumph aloud,—"Arn't I licked him handsome! Hurrah for Kentucky and old Salt—Cock-a-doodle-doo!"

BATTLE OF THE FALLEN TIMBERS

by THOMAS BOYD

HAVING BEEN INSTRUCTED by his friend, President Washington, to make all reasonable efforts toward peace with the Indians, and not to provoke the British unduly, General Wayne made a final effort toward an amicable treaty with the Indian confederacy. And on that he composed a long message to the Miamis, Shawanese, Delawares and Wyandots: "To each and every one of them; and to all other nations of Indians northwest of the Ohio whom it may concern: Brothers, be no longer deceived or led

From: *Shadow of the Long Knives.* Copyright 1928. Charles Scribner's Sons.

astray by the false promises and language of the bad white men at the foot of the rapids; they have neither the power nor the inclination to protect you. No longer shut your eyes to your true interest and happiness, nor your ears to this last overture of peace. But, in pity to your innocent women and children, come and prevent the further effusion of your blood. Let them experience the kindness of the United States of America, and the invaluable blessings of peace and tranquillity." And that this may be done, the hardy old general, still in his saddle a decade after the war of the Revolution, wrote on: "Let each and every hostile tribe of Indians appoint deputies to meet with the commander-in-chief without delay between the mouth of the Oglaize and the foot of the rapids of the Maumee in order to settle the preliminaries of a lasting peace."

This message written, General Wayne sent for Christopher Miller, the white man who had been retaken from the Shawanese after he had been adopted into their tribe, and despatched him to his former brethren.

Miller left at about four o'clock that afternoon, the soldiers watching him as he went out the gate, shouting ribald advice at his departing back:

"Fetch us a fat young squaw there, ol' weasel face!"

"Don't let them Injuns git to chawin' on you, now!"

"Clip one o' them brothers o' your'n for me, hey, Miller?"

Thus they expressed their avid interest as the messenger went forth with the word, the answer to which would mean either war or peace to many thousands of people. The sun sank lower, throwing long shadows of the fort on the darkening surface of the Maumee; it was the end of another day's work on the incompleted fort.

On the eighth day the fort was completed. It stood with a blockhouse at each angle, and all of them connected by a firm line of pickets. Surrounding this was an earthen wall eight feet in thickness, below which another wall of logs and fagots ended at the top of a deep ditch in which a tall man could have stood with his arms upraised without being seen above the parapet. The ditch was fifteen feet wide and encircled the fort, except on the Grand Glaize side. There, the bank being steeper, an extra wall of fagots secured the main works from attack. Entrance to the fort was made by either of two gateways inside the trench, which was crossed at one gate by a foot-bridge, and at the other by a drawbridge, which men behind the pickets raised and lowered by means of pulleys.

It was a solid fort and not uncomfortable inside. There were doors and chimneys in the blockhouses, and room for officers' quarters, the stores of provisions and ammunition. It gave shelter and cooking facilities

better than average. A well had been dug between the ditch and the
river, and passage to it from the fort was made safe, in case of attack, by
two lines of converging pickets. To the west were sanitary vaults among
the trees, and the adjacent forest afforded more fuel than was needed. As
for the outer blockhouse walls, the one looking toward the Maumee and
the other toward the Grand Glaize, there were port-holes where Wayne's
small howitzers were mounted and slits for small-arms firing.

On the evening the work was finished General Wayne walked about
on a tour of inspection accompanied by General Scott, commander of the
volunteer cavalry from Kentucky. Wayne looked at the pickets, stepped
down on the thick earthworks below, and walked along it toward the
drawbridge, where he stood, his jaw grimly set, looking out over the quiet
water toward the forest, deep with shadows. "I defy," he said to Scott as
he thumped his fist into the palm of his hand, "I defy the English, the
Indians, and all the devils in hell, part and parcel, to take this fort!"

General Scott, himself no stranger to tall talk, raised his head smartly
and smoothed the wrinkles of his campaign jacket. "Well now, general, I
declare if I wouldn't call it Fort Defiance."

Wayne squinted his eye at him and remarked with satisfaction: "Why,
general, I named it that two days ago when I sent my report to the secretary of war."

The following morning the main body of the army took up the line
of march down the river in the direction of the British fort, which lay at
the foot of the rapids. They moved cautiously, the scouts in front, and
by the second night they had gone nineteen miles from Fort Defiance.
As they pitched camp that evening General Wayne was restless and irri-
table, and his aides and orderlies were kept running from his quarters to
the picket lines in quest of information about Christopher Miller, who
had been expected even before the march had been taken up. Soldiers
could hear the general barking from his quarters: "The flag! Where in
the devil is that flag I sent, and when is he coming back?"

The flag returned, with the confederacy's reply to Wayne's message,
late that night. Hurried through by the pickets, he was brought to the
general's quarters. By this time the soldiers were nearly as impatient as
their commanding officer to know whether the long journey was to end
in war or a treaty of peace.

They stood about in gossiping groups:

"Bet tomorrer's ration of the wet it's a fight we're agoin' into."

"Cain't fight if the Indians won't fight, I'll allow."

"I'll allow you're a loon an' you don't know Wayne."

"'S right; he wouldn't haul us boys 'way up here an' then not give the Injuns a little seasonin', not the general."

They were still talking when the information contained in the message, by some strange underground current that makes military messages known generally almost as soon as they are known by the commanding officer, became the common knowledge of the camp:

"Ten days! Us wait ten days while they make up their minds whether to go to tanglin' with us or talk nice an' soft!"

"Ol' general'll give 'em ten days on their backsides!"

"I'm set—I'm set fur plain or fancy prancin', an' I'll ride 'em hard!"

"Hark to the catamount!"

Into this talk the commands of an officer penetrated: "Hold your jaws, you buckskins; we take the line of march at daybreak."

☆

☆   ☆

THE CAMP WAS ASTIR in the early dawn and by five o'clock tight-voiced sergeants were rousing sluggards from their blankets and forming their platoons. Everywhere among the soldiers there was a cool excitement. The spirit of recklessness and raillery which had been apparent the day before was gone; now the men looked out of harried eyes and stepped to their places in ranks submissively and with an economy of talk. They carefully inspected their flintlocks and the priming, while a few rubbed shirt-sleeves thoughtfully up and down the blades of their long, slender bayonets. In the growing light could be heard the whinnying of horses and the trampling of many boots through the underbrush. It was the morning of the attack, and they were going into it stripped to their lightest equipment.

By seven o'clock the ranks were organized and ready for the march. Earlier there had been a damp mist, but it was dispersing. Through the trees, where drops of dew on the leaves were opalescent in the sunlight, the men could see their comrades stretched far on either side. In front of the main body General Wayne and his staff, his aide, Major Harrison, and Generals Scott, Todd, and Barbee sat on quiet horses and again went over the battle order.

The units were joined in the standing order of the march. On the extreme right stood the Legion, facing northward, and with its flank covered the rippling Maumee. Next to the Legion, on the left, was a brigade of mounted volunteers under General Todd; another brigade of Kentucky horsemen covered the rear under command of General Barbee.

In front of the Legion Major Price held in check a chosen battalion of horsemen which were to act as advance-guard.

There was no specific and detailed plan of battle. Major Price was instructed to keep sufficiently ahead of the main body so that by the time he met the enemy the troops would be able to prepare before coming upon them. The cavalry were to crash through, followed by an infantry charge with fixed bayonets. Further orders were left for the moment when the enemy had been engaged.

"Arms at the trail, forward . . ." The command came through the forest, repeated by a hundred voices. Slowly the Legion commenced its advance through the wooded ground that sloped down toward the river. On the right General Wilkinson shouted, "Forward!" and Colonel Hamtramck, commanding the Legion's left flank, echoed, "At the trail!" From the mounted ranks adjacent to the infantry's flanks and from the cavalry rear-guard came the scraping sound of sabres being drawn.

The entire body of troops moved warily ahead, following the mounted volunteers under Major Price, who was nearly half a mile to the front of the army.

Price's cavalry rode slowly through the tall grass of the rough terrain, the men bent forward, keeping a tight hand on the bridle-reins. Somewhere ahead of them in this unknown ground the Indians were drawn up for warfare, and the cavalrymen knew they would feel the enemy's bullets before they caught sight of them. They continued grimly, prepared for the shock of contact wherever and whenever it should come.

The sun came out more fully, rose above the forest, and sent rays piercing through the brilliant foliage. Overhead there was a flutter of indignantly chattering birds, and on the earth the small game scurried for cover. Price's vanguard went slowly on, the underbrush breaking gently under the loitering hoofs of the horses. An hour passed, but the enemy were not to be seen.

The forest lay secretively about them. Every tree was a menace from which could be launched a ripping musket-ball. But there was nothing ahead but silence as another hour brought the day closer to noontide heat. Restlessness pervaded the cavalry. The men began to feel their tautened nerves, their stiff-set lips and wary eyes.

"God a'mighty, hain't we never——"

"Don't look like the varmints air around here nohow!"

"Hold your mouths!"

They talked brokenly and in low voices, and the sweat ran down their faces.

It was ten o'clock when unexpectedly the leading fringe of the advance riders reached an opening in the forest and saw before them a great stretch of fallen trees, tangled and sprawling as if they had been blown down by a tornado. Roots reared out of the ground with long, dark tendrils, and there were white, ragged stumps that thrust their splintered remains upward like jagged spikes. The first of the riders had barely paused when a terrific clatter of musketry sounded from the wood beyond the fallen timber, and the balls poured into them with a deadly whining.

A horse stood on its hind legs, its lips working spasmodically over long, white teeth. The rider tightened the bit and the animal went over and lay threshing against a tree, with the man beneath its weight. Another bolted. A cavalryman cried out unintelligibly.

The second round of shot brought worse confusion. A lanky rider pointed to the tangled wood, and called out: "By God, we can't ride through there!" Already horsemen were wheeling their frightened mounts. A spur drove in a mare's flank; with head upflung she plunged recklessly back through the forest.

Major Price worked his blood-drained lips to call the cavalry to stand. The whisper passed unheard, and his gesture with his sword unheeded. He turned and galloped after them.

Ahead and to the right centre of the main body of the Legion marched a front guard of infantry under Captain Cook and Lieutenant Steele. It was their duty to keep within a reasonable distance of the cavalry vanguard, near enough so that they could closely follow into the attack and with their bayonets widen the swath in the enemy ranks cut by the sabres, giving the main guard time to deploy.

The advance of the vanguard being slow, the advance of the infantry guard was even slower. And at moments during the penetration of the forest through the long morning they were almost stationary, thus increasing the general fatigue of the march. In front of them they could see the rumps of the horses between the trees, and the riders with their sabres bared.

Though they had set forth vigilantly spirited that morning, the failure to meet the Indians as the day increased, and the knowledge that the cavalry moved between themselves and surprise made them relax more than they would otherwise have done. They talked and made wry jokes.

A soldier said: "Law, declare if it ain't 'most time to eat again!"

"I don't keer," began another in the front rank, "how long we stay up here long as this Injun green cawn holds out, an' the qua'te'master keeps on rationin' the wet."

"Now hain't that whiskey good! I'll swear ef it don't make yore innards feel right r'yal!"

They were talking when the noise of shot rattled out. A scattering of balls ripped through the foliage and among them.

They wavered a moment, but stood the shock.

Captain Cook shouted and they began to deploy, trailing their arms and staring anxiously ahead.

"Make hell hot for 'em," yelled somebody in a trembling falsetto, "you calv'ry sojers!"

But before the left flank had come up on the advancing line there was a crashing in the wood, and the disordered cavalry were upon them, the horses bolting and mad with fear, and the men doing little to hold them.

"They're acomin' arter us," shouted a cavalryman, and kept on going.

The left flank broke, massed up and faced about to flee.

Lieutenant Steele ran toward them, shaking his sword above his head and thundering: "Hold your ground! Damn it! Damn it! Hold your ground!"

The right flank gave way as the cavalry rode into it, knocking down Captain Cook. He rose to his knee and muttered: "Oh! the cowards; by God! the cowards!" He knelt there, watching his command in flight, half of them run down by the galloping cavalry, and the rest running in uncontrollable panic.

Indians were beginning to appear through the wood and by the bottom-land near the head of the Maumee rapids, armed with muskets, tomahawks, and war-clubs.

The main body of the Legion took up the march that morning in a column of fours, trailing their arms with fixed bayonets, and expecting momentarily to meet the enemy, which, it was said, were somewhere within the half-dozen miles that separated the soldiers' encampment from the British fort that the spies had discovered at the foot of the Maumee rapids. Nearly all of them were eager for the battle to take place, and hoped that it would be decisive. Many of them had been preparing for it during the last two years, when they had volunteered to serve under General Wayne at Legionsville, in June of 1792. But from that month to this they had been engaged by the Indians only once, and that was when they had been attacked under the walls of Fort Recovery, in June of 1794, less than two months ago.

Progress that morning was slower and more wearying than they had ever known it on a march, it seemed to them. Every hour as they tramped ahead there would come the command to halt and ground arms. And there they would stand, wondering what was taking place up in front to cause so many delays, calling, grumbling, and making up absurd explanations of why they were ordered to stop three and four times every hour.

Especially was this true of Captain Howell Lewis's company of light infantry, which advanced at the left centre of the body of the Legion, and had to traverse a rough, brambly and thickly wooded stretch nearly all of the way from Camp Deposit.

Marching at their right flank was Captain Lewis, his mild, light-blue eyes smiling a little at the long, monotonous complaints of the soldiers.

"Tan my britches, but this hain't no Legion; hit's a passel o' turtle varmints!"

"Sho', ain't nobody said it *was* a Legion o' men, it's——"

"I swear," cut in another, "a mortal needs two pairs o' laigs a sight more'n he needs a musket to fight these critters!"

Captain Lewis turned a little and said good-naturedly: "Less noise, boys!"

The light infantry company went on a few paces, then halted again for the twentieth time that morning.

It was while they were deployed and standing with grounded arms that they heard brisk firing in front of them. They stiffened as a body, and their eyes grew anxious. "Whup, cap'n, that might be the Injuns right now!" a front-line soldier said, and looked forward where the infantry front guard could be seen moving on again.

Once more they took up the slow march. They had proceeded to a natural meadow when a man in the first squad sang out excitedly: "Gemini, looky there!"

A riderless horse, its bridle-rein dragging, was bounding toward them in full flight. More cavalrymen were breaking through the wood, and behind them could be seen a mob of infantrymen who, having discarded their muskets, seemed bent on outrunning the disorganized cavalry. It all had the appearance of the beginning of a general rout.

Captain Lewis faced his company as shot rattled out from the pursuing Indians. The left flank, he saw, was wavering uncertainly; there were men staring with horrified eyes at the fleeing soldiers who, mounted and afoot, were running directly for his own ranks.

The sight put a cold fury in him. He rasped out commands, breaking the company into sections. "Second section about face! At the trail . . . double quick time . . . march!" It was a dangerous business, he knew, and he cut around through the moving troops, facing them. When they were forty or more yards from the first section he called out: "Halt! About face and stand fast!" The men were cringing from the anticipated blow, but a sergeant was shouting, "Don't give way! Keep your ranks!" and Lewis had the grim satisfaction of seeing his first section standing fast.

The horsemen swerved from the waiting lines of the second section and went around, hoofs pounding. The retreating front guard of infantry struck and recoiled. Panting and confused, they excitedly fell in on the left flank of the second section at the sharp order of Captain Lewis.

"Second section forward!" shouted Lewis, and the men marched ahead at the trail. His company was rejoined and stood to face the oncoming enemy, who were flinging themselves to the counter-attack with a cry.

Within musket-shot of the Indians General Wayne sat his horse on a knoll, surrounded by his aides, Captains De Butt and T. Lewis, Lieutenant Harrison, and the adjutant-general, Major Mills. The enemy were firing rapidly, and Wayne could tell from the volume of sound that their forces were strongest in the front centre, which was opposite the company commanded by Howell Lewis. Shot was rattling out over a long line, or series of lines—he believed there were three—each extending into the forest for more than a mile. He sat there quietly for some moments, waiting for the action to become clear, apparently oblivious of the fact that he was in any danger.

Young Harrison edged his horse nearer the flank of Wayne's mare. "General," he began hesitantly, "I'm afraid you'll get into this and forget to give me the field orders!"

"Perhaps I may," said Wayne crisply, keeping his eyes ahead, "and if I do, recollect that the standing order of the day is charge the damned rascals with the bayonet."

Shot was rattling out from both sides in terrific bursts. Wayne turned to young Lieutenant Harrison: "Find General Scott and send him around their right flank with every cavalryman he can muster!"

Lieutenant Harrison galloped off through the woods.

"De Butt!" Wayne called.

To the left the roar was growing louder.

Captain De Butt wheeled his horse nearer.

"Where's the Legion cavalry?"

"Back of us, sir, under Campbell."

"Tell him to go 'round our right flank through the bottoms and turn their left!"

Captain De Butt backed his horse and hurried to the rear.

A white-faced orderly broke through and gasped: "Colonel Hamtramck, sir, says to inform General Wayne they're ahammerin' on our left flank."

Wayne said shortly: "Tell Colonel Hamtramck to hold his front line ready for the charge."

Lieutenant Harrison returned. "General Scott's on his way roundabout, sir."

As if he had not heard, General Wayne ordered: "Take word to Wilkinson to prepare his front line for the charge."

A musket-ball tore up the ground in front of Wayne's horse and her flanks began quivering.

While Captain Howell Lewis's company of light infantry were holding their place at the edge of the clearing through which the Indians were attempting a flank attack, a part of Captain Springer's battalion of riflemen were making their way through the woods. They had seen horses running loose among the trees, and had conjectured that as the front guard of cavalry had retreated there was nothing now between themselves and the enemy. They advanced slowly and cautiously, parting the underbrush and staring far ahead toward the sound of firing.

Like the Indians, they slipped from tree to tree. And as the musket-balls flew more thickly many of them went forward on their hands and knees. A corporal and a private, in advance of the rest, stopped and lay still, listening to noises, a muttering and a whimper.

"Think that's Injuns?" asked the private breathlessly.

The corporal shook his head; he could not tell.

As they waited another private crawled up and lay down behind the trunk of a walnut.

Bullets sped overhead. A little to the left there was a cry.

"By God!" said the corporal through nerveless lips, "be here till sundown if we don't take caution!" He stood up on shaky legs and stepped forward.

The private by his side encouraged himself with a shout and arose.

More riflemen from their battalion came up. They reeled ahead after the corporal.

A hundred paces farther they came upon the riddled company of Howell Lewis's, standing the Indian fire alone.

"Go after 'em!" screamed somebody.

The riflemen, joining Lewis's light infantry, surged through the clearing toward the Indians, who were so close that the color of the paint on their faces could be seen.

Captain Campbell, a dark, wiry man with high cheek-bones, in command of the dragoons, or Legion cavalry, sat his horse beside his second-in-command, Lieutenant Covington, at the head of his mounted troop. Moving at the right rear of the infantry, he had ordered a halt when the infantry stopped. Now he was waiting for whatever action was to take place.

Ahead of them and to the left they heard the sound of firing, and the men grew restive. Back of him Campbell could hear their comments:

"That's to'able loud, that is."

"Hain't amovin' none either."

"Sho', an' us a standin' here like this! Tain't right. I'm fixed on fightin', I am." And the speaker ran his finger judiciously along the edge of his sabre-blade.

"Whoa there, Dolly! Stan' still, you ornery critter!"

"Cap'n, flies an' skeeters'll chaw us up if we don't move directly!"

Lieutenant Covington turned about in his saddle: "You'll move soon enough!" he promised.

The firing continued. The smell of gunpowder came to them on a breeze that blew from the northeast.

The hoofs of a swiftly ridden mare were heard at a distance and Captain De Butt appeared. "Captain Campbell!"

"Yes, captain?"

"Orders from General Wayne to advance through the bottom-land and turn the enemy's left flank! You hear me?" He rode away.

"We heered him," called out a cavalryman.

"Draw sabres and forward!" called out Campbell, and led the way through the fringe of trees to the cleared slope by the river. They advanced at a gallop and in close formation.

Half a mile ahead they received their first shot. It came from a shallow trench dug at right angles with the rapids, and slightly protected by a hump of dirt, logs, and boughs. A ball ripped into Campbell's leg. He leaned over with his sabre swinging and shouted: "Forward!" In his mind the scene was clear: a mile of open ground, the forest to the left, the rapids to the right, and down at the foot of them loomed the British fortress. Under him the hoofs of his horse thudded madly on the soft earth, and he saw the Indians springing up out of the trench with musket, tomahawk, and war-club. He slashed out viciously, swinging the heavy sabre until it whistled. A daub of yellow paint that was an Indian's face swam before him and disappeared under the fore legs of his horse. He raised his weapon again, was about to bring it down when his arm lost all its power and his hand slipped out of the guard; simultaneously he felt a blow on his chest where a tomahawk had buried itself.

The horses trampled over his dead body.

"Forward!" yelled Lieutenant Covington. Behind him a soldier shouted a malediction and blew out the face of an Indian with his pistol. Covington's sabre swung into a shoulder, came out with blood and flashed again, cutting a clean slice into the back of a fleeing Indian's neck.

On the knoll General Wayne ordered sharply: "Sound the charge!" And into the noise of shouts and musketry and the air thick with acrid gunpowder came the stirring bleat of the bugle, calling for the advance. All along the line that extended through wood and clearing for more than a mile officers were bellowing: "Front line, at the trail . . . fo-orward!" The string of infantry began to move, wriggling in and out among the trees with the motion of a long snake trying to crawl sideways.

Young George McDermott stood as a file-closer near the extreme right of Colonel Hamtramck's left wing. Earlier in the day, the scouts not engaging in the battle, he had tried to include himself in the ranks of Colonel Hamtramck's brigade as the men fell in for the march. He had joined himself first to one squad and then to another, but each time he was crowded out by the soldier whose place he had unconsciously tried to take. At last he was forced to march among the file-closers.

But when the front line moved to the call of the bugle he saw his chance and stepped between a weazened infantryman on his right and a sallow mountaineer whose jaw hung open dejectedly. Neither noticed him. They were staring beyond through the fringe of trees where there was a small meadow in the forest. George went ahead with them, stealing glances at them now and again to see if they were trembling as badly as he felt himself to be. He had never felt like this before, so scared and shaky and yet with such a curious elation in his heart. It had come with the sound of the clearly trilling bugle that gave the charge. Before that he had listened with restlessness and anxiety to the clatter and rattle of musketry. But now that noise was no longer harrying his ears; it was as if he had grown used to it. Nor did he notice the fumes of the gun-powder which swayed in filmy wreaths among the trees as he followed the advance through the small meadow and into the forest again.

Suddenly he was aware of musket-balls clipping the leaves and fur-rowing the ground about him. They had a deadly singing which made him grit his teeth and try to tighten up his body in a vain effort to pre-sent a smaller target for them. He went ahead and it seemed as though each moment one would strike him. But all along the line he was aware of men trampling forward and he never thought of doing less than they would do on this day.

Farther in the forest lay the body of a dead horse and of a cavalryman pinned under it, his scalp taken off and his face red from the blood that had dripped down. A moment later there was a shout. Ahead George saw the great waste stretch of tangled timber, some trees uprooted and others broken off at the stumps. Behind these trees were heads and mus-ket-barrels and arrows ready to be launched from tight-strung bows. Beside him the weazened infantryman went down, clutching at his mus-ket as he fell. George wondered if he should not stop and pick him up. But it was too much like a fantastic dream, as if it had really never hap-pened. He went forward with a feeling of nakedness, the musketry hum-ming in his ears and the gun-powder stinging his face where rivulets of sweat ran down.

He began working his way through the clutter of fallen timber. Down the line somebody was shouting: "At 'em! at 'em, buckskins!" He went stumbling between the sprawling trees, the prickly vines in the under-brush ripping at his clothing. A few paces ahead was the dark, half-circle of an Indian's skull rising above a log. He brought his musket to his shoulder and fired; the head sank down. A moment later he passed it. The man had been already dead from another shot, it was obvious from his rigidity and the spot of dried rust on the chest of his leather shirt. George went on, sick with disgust.

A charge of shot volleyed forth and officers were making a tumult of orders among which could be heard:

"Close in!"

"Double quick!"

" . . . bayonets!"

Near by an infantryman jabbered, "You G-god-damn whelps, you wh-wh-wh—!" and went stumbling forward with outthrust bayonet through the clutter of timber.

Unexpectedly George broke out of the forest and stood in the natural meadow-land which was dotted all of the way to the British fort with the figures of Indians. As he stood there other soldiers appeared, their faces strained and white and their clothing torn. Though the fort was more than a mile away many of the infantrymen began running over the cleared ground in pursuit of them. George sat down and primed his musket afresh. His hands were unsteady and he was thinking of his father.

The sun was almost directly overhead when a small group of horsemen appeared from the forest and halted in the meadow-land, where they surveyed the British fort. Looking up, George recognized General Wayne, two of his aides, and General Scott, who commanded the volunteer cavalry. General Scott was explaining how his men had made all possible speed to turn the right flank of the enemy but that by the time the cavalry had reached the designated point the Indians had already been driven back by the infantry.

To this explanation General Wayne gave but half of his attention. He was more interested in the British fort toward which the Indians were running. His forehead was wrinkled into an angry bulge above his eyes and he replied briefly to General Scott, obviously trying to discourage a longer recital. At length he broke in: "Harrison, look sharp and tell me if you can see any of the enemy going inside that fortress!"

Lieutenant Harrison stared for a time in silence. "No, they're not going in, General, at least it don't look that way. Seems like they're going around it."

Wayne cursed, "Damn their brass-bound, copper-bottomed effrontery! Establishing a fort within the well-known and acknowledged limits of the United States!"

General Scott looked at him questioningly. . . .

"Come, lieutenant," Wayne spoke brusquely to Harrison, "we'll rub a little dirt under their infernal noses."

General Wayne and his aide moved down the slope, parting from Scott and the other aide, who went slowly toward the river where the soldiers were gathering.

George turned heavily back through the forest. He had been uneasy at the sight of the fleeing Indians and now that General Wayne, collecting a bodyguard on the way, was riding down toward the British fort the whole scene of desolation came sharply to young George's mind: where in it was his father! That he had been in the council and that he would have been somewhere about the battle was certain. Where had they all gone, Little Turtle, Blue Jacket, and the rest? Killed, wounded, running away? It was strange, that place of battle, now that the firing and excitement had ended. There were so many dead. They sprawled in hideous angularity as he ran back over the ground, choking with a sudden fright as it came to him that his father might have been killed.

☆

☆　　☆

ANGUS MCDERMOTT had not fought that day. In fact, he, Little Turtle, and Blue Jacket, who commanded, had not expected that a battle would take place. For this they had a number of reasons.

Four days earlier, when they had returned Miller with the flag, they had sent General Wayne the message that if he waited at Fort Defiance for ten days they would decide whether they would be for peace of war. They did this, not in order to gain time to prepare themselves for fighting, but because Little Turtle and others wanted to make one last effort with the chieftains to arbitrate with Wayne and his army. Now Little Turtle was a brave man; he had been named war-chief of the Miamis for his deeds, but as he had watched Wayne coming up from Fort Greenville, always with his picket chain guarding against surprise and marching ahead with clear-eyed resolution, he had felt that to meet him in warfare would be useless and a criminal act toward the men he commanded. Moreover, when Wayne built his fortress in the heart of the Indian villages and fields, Little Turtle knew that if fighting came the crops would perish and his people go hungry through the long winter.

McDermott likewise had small hope of winning against Wayne's army. They numbered as great a force as the Indians could possibly muster from all of their tribes represented at the council. They were better equipped and ably commanded by a veteran officer who had distinguished himself by taking Stony Point with only the bayonet as a weapon, by holding Chadsford at the battle of Brandywine, by his attack on Cornwallis at the James, by driving both British and Indians from the Georgia colony, and by his fighting at Germantown and Monmouth. But even more than that was McDermott influenced by the fact that George had gone. And as for Charity she had declared herself to be independent of him. George, in whom he had so much pride! Charity, the faithful, who had told him years ago in that sad, awesome intonation of hers that wherever he went and however long he was gone she would always be waiting for him to return. But now all was hopeless. But one spot of light glimmered through the all-embracing darkness: if Wayne would wait, another council could be called and peace might be effected.

But though Little Turtle, a number of lesser Miami chiefs, and Mc-Dermott were anxious for further parley, Blue Jacket, most of the other Shawanese, and the bulk of the Delawares were for war. The Shawanese carried in their hearts the blood feud which had existed between themselves and the Long Knives since the days of Dunmore's war, when they had been driven into the Ohio country there to live under sufferance of the Wyandots. They remembered how their chieftains had been slain and counted the long roll of generations of their dead for which they were bent on repaying these Long Knives in kind. And added to these were the Wyandots, remembering the massacre on the Muskingum years before.

No word came from General Wayne in reply to their request that ten days' grace be given. On the first morning after Miller had returned to Wayne with the message, the Indian spies reported that the army was making ready to move forward. And Blue Jacket ordered his own men into an ambush in the forest where it had been devastated by a storm and where the fallen trees would afford the greatest protection. But that day passed and Wayne did not appear. The Indians, as was their custom when on the verge of battle, had eaten nothing the night before or in the morning following. The day passed and Wayne did not appear. Another night came and still the Indians waited.

Meanwhile Little Turtle, McDermott, and others had contrived to call a council. It met on the third night after Miller had departed with the message. About the fire lighted in that darkness were more than a dozen chiefs. Shortly after they had met Little Turtle addressed them.

Little Turtle spoke earnestly. After the peroration he said: "We have beaten the Long Knives twice, under separate commanders. It is the truth. But we cannot always expect the same good fortune. The Long Knives are now led by a chief who never sleeps. Night and day are alike to him. Through all his long march to our villages our young men have never been able to surprise him. It is not too late to listen to his offer of peace. Hearken to it well! It may save us our hunting-grounds. Beware lest in endeavoring to keep all we should lose all!" He strode about in the firelight, chanting his plea that General Wayne be reconciled before it was too late. At last he sat down.

Little Turtle had no sooner resumed his seat on his blanket than Manato, a young chief of the Shawanese, jumped up and said craftily: "The Little Turtle is growing old! Nearly fifty summers and fifty winters he has seen! His blood may be cool and his arm no longer mighty! But that is not true of the young chiefs. Their blood is warm and many grand-fathers look down on them to be avenged against the Long Knives. Let the brave men stay to defeat the Long Knives! Let the cowards run!" Manato's full lips curved and he stared triumphantly about him.

Little Turtle winced, knotted his fists, and remained silent.

Blue Jacket nodded solemnly.

In praise of Manato's speech Bockongahelas intoned: "It is the truth, the very truth Manato speaks!"

Mournfully, Little Turtle arose. Further pleading was useless. He said in a steadfast voice: "I lead my young men to the battle."

The council broke up.

That was on the night before General Wayne's attack and he was still some miles distant. Morning came and as there was no sight of him the braves concluded that they would be safe in cooking breakfast. The front line went to their posts in a long stretch at right angles with the rapids, there to wait in the fallen timber. The men who were to form the two support lines cooked up provisions while the squaws and their families trailed up the river to the woods behind the British fort.

McDermott had not spoken at the council. For he knew that if he had, once Little Turtle had failed, he would have been looked on as a traitor and his words would have passed unheeded. The promised aid of more than two hundred volunteers from the British under Captain Cald-well had come and they were ready to go into action; it was too late for McDermott to face about.

He felt that sharply, and the poignant loneliness that went with it. George and Charity were separated from him and the world was empty. As the sun rose toward midday on the morning of the attack he left the camp and went down by the river between the forest and the foot of the rapids near the looming British fort. Sitting on the bank, he could do no more than stare wofully down at the bright water splashing and tum-bling over the vari-colored rocks.

It was while he sat there that he heard the staccato of musketry sound-ing from the forest down the river to the southwest, a ragged round of shot followed by a silence that seemed to be drawing out interminably. He listened, speculating vaguely as to whether it had been fired by the Indians or by Wayne's army. Probably the Indians, he thought, for the shot would be still more scattered if it came from advancing troops.

The silence puzzled him. It could not be possible that Wayne's troops would be routed, yet there was no further evidence of conflict. He watched the forest edge incuriously. Strange that there was so long a stillness.

Unexpectedly from the depths of the forest there broke forth an exultant crackling. The noise seemed to be stationary for a while, then drew nearer. And looking up the slope of bottom-land toward the tree-tops he could see a gray wraith of smoke hanging irresolutely above the trees. Now it was a pitched battle, he decided.

As he watched he saw three Indians break through the edge of the woods, looking furtively behind them as they stepped into the tall grass of the prairie. One had a musket, but the other two had abandoned all but their side-arms. The firing was coming closer, he could tell by the sound of it.

Young George! Would he be in it? Like the headstrong boy he was, running off like that, always talking about his own folks. As if one set of people weren't like any other! He for his part had always got along wherever he had been; and Colonel Elliott, now, there was a right good man! Of course the British weren't his people; he had never thought they were. But who were his people? That was the point he could not find. When he had left the Virginia country it was governed through Lord Dunmore by his majesty, King George. And then there had been some rebels—he didn't even know their names or what they looked like. There hadn't been many at first, but then after a while it seemed as if everybody, not only in the Virginia country, but in Pennsylvania and the Carolinas and in those countries to the north and by the sea, had become rebels! And then there were no rebels at all, all the rebels had set up a government of their own—the United States of America.

More Indians were appearing on the prairie, some of them in full flight, as if they had a long way to go and little time in which to get there. McDermott looked down to the British fort, wondering what the commandant, Major Campbell, would be up to now that the Indians were running. And he thought that Campbell would be mustering his troops to their places and waiting for Wayne's army to break through and draw up on the prairie. There would be a wide swath of devastation then, he calculated. For Major Campbell had four nine-pounders, two howitzers, and some smaller guns mounted inside his fortress.

He turned from the fortress and looked up the bottom-lands along the river. There was a dark mêlée of cavalry riding low in their saddles, he judged, cutting and slashing at the Indians' right flank. All he could see was a whirling mass and an occasional gleam as a sabre swung, reflecting the glint of the sun. Blue Jacket would be somewhere in there, fighting man to man with his braves as he always did. A stout man, Blue Jacket, but a headstrong fool, and his pride high because the British had given him a high officer's commission and sent two of his boys to school across the water—the big water.

From the edge of the forest stepped a familiar Indian figure in warrior dress. Even from that distance McDermott could see that he moved in pain, all drawn up on one side. As the man came closer he recognized Bockongahelas. Must be a general rout if Bockongahelas was running away; that warrior scarcely got out of the way of anything, McDermott told himself.

Another round of shot crackled in the forest and balls went spinning through the light, mid-morning air. They must be very near, that army. McDermott lifted his hand to Bockongahelas, but Bockongahelas only shook his head in a slow, heart-broken sort of way.

A great gathering of Indians momentarily debouched from the forest, leaping for cover into the tall prairie-grass. Back of them McDermott saw a ragged, hesitant soldier of the Legion.

They were coming swiftly now, Wayne's army, and the firing sounded only in small, isolated bursts through the forest. Cavalrymen and infantrymen alike were coming, the one from among the trees and the others up from the bottom-lands. But McDermott scarcely cared whether they came or not. Slowly, without thought of cowardice or personal danger, he got up and walked toward the British fort, expecting that at any moment the guns would rumble forth their shot over the breastworks, now that Wayne's army was massing in the prairie.

By the fort the remnant of Blue Jacket's command were gathering. And seeing them McDermott thought automatically that some one, Captain Caldwell or Major Campbell, would step forth and form them to meet the enemy. They stood outside, milling about, and it seemed to McDermott as if this uncertainty of theirs was but a prelude to a new formation and that soon the guns would be barking.

But as he drew nearer he discovered the reason why the Indians were waiting outside the fort and making no effort at order. For there were British redcoats with bayonets at the gate and the sergeant who commanded them was shouting angrily to the Indians: "Get out, you rascals! You can't come in! Get out, get out!" And the Indians, confused by this change of face on the part of the British in the fort, were trying desperately to push their way inside.

McDermott stared in bewilderment. A sharp pain cut through him. He could hear the sergeant's high-pitched voice, but the words were unbelievable. The British were there to help; they had promised the Indians support not only in keeping the ground on which they now lived but also in winning back all of the country west and north of the Ohio from the settlers. And yet at this crucial time the guns were silent and the bayonets were sharply pointed against the breasts of those who had fled there for security! McDermott's mind could not take it in. The thing was too sudden and unanticipated. But he felt the treachery in his heart, as strongly as if it had been directed against himself. As in a sense it was. Those long journeys, the parleys that led to the forming of the confederacy; all had gone for nothing, there was no more hope. The confederacy was dead and could never be reborn. For a moment he stood there with his shoulders slumped dejectedly forward. Ahead of him the Indians were still clamorous about the unyielding fortress; behind him Wayne's army was coming on, scattering shot before them. He turned down toward the river where a canoe lay hidden among the drooping willows. Not that it mattered greatly, but he could stay there no longer. Walking quickly, he stepped along the overhanging willow trunk and dropped into the bark vessel; the paddle dipped and the bow shot down the rapids toward the opposite bank.

ASSINIBOINS

by STEWART EDWARD WHITE

IT WAS BUT A SCANT two hours until dawn before the late waning moon had risen above the ranges to give sufficient light. To these white men huddling in the cabin the time from midnight on seemed interminable. Every minute that passed seemed a minute wasted. Yet if the escape was to prove successful they must wait. No man can walk the crisscross of bottomland windfalls in pitch darkness: if they were to leave no trail for the Blackfeet they must keep their moccasins from earth and snow.

Their preparations were necessarily simple. Andy loaded the Boone gun. The powder smuggled to him by Nit-o-ké-man was his own, and therefore of good quality. The shot pouch also was his own. This was sheer good luck. Nit-o-ké-man might well have brought the ammunition belonging to some of the old fusees owned by the Indians. Of course they could have made shift. Trade powder burned slow and dirty, but it

From: *The Long Rifle.* Copyright 1930, 1932, reprinted by permission from Doubleday, Doran and Company, Inc.

exploded—generally. The lead of the musket balls could have been re-fashioned to the grooved barrel. But it would have been an inaccurate makeshift. Here lacked only patches for a proper loading, fit for nail-driving. There were a few in the patch box in the butt, but not many. Joe rummaged the crevice under the rafters to haul out the ragged remains of the garments Andy had long since discarded for his buckskins.

"Thar you be!" he cried triumphantly. "Didn't I tell you not to throw nothin' away—that it shore would come in handy sometime? Cut yo' patches from that shirt."

And when the time came to venture, the old clothes justified Joe once more by "coming in handy" again. They were wetted, then laid craftily in and around the freshly fueled fire. There they would smolder for hours. The resultant smoke, escaping through the cowled hole in the roof, would give the cabin the appearance of habitation; and as none of the Blackfeet, with the exception of the old woman who brought food, ever came near the place, this should afford the fugitives a start of hours, even in daylight.

The morning was snapping with cold. The sky was blue black, asparkle with stars. Only, over the high eastern ranges, spread the milky extinguishing paleness of the moon. At first the fugitives could see nothing. They stood patiently until their irises expanded; until they could make out, dimly, the markings on the snow's surface. Then, stepping carefully in the old moccasin trails, they stole down toward the river bottom.

All went well for a time. They were nearly past the sleeping village. Then the breeze, which had been blowing steadily downstream, suddenly fell flat, whirled a stray gust in the opposite direction.

A dog barked.

"Down! Down!" hissed Joe.

The three threw themselves on their faces.

But the dog had had a noseful, and he clamored excitedly in the strange mixture of bark and wailing howl peculiar to Indian canines. In two seconds the night was hideous with sound as every other dog in the encampment—and there were dozens of them—joined the chorus. The men flattened themselves close to the earth, cursing steadily under their breaths.

The clamor was enough to wake the dead. The fugitives caught momentarily red gleams as opening tent flaps showed the coals of fires within. Against the sky they made out, here and there, the silhouettes of men peering, listening.

Encouraged by this human reinforcement the dogs redoubled their outcries. Some of the bolder even made short dashes toward the outer darkness, but with hind legs in reverse, ready to scuttle back. They were, however, very bold with their tongues; daring the hidden monster; hurling opprobrious epithets; histrionic, after the manner of dogs showing off their zeal before their masters.

A fox barked sharply in reply, so close to Andy's elbow as almost to startle him into movement. A touch of Joe's hand restrained him. The fox barked again, and yet again. Obviously it returned the dogs as good as they sent. Obviously it gave its contemptuous opinion of dogs in general and these dogs in particular. It defied the whole race of dogs.

The hullabaloo in the encampment trebled in volume. The dogs told the fox just what they would do to him if only stern duty did not hold them. But they did not venture. Deep-seated racial experience had taught them the extreme insalubrity of the wilderness night.

The chorus broke up in a medley of astounded and indignant yelps, through which could be distinguished sharp human language and a dull thud or so as a moccasined foot or a billet of wood found its mark. Evidently the Indians also had heard the fox. Only the original dog, the one whose nostrils had caught veritable evidence, persisted self-righteously in his warning. But his quavering howl too terminated in a sharp *yip* of pain. His fleeing form darted across the skyline to plunge precipitately to the haven of a lodge flap, where presumably he brooded on the injustice of man.

After a few moments the white men rose cautiously to their feet, and so reached the river bank undiscovered.

Joe removed his cap and wiped his forehead.

"Whew!" he breathed. "Thought shore our powder was all wet that time. Good thing I larned to talk fox!"

"Was that *you?*" whispered Andy, astonished.

"What'd you think?" asked Joe sarcastically. "Think I had me a tame fox to foller me around?"

"Let's get on," said Kelly with a touch of impatience. "It's getting to be daylight."

Indeed the delay had been longer than they had supposed. The sun, in close pursuit of the moon, was filling the sky with an added paleness. Apparently there was as yet no actual light; and yet, dimly, objects about them were becoming distinguishable. Although they had escaped discovery thus far, the check was like to prove disastrous yet.

But it turned out to be good fortune in disguise. The original plan had been to make their way up the river bottom over the jackstraws of fallen aspens, which would leave no trail; then to swim the river. But the new visibility revealed to them a great cottonwood, loosened at the roots by the thaws, and newly fallen in such fashion that it spanned the stream. In complete darkness they would have passed it by.

"Wagh!" cried Joe under his breath, when he saw this. "She's a lucky trip. We gits our powder and ball, we gits our jerky, now we gits our bridge!" His irrepressible spirits were bubbling again. "No cold water for this child!"

He untied his moccasins and slung them about his neck.

"Barefoot holds better'n parfleche," said he. "Take 'em off, Andy."

"And hurry!" urged Kelly. "We're in plain sight of camp."

The crossing was a ticklish business, for while the tree trunk was thick, the dark water thrust against it strongly. Its whole length was aquiver. Andy had to use great will power to hold his attention away from the whirl and boil of the rushing current. He felt that if he yielded for the fraction of a second he must topple into giddiness. He gave his whole mind to reaching one bare foot sideways to the left, bringing the other bare foot alongside, over and over again, sidling slowly like a crab. The log seemed of interminable length. He did not dare look up to see what progress he had made. He was among branches around which he must squirm and still retain his upright equilibrium. The trunk had divided, become small. Its trembling had increased to a veritable swaying. Then from the corner of his eye he saw the beach. He made a single desperate leap sideways. He was ashore.

Hastily retying their moccasins they ran rapidly down the stony stream bed past betraying snowfields to a point where naked talus afforded them an unmarked ascent. Up this they toiled as fast as they could climb. It was full daylight. The camp was directly across from them, distant by only the width of the stream. If any early riser were to emerge from one of the lodges, were to glance in their direction, discovery was inevitable. They scrambled desperately, gasping for breath, their hearts pounding in their breasts. Andy's legs were leaden. He felt that he could not lift his feet another dozen paces; and yet, paradoxically, he seemed to himself to be raising his knees absurdly, inordinately high, an illusion of exhaustion.

"Wagh!" exploded Joe, suddenly. "Down! Down!"

They dropped behind a talus block, breathing heavily.

2

At the very instant of their disappearance a devilish outbreak of shrieks, cries, yells, and whoops, punctuated by musket shots, burst from the village across the way. Andy gripped his rifle and peered around the edge of the talus block. At first, so certain was his preconception of discovery, he did not understand what he saw. He was aware merely of a confusion of figures running about. Joe's comment focused the situation for him.

"Told you she's a lucky trip!" exulted the trapper. "Now they're so busy they won't *never* pay us no attention!"

It was now clear that the Blackfoot camp was the subject of a surprise attack.

"Assiniboins," said Kelly after an attentive examination.

"Who'd have thought they'd ever git west the divide this time of year!" marveled Joe.

"Not the Blackfeet, evidently," said Kelly. "They're caught as flatfooted as we were."

The Assiniboins had crept up on foot; had at a signal made a concerted rush from three sides. The Blackfeet, caught totally unprepared, awakened from sleep, catching up what weapons were next their hands, stumbling scattered from their lodges, were pounced upon before they had gathered their wits to offer defense. For a moment or so the slaughter was almost unopposed. Then here and there single champions, reckless with desperation, began to fight back. Many of them were overwhelmed; but not before they had done some damage. Others made head, slowly forced a way to coherence in small groups. The din was fearful; for to the cries of the warriors were added the shrieks of the women and the wails of the children.

The Assiniboins were darting alertly and eagerly about, doing just as much damage as they possibly could in the briefest possible time. That was what they were there for. They kept after the individual warriors just as long, and only as long, as the odds were overwhelmingly in their favor. As soon as a Blackfoot succeeded in struggling to the nucleus near the chief's lodge, they abandoned him for easier prey. If enough Blackfeet survived and got together to warrant a counter attack, then the Assiniboins would withdraw. They were comparatively few in numbers. If they could wipe out the camp without a pitched battle, well and good. If not they would be abundantly satisfied with the scalps they could take and the destruction they could inflict. In the meantime others of the band would be gathering the horses and running them up the valley toward the low passes to the north. That was the method of Indian warfare.

Joe, watching critically the course of events, explained these things to Andy in running comment. Kelly, at the other side of the talus block, occasionally added a word. Both the older trappers were calm and obviously pleased with the shaping of events.

"Told you she was a lucky trip!" Joe kept repeating. "Everything laid out to order. We'll jist cache right here until the Blackfeet put up a real fight. Ef'n we move now some stray mout look up and see us. When the real fight starts all hands will be too busy. Set still, Andy; we'll tell you when."

This was directed at Andy's obvious restlessness. The younger man could not share his companions' cool detachment. The affair was dreadful, agonizing. From inside the lodges women, little children ran shrieking; were overtaken by bounding Assiniboin warriors; felled by blows from the terrible "warhawks." Brave men, fighting bravely, went down overcome by the press of numbers, and their bleeding scalps were brandished in triumph. Lodges toppled; came down with a crash, enveloping their floundering inmates, who were pounced upon and slaughtered out of hand. It was a nightmare, in the rapid and confused movement of which no detail could be seized and held; on no single incident of which the eye could rest long enough to catch an outcome.

Then suddenly one situation leaped from chaos very clearly. A tall warrior emerged from the interior of one of the lodges dragging a woman by the hair. These figures Andy distinguished plainly; so plainly that for the moment all else of the swift terrible confusion faded into a mere background of commotion. Details irrelevant and unimportant registered on his mind. For example, somehow he had space of leisure to notice such small things as that the Assiniboin wore a white buckskin cap; that he was naked to the waist; that he wore a peculiar necklace made of wolves' tails; that his warhawk was decorated with feathers. There things registered instantaneously, as a lightning flash reveals. Andy saw at the same time that the woman was Nit-o-ké-man.

Motion seemed suspended. The warhawk was raised for the blow, but did not descend. Andy appeared to himself to be moving with a cool deliberation in an ample leisure. He thrust forward the muzzle of the long rifle; he assured a careful sight on the Assiniboin's head; he slowly squeezed the trigger. As he did so a story told by his grandmother recalled itself in complete detail; how in the siege of Boonesborough Colonel Boone had dropped a sharpshooter from a distant tree—"a notable feat," the old lady had said. As a matter of fact Andy flung the rifle to his face and fired as the butt touched his shoulder. The savage wilted in his tracks. Nit-o-ké-man tore herself from his dying grasp and darted back into the lodge.

Andy was down the slope of the talus running along the beach. Faintly in his preoccupation he heard Joe's astonished ejaculation behind him. Somehow he was across the log. Somehow he had reloaded as he ran. Somehow he was yelling at the top of his voice. These matters seemed to have nothing to do with himself.

His sudden appearance for a moment struck the turmoil flat. Straight through the paralyzed Assiniboins he darted to the lodge in which the Blackfoot woman had taken refuge.

He had no chance to look within. The Assiniboins recovered promptly from their first surprise. Andy found himself beset. The foremost he killed with a shot; then clubbed his rifle and laid about him. For a moment he swept a space clear. An arrow thudded into his left shoulder. He leaped backward with a roar so formidable that again his assailants paused.

Andy faced them in the brief respite. His left arm was numb and useless. He dropped his rifle to the ground, and his hand sought the knife at his belt. The Assiniboins ringed him close, stooping for a last rush. Andy saw them all clearly, individually. His mind, back of the great excitement that sustained him, was working clearly, coolly, in a strange hypnotic calm. The occasion pressed, was a matter of split seconds; yet he seemed to have all eternity for decision. Outside and beyond the ring of warriors and some fifty feet or more distant stood a man apart. He too wore a cap of white buckskin to which he had attached upright a pair of buffalo horns. His face was painted black. He took no part in the fighting, but watched.

Why he selected this man Andy could not have told—certainly this Assiniboin was no immediate threat, as were the others—but he swept back his arm in the long overhand throw he had so often practised, and the knife flashed, turning over and over, to bury itself hilt deep in the warrior's neck.

A loud wail burst from the throats of Andy's assailants. One leaped forward and struck Andy a glancing blow on the head. The next instant they were swept aside by the rush of the Blackfeet. Andy's clarity broke. He stood helpless and bewildered in mind. He saw a confusion of struggling bodies. He caught a glimpse of Joe's tall figure, of Kelly laying about him with a warhawk. He heard wild yells of triumph as the Assi-

niboins gave way, scattered running in all directions. He was feeling
giddy, a little sick.

Then Joe was pounding him on the back. The trapper was wildly
excited.

"Quit that; it hurts," protested Andy.

But Joe was with difficulty dissuaded.

"That's the quickest, fastest, longest shot I ever see mortal man make
with a rifle!" cried the trapper. "That's the longest, straightest throw I
ever see made with a knife! Boy, you do make 'em *come!*" He thrust a
mass of hair and blood enthusiastically into Andy's lap. "Thar's yore
sculps; four on 'em," he exulted. "I took 'em fer ye!"

"Good lad," Kelly was saying quietly. "Killed their chief. That's
using your head."

Andy shuddered and thrust the scalps violently from him. The world
was very confused. He fainted away.

3

When he came to he found himself on a robe in the lodge's interior.
For a moment or so he stared at the smoke hole, unable to figure out
just where he was. The voice of Nit-o-ké-man oriented him.

"He has ceased from dying," she cried joyously.

Andy turned his head. Though his mind was still strangely confused,
it was clearing; but as it cleared he became more and more painfully
aware of a throbbing shoulder and an aching head. He saw Nit-o-ké-man
kneeling at a cooking pot over the fire. Beyond her sat Kiasax, and by
him, bolt upright, stood the Little Warrior. Kiasax's head was big with
a bloody bandage.

"You have been dead a long time, my brother," said he. "I too was
dead,"—he touched his head—"but I have heard. Your Sun-power is great
but it cannot fill the whole of your heart. I have no more words."

"What has happened?" asked Andy.

"I do not know. I too have been dead," Kiasax repeated.

Andy listened. From the outside came no sounds save a thin low
wailing. He arose to his feet, steadied himself, went to the lodge opening
to look.

The camp was empty of men. The presence of the women was attested
only by the mourning from within the lodges whither they had carried
their dead. The slain and scalped Assiniboins lay as they had fallen. The
dogs prowled furtively among them. Overhead wheeled ravens, material-

ized from nowhere at the summons of no one knows what mysterious perception.

Andy cocked his ear to a faint clamor over the tableland. It increased. Then around the end of the willow thicket swept a dozen men on horseback. At their head rode Joe Crane. He was yelling at the top of his voice. He brandished his rifle in one hand, waved a handful of scalps in the other. The pony he bestrode ran recklessly unguided; its ears flattened; its head extended; its nostrils wide. The Indians at its heels were pressing him close, both in speed, in excitement and in noise. After a brief interval came Kelly, jogging soberly. He too had somehow reclaimed his rifle, which he carried across his saddle. A larger number of Blackfeet afoot jogged tirelessly alongside him.

The cavalcade swept the village like a whirlwind, plowed to a stop. Joe was afoot. He rushed up to Andy, enveloped him in a mighty bear hug, scalps, rifle, and all. Andy nearly fainted again from the pain of his shoulder. He half hit, half shoved Joe so mighty a buffet on the chest that the trapper's hold was torn loose and he staggered back several paces. The Indians, who had also dismounted, and were crowding close, laughed delightedly at this exhibition of strength.

"Lay off, you old idiot!" growled Andy. "I've got a hole in me."

"Wagh, I forgot!" But Joe was unabashed. "Boy! That was a fight! We made 'em come!" He slapped the nearest warrior so mightily on the back as nearly to overset him. "Hey, old hoss?" He crow-hopped in absurd caricature of the war dance; leaped in the air to crack his heels together; crowed like a cock. The Blackfeet crowded close, laughing, as much excited as he. Andy could get no sense out of anybody.

Kelly had ridden up and dismounted. Small boys swarmed from the lodges to hold the horses. Women followed them. The men who had been running afoot joined the shouting, exulting mob milling restlessly before the lodge door. Hands brandished scalps aloft. A score of voices shouted, declaimed, chanted. The noise was distracting. Yet somehow below it, through it, persisted the thin low wailing of the hidden women mourning the dead.

Andy was suddenly invaded by a deadly weariness. He could make nothing of it all, except that a victory had been won. Joe was hopeless. His caperings had become a center about which a rough impromptu dance of triumph was forming. The young man suddenly abandoned it all with a gesture of despair.

But Kelly was at his elbow, cool, collected, smiling faintly.

"Come inside, lad," he advised.

They entered the lodge and sat side by side on the robe. Kelly re-counted, accompanying his recital by a running translation of sign talk for the benefit of the young Blackfoot.

Andy's knife throw had turned the tide of battle. The death of their chief had cast the Assiniboins into a momentary confusion. Before they could recover, the Blackfeet had gained the upper hand. Furthermore their plans had been wholly upset by a clever bit of strategy. A small de-tachment of the Blackfeet had avoided the fight to execute a swift move-ment in capture of the attacking party's riding horses, which were being held convenient for the retreat when the time was ripe. Kelly did not mention the fact that this thought was his own. The raiders had to fight it out afoot, which was no part of their original intention. The sudden injection of the white men into the mêlée had upset all their calculations, which, naturally, had not taken such a reinforcement into account. Nor could they have foreseen the moral effect of that reinforcement, with its deadly long rifles, which had been promptly restored to their owners. In fact the whole of their strategy had blown up. Such of them as survived had made their way to the willow bottoms where they were being hunted down one by one. In the meantime a sufficient band, mounted on the enemies' own ponies, had followed the trail of the horses.

"They'll recapture them," said Kelly confidently. "You can't drive loose horses very fast. They leave a plain trail, and there can't be many men in charge of them."

The triumph had been complete. Kiasax's eyes glowed with gratifica-tion, though he made no comment.

Nit-o-ké-man stood before them, smiling shyly, offering each a wooden bowl filled with a savory stew of venison. Andy accepted it eagerly. To his surprise he discovered himself to be suddenly very hungry.

"This is something like!" he cried to his companion. "I'm starved!"

But Kelly expressed a gratification over and above the mere satisfac-tion of appetite.

"Better than you think," said he. "Once you have eaten in an Indian lodge you are a guest; and a guest is sacred from hurt or theft. I have known them to sleep in the snow outside while guests occupy the lodge. This is the best news yet."

However that might be, Andy found the food most grateful.

"Well," said Kelly, after the bowls had been emptied, "we're back again. We'd better collect that wild Indian of ours and get back to the cabin. What next?"

But when Andy would have departed, Kiasax would have none of it.

Staggering weakly to his feet, his hands on Andy's shoulders, he forced him gently back to the robe.

"No, my brother," said he. "You are now a dweller of this lodge."

SIOUX

by HAL G. EVARTS

THE BRIGADE LEFT in mid-April. During the last week in May, Breckenridge, leaving Brady and Little Bull in charge of the post, struck out alone to cross the prairies to the Saskatchewan country for the purpose of locating McKenzie's post. New spring flowers painted the green prairies. Game ranged upon them in unbelievable profusion. Buffalo and antelope appeared in vast herds in every direction upon the plains; deer and elk abounded along the streams. The waters were swarming with geese, ducks, shore birds and other wild fowl. Prairie hens, upland plovers and curlews nested in the open prairies and great white whooping cranes, sand-hills and whistling swans nested in every strip of marshland. It was a land of plenty through which he rode. He took two horses, riding one and leading the other, changing mounts at frequent intervals, as was the Indian custom when making forced marches. He covered fifty miles a day for the first three days, then, to rest his mounts, traveled but a dozen miles on the fourth day out. His only equipment, aside from his weapon, consisted of a soft-tanned buffalo robe that was used as saddle blanket by day and bedding by night. He shot his food as he required it, subsisting on a diet of straight meat. Lest his scalp should prove too great a temptation to some prowling band of Assiniboines, he followed his usual custom of cooking his meat early, then putting out his fire and moving on to some other spot to sleep. In this fashion he covered three hundred miles in seven days. The creeks now drained north to the Saskatchewan. On the seventh night he made camp on a timbered stream along the course of which was a broad Indian trail that showed signs of recent and frequent travel. It would lead either to a big Assiniboine village or to a post of the Northwest Company.

From: *Fur Brigade.* Copyright 1928, by Hal G. Evarts.

It proved to be the latter. The factor, a French Canadian, greeted him cordially enough. His identity as the Big Mandan from the post on the Missouri was circulated among the Assiniboines that were present at the post. The host was geniality itself but decidedly non-committal regarding company affairs. The McKenzies? Oh, yes—Big Mack. He couldn't say where Big Mack was. Way off to the east, though—a thousand, two thousand miles perhaps; who could say?

"East!" Hunter exclaimed. "But he was intending to open up as a free trader, or perhaps to take a post in the prairies for the Northwest Company."

"Yes," the French Canadian agreed. "But free traders cannot operate in the territory of the Northwest Company. It has been given a monopoly by the government in return for establishing its forts and advancing Canadian civilization and territorial rights across the mountains to the Pacific. Big Mack was an old-time employee of the company and was taken back by it. At least, I heard talk to that effect. He was old, unfit for the strenuous job of factor in some prairie fort. He and his daughter were to go to some eastern fort, perhaps even to Montreal in an office job—who knows?"

"And Leroux?" Hunter queried.

"He was sent northwest, perhaps to the Athabasca country," the factor informed. "Or so I heard."

Hunter headed back toward the Mandan country, his plans all gone awry. He must some day find Hair-that-shines. That much was certain. But Montreal seemed very far away. One could not travel those thickly settled eastern districts and live off the country as he journeyed, as one could in the West. And the search for her might be long.

A new significance of his present employment came to him as he rode. He would require money to facilitate his travels in searching for Nepanamo through the provinces of Eastern Canada. For the first time, he was conscious of a desire for money. Fortunately, he was also situated for the first time so that he could acquire money. He would work for two years with the Rocky Mountain Company. That would provide the necessary funds. But the time seemed long and his heart was heavy. He was half tempted to turn his horse's head to the east and begin his search at once. Strangely enough, it did not occur to him that the factor of the Northwest post had deliberately lied to him; and it would be many a moon before he was to discover that fact.

Upon his return, it was to find the Mandan village in the first throes of mourning. Two lodges, numbering some twenty-odd souls, had set out on a short expedition to trap beaver and had been annihilated by the

Sioux. Every face was daubed black with a mixture of soot and bear grease. Lamentations made the night hideous. The Indians lacerated their bodies so that the blood might run in sympathy with that spilled by the departed ones. Several bereaved relatives lopped off fingers. Some squaws split their ear lobes. Others inflicted wounds in their scalps so that the blood might run down across their blackened faces. Brady and Little Bull were inured to such mourning from long experience but the continuous screeching disturbed Hunter's slumber and added to the restlessness that had come to him with the knowledge that Hair-that-shines had gone to parts unknown. Inactivity added to his depression. The appalling volume of the wailing decreased as the days passed but at the expiration of the second week there were still sporadic outbursts of screeching that punctuated the nights. Faces were still blackened and would remain so until enemy scalps were brought in without loss of Mandan life. The lamentations had almost ceased when a party of a half dozen squaws and children, journeying from a hunting camp to the village, were waylaid and killed by a band of Assiniboines.

Wailing and self-laceration broke out afresh. In vain Hunter urged the Indians to go out and trap beaver, the squaws to dress buffalo hides. But the Mandan nation was given over to mourning. Brady and Little Bull endured it stoically, no more concerned than if the uproar had been merely the chattering of blackbirds; but Hunter, his mind seething with disappointment at the unexpected disappearance of Ann McKenzie and his uncertainty as to her whereabouts, was nearing the limit of his endurance. There was but one remedy for such mental tension known to his breed —activity! The Mandans held frequent councils and planned revenge upon their foes but talked in circles and arrived nowhere.

Then Breckenridge rose one night in council.

"Hear me, Warriors! Big Mandan, the slayer of Sioux, speaks to you. The Mandans are my brothers and I cry to hear them wail in mourning for the brave warriors and the women that were slain by cowardly foes. Give me fifty of the best warriors and Big Mandan will ride forth at their head to avenge these wrongs. We will not return until we come with many horses that we have stolen and bring fresh scalps, so that my people may wash their faces and rejoice. The village will ring with the glad cry of the scalp dance. Big Mandan pledges it. I have spoken."

Eventually, it was so arranged. The comely young squaw, who had been complimented by Breckenridge during the first days of his stay among the Mandans, presented him with a shield fashioned and decorated by her own hand. It was made of double thickness of the back hide of bull buffalo, shrunken by heat while still green. It was incredibly tough and would turn arrow or lance thrust and, if struck at the slightest angle, would even deflect a ball fired from the inferior smooth-bore trade guns of the Indians.

The war party set off in high spirits and at its head rode big Mandan and Little Bull Buffalo of the Loup Pawnees.

There was one vital weakness in the fighting tactics of all mounted Indians of the West. Every white trapper was aware of it. A war party invariably charged the enemy at a furious run, frequently advancing to within a few feet, but not one charge in a thousand was pressed home. After dashing down and firing arrows or musket shots at close range, the custom was to veer off, wheel and retreat, form and charge again. This afforded the enemy time to reload. On literally thousands of occasions a mere handful of white trappers, caught on the open prairies and with no more than a coulee bank or the bodies of their slain horses behind which to take shelter, were thus able to sell their lives at dear cost to the Indians. In such a battle, it was the custom of the whites to hold their fire until the furious charge was fairly upon them, then each pick a foe and shoot him from his horse. At that instant, with their flintlocks uncharged, they were at the mercy of the Indians, if only the latter should press the charge home, which was seldom done.

It was not lack of bravery that prevented the Indians from charging home upon inferior numbers. It was merely habit. The overwhelming charge had not appealed to the horse Indians as good tactics and it was destined to be many a year before they adopted it from the whites.

As they rode into Sioux territory, Hunter harangued the warriors on this fatal defect.

"When we charge the Sioux they will fire upon us too soon," he said. "We will hold our own fire until right upon them and shoot in their very faces. Their guns will be empty. Instead of wheeling to reload, we will hurl ourselves upon them and cut them down like blades of grass."

Almost hourly he repeated the formula, so that his words would be implanted in their minds.

On the eighth day they were apprised of the location of an encampment by a thin film of smoke. Scouts, signalling with looking-glasses, flashed the report of a Sioux hunting party of twenty-odd lodges. That would mean probably a hundred warriors. Hunter led his band into camp on another creek ten miles distant. They camped without fires. The returning scouts reported that the Sioux had made camp at the head of a shallow valley earlier in the afternoon. A few miles down its course, the valley was alive with buffalo and it was evident that the Sioux intended to stage a surround, their favorite method of hunting those animals. Five or six hundred head of horses accompanied the party.

The concensus of opinion was to the effect that the Sioux were in too great numbers to attack and that the best plan was to swoop down under cover of darkness and steal the horses, shooting into the encampment as they charged past.

"We came to give battle and to take scalps," Breckenridge declared. "If you follow me and do as I do, we will cut them down as ripe plums fall with the first frost."

They were on the march two hours before dawn, riding slowly in order that their war horses might be fresh when they went into battle. Breckenridge and Little Bull reconnoitered from the rims of the valley at sunrise. The camp was a mile above them. The buffalo herds had moved some three or four miles farther down the bottoms. Breckenridge marshalled his party in the mouth of a tributary valley that opened into the main bottoms something over a mile below the camp. A fringe of brush just within its mouth concealed the Mandan war party from the view of any who might ride down the main valley.

A lookout, peering from behind a bush on the banks above, signalled that the Sioux were leaving the village to ride down and stage the surround. He slid down from his post and mounted his horse.

"Remember!" Breckenridge said in final admonishment. "The Sioux will be startled and will shoot too soon. Their guns will be empty. Every man hold his fire until I shoot. Then every man of you fire. Do not so much as swerve from your course. Hurl yourselves upon them while their guns are empty. They go forth to hunt, not to war, and will carry no shields. They will be meat for our lances and our war axes. Let no man slacken speed until his lance or war ax drips red with the blood of a Sioux."

The Sioux hunters, ninety-odd strong, rode down the bottoms. Behind Breckenridge and Little Bull, the war horses of the Mandans stamped eagerly, quivering to be off. The Sioux, riding a hundred and fifty yards out in the open bottoms, came abreast of the Mandan ambush. The first were allowed to pass. When the center of the party drew abreast of him, Hunter raised his shield in the signal to charge and jumped his horse through the fringe of brush. His voice rang out in the high-pitched Missouri yell, and from the throat of Little Bull sounded the war whoop of the Loup Pawnees, followed by that of half a hundred Mandans.

The startled Sioux whirled to see this array of mounted warriors charging down upon their flank at a furious run. As Breckenridge had predicted, in the first confusion half of the Sioux discharged their guns at once, the others following suit raggedly. They wavered and many of them turned to flee, but a great chief among them, observing the inferior numbers of the attacking party, shouted swift orders and they rallied into battle line to face the oncoming foe.

An arrow thudded home in Hunter's bull hide shield; another zipped nastily past his ear. At a distance of twenty yards, he fired, shooting an Indian through the body and toppling him from his horse. Then he thrust his rifle into the slanting buckskin scabbard and transferred his grip to the handle of a heavy war ax that was suspended from his right wrist by a thong. He rode straight at the Sioux chief. The Indian met him with levelled lance. With his left hand, Breckenridge executed an upward sweep of his shield at the instant of contact, carrying the point of the lance aloft to glance harmlessly off the tough bull hide and pass above his head. At the same instant his right hand swept under it with a mighty swing of his war ax. Its blade caught the Sioux chief on the chin and split his head in half.

Instantly, Hunter shifted his shield to interpose it between his body and the blow of a tomahawk aimed at him by the Sioux on his left, deflected it and with an overhand cross swing, brought the blade of his own war ax down across the base of the savage's skull. Three more Sioux tilted at him. He met the central one and cut him down. Little Bull split the skull of the one on the right and a Mandan drove his lance through the body of the third. The center of the Sioux line wavered, broke and fled. Breckenridge had chosen a dozen Mandan warriors to ride on either side of himself and Little Bull, selecting those most likely to obey his instructions and press home the charge. They had hit the line to a man. Those on the flanks, however, after delivering their fire at close range, forgetting instructions in the excitement of battle, had wavered. Some of them had wheeled their horses to the rear and several, thus exposing their unprotected backs, had been transfixed by Sioux arrows. It was no lack of bravery that had occasioned their failure to press home, but merely an instinctive reversion to established tactics in the excitement of battle. The extremities of the Sioux line, appalled by the unexampled ferocity of the charge that had dispersed their center, whirled and joined the flight. No Mandan was now in doubt. They had now but to follow custom without puzzling over strange instructions. Every man knew his job, which was to overhaul and cut down as many as possible of the scattered and routed foe. The Sioux would have been killed to the last man, except for the

Indian custom of dismounting to strike a fallen enemy and thus count coos. As it was, over fifty Sioux were slain, scalped and hastily despoiled of gun, war axes, knives and other treasures. The survivors were not pursued beyond the high headlands that constituted the far rims of the valley. Scouts that Breckenridge dispatched to those heights immediately signalled the presence of a huge encampment of Sioux in another shallow valley some five miles distant. It would be but a matter of minutes until the fugitives would signal the news to the big village and hundreds of Sioux warriors would be dashing down upon the Mandans.

The squaws and children of the smaller village whose men had just suffered defeat were already in flight, some of them having mounted hastily, others departing on foot. The Mandans rallied swiftly to Breckenridge as the scouts signalled the news of the big village. They were in favor of departing at once, without taking time to run off the five hundred or more head of horses that grazed near the head of the valley. Breckenridge held up his hand.

"There is time. We must have those horses. Without them, we are lost. Our ponies are tired, those of the Sioux are fresh. We are in the heart of the Sioux country with three hundred miles to ride. Big Mandan has spoken. Follow me, Warriors."

He put his horse at the run and headed up the valley. Already a few of the hardier young spirits of the demoralized village were endeavoring to attain the far side of the horses for the purpose of heading them back across the valley toward the main Sioux encampment. They abandoned the purpose and fled when it became apparent that the racing Mandan war party would arrive in time to cut them off. Several Mandan warriors darted aside to capture fleeing young women, forcing the captives to mount behind them. Breckenridge veered aside to capture a Sioux lad in his early teens and the boy mounted behind him. The Mandans were expert horse thieves. Little Bull and half a dozen warriors had angled to reach the far edge of the grazing herd. The main body of Mandans, fanning out in a wide crescent, bore down upon the rear of the drove. The horses moved away from them and instinctively followed the little cluster of riders out ahead of them, as Little Bull and his companions led the way toward the distant Mandan village on the Missouri. The rearmost Mandans hazed the horses forward. Others rode at close intervals along either flank, to prevent sporadic attempts to cut out to the side. Within half a mile from the start, the entire outfit was flying across the prairies at a smooth run, long manes and tails streaming in the wind.

Hunter's war horse was tiring under his double load. Breckenridge urged the animal forward until he was riding among the rearmost of the herd of loose horses. He snared one with his rawhide cord and the animal halted instantly.

"Mount him," Breckenridge instructed his youthful captive. "You shall be treated well and returned to your people. If you try to escape you will be slain. Ride!"

The young Sioux leaped to the bare back of the horse and rode on. Here and there, Mandans were similarly disposing of their captive young women. The war horse, thus relieved of a part of his burden, forged gallantly on until Hunter was once more riding among the rearmost Sioux horses. He selected a big pinto that gave promise of speed and endurance, slipped a noose round the animal's neck and brought it to a halt. Dismounting, he effected a quick change of equipment. Several Mandan warriors were similarly engaged. Mounting his fresh steed, Breckenridge drove his own horse ahead of him until it joined the main band.

Looking back, he saw the first of the Sioux pursuers top out on a swell of the prairie some four or five miles behind. These foremost riders were followed by others, an ominous dark cloud sweeping down upon the audacious handful of Mandans. There were not less than five hundred warriors in that crew, Hunter estimated; probably more.

"They will never overtake us now," he shouted to the nearest warriors. The Mandans grinned acknowledgment. Turning upon the backs of their running ponies, they levelled derisive and insulting gestures at the Sioux, who were too distant to observe them. However, the gestures were no less sincere and triumphant for that.

Instead of a large band of stolen horses being a handicap to the pursued thieves, they constituted the greatest possible asset. The tough little prairie steeds could run endlessly at a smooth flowing gait if unburdened, and for considerable distances when carrying a man. The horse herd afforded frequent changes of mounts for the pursued while the pursuers must ride the same horse throughout the chase. The loose horses also could be viewed as a traveling commissary in addition to furnishing means of locomotion.

Hour after hour the Mandans held their charges at a run. Whenever a steed showed evidence of weariness the rider effected a quick change of mounts. Some few of the pursuing Sioux, up on particularly fleet and staunch horses, gained slightly at first. None drew nearer than two miles and those were but a handful. Then even these foremost ones began to lose ground; imperceptibly at first, then noticeably. The gap gradually widened. After a run of perhaps five hours, a group of Mandans selected a fat yearling colt and shot it. It was but the work of a very few minutes to cut off the best of the meat, mount and ride on after their comrades, among whom the meat was distributed and devoured as they rode. Another two hours and the whole cavalcade was slowed to a trot, then urged on at a run after an hour's travel at the restful slower gait.

Two miles out ahead rode Little Bull and three Mandans. The danger from behind was now negligible, the chief danger consisting of the possibility that they might ride unexpectedly upon some big Sioux encampment; and it was to guard against this contingency that Little Bull and three experienced Mandan warriors rode in advance. A swift alteration of route could be effected on the instant that the peak riders should signal the direction of the danger. Smoke columns had long since apprised the Mandans of the fact that the news had been signalled far and wide, and that the whole Brule nation was on the lookout for a chance to intercept the audacious little party of Mandan raiders.

At nightfall they were still holding on, a flying cloud on the prairies, riding hard and fast toward the distant Mandan village on the Missouri. Two hours after sundown, Breckenridge called a halt. The horses were rested for an hour and given a chance to graze. Then the flight was resumed. Again, three hours before dawn, a similar stop was made. At sunup they were still traveling, splashing across streams that were fordable, swimming those that were too deep. When the sun was two hours high they forded a wide shallow stream and ascended a high prairie headland that flanked the valley through which it flowed. These heights afforded an unobstructed view for miles to the rear.

Here Breckenridge halted the outfit for some three hours. Scouts sent on ahead relayed back the message that all was clear in that direction. It was evident that the Sioux behind had abandoned the pursuit. The tired ponies grazed, rolled and kicked their heels and some bedded down.

Breckenridge summoned his young captive.

"The Brules sent a thousand warriors to raid the Mandan villages. Some of their young men crept upon four sleeping whites with intent to kill them in their beds. But among the white men was Big Mandan and Little Bull Buffalo, who sleep with their eyes open and their ears wi'
Big Mandan took four Sioux scalps and Little Bull took three. The ad.
Sioux war party turned back without a scalp, leaving seven of scalps of
But Big Mandan and Little Bull were not content with eir rage was
the dogs who sought to creep upon them in their slee
great."

He thumped his chest impressively. The Ma ans were not too tired to listen with vast relish to this imposing and boastful oratory, so dear to the savage heart. They grunted approval, punctuating the Big Mandan's speech.

"Then the Sioux killed the women and children of the Mandans. Our rage increased. Big Mandan and Little Bull led, not a thousand warriors, but only fifty, into the heart of the Sioux country. Big Mandan counted five coos in the battle, Little Bull five more. The scalps hang at our saddles. It is thus that we repay enemies that would kill us in our sleep. Fifty Sioux scalps were taken and there will be wailing in the villages of the Burnt-thighs for months to come. More than five hundred horses we have captured. Sioux hunters will go afoot. Your captive young women are overjoyed at the prospect of being adopted into the lodges of the Mandans, who are well known to treat their women better than do the Brules. It is Big Mandan who speaks." Again he thumped his chest. "It is not good to rouse the wrath of Big Mandan, as the Sioux scalps at my saddle testify. My lodge will be black with Burnt-thigh scalps if they anger us again. You expected to be killed; but Big Mandan does not make war upon half-grown lads. Mount your pony and return to your people. Give them the message that Big Mandan has spoken."

A chorus of approving grunts testified to the admiration with which this speech had been received. Big Mandan rose even higher in the estimation of the warriors. The liberated youth would deliver the message word for word, and thus would the famous exploit of the war party spread.

The hours of rest had refreshed the horses and Breckenridge ordered a resumption of the march. Night and day, with brief and infrequent halts, the tough prairie horses and the tireless, iron-hard riders sped across the plains. On the morning of the fifth day, having camped some miles away in order to make a spectacular daylight entry, they rode full tilt up to the village. They were greeted with wild enthusiasm for their great victory and the richness of their spoils.

Nevertheless, preparations were made for a fresh outburst of wailing the three Mandan warriors—shot in the back by arrows when they ha_vered and wheeled back instead of driving home the charge—who Manda_brought home lashed upon the backs of ponies. Not one dead lost. Accor_been left upon the field of battle, not one scalp had been ern Indian, a l_any military reckoning save that of the early-day West- three men on the v_f fifty inflicted upon the enemy with but a loss of victory. Mandan reason_rious side would have been deemed a crushing _however, had upheld for centuries the conclusion that a single scalp brought in by a party with no loss of Mandan life was a more complete victory than when a thousand enemy scalps were taken and one Mandan lost. There would be no scalp dance. Not yet could the women wash their faces. Wailing was resumed.

ACROSS THE PLAINS

by ZANE GREY

BENTON HAD TWO TRAINS each day now. This one, just in, was long and loaded to its utmost capacity. Neale noticed an Indian arrow sticking fast over a window of one of the coaches. There were flat cars loaded with sections of houses, and box-cars full of furniture. Benton was growing every day. At least a thousand persons got off that train, adding to the dusty, jostling mêlée.

Suddenly Neale came face to face with Larry King.

"Red!" he yelled, and made at the cowboy.

"I'm shore glad to see you," drawled Larry. "What'n hell busted loose round heah?"

Neale drew Larry out of the crowd. He carried a small pack done up in a canvas covering.

"Red, your face looks like home to a man in a strange land," declared Neale. "Where are your horses?"

Larry looked less at his ease.

"Wal, I sold them."

"Sold them! Those great horses? Oh, Red, you didn't!"

"Hell! It costs money to ride on this heah U.P.R. thet we built, an' I had no money."

"But what did you sell them for? I—I cared for those horses."

"Will you keep quiet aboot my hosses?"

Neale had never before seen the tinge of gray in that red-bronze face.

"But I told you to straighten up!"

"Wal, who hasn't?" retorted Larry.

"You haven't! Don't lie."

From: *The U.P. Trail.* Copyright 1918. Harper and Brothers.

"If you put it thet way, all right. Now what're you-all goin' to do aboot it?"

"I'll lick you good," declared Neale, hotly. He was angry with Larry, but angrier with himself that he had been the cause of the cowboy's loss of work and of his splendid horses.

"Lick me!" ejaculated Larry. "You mean beat me up?"

"Yes. You deserve it."

Larry took him in earnest and seemed very much concerned. Neale could almost have laughed at the cowboy's serious predicament.

"Wal, I reckon I ain't much of a fighter with my fists," said Larry, soberly. "So come an' get it over."

"Oh, damn you, Red! . . . I wouldn't lay a hand on you. And I am sick, I'm so glad to see you! . . . I thought you got here ahead of me."

Neale's voice grew full and trembling.

Larry became confused, his red face grew redder, and the keen blue flash of his eyes softened.

"Wal, I heerd what a tough place this heah Benton was—so I jest come."

Larry ended this speech lamely, but the way he hitched at his belt was conclusive.

"Wal, by Gawd! Look who's heah!" he suddenly exclaimed.

Neale wheeled with a start. He saw a scout, in buckskin, a tall form with the stride of a mountaineer, strangely familiar.

"Slingerland!" he cried.

The trapper bounded at them, his tanned face glowing, his gray eyes glad.

"Boys, it's come at last! I knowed I'd run into you some day," he said, and he gripped them with horny hands.

☆   ☆   ☆   ☆

"No. Boys, I hed to give up trappin'. I couldn't stand the loneliness . . . An' now I'm killin' buffalo meat for the soldiers an' the construction gangs. Jest got in on thet train with a car-load of fresh meat."

"Buffalo meat," echoed Neale. His mind wandered.

"Son, how's your work goin'?"

Neale shook his head.

The cowboy, answering for him, said, "We kind of chucked the work, Slingerland."

"What? Are you hyar in Benton, doin' nothin'?"

"Shore. Thet's the size of it."

The trapper made a vehement gesture of disapproval and he bent a scrutinizing gaze upon Neale.

"Son, you've not gone an'—an'—"

"Yes," replied Neale, throwing out his hands. "I quit. I couldn't work. I *can't* work. I *can't* rest or stand still!" . . .

A spasm of immense regret contracted the trapper's face. And Larry King, looking away over the sordid, dusty passing throng, cursed under his breath. Neale was the first to recover his composure.

"Let's say no more. What's done is done," he said. "Suppose you take us on one of your buffalo-hunts."

Slingerland grasped at straws. "Wal, now, thet ain't a bad idee. I can use you," he replied, eagerly. "But it's hard an' dangerous work. We git chased by redskins often. An' you'd hev to ride. I reckon, Neale, you're good enough on a hoss. But our cowboy friend hyar, he can't ride, as I recollect your old argyments."

"My job was hosses," drawled Larry.

"An' besides, you've got to shoot straight, which Reddy hasn't hed experience of," went on Slingerland, with a broader smile.

"I seen you was packin' a Winchester all shiny an' new," replied Larry. "Shore I'm in fer anythin' with ridin' an' shootin'."

"You'll both go, then?"

Neale and Larry accepted the proposition then and there.

"You'll need to buy rifles an' shells, thet's all," said Slingerland. "I've hosses an' outfit over at the work camp, an' I've been huntin' east of thar. Come on, we'll go to a store. Thet train's goin' back soon."

"Wal, I come in on thet train an' now I'm leavin' on it," drawled Larry. "Shore is funny. Without even lookin' over this heah Benton."

☆   ☆   ☆   ☆

Both Indians and buffalo were sighted from the train before the trio got to the next camp.

"I reckon I don't like thet," declared Slingerland. "I was friendly with the Sioux. But now thet I've come down hyar to kill off their buffalo fer the whites they're ag'in' me. I know thet. An' I allus regarded them buffalo as Injun property. If it wasn't thet I seen this railroad means the end of the buffalo, an' the Indians, too, I'd never hev done it. Thet I'll swar."

It was night when they reached their destination. How quiet and dark after Benton! Neale was glad to get there. He wondered if he could conquer his unrest. Would he go on wandering again? He doubted himself and dismissed the thought. Perhaps the companionship of his old friends and the anticipation of action would effect a change in him.

Neale and Larry spent the night in Slingerland's tent. Next morning the trapper was ready with horses at an early hour, but, owing to the presence of Sioux in the vicinity, it was thought best to wait for the work-train and ride out on the plains under its escort.

By and by the train, with its few cars and half a hundred workmen, was ready, and the trapper and his comrades rode out alongside. Some few miles from camp the train halted at a place where stone-work and filling awaited the laborers. Neale was again interested, in spite of himself. Yet his love for that railroad was quite as hopeless as other things in his life.

These laborers were picked men, all soldiers, and many Irish; they stacked their guns before taking up shovels and bars.

"Dom me if it ain't me ould fri'nd Neale!" exclaimed a familiar voice.

And there stood Casey, with the same old grin, the same old black pipe.

Neale's first feeling of pleasure at seeing the old flagman was counteracted by one of dismay at the possibility of coming in contact with old acquaintances. It would hurt him to meet General Lodge or any of the engineers who had predicted a future for him.

Shane and McDermott were also in this gang, and they slouched forward.

"It's thot gun-throwin' cowboy as wuz onct goin' to kill Casey!" exclaimed McDermott, at sight of Larry.

Neale, during the few moments of reunion with his old comrades of the survey, received a melancholy insight into himself and a clearer view of them. The great railroad had gone on, growing, making men change. He had been passed by. He was no longer a factor. Along with many, many other men, he had retrograded. The splendid spirit of the work had not gone from him, but it had ceased to govern his actions. He had ceased to grow. But these uncouth Irishmen, they had changed. In many ways they were the same slow, loquacious, quarreling trio as before, but they showed the effect of toil, of fight, of growth under the great movement and its spirit—the thing which great minds had embodied; and these laborers were no longer ordinary men. Something shone out of them. Neale saw it. He felt an inexplicable littleness in their presence. They had gone on; he had been left. They would toil and fight until they filled nameless graves. He, too, would find a nameless grave, he thought, but he would not lie in it as one of these. The moment was poignant for Neale, exceedingly bitter, and revealing.

Slingerland was not long in sighting buffalo. After making a careful survey of the rolling country for lurking Indians he rode out with Neale, Larry, and two other men—Brush and an Irishman named Pat—who were to skin the buffalo the hunters killed, and help load the meat into wagons which would follow.

"It ain't no trick to kill buffalo," Slingerland was saying to his friends. "But I don't want old bulls an' old cows killed. An' when you're ridin' fast an' the herd is bunched it's hard to tell the difference. You boys stick close to me·an' watch me first. An' keep one eye peeled fer Injuns!"

Slingerland approached the herd without alarming it, until some little red calves on the outskirts of the herd became frightened. Then the herd lumbered off, raising a cloud of dust. The roar of hoofs was thunderous.

"Ride!" yelled Slingerland.

Not the least interesting sight to Neale was Larry riding away from them. He was whacking the buffalo on the rumps with his bare hand before Slingerland and Neale got near enough to shoot.

At the trapper's first shot the herd stampeded. Thereafter it took fine riding to keep up, to choose the level ground, and to follow Slingerland's orders. Neale got up in the thick of the rolling din and dust. The pursuit liberated something fierce within him which gave him a measure of freedom from his constant pain. All before spread the great bobbing herd. The wind whistled, the dust choked him, the gravel stung his face, the strong, even action of his horse was exhilarating. He lost track of Larry, but he stayed close to Slingerland. The trapper kept shooting at intervals. Neale saw the puffs of smoke, but in the thundering din he could not hear a report. It seemed impossible for him to select the kind of buffalo Slingerland wanted shot. Neale could not tell one from the other. He rode right upon their flying heels. Unable, finally, to restrain himself from shooting, he let drive and saw a beast drop and roll over. Neale rode on.

Presently out of a lane in the dust he thought he saw Slingerland pass. He reined toward the side. Larry was riding furiously at him, and Slingerland's horse was stretched out, heading straight away. The trapper madly waved his arms. Neale spurred toward them. Something was amiss. Larry's face flashed in the sun. He whirled his horse to take Neale's course and then he pointed.

Neale thrilled as he looked. A few hundred rods in the rear rode a band of Sioux, coming swiftly. A cloud of dust rose behind them. They had, no doubt, been hiding in the vicinity of the grazing buffalo, lying in wait.

As Neale closed in on Larry he saw the cowboy's keen glance measuring distance and speed.

"We shore got to ride!" was what Larry apparently yelled, though the sound of words drifted as a faint whisper to Neale. But the roar of buffalo hoofs was rapidly diminishing.

Then Neale realized what it meant to keep close to the cowboy. Every moment Larry turned round both to watch the Indians and to have a glance at his comrade. They began to gain on Slingerland. Brush was riding for dear life off to the right, and the Irishman, Pat, still farther in that direction, was in the most perilous situation of all. Already the white skipping streaks of dust from bullets whipped up in front of him. The next time Neale looked back the Sioux had split up; some were riding hard after Brush and Pat; the majority were pursuing the other three hunters, cutting the while a little to the right, for Slingerland was working round toward the work-train. Neale saw the smoke of the engine and then the train. It seemed far away. And he was sure the Indians were gaining. What incomparable riders! They looked half naked, dark, gleaming, low over their mustangs, feathers and trappings flying in the wind— a wild and panic-provoking sight.

"Don't ride so close!" yelled Larry. "They're spreadin'!"

Neale gathered that the Indians were riding farther apart because they soon expected to be in range of bullets; and Larry wanted Neale to ride farther from him for the identical reason.

Neale saw the first white puff of smoke from a rifle of the leader. The bullet hit far behind. More shots kept raising the dust, the last time still a few yards short.

"Gawd! Look!" yelled Larry. "The devils hit Pat's hoss!"

Neale saw the Irishman go down with his horse, plunge in the dust, and then roll over and lie still.

"They got him!" he yelled at Larry.

"Ride thet hoss!" came back grimly and appealingly from the cowboy.

Neale rode as he had never before ridden. Fortunately his horse was fresh and fast, and that balanced the driving the cowboy was giving his mount. For a long distance they held their own with the Sioux. They had now gained a straightaway course for the work-train, so that with the Sioux behind they had only to hold out for a few miles. Brush appeared as well off as they were. Slingerland led by perhaps a hundred feet, far over to the left, and he was wholly out of range.

It took a very short time at that pace to cover a couple of miles. And then the Indians began to creep up closer and closer. Again they were shooting. Neale heard the reports and each one made him flinch in expectation of feeling the burn of a bullet. Brush was now turning to fire his rifle.

Neale bethought himself of his own Winchester, which he was carrying in his hand. Dropping the rein over the horn of his saddle, he turned half round. How close, how red, how fierce these Sioux were! He felt his hair rise stiff under his hat. And at the same instant a hot wrath rushed over him, madness to fight, to give back blow for blow. Just then several of the Indians fired. He heard the sharp cracks, then the spats of bullets striking the ground, he saw the little streaks of dust in front of him. Then the whistle of lead. That made him shoot in return. His horse lunged forward, almost throwing him, and ran the faster for his fright. Neale heard Larry begin to shoot. It became a running duel now, with the Indians scattering wide, riding low, yelling like demons, and keeping up a continuous volley. They were well armed with white men's guns. Neale worked the lever of his rifle while he looked ahead for an instant to see where his horse was running; then he wheeled quickly and took a snap shot at the nearest Indian, no more than three hundred yards distant now. He saw where his bullet, going wide, struck up the dust. It was desperately hard to shoot from the back of a scared horse. Neale did not notice that Larry's shots were any more effective than his own. He grew certain that the Sioux were gaining faster now. But the work-train was not far away. He saw the workmen on top of the cars waving their arms. Rougher ground, though, on this last stretch.

Larry was drawing ahead. He had used all the shells in his rifle and now with hand and spur was goading his horse.

Suddenly Neale heard the soft thud of lead striking flesh. His horse leaped with a piercing snort of terror, and Neale thought he was going down. But he recovered, and went plunging on, still swift and game, though with uneven gait. Larry yelled. His red face flashed back over his shoulder. He saw something was wrong with Neale's horse and he pulled his own.

"Save your own life!" yelled Neale, fiercely. It enraged him to see the cowboy holding back to let him come up. But he could not prevent it.

"He's hit!" shouted Larry.

"Yes, but not badly," shouted Neale, in reply. "Spread out!"

The cowboy never swerved a foot. He watched Neale's horse with keen, sure eyes.

"He's breakin'! Mebbe he can't last!"

Bullets whistled all around Neale now. He heard them strike the stones on the ground and sing away; he saw them streak through the scant grass; he felt the tug at his shoulder where one cut through his coat, stinging the skin. That touch, light as it was, drove the panic out of him. The strange darkness before his eyes, hard to see through, passed away. He wheeled to shoot again, and with deliberation he aimed as best he could. Yet he might as well have tried to hit flying birds. He emptied the Winchester.

Then, hunching low in the saddle, Neale hung on. Slingerland was close to the train; Brush on his side appeared to be about out of danger; the pursuit had narrowed down to Neale and Larry. The anger and the grimness faded from Neale. He did not want to go plunging down in front of those lean wild mustangs, to be ridden over and trampled and mutilated. The thought sickened him. The roar of pursuing hoofs grew distinct, but Neale did not look back.

Another roar broke on his ear—the clamor of the Irish soldier-laborers as they yelled and fired.

"Pull him! Pull him!" came the piercing cry from Larry.

Neale was about to ride his frantic horse straight into the work-train. Desperately he hauled the horse up and leaped off. Larry was down, waiting, and his mount went plunging away. Bullets were pattering against the sides of the cars, from which puffed streaks of flame and smoke.

"Up wid yez, lads!" sang out a cheery voice. Casey's grin and black pipe appeared over the rim of the car, and his big hands reached down.

One quick and straining effort and Neale was up, over the side, to fall on the floor in a pile of sand and gravel. All whirled dim round him for a second. His heart labored. He was wet and hot and shaking.

"Shure yez ain't hit now!" exclaimed Casey.

Larry's nervous hands began to slide and press over Neale's quivering body.

"No—I'm—all—safe!" panted Neale.

The engine whistled shrilly, as if in defiance of the Indians, and with a jerk and rattle the train started.

Neale recovered to find himself in a novel and thrilling situation. The car was of a gondola type, being merely a flat-car, with sides about four feet high, made of such thick oak planking that bullets did not penetrate it. Besides himself and Larry there were half a dozen soldiers, all kneeling at little port-holes. Neale peeped over the rim. In a long thinned-out line the Sioux were circling round the train, hiding on the off sides of their mustangs, and shooting from these difficult positions. They were going at full speed, working in closer. A bullet, striking the rim of the car and showering splinters in Neale's face, attested to the fact that the Sioux were still to be feared, even from a moving fort. Neale dropped back and, reloading his rifle, found a hole from which to shoot. He emptied his magazine before he realized it. But what with his trembling hands, the jerking of the train, and the swift motion of the Indians, he did not do any harm to the foe.

Suddenly, with a jolt, the train halted.

"Blocked ag'in, b'gorra," said Casey, calmly. "Me pipe's out. Sandy, gimme a motch."

The engine whistled two shrill blasts.

"What's that for?" asked Neale, quickly.

"Them's for the men in the foist car to pile over the engine an' remove obstruchtions from the track," replied Casey.

Neale dared to risk a peep over the top of the car. The Sioux were circling closer to the front of the train. All along the half-dozen cars ahead of Neale puffs of smoke and jets of flame shot out. Heavy volleys were being fired. The attack of the savages seemed to be concentrating forward, evidently to derail the engine or kill the engineer.

Casey pulled Neale down. "Risky fer yez," he said. "Use a port-hole an' foight."

"My shells are gone," replied Neale.

He lay well down in the car then, and listened to the uproar, and watched the Irish trio. When the volleys and the fiendish yells mingled he could not hear anything else. There were intervals, however, when the uproar lulled for a moment.

Casey got his black pipe well lit, puffed a cloud of smoke, and picked up his rifle.

"Drill, ye terriers, drill!" he sang, and shoved his weapon through a port-hole. He squinted over the breech.

"Mac, it's the same bunch as attackted us day before yisteddy," he observed.

"It shure ain't," replied McDermott. "There's a million of thim to-day."

He aimed his rifle as if following a moving object, and fired.

"Mac, you git excited in a foight. Now I niver do. An' I've seen thot pinto hoss an' thot dom' redskin a lot of times. I'll kill him yit."

Casey kept squinting and aiming, and then, just as he pressed the trigger, the train started with a sudden lurch.

"Sp'iled me aim! Thot engineer's savin' of the Sooz tribe! . . . Drill, ye terriers, drill! Drill, ye terriers, drill! . . . Shane, I don't hear yez shootin'."

"How'n hell can I shoot whin me eye is full of blood?" demanded Shane.

Neale then saw blood on Shane's face. He crawled quietly to the Irishman.

"Man, are you shot? Let me see."

"Jist a bullet hit me, loike," replied Shane.

Neale found that a bullet, perhaps glancing from the wood, had cut a gash over Shane's eye, from which the blood poured. Shane's hands and face and shirt were crimson. Neale bound a scarf tightly over the wound.

"Let me take the rifle now," he said.

"Thanks, lad. I ain't hurted. An' hev Casey make me loife miserable foriver? Not much. He's a harrd mon, thot Casey."

Shane crouched back to his port-hole, with his bloody bandaged face and his bloody hands. And just then the train stopped with a rattling crash.

"Whin we git beyond thim ties as was scattered along here mebbe we'll go on in," remarked McDermott.

"Mac, yez looks on the gloomy side," replied Casey. Then quickly he aimed the shot. "I loike it better whin we ain't movin'," he soliloquized, with satisfaction. "Thot redskin won't niver scalp a soldier of the U.P.R. . . . Drill, ye terriers! Drill, ye terriers, drill!"

The engine whistle shrieked out and once more the din of conflict headed to the front. Neale lay there, seeing the reality of what he had so often dreamed. These old soldiers, these toilers with rail and sledge and shovel, these Irishmen with the rifles, they were the builders of the great U.P.R. Glory might never be theirs, but they were the battle-scarred heroes. They were as used to fighting as to working. They dropped their sledges or shovels to run for their guns.

Again the train started up and had scarcely gotten under way when with jerk and bump it stopped once more. The conflict grew fiercer as the Indians became more desperate. But evidently they were kept from closing in, for during the thick of the heaviest volleying the engine again began to puff and the wheels to grind. Slowly the train moved on. Like hail the bullets pattered against the car. Smoke drifted away on the wind.

Neale lay there, watching these cool men who fought off the savages. No doubt Casey and Shane and McDermott were merely three of many thousands engaged in building and defending the U.P.R. This trio liked the fighting, perhaps better than the toiling. Casey puffed his old black pipe, grinned and aimed, shot and reloaded, sang his quaint song, and joked with his comrades, all in the same cool, quiet way. If he knew that the shadow of death hung over the train, he did not show it. He was not a thinker. Casey was a man of action. Only once he yelled, and that was when he killed the Indian on the pinto mustang.

Shane grew less loquacious and he dropped and fumbled over his rifle, but he kept on shooting. Neale saw him feel the hot muzzle of his gun and shake his bandaged head. The blood trickled down his cheek.

McDermott plied his weapon, and ever and anon he would utter some pessimistic word, or presage dire disaster, or remind Casey that his scalp was destined to dry in a Sioux's lodge, or call on Shane to hit something to save his life, or declare the engine was off the track. He rambled on. But it was all talk. The man had gray hairs and he was a born fighter.

This time the train gained more headway, and evidently had passed the point where the Indians could find obstructions to place on the track. Neale saw through a port-hole that the Sioux were dropping back from the front of the train and were no longer circling. Their firing had become desultory. Medicine Bow was in sight. The engine gathered headway.

"We'll git the rest of the day off," remarked Casey, complacently. "Shane, yez are dom' quiet betoimes. An' Mac, I shure showed yez up to-day."

"Ye *did* not," retorted McDermott. "I kilt jist twinty-nine Sooz!"

"Jist thorty wus moine. An', Mac, as they wus only about fifthy of thim, yez must be a liar."

The train drew on toward Medicine Bow. Firing ceased. Neale stood up to see the Sioux riding away. Their ranks did not seem noticeably depleted.

"Drill, ye terriers, drill!" sang Casey, as he wiped his sweaty and be-grimed rifle. "Mac, how many Sooz did Shane kill?"

"B'gorra, he ain't said yit," replied McDermott. "Say, Shane . . . Casey!"

Neale whirled at the sharp change of tone.

Shane lay face down on the floor of the car, his bloody hands gripping his rifle. His position was inert, singularly expressive.

Neale strode toward him. But Casey reached him first. He laid a hesitating hand on Shane's shoulder.

"Shane, old mon!" he said, but the cheer was not in his voice.

Casey dropped his pipe! Then he turned his comrade over. Shane had done his best and his last for the U.P.R.

THE BATTLE OF BEECHER'S ISLAND

by MARGARET HILL MCCARTER

BUT WITH THE MORNING all my sentiment vanished and I was eager for the thing before me. Two hundred Indians we were told we should find and every man of us was accounted good for at least five redskins. At sunrise on the twenty-ninth day of August in the year of our Lord 1868, Colonel Forsyth's little company started on its expedition of defence for the frontier settlements, and for just vengeance on the Cheyennes of the plains and their allied forces from kindred bands. Fort Hays was the very outpost of occupation. To the north and west lay a silent, pathless country which the finger of the white man had not touched. We knew we were bidding good-bye to civilization as we marched out that morning, were turning our backs on safety and comfort and all that makes life fine. Before us was the wilderness, with its perils and lonely desolation and mysteries.

But the wilderness has a siren's power over the Anglo-Saxon always. The strange savage land was splendid even in its silent level sweep of distance. When I was a boy I used to think that the big cottonwood beyond the West Draw was the limit of human exploration. It marked the world's western bound for me. Here were miles on miles of landscape opening wide to more stretches of leagues and leagues of far boundless plains, and all of it was weird, unconquerable, and very beautiful. The earth was spread with a carpet of gold splashed with bronze and scarlet and purple, with here and there a shimmer of green showing through the yellow, or streaking the shallow waterways. Far and wide there was not a tree to give the eye a point of attachment; neither orchard nor forest nor lonely sentinel to show that Nature had ever cherished the land for the white man's home and joy. The buffalo herd paid little heed to our brave company marching out like the true knights of old to defend the weak and oppressed. The gray wolf skulked along in the shadows of the draws behind us and at night the coyotes barked harshly at the invading band. But there was no mark of civilized habitation, no friendly hint that aught but the unknown and unconquerable lay before us.

I was learning quickly in those days of marching and nights of dreamless sleep under sweet, health-giving skies. After all, Harvard had done

From: *The Price of the Prairie.*

414

me much service; for the university training, no less than the boyhood on the Territorial border, had its part in giving me mental discipline for my duties now. Camp life came easy to me, and I fell into the soldier way of thinking, more readily than I had ever hoped to do.

On we went, northward to the Saline Valley, and beyond that to where the Solomon River winds down through a region of summer splendor, its rippling waves of sod a-tint with all the green and gold and russet and crimson hues of the virgin Plains, while overhead there arched the sky, tenderly blue in the morning, brazen at noon-day, and pink and gray and purple in the evening lights. But we found no Indians, though we followed trail on trail. Beyond the Solomon we turned to the south-west, and the early days of September found us resting briefly at Fort Wallace, near the western bound of Kansas.

The real power that subdues the wilderness may be, nay, is, the spirit of the missionary, but the mark of military occupation is a tremendous convincer of truth. The shotgun and the Bible worked side by side in the conquest of the Plains; the smell of powder was often the only incense on the altars, and human blood was sprinkled for holy water. Fort Wallace, with the Stars and Stripes afloat, looked good to me after that ten days in the trackless solitude. And yet I was disappointed, for I thought our quest might end here with nothing to show in results for our pains. I did not know Forsyth and his band, as the next twenty days were to show me.

While we were resting at the Fort, scouts brought in the news of an Indian attack on a wagon train a score of miles eastward, and soon we were away again, this time equipped for the thing in hand, splendidly equipped, it seemed, for what we should really need to do. We were all well mounted, and each of us carried a blanket, saddle, bridle, picket-pin, and lariat; each had a haversack, a canteen, a butcher knife, a tin plate and tin cup. We had Spencer rifles and Colt's revolvers, with rounds of ammunition for both; and each of us carried seven days' rations. Besides this equipment the pack mules bore a large additional store of ammunition, together with rations and hospital supplies.

Northward again we pushed, alert for every faint sign of Indians. Those keen-eyed scouts were a marvel to me. They read the ground, the streams, the sagebrush, and the horizon as a primer set in fat black type. Leader of them, and official guide, was a man named Grover, who could tell by the hither side of a bluff what was on the farther side. But for five days the trails were illusive, finally vanishing in a spread of faint footprints radiating from a centre telling us that the Indians had broken up and scattered over separate ways. And so again we seemed to have been deceived in this unmapped land.

We were beyond the Republican River now, in the very northwest corner of Kansas, and the thought of turning back toward civilization had come to some of us, when a fresh trail told us we were still in the Indian country. We headed our horses toward the southwest, following the trail that hugged the Republican River. It did not fade out as the others had done, but grew plainer each mile.

The whole command was in a fever of expectancy. Forsyth's face was bright and eager with the anticipation of coming danger. Lieutenant Beecher was serious and silent, while the guide, Sharp Grover, was alert and cool. A tenseness had made itself felt throughout the command. I learned early not to ask questions; but as we came one noon upon a broad path leading up to the main trail where from this union we looked out on a wide, well-beaten way, I turned an inquiring face toward Morton, who rode beside me. There was strength in the answer his eyes gave mine. He had what the latter-day students of psychology call "poise," a grip on himself. It is by such men that the Plains have been won from a desert demesne to fruitful fields.

"I gave you warning it was no boy's play," he said simply.

I nodded and we rode on in silence. We pressed westward to where the smaller streams combine to form the Republican River. The trail here led us up the Arickaree fork, a shallow stream at this season of the year, full of sand-bars and gravelly shoals. Here the waters lost themselves for many feet in the underflow so common in this land of aimless, uncertain waterways.

On the afternoon of the sixteenth of September the trail led to a little gorge through which the Arickaree passes in a narrower channel. Beyond it the valley opened out with a level space reaching back to low hills on the north, while an undulating plain spread away to the south. The grass was tall and rank in this open space, which closed in with a bluff a mile or more to the west. Although it was hardly beyond midafternoon, Colonel Forsyth halted the company, and we went into camp. We were almost out of rations. Our horses having no food now, were carefully picketed out to graze at the end of their lariats. A general sense of impending calamity pervaded the camp. But the Plainsmen were accustomed to this kind of thing, and the Civil War soldiers had learned their lesson at Gettysburg and Chickamauga and Malvern Hill. I was the green hand, and I dare say my anxiety was greater than that of any other one there. But I had a double reason for apprehension.

As we had come through the little gorge that afternoon, I was riding some distance in the rear of the line. Beside me was a boy of eighteen, fair-haired, blue-eyed, his cheek as smooth as a girl's. His trim little figure, clad in picturesque buckskin, suggested a pretty actor in a Wild West play. And yet this boy, Jack Stillwell, was a scout of the uttermost daring and shrewdness. He always made me think of Bud Anderson. I even missed Bud's lisp when he spoke.

"Stillwell," I said in a low tone as we rode along, "tell me what you think of this. Aren't we pretty near the edge? I've felt for three days as if an Indian was riding beside me and I couldn't see him. It's not the mirage, and I'm not locoed. Did you ever feel as if you were near somebody you couldn't see?"

The boy turned his fair, smooth face toward mine and looked steadily at me.

"You must n't get to seein' things," he murmured. "This country turns itself upside down for the fellow who does that. And in Heaven's name we need every man in his right senses now. What do I think? Good God, Baronet! I think we are marching straight into Hell's jaws. Sandy knows it"—"Sandy" was Forsyth's military pet name—"but he's too set to back out now. Besides, who wants to back out? or what's to be gained by it? We've come out here to fight the Cheyennes. We're gettin' to 'em, that's all. Only there's too damned many of 'em. This trail's like the old Santa Fé Trail, wide enough for a Mormon church to move along. And as to feelin' like somebody's near you, it's more'n feelin'; it's fact. There's Injuns on track of this squad every minute. I'm only eighteen, but I've been in the saddle six years, and I know a few things without seein' 'em. Sharp Grover knows, too. He's the doggondest scout that ever rode over these Plains. He knows the trap we've got into. But he's like Sandy, come out to fight, and he'll do it. All we've got to do is to keep our opinions to ourselves. They don't want to be told nothin'; they know."

The remainder of the company was almost out of sight as we rounded the shoulder of the gorge. The afternoon sunlight dazzled me. Lifting my eyes just then I saw a strange vision. What I had thought to be only a piece of brown rock, above and beyond me, slowly rose to almost a sitting posture before my blinking eyes, and a man, no, two men, seemed to gaze a moment after our retreating line of blue-coats. It was but an instant, yet I caught sight of two faces. Stillwell was glancing backward at that moment and did not see anything. At the sound of our horses' feet on the gravel the two figures changed to brown rock again. In the moment my eye had caught the merest glint of sunlight on an artillery bugle, a gleam, and nothing more.

"What's the matter, Baronet? You're white as a ghost. Are you scared or sick?" Stillwell spoke in a low voice. We didn't do any shouting in those trying days.

"Neither one," I answered, but I had cause to wonder whether I was insane or not. As I live, and hope to keep my record clear, the two figures I had seen were not strangers to me. The smaller of the two had the narrow forehead and secretive countenance of the Reverend Mr. Dodd. In his hand was an artillery bugle. Beyond him, though he wore an Indian dress, rose the broad shoulders and square, black-shadowed forehead of Father Le Claire.

"It is the hallucination of this mirage-girt land," I told myself. "The Plains life is affecting my vision, and then the sun has blinded me. I'm not delirious, but this marching is telling on me. Oh, it is at a fearful price that the frontier creeps westward, that homes are planted, and peace, blood-stained, abides with them."

So I meditated as I watched the sun go down on that September night on the far Colorado Plains by the grassy slopes and yellow sands and thin, slow-moving currents of the Arickaree.

☆

☆   ☆

Stillwell was right. Sharp Grover knew, as well as the boy knew, that we were trapped, that before us now were the awful chances of unequal Plains warfare. A mere handful of us had been hurrying after a host, whose numbers the broad beaten road told us was legion. There was no mirth in that little camp that night in mid-September, and I thought of other things besides my strange vision at the gorge. The camp was the only mark of human habitation in all that wide and utterly desolate land. For days we had noted even the absence of all game—strong evidence that a host had driven it away before us. Everywhere, save about that winking camp fire was silence. The sunset was gorgeous, in the barbaric sublimity of its seas of gold and crimson atmosphere. And then came the rich coloring of that purple twilight. It is no wonder they call it regal. Out on the Plains that night it swathed the landscape with a rarer blue than I have ever seen anywhere else, although I have watched the sun go down into the Atlantic off the Rockport coast, and have seen it lost over the edge of the West Prairie beyond the big cottonwood above the farther draw. As I watched the evening shadows deepen, I remembered what

Morton had told me in the little cabin back in the Saline country, "Whoever fights the Indians must make his will before the battle begins." Now that I was face to face with the real issue, life became very sweet to me. How grand over war and hate were the thoughts of peace and love! And yet every foot of this beautiful land must be bought with a price. No matter where the great blame lies, nor who sinned first in getting formal possession, the real occupation is won only by sacrifice. And I was confronted with my part of the offering. Strange thoughts come in such an hour. Sitting there in the twilight, I asked myself why I should want to live; and I realized how strong, after all, was the tie that bound me to Springvale; how under all my pretence of beginning a new life I had not really faced the future separated from the girl I loved. And then I remembered that it would mean nothing serious to her how this campaign ended. Oh! I was in the crucible now. I must prove myself the thing I always meant to be. God knew the heroic spirit I needed that lonely September night. As I sat looking out toward the west the years of my boyhood came back to me, and then I remembered O'mie's words when he told me of his struggle:

"It was to save a woman, Phil. He could only kill me. He wouldn't have been that good to her. You'd have done the same to save any woman, aven a stranger to you. Wait an' see."

I thought of the two women in the Solomon Valley, whom Black Kettle's band had dragged from their homes, tortured inhumanly, and at last staked out hand and foot on the prairie to die in agony under pitiless skies.

"When the day av choosin' comes," O'mie said, "we can't do no more'n to take our places. We all do it. When you git face to face with a thing like that, somehow the everlastin' arms Dr. Hemingway preaches about is strong underneath you."

Oh, blessed O'mie! Had he told me that to give me courage in my hour of shrinking? Wherever he was tonight I knew his heart was with me, who so little deserved the love he gave me. At last I rolled myself snugly in my blanket, for the September evenings are cold in Colorado. The simple prayers of childhood came back to me, and I repeated the "Now I lay me" I used to say every night at Aunt Candace's knee. It had a wonderful meaning to me to-night. And once more I thought of O'mie and how his thin hand gripped mine when he said: "Most av all, don't niver forget it, Phil, when the thing comes to you, aven in your strength. Most av all, above all sufferin', and natural longin' to live, there comes the reality av them words Aunt Candace taught us: 'Though I walk through the valley av the shadow av death, I will fear no evil.' "

"It may be that's the Arickaree Valley for me," I said to myself. "If it is, I will fear no evil." And I stretched out on the brown grasses and fell asleep.

About midnight I wakened suddenly. A light was gleaming near. Some one stood beside me, and presently I saw Colonel Forsyth looking down into my face with kindly eyes. I raised myself on my elbow and watched him passing among the slumbering soldiers. Even now I can see Jack Stillwell's fair girl-face with the dim light on it as he slept beside me. What a picture that face would make if my pen were an artist's brush! At three in the morning I wakened again. It was very dark, but I knew some one was near me, and I judged instinctively it was Forsyth. It was sixty hours before I slept again.

For five days every movement of ours had been watched by Indian scouts. Night and day they had hung on our borders, just out of sight, waiting their time to strike. Had we made a full march on that sixteenth day of September, instead of halting to rest and graze our horses, we should have gone, as Stillwell predicted, straight into Hell's jaws. As it was, Hell rose up and crept stealthily toward us. For while our little band slept, and while our commander passed restlessly among us on that night, the redskins moved upon our borders.

Morning was gray in the east and the little valley was full of shadows, when suddenly the sentinel's cry of "Indians! Indians!" aroused the sleeping force. The shouts of our guards, the clatter of ponies' hoofs, the rattling of dry skins, the swinging of blankets, the fierce yells of the invading foe made a scene of tragic confusion, as a horde of redskins swept down upon us like a whirlwind. In this mad attempt to stampede our stock nothing but discipline saved us. A few of the mules and horses not properly picketed, broke loose and galloped off before the attacking force, the remaining animals held as the Indians fled away before the sharp fire of our soldiers.

"Well, we licked them, anyhow," I said to myself exultantly as we obeyed the instant orders to get into the saddle.

The first crimson line of morning was streaking the east and I lifted my face triumphantly to the new day. Sharp Grover stood just before me; his hand was on Forsyth's shoulder.

Suddenly he uttered a low exclamation. "General, look at the Indians."

This was no vision of brown rock and sun-blinded eyes. From every direction, over the bluff, out from the tall grass, across the slope on the south, came Indians, hundreds on hundreds. They seemed to spring from the sod like Roderick Dhu's Highland Scots, and people every curve and hollow. Swift as the wind, savage as hate, cruel as hell, they bore down upon us from every way the wind blows. The thrill of that moment is in my blood as I write this. It was then I first understood the tie between the commanding officer and his men. It is easy to lead the file of privates on dress parade, but the man who directs the file in the hour of battle is the real power. In that instant of peril I turned to Forsyth with the trust that the little child gives to its father. How cool he was, and yet how lightning-swift in thought and action.

In all the valley there was no refuge where we might hide, nor height on which we might defend ourselves. The Indians had counted on our making a dash to the eastward, and had left that way open for us. They had not reckoned well on Colonel Forsyth. He knew intuitively that the gorge at the lower end of the valley was even then filled with a hidden foe, and not a man of us would ever have passed through it alive. To advance meant death, and there was no retreat possible. Out in the middle of the Arickaree, hardly three feet above the river-bed, lay a little island. In the years to be when the history of the West shall be fully told, it may become one of the Nation's shrines. But now in this dim morning light it showed only an insignificant elevation. Its sandy surface was grown over with tall sage grasses and weeds. A few wild plums and alder bushes, a clump of low willow shrubs, and a small cottonwood tree completed its vegetation.

"How about that island, Grover?" I heard Forsyth ask.

"It's all we can do," the scout answered; and the command: "Reach the island! hitch the horses!" rang through the camp.

It takes long to tell it, this dash for the island. The execution of the order was like the passing of a hurricane. Horses, mules, men, all dashed toward the place, but in the rush the hospital supplies and rations were lost. The Indians had not counted on the island, and they raged in fury at their oversight. There were a thousand savage warriors attacking half a hundred soldiers, and they had gloated over the fifty scalps to be taken in the little gorge to the east. The break in their plans confused them but momentarily, however.

On the island we tied our horses in the bushes and quickly formed a circle. The soil was all soft sand. We cut the thin sod with our butcher knives and began throwing up a low defence, working like fiends with our hands and elbows and toes, scooping out the sand with our tin plates, making the commencement of shallow pits. We were stationed in couples,

and I was beside Morton when the onslaught came. Up from the undulating south, and down over the north bluff swept the furious horde. On
they came with terrific speed, their blood-curdling yells of hate mingling
with the wild songs, and cries and taunts of hundreds of squaws and
children who crowded the heights out of range of danger, watching the
charge and urging their braves to battle. Over the slopes to the very banks
of the creek, into the sandy bed of the stream, and up to the island they
hurled their forces, while bullets crashed murderously, and arrows whizzed
with deadly swiftness into our little sand-built defence.

In the midst of the charge, twice above the din, I caught the clear
notes of an artillery bugle. It was dim day-light now. Rifle-smoke and
clouds of dust and gray mist shot through with flashes of powder, and the
awful rage, as if all the demons of Hell were crying vengeance, are all in
that picture burned into my memory with a white-hot brand. And above
all these there come back to me the faces of that little band of resolute
men biding the moment when the command to charge should be given.
Such determination and such splendid heroism, not twice in a lifetime is
it vouchsafed to many to behold.

We held our fire until the enemy was almost upon us. At the right
instant our rifles poured out a perfect billow of death. Painted bodies
reeled and fell; horses sank down, or rushed mad with pain, upon their
fallen riders; shrieks of agony mingled with the unearthly yells; while
above all this, the steady roar of our guns—not a wasted bullet in all the
line—carried death waves out from the island thicket. To me that first
defence of ours was more tragic than anything in the days and nights
that followed it. The first hour's struggle seasoned me for the siege.

The fury of the Indian warriors and of the watching squaws is inde-
scribable. The foe deflected to left and right, vainly seeking to carry their
dead from the field with them. The effort cost many Indian lives. The
long grass on either side of the stream was full of sharp-shooters. The
morning was bright now, and we durst not lift our heads above our low
entrenchment. Our position was in the centre of a space open to attack
from every arc of the circle. Caution counted more than courage here.
Whoever stood upright was offering his life to his enemy. Our horses suffered first. By the end of an hour every one of them was dead. My own
mount, a fine sorrel cavalry horse, given to me at Fort Hays, was the last
sacrifice. He was standing near me in the brown bushes. I could see his
superb head and chest as, with nostrils wide, and flashing eyes, he saw
and felt the battle charge. Subconsciously I felt that so long as he was
unhurt I had a sure way of escape. Subconsciously, too, I blessed the day

that Bud Anderson taught O'mie and me to drop on the side of Tell Mapleson's pony and ride like a Plains Indian. But even as I looked up over my little sand ridge a bullet crashed into his broad chest. He plunged forward toward us, breaking his tether. He staggered to his knees, rose again with a lunge, and turning half way round reared his fore feet in agony and seemed about to fall into our pit. At that instant I heard a laugh just beyond the bushes, and a voice, not Indian, but English, cried exultingly, "There goes the last damned horse, anyhow."

It was the same voice that I had heard up on "Rockport" one evening, promising Marjie in pleading tones to be a "good Indian." The same hard, cold voice I had heard in the same place saying to me, as a promise before high heaven: "I will go. But I shall see you there. When we meet again my hand will be on your throat and—I don't care whose son you are."

Well, we were about to meet. The wounded animal was just above our pit. Morton rose up with lifted carbine to drive him back when from the same gun that had done for my horse came a bullet full into the man's face. It ploughed through his left eye and lodged in the bones beyond it. He uttered no cry, but dropped into the pit beside me, his blood, streaming from the wound, splashed hot on my forehead as he fell. I was stunned by his disaster, but he never faltered. Taking his handkerchief from his pocket, he bound it tightly about his head and set his rifle ready for the next charge. After that, nothing counted with me. I no longer shrank in dread of what might happen. All fear of life, or death, of pain, or Indians, or fiends from Hades fell away from me, and never again did my hand tremble, nor my heart-beat quicken in the presence of peril. By the warm blood of the brave man beside me—I was baptized a soldier.

The force drew back from this first attempt to take the island, but the fire of the hidden enemy did not cease. In this brief breathing spell we dug deeper into our pits, making our defences stronger where we lay. Disaster was heavy upon us. The sun beat down pitilessly on the hot, dry earth where we burrowed. Out in the open the Indians were crawling like serpents through the tall grasses toward our poor house of sand, hoping to fall upon us unseen. They had every advantage, for we did not dare to let our bodies be exposed above the low breastworks, and we could not see their advance. Nearly one-half of our own men were dead or wounded. Each man counted for so much on that battle-girt island that day. Our surgeon had been struck in the first round and through all the rest of his living hours he was in a delirium. Forsyth himself, grievously wounded in both lower limbs, could only drag his body about by his arms. A rifle ball had grazed his scalp and fractured his skull. The pain from this wound was almost unbearable. But he did not loosen his grip on the military power delegated to him. From a hastily scooped-out pit where we laid him he directed the whole battle.

And now we girded on our armor for the supreme ordeal. The unbounded wrath of the Indians at their unlooked-for failure on their first attack told us what to expect. Our own guns were ready for instant use. The arms of our dead and wounded comrades were placed beside our own. No time was there in those awful hours to listen to the groans of the stricken ones nor to close the dying eyes. Not a soul of us in those sand-pits had any thought that we should ever see another sunset. All we could do was to put the highest price upon our lives. It was ten o'clock in the forenoon. The firing about the island had almost ceased, and the silence was more ominous than the noise of bullets. Over on the bluff the powers were gathering. The sunlight glinted on their arms and lighted up their fantastic equipments of war. They formed in battle array. And then there came a sight the Plains will never see again, a sight that history records not once in a century. There were hundreds of these warriors, the flower of the fierce Cheyenne tribe, drawn up in military order, mounted on great horses, riding bareback, their rifles held aloft in their right hands, the left hand grasping the flowing mane, their naked bodies hideously adorned with paint, their long scalp-locks braided and trimmed with plumes and quills. They were the very acme of grandeur in a warfare as splendid as it was barbaric. And I, who live to write these lines, account myself most fortunate that I saw it all.

They were arrayed in battle lines riding sixty abreast. It was a man of genius who formed that military movement that day. On they came in orderly ranks but with terrific speed, straight down the slope, across the level, and on to the island, as if by their huge weight and terrible momentum they would trample it into the very level dust of the earth, that the winds of heaven might scatter it broadcast on the Arickaree waters. Till the day of my death I shall hear the hoof-beats of that cavalry charge.

Down through the centuries the great commanders have left us their stories of prowess, and we have kept their portraits to adorn our stately halls of fame; and in our historic shrines we have preserved their records —Cyrus, Alexander, Leonidas at Thermopylæ, Hannibal crossing the Alps, Charles Martel at Tours, the white-plumed Henry of Navarre leading his soldiers in the battle of Ivry, Cromwell with his Ironsides—godly men who chanted hymns while they fought—Napoleon's grand finale at Waterloo, with his three thousand steeds mingling the sound of hoof-beats with the clang of cuirasses and the clash of sabres; Pickett's grand sweep at Gettysburg, and Hooker's charge up Lookout Mountain.

But who shall paint the picture of that terrific struggle on that September day, or write the tale of that swirl of Indian warriors, a thousand strong, as they swept down in their barbaric fury upon the handful of Anglo-Saxon soldiers crouching there in the sand-pits awaiting their onslaught? It was the old, old story retold that day on the Colorado plains by the sunlit waters of the Arickaree—the white man's civilization against the untamed life of the wilderness. And for that struggle there is only one outcome.

Before the advancing foe, in front of the very centre of the foremost line, was their leader, Roman Nose, chief warrior of the Cheyennes. He was riding a great, clean-limbed horse, his left hand grasping its mane. His right hand was raised aloft, directing his forces. If ever the moulds of Nature turned out physical perfection, she realized her ideal in that superb Cheyenne. He stood six feet and three inches in his moccasins. He was built like a giant, with a muscular symmetry that was artistically beautiful. About his naked body was a broad, blood-red silken sash, the ends of which floated in the wind. His war bonnet, with its two short, curved, black buffalo horns, above his brow, was a magnificent thing crowning his head and falling behind him in a sweep of heron plumes and eagle feathers. The Plains never saw a grander warrior, nor did savage tribe ever claim a more daring and able commander. He was by inherent right a ruler. In him was the culmination of the intelligent prowess and courage and physical supremacy of the free life of the broad, unfettered West.

On rushed that host of eager warriors. The hills behind them swarmed with squaws and children. Their shrieks of grief and anger and encouragement filled the air. They were beholding the action that down to the last of the tribe would be recounted a victory to be chanted in all future years over the graves of their dead, and sung in heroic strain when their braves went forth to conquest. And so, with all the power of heart and voice, they cried out from the low hill-tops. Just at the brink of the stream the leader, Roman Nose, turned his face a moment toward the watching women. Lifting high his right hand he waved them a proud salute. The gesture was so regal, and the man himself so like a king of men, that I involuntarily held my breath. But the set blood-stained face of the wounded man beside me told what that kingship meant.

As he faced the island again, Roman Nose rose up to his full height and shook his clenched fist toward our entrenchment. Then suddenly lift-

ing his eyes toward the blue sky above him, he uttered a war-cry, unlike
any other cry I have ever heard. It was so strong, so vehement, so full of
pleading, and yet so dominant in its certainty, as if he were invoking the
gods of all the tribes for their aid, yet sure in his defiant soul that victory
was his by right of might. The unearthly, blood-chilling cry was caught
up by all his command and reëchoed by the watchers on the hills till, away
and away over the undulating plains it rolled, dying out in weird cadences
in the far-off spaces of the haze-wreathed horizon.

Then came the dash for our island entrenchment. As the Indians entered the stream I caught the sound of a bugle note, the same I had heard
twice before. On the edge of the island through a rift in the dust-cloud,
I saw in the front line on the end nearest me a horse a little smaller than
the others, making its rider a trifle lower than his comrades. And then I
caught one glimpse of the rider's face. It was the man whose bullet had
wounded Morton—Jean Pahusca.

We held back our fire again, as in the first attack, until the foe was
almost upon us. With Forsyth's order, "Now! now!" our part of the
drama began. I marvel yet at the power of that return charge. Steady,
constant, true to the last shot, we swept back each advancing wave of
warriors, maddened now to maniac fury. In the very moment of victory
defeat was breaking the forces, mowing down the strongest, and spreading
confusion everywhere. A thousand wild beasts on the hills, frenzied with
torture, could not have raged more than those frantic Indian women and
shrieking children watching the fray.

With us it was the last stand. We wasted no strength in this grim
crisis; each turn of the hand counted. While fearless as though he bore a
charmed life, the gallant savage commander dared death at our hands,
heeding no more our rain of rifle balls than if they had been the drops of
a summer shower. Right on he pressed regardless of his fallen braves.
How grandly he towered above them in his great strength and superb
physique, a very prince of prowess, the type of leader in a land where the
battle is always to the strong. And no shot of our men was able to reach
him until our finish seemed certain, and the time-limit closing in. But
down in the thick weeds, under a flimsy rampart of soft sand, crouched a
slender fair-haired boy. Trim and pink-cheeked as a girl, young Stillwell
was matching his cool nerve and steady marksmanship against the exultant
dominance of a savage giant. It was David and Goliath played out in the
Plains warfare of the Western continent. At the crucial moment the
scout's bullet went home with unerring aim, and the one man whose
power counted as a thousand warriors among his own people received his

mortal wound. Backward he reeled, and dead, or dying, he was taken from the field. Like one of the anointed he was mourned by his people, for he had never known fear, and on his banners victory had constantly perched.

In the confusion over the loss of their leader the Indians again divided about the island and fell back out of range of our fire. As the tide of battle ebbed out, Colonel Forsyth, helpless in his sand pit, watching the attack, called to his guide.

"Can they do better than that, Grover?"

"I've been on the Plains since I was a boy and I never saw such a charge as that. I think they have done their level best," the scout replied.

"All right, then, we are good for them." How cheery the Colonel's voice was! It thrilled my spirits with its courage. And we needed courage, for just then, Lieutenant Beecher was stretching himself wearily before his superior officer, saying briefly:

"I have my death-wound; good-night." And like a brave man who had done his best he pillowed his head face downward on his arms, and spoke not any more on earth forever.

It has all been told in history how that day went by. When evening fell upon that eternity-long time, our outlook was full of gloom. Hardly one-half of our company was able to bear arms. Our horses had all been killed, our supplies and hospital appliances were lost. Our wounds were un-dressed; our surgeon was slowly dying; our commander was helpless, and his lieutenant dead. We had been all day without food or water. We were prisoners on this island, and every man of us had half a hundred jailers, each one a fiend in the high art of human torture.

I learned here how brave and resourceful men can be in the face of disaster. One of our number had already begun to dig a shallow well. It was a muddy drink, but, God be praised, it was water! Our supper was a steak cut from a slaughtered horse, but we did not complain. We gathered round our wounded commander and did what we could for each other, and no man thought of himself first. Our dead were laid in shallow graves, without a prayer. There was no time here for the ceremonies of peace; and some of the men, before they went out into the Unknown that night, sent their last messages to their friends, if we should ever be able to reach home again.

At nightfall came a gentle shower. We held out our hands to it, and bathed our fevered faces. It was very dark and we must make the most of every hour. The Indians do not fight by night, but the morrow might bring its tale of battles. So we digged, and shaped our stronghold, and told over our resources, and planned our defences, and all the time hunger and suffering and sorrow and peril stalked about with us. All night .the Indians gathered up their dead, and all night they chanted their weird, blood-chilling death-songs, while the lamentations of the squaws through that dreadful night filled all the long hours with hideous mourning unlike any other earthly discord. But the darkness folded us in, and the blessed rain fell softly on all alike, on skilful guide, and busy soldier, on the wounded lying helpless in their beds of sand, on the newly made graves of those for whom life's fitful fever was ended. And above all, the loving Father, whose arm is never shortened that He cannot save, gave His angels charge over us to keep us in all our ways.

☆

☆   ☆

"Baronet, we must have that spade we left over there this morning. Are you the man to get it?" Sharp Grover said to me just after dusk. "We've got to have water or die, and Burke here can't dig a well with his toe nails, though he can come about as near to it as anybody." Burke was an industrious Irishman who had already found water for us. "And then we must take care of these." He motioned toward a still form at my feet, and his tone was reverent.

"Over there" was the camp ground of the night before. It had been trampled by hundreds of feet. Our camp was small, and finding the spade by day might be easy enough. To grope in the dark and danger was another matter. Twenty-four hours before, I would not have dared to try. Nothing counted with me now. I had just risen from the stiffening body of a comrade whom I had been trying to compose for his final rest. I had no more sentiment for myself than I had for him. My time might come at any moment.

"Yes, sir, I'll go," I answered the scout, and I felt of my revolvers; my own and the one I had taken from the man who lay at my feet.

"Well, take no foolish chances. Come back if the way is blocked, but get the spade if you can. Take your time. You'd better wait an hour than be dead in a minute," and he turned to the next work before him.

He was guide, commander, and lieutenant all in one, and his duties were many. I slipped out in the danger-filled shadows toward our camping place of the night before. Every step was full of peril. The Indians had no notion of letting us slip through their fingers in the dark. Added to their day's defeats, we had slain their greatest warrior, and they would have perished by inches rather than let us escape now. So our island was guarded on every side. The black shadowed Plains were crossed and re-crossed by the braves silently gathering in their lost ones for burial. My scalp would have been a joy to them who had as yet no human trophy to gloat over. Surely a spade was never so valuable before. My sense of direction is fair and to my great relief I found that precious implement marvellously soon, but the creek lay between me and the island. Just at its bank I was compelled to drop into a clump of weeds as three forms crept near me and straightened themselves up in the gloom. They were speaking in low tones, and as they stood upright I caught their words.

"You made that bugle talk, anyhow, Dodd."

So Dodd was the renegade, whom I had heard three times in the conflict. My vision at the gorge was not the insanity of the Plains, after all. I was listening ravenously now. The man who had spoken stood nearest me. There was a certain softness of accent and a familiar tone in his speech. As he turned toward the other two, even in the dim light, the outline of his form and the set of his uncovered head I knew.

"That's Le Claire, as true as heaven, all but the voice," I said to myself. "But I'll never believe that metallic ring is the priest's. It is Le Claire turned renegade, too, or it's a man on a pattern so like him, they couldn't tell themselves apart."

I recalled all the gentleness and manliness of the Father. Never an act of his was cruel, or selfish, or deceptive. True to his principles, he had warned us again and again not to trust Jean. And yet he had always seemed to protect the boy, always knew his comings and goings, and the two had grown yearly to resemble each other more and more in face and form and gesture. Was Le Claire a villain in holy guise?

I did not meditate long, for the third man spoke. Oh, the "good Indian"! Never could he conceal his voice from me.

"Now, what I want you to do is to tell them all which one he is. I've just been clear around their hole in the sand. I could have hit my choice of the lot. But he wasn't there."

No, I had just stepped out after the spade.

"If he had been, I'd have shot him right then, no matter what come next. But I don't want him shot. He's mine. Now tell every brave to leave him to me, the big one, nearly as big as Roman Nose, whiter than the others, because he's not been out here long. But he's no coward. The one with thick dark curly hair; it would make a beautiful scalp. But I want him."

"What will you do with him?" the man nearest to me queried.

"Round the bend below the gorge the Arickaree runs over a little strip of gravel with a ripple that sounds just like the Neosho above the Deep Hole. I'll stake him out there where he can hear it and think of home until he dies. And before I leave him I've got a letter to read to him. It'll help to keep Springvale in his mind if the water fails. I've promised him what to expect when he comes into my country."

"Do it," the smallest of the three spoke up. "Do it. It'll pay him for setting Bud Anderson on me and nearly killing me in the alley back of the courthouse the night we were going to burn up Springvale. I was making for the courthouse to get the papers to burn sure. I'd got the key and could have got them easy—and there's some needed burning specially —when that lispin' tow-head caught my arm and gave my head such a cut that I'll always carry the scar, and twisted my wrist so I've never been able to lift anything heavier than an artillery bugle since. Nobody ever knew it back there but Mapleson and Conlow and Judson. Funny nobody ever guessed Judson's part in that thing except his wife, and she kept it to herself and broke her heart and died. Everybody else said he was water-bound away from home. He wasn't twenty feet from his own house when the Whately girl come out. He was helpin' Jean then. Thought her mother'd be killed, and Whately'd never get home alive—as he didn't—and he'd get the whole store; greediest man on earth for money. He's got the store anyhow, now, and he's going to marry the girl he was helpin' Jean to take out of his way. That store never would have been burnt that night. I wish Jean had got her, though. Then I'd turned things against Tell Mapleson and run him out of town instead of his driving me from Springvale. Tell played a double game damned well. I'm outlawed and he's gettin' richer every day at home."

So spoke the Rev. Mr. Dodd, pastor of the Methodist Church South. It may be I needed the discipline of that day's fighting to hold me motionless and silent in the clump of grass beside these three men.

"Well, let's get up there and watch the fool women cry for their men." It was none other than Father Le Claire's form before me, but this man's voice was never that soft French tone of the good man's—low and musical, matching his kindly eyes and sweet smile. As the three slipped away I did the only foolish act of mine in the whole campaign: I rose from my hiding place, shouldered that spade, and stalked straight down the bank, across the creek, and up to our works in the centre of the island as upright and free as if I were walking up Cliff Street to Judge Baronet's front door. Jean's words had put into me just what I needed—not acceptance of the inevitable, but a power of resistance, the indomitable spirit that overcomes.

History is stranger than fiction, and the story of the Kansas frontier is more tragical than all the Wild West yellow-backed novels ever turned off the press. To me this campaign of the Arickaree has always read like a piece of bloody drama, so terrible in its reality, it puts the imagination out of service.

We had only one chance for deliverance, we must get the tidings of our dreadful plight to Fort Wallace, a hundred miles away. Jack Stillwell and another brave scout were chosen for the dangerous task. At midnight they left us, moving cautiously away into the black blank space toward the southwest, and making a wide detour from their real line of direction. The Indians were on the alert, and a man must walk as noiselessly as a panther to slip between their guards.

The scouts wore blankets to resemble the Indians more closely in the shadows of the night. They made moccasins out of boot tops, that their footprints might tell no story. In sandy places they even walked backward that they should leave no tell-tale trail out of the valley.

Dawn found them only three miles away from their starting place. A hollow bank overhung with long, dry grasses, and fronted with rank sunflowers, gave them a place of concealment through the daylight hours. Again on the second night they hurried cautiously forward. The second morning they were near an Indian village. Their only retreat was in the tall growth of a low, marshy place. Here they crouched through another long day. The unsuspecting squaws, hunting fuel, tramped the grasses dangerously near to them, but a merciful Providence guarded their hiding-place.

On the third night they pushed forward more boldly, hoping that the next day they need not waste the precious hours in concealment. In the early morning they saw coming down over the prairie the first guard of a Cheyenne village moving southward across their path. The Plains were flat and covertless. No tall grass, nor friendly bank, nor bush, nor hollow of ground was there to cover them from their enemies. But out before them lay the rotting carcass of an old buffalo. Its hide still hung about its bones. And inside the narrow shelter of this carcass the two concealed themselves while a whole village passed near them trailing off toward the south.

Insufficient food, lack of sleep, and poisonous water from the buffalo wallows brought nausea and weakness to the faithful men making their way across the hostile land to bring help to us in our dire extremity. It is all recorded in history how these two men fared in that hazardous undertaking. No hundred miles of sandy plain were ever more fraught with peril; and yet these two pressed on with that fearless and indomitable courage that has characterized the Saxon people on every field of conquest.

Meanwhile day crept over the eastern horizon, and the cold chill of the shadows gave place to the burning glare of the September sun. Hot and withering it beat down upon us and upon the unburied dead that lay all about us. The braves that had fallen in the strife strewed the island's edges. Their blood lay dark on the sandy shoals of the stream and stained to duller brown the trampled grasses. Daylight brought the renewal of the treacherous sharpshooting. The enemy closed in about us and from their points of vantage their deadly arrows and bullets were hurled upon our low wall of defence. And so the unequal struggle continued. Ours was henceforth an ambush fight. The redskins did not attack us in open charge again, and we durst not go out to meet them. And so the thing became a game of endurance with us, a slow wearing away of ammunition and food, a growing fever from weakness and loss of blood, a festering of wounds, the ebbing out of strength and hope; while putrid mule meat and muddy water, the sickening stench from naked bloated bodies under the blazing heat of day, the long, long hours of watching for deliverance that came not, and the certainty of the fate awaiting us at last if rescue failed us—these things marked the hours and made them all alike. As to the Indians, the passing of Roman Nose had broken their fighting spirit; and now it was a mere matter of letting us run to the end of our tether and then—well, Jean had hinted what would happen.

On the third night two more scouts left us. It seemed an eternity since Stillwell and his comrade had started from the camp. We felt sure that they must have fallen by the way, and the second attempt was doubly hazardous. The two who volunteered were quiet men. They knew what the task implied, and they bent to it like men who can pay on demand the price of sacrifice. Their names were Donovan and Pliley, recorded in the military roster as private scouts, but the titles they bear in the memory of every man who sat in that grim council on that night, has a grander sound than the written records declare.

"Boys," Forsyth said, lifting himself on his elbow where he lay in his sand bed, "this is the last chance. If you can get to the fort and send us help we can hold out a while. But it must come quickly. You know what it means for you to try, and for us, if you succeed."

The two men nodded assent, then girding on their equipments, they gave us their last messages to be repeated if deliverance ever came to us and they were never heard of again. We were getting accustomed to this now, for Death stalked beside us every hour. They said a brief good-bye and slipped out from us into the dangerous dark on their chosen task.

Then the chill of the night, with its uncertainty and gloom, with its ominous silences broken only by the howl of the gray wolves, who closed in about us and set up their hunger wails beyond the reach of our bullets; and the heat of the day with its peril of arrow and rifle-ball filled the long hours. Hunger was a terror now. Our meat was gone save a few decayed portions which we could barely swallow after we had sprinkled them over with gunpowder. For the stomach refused them even in starvation. Dreams of banquets tortured our short, troubled sleep, and the waking was a horror. A luckless little coyote wandered one day too near our fold. We ate his flesh and boiled his bones for soup. And one day a daring soldier slipped out from our sand pit in search of food—anything—to eat in place of that rotting horseflesh. In the bushes at the end of the island, he found a few wild plums. Oh, food for the gods was that portion of stewed plums carefully doled out to each of us.

Six days went by. I do not know on which one the Sabbath fell, for God has no holy day in the Plains warfare. Six days, and no aid had come from Fort Wallace. That our scouts had failed, and our fate was decreed, was now the settled conclusion in every mind.

On the evening of this sixth day our leader called us about him. How gray and drawn his face looked in the shadowy gray light, but his eyes were clear and his voice steady.

"Boys, we've got to the end of our rope, now. Over there," pointing to the low hills, "the Indian wolves are waiting for us. It's the hazard of war; that's all. But we needn't all be sacrificed. You, who aren't wounded, can't help us who are. You have nothing here to make our suffering less. To stay here means—you all know what. Now the men who can go must leave us to what's coming. I feel sure now that you can get through together somehow, for the tribes are scattering. It is only the remnant left over there to burn us out at last. There is no reason why you should stay here and die. Make your dash for escape together to-night, and save your lives if you can. And"—his voice was brave and full of cheer—"I believe you can."

Then a silence fell. There were two dozen of us gaunt, hungry men, haggard from lack of sleep and the fearful tax on mind and body that tested human endurance to the limit—two dozen, to whom escape was not impossible now, though every foot of the way was dangerous. Life is sweet, and hope is imperishable. We looked into one another's face grimly, for the crisis of a lifetime was upon us. Beside me lay Morton. The handkerchief he had bound about his head in the first hour of battle had not once been removed. There was no other handkerchief to take its place.

"Go, Baronet," he said to me. "Tell your father, if you see him again, that I remembered Whately and how he went down at Chattanooga."

His voice was low and firm and yet he knew what was awaiting him. Oh! men walked on red-hot ploughshares in the days of the winning of the West.

Sharp Grover was sitting beside Forsyth. In the silence of the council the guide turned his eyes toward each of us. Then, clenching his gaunt, knotted hands with a grip of steel, he said in a low, measured voice:

"It's no use asking us, General. We have fought together, and, by Heaven, we'll die together."

In the great crisis of life the only joy is the joy of self-sacrifice. Every man of us breathed freer, and we were happier now than we had been at any time since the conflict began. And so another twenty-four hours, and still another twenty-four went by.

> The sun came up and the sun went down,
> And day and night were the same as one.

And any evil chance seemed better than this slow dragging out of misery-laden time.

"Nature meant me to defend the weak and helpless. The West needs me," I had said to my father. And now I had given it my best. A slow fever was creeping upon me, and weariness of body was greater than pain and hunger. Death would be a welcome thing now that hope seemed dead. I thought of O'mie, bound hand and foot in the Hermit's Cave, and like him, I wished that I might go quickly if I must go. For back of my stolid mental state was a frenzied desire to outwit Jean Pahusca, who was biding his time, and keeping a surer watch on our poor battle-wrecked, starving force than any other Indian in the horde that kept us imprisoned.

The sunrise of the twenty-fifth of September was a dream of beauty on the Colorado Plains. I sat with my face to the eastward and saw the whole pageantry of morning sweep up in a splendor of color through stretches of far limitless distances. Oh! it was gorgeous, with a glory fresh from the hand of the Infinite God, whose is the earth and the seas. Mechanically I thought of the sunrise beyond the Neosho Valley, but nothing there could be half so magnificent as this. And as I looked, the thought grew firmer that this sublimity had been poured out for me for the last time, and I gazed at the face of the morning as we look at the face awaiting the coffin lid.

And even as the thought clinched itself upon me came the sentinel's cry of "Indians! Indians!"

We grasped our weapons at the shrill warning. It was the death-grip now. We knew as surely as we stood there that we could not resist this last attack. The red-skins must have saved themselves for this final blow, when resistance on our part was a feeble mockery. The hills to the north-ward were black with the approaching force, but we were determined to make our last stand heroically, and to sell our lives as dearly as possible. As with a grim last measure of courage we waited, Sharp Grover, who stood motionless, alert, with arms ready, suddenly threw his rifle high in air, and with a shout that rose to heaven, he cried in an ecstasy of joy:

"By the God above us, it's an ambulance!"

To us for whom the frenzied shrieks of the squaws, the fiendish yells of the savage warriors, and the weird, unearthly wailing for the dead were the only cries that had resounded above the Plains these many days, this shout from Grover was like the music of heaven. A darkness came before me, and my strength seemed momentarily to go from me. It was but a moment, and then I opened my eyes to the sublimest sight it is given to the Anglo-American to look upon.

Down from the low bluffs there poured a broad surge of cavalry, in perfect order, riding like the wind, the swift, steady hoof-beats of their horses marking a rhythmic measure that trembled along the ground in musical vibration, while overhead—oh, the grandeur of God's gracious dawn fell never on a thing more beautiful—swept out by the free winds of heaven to its full length, and gleaming in the sunlight, Old Glory rose and fell in rippling waves of splendor.

On they came, the approaching force, in a mad rush to reach us. And we who had waited for the superb charge of Roman Nose and his savage warriors, as we wait for death, saw now this coming in of life, and the regiment of the unconquerable people.

We threw restraint to the winds and shouted and danced and hugged each other, while we laughed and cried in a very transport of joy.

It was Colonel Carpenter and his colored cavalry who had made a dash across the country rushing to our rescue. Beside the Colonel at their head, rode Donovan the scout, whom we had accounted as dead. It was his unerring eye that had guided this command, never varying from the straight line toward our danger-girt entrenchment on the Arickaree.

Before Carpenter's approaching cavalry the Indians fled for their lives, and they who a few hours hence would have been swinging bloody toma-hawks above our heads were now scurrying to their hiding-places far away.

Never tenderer hands cared for the wounded, and never were bath and bandage and food and drink more welcome. Our command was shifted to a clean spot where no stench of putrid flesh could reach us. Rest and care, such as a camp on the Plains can offer, was ours luxuriously; and hard-tack and coffee, food for the angels, we had that day, to our intense satisfaction. Life was ours once more, and hope, and home, and civilization. Oh, could it be true, we asked ourselves, so long had we stood face to face with Death.

The import of this struggle on the Arickaree was far greater than we dreamed of then. We had gone out to meet a few foemen. What we really had to battle with was the fighting strength of the northern Cheyenne and Sioux tribes. Long afterwards it came to us what this victory meant. The broad trail we had eagerly followed up the Arickaree fork of the Republican River had been made by bands on bands of Plains Indians mobilizing only a little to the westward, gathering for a deadly purpose. At the full of the moon the whole fighting force, two thousand strong, was to make a terrible raid, spreading out on either side of the Republican River, reaching southward as far as the Saline Valley and northward to the Platte, and pushing eastward till the older settlements turned them back. They were determined to leave nothing behind them but death and desolation. Their numbers and leadership, with the defenceless condition of the Plains settlers, give broad suggestion of what that raid would have done for Kansas. Our victory on the Arickaree broke up that combination of Indian forces, for all future time. It was for such an unknown purpose, and against such unguessed odds, that fifty of us led by the God of all battle lines, had gone out to fight. We had met and vanquished a foe two hundred times our number, aye, crippled its power for all future years. We were lifting the fetters from the frontier; we were planting the standards westward, westward. In the history of the Plains warfare this fight on the Arickaree, though not the last stroke, was one of the decisive struggles in breaking the savage sovereignty, a sovereignty whose wilderness demesne to-day is a land of fruit and meadow and waving grain, of peaceful homes and wealth and honor.

It was impossible for our wounded comrades to begin the journey to Fort Wallace on that day. When evening came, the camp settled down to quiet and security: the horses fed at their rope tethers, the fires smouldered away to gray ashes, the sun swung down behind the horizon bar, the gold and scarlet of evening changed to deeper hues and the long, purple twilight was on the silent Colorado Plains. Over by the Arickaree the cavalry men lounged lazily in groups. As the shades of evening gathered, the soldiers began to sing. Softly at first, but richer, fuller, sweeter their voices rose and fell with that cadence and melody only the negro voice can compass. And their song, pulsing out across the undulating valley wrapped in the twilight peace, made a harmony so wonderfully tender that we who had dared danger for days unflinchingly now turned our faces to the shadows to hide our tears.

> We are tenting to-night on the old camp ground.
> Give us a song to cheer
> Our weary hearts, a song of home
> And friends we love so dear.
> Many are the hearts that are weary to-night,
> Wishing for this war to cease,
> Many are the hearts looking for the right
> To see the dawn of peace.

So the cavalry men sang, and we listened to their singing with hearts stirred to their depths. And then with prayers of thankfulness for our deliverance, we went to sleep. And over on the little island, under the shallow sands, the men who had fallen beside us lay with patient, folded hands waiting beside the Arickaree waters till the last reveille shall sound for them and they enter the kingdom of Eternal Peace.

THE CIVIL WAR
1861–1865

THE CIVIL WAR
1861-1865

The War with Mexico proved a fertile training ground for a majority of the general officers, Union and Confederate, who took the field at the outbreak of the War Between the States. Imbued with the traditions of the old army, and fully aware of one another's strengths and weaknesses, they were prepared for a war to be fought along the classic lines of the War with Mexico.

Unfortunately, politicians took a hand on both sides so, for two years, the armies suffered staggering blows with the North getting much the worst of it. Nor was all easy and efficient on the Confederate side. The meddling of Jefferson Davis, who had been a soldier, did much to cripple the Southern effort.

Finally, McClellan was able to enforce discipline upon the willing but wayward soldiers of the Army of the Potomac and so forged them into a potentially fine battle instrument.

The character of Praxiteles Swan, Methodist elder from Texas, is an example of the fighting Americans who enter battle in the exalted mood of Cromwell's Ironsides.

There is more than a trace of knightliness in several of the tales; this was the last of our wars in which a sense of chivalry played any real part. The account of Antietam is excellent, whereas the picture of Gettysburg, in a wild flurry of words, depicts some of the bewilderment of conflict.

Mark Twain figures in this anthology because it may be interesting to note what kind of fighting American he was, a humorous cynic of a soldier of which there are many in every army. Fort Donelson is an exciting bit of work, neither pure prose nor pure poetry, and remarkably like some more recent works in detailing narrative action.

FORT DONELSON

by HERMAN MELVILLE

Donelson

(FEBRUARY, 1862)

THE BITTER CUP
  Of that hard countermand
Which gave the Envoys up,
Still was wormwood in the mouth,
  And clouds involved the land,
When, pelted by sleet in the icy street,
  About the bulletin-board a band
Of eager, anxious people met,
And every wakeful heart was set
On latest news from West or South.
"No seeing here," cries one—"don't crowd"—
"You tall man, pray you, read aloud."

IMPORTANT.

> *We learn that General Grant,*
> *Marching from Henry overland,*
> *And joined by a force up the Cumberland sent*
> *(Some thirty thousand the command),*
> *On Wednesday a good position won—*
> *Began the siege of Donelson.*

> *This stronghold crowns a river-bluff,*
> *A good broad mile of leveled top;*
> *Inland the ground rolls off*
> *Deep-gorged, and rocky, and broken up—*
> *A wilderness of trees and brush.*

From: *Battle Pieces.*

The spaded summit shows the roods
Of fixed intrenchments in their hush;
Breast-works and rifle-pits in woods
Perplex the base.—
                         The welcome weather
Is clear and mild; 'tis much like May.
The ancient boughs that lace together
Along the stream, and hang far forth,
Strange with green mistletoe, betray
A dreamy contrast to the North.

Our troops are full of spirits—say
    The siege won't prove a creeping one.
They purpose not the lingering stay
Of old beleaguerers; not that way;
    But, full of vim *from Western prairies won,*
    They'll make, ere long, a dash at Donelson.
Washed by the storm till the paper grew
Every shade of a streaky blue,
That bulletin stood. The next day brought
A second.

LATER FROM THE FORT.
Grant's investment is complete—
    A semicircular one.
Both wings the Cumberland's margin meet,
Then, backward curving, clasp the rebel seat.
    On Wednesday this good work was done;
    But of the doers some lie prone.
Each wood, each hill, each glen was fought for;
The bold inclosing line we wrought for
Flamed with sharpshooters. Each cliff cost
A limb or life. But back we forced
Reserves and all; made good our hold;
And so we rest.

                    Events unfold.
On Thursday added ground was won,
    A long bold steep: we near the Den.

Later the foe came shouting down
  In sortie, which was quelled; and then
We stormed them on their left.
A chilly change in the afternoon;

The sky, late clear, is now bereft
Of sun. Last night the ground froze hard—
Rings to the enemy as they run
Within their works. A ramrod bites
The lip it meets. The cold incites
To swinging of arms with brisk rebound.
Smart blows 'gainst lusty chests resound.

Along the outer line we ward
  A crackle of skirmishing goes on,
Our lads creep round on hand and knee,
  They fight from behind each trunk and stone;
  And sometimes, flying for refuge, one
Finds 'tis an enemy shares the tree.
Some scores are maimed by boughs shot off
  In the glades by the Fort's big gun.
  We mourn the loss of Colonel Morrison,
  Killed while cheering his regiment on.
Their far sharpshooters try our stuff;
And ours return them puff for puff:
'Tis diamond-cutting-diamond work.
  Woe on the rebel cannoneer
Who shows his head. Our fellows lurk
  Like Indians that waylay the deer
By the wild salt-spring.—The sky is dun,
Foredooming the fall of Donelson.

Stern weather is all unwonted here.
  The people of the country own
We brought it. Yea, the earnest North
Has elementally issued forth
  To storm this Donelson.

FURTHER.

A yelling rout
Of ragamuffins broke profuse
To-day from out the Fort.
Sole uniform they wore, a sort
Of patch, or white badge (as you choose)
Upon the arm. But leading these,
Or mingling, were men of face
And bearing of patrician race,
Splendid in courage and gold lace—
The officers. Before the breeze
Made by their charge, down went our line;
But, rallying, charged back in force,
And broke the sally; yet with loss.
This on the left; upon the right
Meanwhile there was an answering fight;
Assailants and assailed reversed.
The charge too upward, and not down—
Up a steep ridge-side, toward its crown,
A strong redoubt. But they who first
Gained the fort's base, and marked the trees
Felled, heaped in horned perplexities,
And shagged with brush; and swarming there
Fierce wasps whose sting was present death—
They faltered, drawing bated breath,
And felt it was in vain to dare;
Yet still, perforce, returned the ball,
Firing into the tangled wall
Till ordered to come down. They came;
But left some comrades in their fame,
Red on the ridge in icy wreath
And hanging gardens of cold Death.
But not quite unavenged these fell;
Our ranks once out of range, a blast
Of shrapnel and quick shell
Burst on the rebel horde, still massed,
Scattering them pell-mell.
(This fighting—judging what we read—
Both charge and countercharge,

Would seem but Thursday's told at large,
Before in brief reported.—Ed.)
Night closed in about the Den
  Murky and lowering. Ere long, chill rains.
A night not soon to be forgot,
  Reviving old rheumatic pains
And longings for a cot.
  No blankets, overcoats, or tents.
Coats thrown aside on the warm march here—
We looked not then for changeful cheer;
Tents, coats, and blankets too much care.
  No fires; a fire a mark presents;
  Near by, the tree shows bullet-dents.
Rations were eaten cold and raw.
  The men well soaked, came snow; and more—
A midnight sally. Small sleeping done—
    But such is war;
No matter, we'll have Fort Donelson.

"Ugh! Ugh!
'Twill drag along—drag along,"
Growled a cross patriot in the throng,
His battered umbrella like an ambulance-cover
Riddled with bullet-holes, spattered all over.
"Hurrah for Grant!" cried a stripling shrill;
Three urchins joined him with a will,
And some of taller stature cheered.
Meantime a Copperhead passed; he sneered.
  "Win or lose," he pausing said,
"Caps fly the same; all boys, mere boys;
Any thing to make a noise.
  Like to see the list of the dead;
These 'craven Southerners' hold out;
Ay, ay, they'll give you many a bout."
  "We'll beat in the end, sir,"
Firmly said one in staid rebuke,
A solid merchant, square and stout.
  "And do you think it that way tend, sir?"
Asked the lean Copperhead, with a look
Of splenetic pity. "Yes, I do."

His yellow death's head the croaker shook:
"The country's ruined, that I know."
A shower of broken ice and snow,
 In lieu of words, confuted him;
They saw him hustled round the corner go,
 And each by-stander said—Well suited him.

Next day another crowd was seen
In the dark weather's sleety spleen.
Bald-headed to the storm came out
A man, who, 'mid a joyous shout,
Silently posted this brief sheet:

 GLORIOUS VICTORY OF THE FLEET!

 FRIDAY'S GREAT EVENTS!

 THE ENEMY'S WATER-BATTERIES BEAT!

 WE SILENCED EVERY GUN!

 THE OLD COMMODORE'S COMPLIMENTS SENT
 PLUMP INTO DONELSON!

"Well, well, go on!" exclaimed the crowd
To him who thus much read aloud.
"That's all," he said. "What! nothing more?"
"Enough for a cheer, though—hip, hurrah!
"But here's old Baldy come again—
"More news!"—And now a different strain.

 (Our own reporter a dispatch compiles,
  As best he may, from varied sources.)

 Large re-enforcements have arrived—
  Munitions, men, and horses—
 For Grant, and all debarked, with stores.

  The enemy's field-works extend six miles—
 The gate still hid; so well contrived.

Yesterday stung us; frozen shores
  Snow-clad, and through the drear defiles

And over the desolate ridges blew
A Lapland wind.
                    The main affair
  Was a good two hours' steady fight
Between our gun-boats and the Fort.
  The Louisville's wheel was smashed outright.
A hundred-and-twenty-eight-pound ball
Came planet-like through a starboard port,
Killing three men, and wounding all
The rest of that gun's crew,
(The captain of the gun was cut in two);
Then splintering and ripping went—
Nothing could be its continent.
  In the narrow stream the Louisville,
Unhelmed, grew lawless; swung around,
  And would have thumped and drifted, till
All the fleet was driven aground,
But for the timely order to retire.

Some damage from our fire, 'tis thought,
Was done the water-batteries of the Fort.

Little else took place that day,
  Except the field artillery in line
Would now and then—for love, they say—
  Exchange a valentine.

The old sharpshooting going on.
Some plan afoot as yet unknown;
So Friday closed round Donelson.

LATER.
        Great suffering through the night—
A stinging one. Our heedless boys
  Were nipped like blossoms. Some dozen
  Hapless wounded men were frozen.

During day being struck down out of sight,
And help-cries drowned in roaring noise,
They were left just where the skirmish shifted—
Left in dense underbrush snow-drifted.
Some, seeking to crawl in crippled plight,
So stiffened—perished.
                  Yet in spite
Of pangs for these, no heart is lost.
Hungry, and clothing stiff with frost,
Our men declare a nearing sun
Shall see the fall of Donelson.
  And this they say, yet not disown
The dark redoubts round Donelson,
    And ice-glazed corpses, each a stone—
      A sacrifice to Donelson;
They swear it, and swerve not, gazing on
A flag, deemed black, flying from Donelson.
Some of the wounded in the wood
 Were cared for by the foe last night,
Though he could do them little needed good,
    Himself being all in shivering plight.
The rebel is wrong, but human yet;
He's got a heart, and thrusts a bayonet.
He gives us battle with wondrous will—
This bluff's a perverted Bunker Hill.

The stillness stealing through the throng
The silent thought and dismal fear revealed;
     They turned and went,
    Musing on right and wrong
    And mysteries dimly sealed—
Breasting the storm in daring discontent;
The storm, whose black flag showed in heaven,
As if to say no quarter there was given
     To wounded men in wood,
  Or true hearts yearning for the good—
All fatherless seemed the human soul.
But next day brought a bitterer bowl—
  On the bulletin-board this stood:

Saturday morning at 3 A. M.
  A stir within the Fort betrayed
That the rebels were getting under arms;
  Some plot these early birds had laid.
But a lancing sleet cut him who stared
Into the storm. After some vague alarms,
Which left our lads unscared,
Out sallied the enemy at dim of dawn,
  With cavalry and artillery, and went
  In fury at our environment.
Under cover of shot and shell
  Three columns of infantry rolled on,
  Vomited out of Donelson—
Rolled down the slopes like rivers of hell,
  Surged at our line, and swelled and poured
Like breaking surf. But unsubmerged
  Our men stood up, except where roared
The enemy through one gap. We urged
Our all of manhood to the stress,
But still showed shattered in our desperateness.
      Back set the tide,
But soon afresh rolled in;
  And so it swayed from side to side—
Far batteries joining in the din,
Though sharing in another fray—
  Till all became an Indian fight,
Intricate, dusky, stretching far away,
Yet not without spontaneous plan
  However tangled showed the plight:
Duels all over 'tween man and man,
Duels on cliff-side, and down in ravine,
  Duels at long range, and bone to bone;
Duels every where flitting and half unseen.
  Only by courage good as their own,
And strength outlasting theirs,
  Did our boys at last drive the rebels off.
Yet they went not back to their distant lairs
  In strong-hold, but loud in scoff
Maintained themselves on conquered ground—
Uplands; built works, or stalked around.

Our right wing bore this onset. Noon
Brought calm to Donelson.

The reader ceased; the storm beat hard;
   'Twas day, but the office-gas was lit;
   Nature retained her sulking-fit,
      In her hand the shard.
Flitting faces took the hue
Of that washed bulletin-board in view,
And seemed to bear the public grief
As private, and uncertain of relief;
Yea, many an earnest heart was won,
   As broodingly he plodded on,
To find in himself some bitter thing,
Some hardness in his lot as harrowing
            As Donelson.
That night the board stood barren there,
   Oft eyed by wistful people passing,
   Who nothing saw but the rain-beads chasing
Each other down the wafered square,
As down some storm-beat grave-yard stone.
But next day showed—

MORE NEWS LAST NIGHT

STORY OF SATURDAY AFTERNOON.

VICISSITUDES OF THE WAR.

The damaged gun-boats can't wage fight
For days; so says the Commodore.
Thus no diversion can be had.
Under a sunless sky of lead
   Our grim-faced boys in blackened plight
Gaze toward the ground they held before,
And then on Grant. He marks their mood,
And hails it, and will turn the same to good.
Spite all that they have undergone,
Their desperate hearts are set upon

FORT DONELSON

This winter fort, this stubborn fort,
This castle of the last resort,
    This Donelson.

1 P. M.
              An order given
  Requires withdrawal from the front
  Of regiments that bore the brunt
Of morning's fray. Their ranks all riven
Are being replaced by fresh, strong men.
Great vigilance in the foeman's Den;
He snuffs the stormers. Need it is
That for that fell assault of his,
That rout inflicted, and self-scorn—
Immoderate in noble natures, torn
By sense of being through slackness overborne—
The rebel be given a quick return:
The kindest face looks now half stern.
Balked of their prey in airs that freeze,
Some fierce ones glare like savages.
And yet, and yet, strange moments are—
Well—blood, and tears, and anguished War!
The morning's battle-ground is seen
  In lifted glades, like meadows rare;
  The blood-drops on the snow-crust there
Like clover in the white-weed show—
  Flushed fields of death, that call again—
  Call to our men, and not in vain,
For that way must the stormers go.

3 P. M.
           The work begins.
Light drifts of men thrown forward, fade
  In skirmish-line along the slope,
Where some dislodgments must be made
  Ere the stormer with the strong-hold cope.

Lew Wallace, moving to retake
The heights late lost—

(Herewith a break,
Storms at the West derange the wires.
Doubtless, ere morning, we shall hear
The end; we look for news to cheer—
Let Hope fan all her fires.)

Next day in large bold hand was seen
The closing bulletin:

VICTORY!
Our troops have retrieved the day
By one grand surge along the line;
The spirit that urged them was divine.
The first works flooded, naught could stay
The stormers: on! still on!
Bayonets for Donelson!
Over the ground that morning lost
Rolled the blue billows, tempest-tossed,
Following a hat on the point of a sword.
Spite shell and round-shot, grape and canister,
Up they climbed without rail or banister—
Up the steep hill-sides long and broad
Driving the rebel deep within his works.
'Tis nightfall; not an enemy lurks
In sight. The chafing men
Fret for more fight:
"To-night, to-night let us take the Den!"
But night is treacherous, Grant is wary;
Of brave blood be a little chary.
Patience! the Fort is good as won;
To-morrow, and into Donelson.

LATER AND LAST.
THE FORT IS OURS.
A flag came out at early morn
Bringing surrender. From their towers
Floats out the banner late their scorn.
In Dover, hut and house are full
Of rebels dead or dying.

The National flag is flying
From the crammed court-house pinnacle.
Great boat-loads of our wounded go
To-day to Nashville. The sleet-winds blow;
But all is right: the fight is won,
The winter-fight for Donelson.
                    Hurrah!
The spell of old defeat is broke,
   The habit of victory begun;
Grant strikes the war's first sounding stroke
                    At Donelson.
For lists of killed and wounded, see
The morrow's dispatch: to-day 'tis victory.

The man who read this to the crowd
   Shouted as the end he gained;
      And though the unflagging tempest rained,
         They answered him aloud.
And hand grasped hand, and glances met
In happy triumph; eyes grew wet.
O, to the punches brewed that night
Went little water. Windows bright
Beamed rosy on the sleet without,
And from the deep street came the frequent shout;
While some in prayer, as these in glee,
Blessed heaven for the winter-victory.
But others were who wakeful laid
   In midnight beds, and early rose,
      And, feverish in the foggy snows,
Snatched the damp paper--wife and maid.
   The death-list like a river flows
      Down the pale sheet,
And there the whelming waters meet.

      Ah, God! may Time with happy haste
      Bring wail and triumph to a waste,
         And war be done;
      The battle flag-staff fall athwart
      The curs'd ravine, and wither; naught

Be left of trench or gun;
The bastion, let it ebb away,
Washed with the river bed; and Day
In vain seek Donelson.

GAINES' MILL

by JOHN W. THOMASON, JR.

OF THE REV. PRAXITELES SWAN, it is related elsewhere how he rode out from Virginia to Texas in the days before the war, ordained to preach the Gospel after the style of the Methodist Episcopal Church, South; and how he came, on a blooded mare, with salvation in his saddlebags, to establish himself on the front rank of the battle line Methodism maintained against the powers of darkness in those parts. They relate also that he was redheaded and slabsided, and pretty nearly as tall, and as loud in the mouth, as Gen. Sam Houston. In the Rutersville District at Washington on the Brazos, he immediately thrashed the two toughest men in the community, commandeered a saloon for his tabernacle, and married the local heiress. Forthwith, he preached and practised a militant religion immensely appealing to East Texas of that ardent time. The years passed over him, and he entered into the legends and the folk tales of the region, for he was of the material from which the narrators make such things. You will find his acts set forth in certain old books; and the elders of my youth remembered him, particularly Uncle Jimmy Farrow, the Quantrill raider, who taught me the refinements of squirrel hunting by Patterson Lake; and my uncles, who fought the war in the Fifth Texas Volunteer Infantry, Confederate States Provisional Army.

From these sources, then, and from old letters in a cowhide trunk, I make this story. Praxiteles Swan was a thoughtful man and liked to analyze his personal acts. He says somewhere that the first important decision in his life was that which led him to turn his back on the tempestuous blue-blood uncle in Virginia, who brought him up, and to enter the Methodist ministry. For this decision, he felt, he had a basis of high conviction and sound scriptural precept, and he was proud of it. The sec-

From: *Lone Star Preacher.* Copyright 1941. Charles Scribner's Sons.

ond, however, he considered to have been forced upon him by no less an event than the War of the Southern Confederacy, and he was never quite certain that it carried a blessing with it.

But as for this story: The opening of the year 1861 found him in health and high condition, his circumstances better than a bishop's in most respects; a lean column of a man, red-maned and red-bearded. Named presiding elder for the Huntsville District in 1859, he had brought his family to a farm a few miles west of that pleasant little town, so that the children might have advantage of the schools which caused Huntsville to be called, in those days, the Athens of Texas. Mrs. Swan's money had provided the farm, her Negroes worked it, and she herself, Praxiteles said with pride, ran it as well as a man. For the Swans were folks who got ahead. Praxiteles himself had ever an eye for horse-flesh, and talent for occasional judicious horse trading, and saw nothing wrong about it, any more than he saw evil for his cloth in hunting and fishing. Nor did he see why he shouldn't wear a good coat and ride a good horse on his pastoral rounds, and he did both all his life. While he conceded the spirituality of his colleagues, he privately considered most of them a shiftless lot; he was never able to associate starvation, even the genteel starvation of the Methodist preacher, with a state of grace. That was the year the state seceded from the Federal Union.

The war was seen far in advance by knowledgeable men, and there were signs and portents, such as go before great events. The old folks, white and black, still remember the comet blazing in the sky, about the winter of '59 and '60; it had a tail shaped like a sword; and they recall the other omens also. When men met, throughout the South, they talked politics, and the women showed an uneasy interest, and every scrap of newspaper that penetrated to the settlements was read to tatters. Not a few of the preachers took sides and held forth from their pulpits on a tariff for revenue only, and states' rights, and brave little South Carolina. But Praxiteles Swan was not one of these; he despised politicians, and notably lacked patience with fools. He considered that preachers should abjure the things of this world, and that his Lord and Master was not in politics, and that war talk was idle and wicked. Such sentiments got him into continual argument, because tempers were running high all over the South, and Praxiteles, for all his weight and inches and red hair, was more than once forced to support his principles with his hands.

Indeed, his conduct had come to a point of issue before the last East Texas Conference of 1860. Praxiteles' presiding elder—a divine famous for his warlike sentiments, who ate fire to public admiration all over his district, and then went to California when the war broke out and stayed there—publicly cited Brother Swan for fighting—this to the scandal of the cloth. And it is one of the stories they tell: How the deliberations of the conference on the unchristian violence of Brother Swan were guided tactfully by the bishop, because Praxiteles, with his white face and flaming hair and dilated nostrils, was rather frightening. The evidence allowed no doubt that Brother Swan had, in fact, whaled the daylights out of a Mr. Ellers, of Old Waverly: and the bishop announced, uneasily: "Brother Swan must be admonished before the conference, and have prayer offered for him." They relate that the accused stood up, with the effect of a tree standing, and the bishop added hastily that Brother Abner Smedes would offer the prayer "for our dearly beloved brother, yonder." Praxiteles sat down and Brother Smedes rose; he was oldest and gentlest of them all; his hair was white as carded wool, and he was round and pink and benevolent. He stood and raised a face of beatitude and a smooth voice, saying: "O Lord! Brother Swan has been a-fightin' again. We're mighty sorry about this, Lord. We know he oughtn' to be a-fightn' like this all the time, and we hope, O Lord! you'll help him not to, any more. But if he does have to fight, O Lord, please, Seh, arrange it so he'll whup!"

After that, Praxiteles, not at all chastened, was sent into the North Texas Conference to fill the pulpit of a furloughed preacher, and the North Texas counties were close enough to Kansas to be infected with the Free Soil violence which was tearing the border to pieces. In February, Texas seceded from the Union and joined the Confederacy. Praxiteles Swan was one of the two Methodist preachers sitting on the Gainesville citizens' committee to try the bushwhackers who killed Col. Bill Young in Cooke County, and that committee tranquilized the section by hanging forty-eight men on the same tree, as it is told, and in the same day. This event, more than any other, forced Praxiteles Swan to turn his thoughts from his calling, his family and his brood mares.

The entries in his journal indicate a certain agony of spirit; he didn't believe in secession, but he wanted to do what was right: "I am still visiting, praying, and preaching as hard as I can, with fear and trembling. . . . The people are so absorbed in the 'Crisis' that they have forgotten they have souls. . . . I think the moral crisis in this country is much greater than the political. . . . I am going to throw a few Bum shells into my congregation this very Sunday. . . ." Everywhere he went, that winter, prominent gentlemen were raising military companies and regiments. The divine who served the Galveston charge wrote him in winged words: "If Lincoln's fleet should come now . . . I am satisfied that their blood will make the grass come up a foot higher on our prairie here. . . . I shall die a true patriot and a soldier of the Cross, the gun in hand and Christ within my heart. . . ." This letter further stated that the writer was joining the MacDonald Rangers.

Praxiteles asked about the Rangers of a state militia officer in Houston, and learned that they were frontier guards; the authorities were apprehensive for the western regions of the state. Praxiteles shrugged and went his way; the approach of war, he reflected, brought out a lot of human nature. I find in this part of his diary references which, on examination, prove to be from the more sanguinary passages of the Old Testament. Praxiteles was an Old Testament man; the New Testament was for his softer moods, and he had few soft moods that one can verify. It should be added that there was no pressure on him, nor any preacher, to bear arms. The old South held its preachers high and rarely sat in judgment on their conduct. But he realized presently that he was one crying "Peace, peace," when there was no peace.

The thing came clear for him one raw March evening, after his return to Huntsville; the children, having done their lessons—young Prax, the oldest, was deep in the *Commentaries of Caesar* and most insistent to discover the age at which Roman boys were allowed to go to war—had yawned off to bed; the two girls were tucked away; and Mrs. Swan was reading, with much indignation, a book by a Mrs. Stowe called *Uncle Tom's Cabin,* which had come into the community—although Mrs. Swan wasn't a reading woman, really. Praxiteles, since supper, had walked up and down before the fire, his face withdrawn and shadowed, his brows knitted.

Now he stopped pacing, and faced his wife. "Mrs. Swan, the thing is clear to me. I have wrestled, as Jacob on Peniel, and I have my answer. I must join this war."

"Yes, Mr. Prax," she replied, not lifting her eyes from the page. "Yes, Mr. Prax. I thought you would."

"You thought I would!" His tone implied that she had taken a liberty, thinking about his actions. "It is a plain duty. Our young men in these camps of instruction are sheep without a shepherd, if I ever saw any in my life. Most of them are from Christian homes, but there are godless young hellions at large among them. And the officers—I declare to you, Mrs. Swan, I don't believe the officers, especially the majors and colonels, do a thing but drink whisky and chew tobacco! And the generals!" He stopped to search a usually adequate vocabulary, without success. "I am no part of a soldier. I am a man of peace. I don't pretend to understand the politics of the affair. But there can be no dispensation of grace on the godless and the wrathful, and who wins must have God on his side! Where, then"—his great voice mounted and the flame fluttered in the lamp—"is the preacher's place but in the forefront of the fight? I mean, the unremitting war we wage against Apollyon and his host."

Mrs. Swan rose deliberately, went to the fireplace and laid the Stowe book well back on the logs. She returned to her chair, and you saw that she was repressing sentiments of extraordinary violence. "Don't you preach at me, Mr. Swan," she told him. "I knew you were going to the war, one way or another. You couldn't see a fuss as big as that and not get yourself into it. It was just a question in my mind, when you'd choose to join. I've got your clothes together, ready to go in the portmanteau, and—"

"Woman, you're crazy!" Praxiteles had never heard such language from her in eighteen years of married life. This dutiful and tender wife of his—"Woman, the events happening have upset you! What is this book you burn? What—"

"Nothing's upset me," Mrs. Swan told him evenly. "As to that Stowe hussy, I'd like to have my fingers"—she crooked and flexed her strong, well-kept hands—"in her back hair for about two minutes! Pah!" She came as near spitting as a refined female might, and not do so. "I'll not vex myself discussing it. But why don't they let us alone, those Yankees? I tell you, Mr. Swan, if I was a man, I'd have gone myself before now— indeed I would." Mrs. Swan's black eyes snapped and her nostrils dilated, and she breathed strongly through her nose. She straightened herself in her chair, and you observed that she still had a figure. "I wish the Yankee nation was in the Bad Place, John Brown and that Garrison man and all," she stated, "and that I could help send them there! Well, go on and preach to your young men, Mr. Prax. I can take care of things here. But," she concluded darkly, "I don't think you'll be preaching very long." She sought with fumbling hands for her sewing basket. All at once her eyes were bright with tears, but Praxiteles observed that they were tears of pure rage. The woman Stowe's book was burning unwillingly, with a great smoke and a strong smell of glue. Come to think of it, he'd heard the book mentioned, although he discouraged among his flocks the reading of secular works—novels and such. Would that be the spark that had struck such fire from this meek wife of his bosom? She had never spoken so to him before; had been, all these years, a jewel among women. Now . . . *Jael—Jael—Jael*. The text came to him: "Blessed above women shall Jael . . . be. . . . She put her hand to the nail, and her right hand to the workman's hammer; and with the hammer she smote Sisera, she smote off his head, when she had pierced and stricken through his temples."

Praxiteles Swan turned and leaned against the mantel, and poked *Uncle Tom's Cabin* deeper into the logs; now it burned more strongly. He looked again at his wife over his arm. Her eyes were the eyes of one seeing visions.

"My dear," he said gently, almost timidly. "My dear."

She got up and came over to him. "Mr. Prax," she said, "you're a good man and you've been a good husband to me all these years. I was never in a war, but women know all about war—women who bear men-children know all about war. This war will be terrible. I only hope it's finished before young Prax is old enough to go. But if it's not, I'll send him too."

He told her, presently, that she was overwrought; it was time they had the evening lesson and sought their rest, and he picked up his Bible. First he looked for that eloquent passage in which Paul, a bachelor, discusses matrimony, but he changed his mind and read aloud the ninety-first psalm, which is a good psalm for a man going away to war; and the prayer he prayed that night was Mizpah—Laban's "The Lord watch between me and thee when we are absent one from another."

The next day, Elder Swan set out for Houston, to enroll himself as chaplain in the Fifth Texas Regiment of Volunteer Infantry. As far as Montgomery he had a fellow traveller, his friend, Gen. Sam Houston, lately ejected from the governor's chair at Austin, after he had declined to take the oath of allegiance to the Confederacy. The vast old general was in great form, his eyes bright with some scheme he had, and he talked for forty miles. One passage Praxiteles was to remember all his life, although he never saw Sam Houston again.

"All the young men are going to this war, Elder, and you, who are old enough to know better, are going with them. And old Sam Houston tells you, Elder, that it is madness. *Quem Deus vult perdere*—As the Gadarene swine, you rush on destruction! And you who live will see your substance wasted, your women and children homeless, your very social order destroyed. Elder, the day will come—and you will see it—oh, a chaplain seldom gets hurt—you'll see people draw the nails from those cotton sheds out there to fasten planks above their heads against the elements! You'll see gentlefolk working with their hands where your Negroes work now—only a damned sight harder. Remember, in those days, that old Sam warned ye and you would not hear."

II

Of the Texas Brigade which served with the Army of Northern Virginia many books have been written, some of them still available in the older libraries. There were the First, Fourth and Fifth Regiments, assembled from thirty-two militia companies over the eastern portion of the state in early 1861. The Fourth and Fifth formed at Houston and were sworn in by a picturesque Old Army officer named Earl Van Dorn, then major, C. S. A. In August they were ordered to Virginia, and marched through Eastern Texas and Western Louisiana to New Iberia on the Teche, a twelve-day march in the hottest and unhealthiest season of the year, which stripped away their weaklings before they reached the railhead. They arrived in Richmond, already very tough men, in September. The First Texas came in a little later by a sort of unofficial movement still unexplained in the annals; it was John Bell Hood's word that the First Texas simply straggled to the front.

They were sent to the Army on the Alexandria Line—as the loose irregular front from Winchester down through the plains of Manassas, Fredericksburg and Yorktown was called—and were brigaded with the 18th Georgia and Hampton's Legion, under the famous fire-eater, General Wigfall. Their time passed without alarms, in drills and instruction; the war was urbane and far away. It was by no means certain, after the sweeping victory at Manassas in July, that there would be any fighting with the North. It was generally believed that the mudsills were well whipped, and would presently go home; although Praxiteles Swan, from his travels in the North, didn't think so himself.

Praxiteles Swan made the march to New Iberia, and the steam-car ride thereafter. He was a great help to the colonel in minor disciplinary matters, and his regiment left no trail of wrecked barrooms along the road to Richmond, as did certain other formations whose misdeeds are even now embalmed in the official records. At the Richmond camp of instruction, up river by the fairgrounds, he became interested in drills and bought himself a *Gilham's Manual*. He also added to his field library the *Commentaries of Caesar* and Xenophon's books. But the best soldier of them all, he considered, was Joshua; he had Joshua by heart. What he saw of the Provisional Government—the Jeff Davis Government it was beginning to be called—did not impress him. He renewed no old acquaintances in Richmond. He had, he conceded, completely severed himself from his beginnings; that soft drawl of the Texans made him homesick, not for his Virginia birthplace, but for the East Texas hills and the Trinity bottom lands where Mrs. Swan and his children waited for him. Up at Charlottesville there still must live, he supposed, the furious old uncle who had brought him up, and thrown him out when he joined the ministry. No word from the uncle, all the years since he went out to Texas; the old rascal would be in a fine humor over this war, although too old to serve in it. One day, while Praxiteles played with the idea of asking leave to visit him, he learned, casually, that the gentleman was dead—dead of a thundering apoplexy induced by the news that Gen. Joe Johnston failed to pursue the broken foe after the Battle of Manassas. Also, that he had left his property—which was considerable—to a nephew who ran off to Texas some years back. Praxiteles took furlough and went to Charlottesville, and made himself known to the lawyers who were tracing him in Texas. Such was the lighthearted inefficiency of the Confederate postal service that their letters would be another year finding him.

When the uncle's affairs were settled, the Reverend Praxiteles Swan was a well-to-do man, as such things went in that section. He inherited three fat Piedmont farms, some blooded stock, and a hundred slaves. Praxiteles did not hesitate over the slaves. He considered the institution legal and ethical, but prohibitively wasteful. He had no intention, he stated, of undertaking the upkeep of a parcel of lazy, heavy-eating blacks, nor did he care for the hiring-out system. He directed the legal gentlemen to manumit the able-bodied and their families as fast as work could be found for them, and he arranged living quarters and kitchen gardens for the few incapables in the back areas of the great house, which he would hold.

The farms rented readily, for it looked as though the armies would need a lot of wheat, and farmers were increasing their acreages. The horses offered no problem. Confederate remount officers snapped at them, and Praxiteles saved two for his personal use—a thoroughbred bay mare, and a strong young gelding, three-quarter strain, that promised well. There was some cash, too; the old colonel had thought highly of gold. Praxiteles put as much as he considered patriotic in Confederate bonds, and set aside a respectable sum for soldier uses. He bought no tracts; he considered that tracts did no good to anybody, and he argued the matter hotly and publicly with a Presbyterian divine in the post office at Charlottesville, to the great delight of the bystanders. His business concluded, he stood bareheaded for a space in the keen November wind by his uncle's grave, under the cedar trees in the garden, where the old gentleman loved to sit through hot afternoons. He found no feeling save a mild regret, and his uncle, he was convinced, lay securely in hell. Then he returned to his regiment and found the army going into winter quarters, after the genteel fashion of that war.

The Texas Brigade was building huts on the hills by Dumfries, with the flats of Quantico Creek below and the Potomac making a great shimmering loop toward the east. Four men would join forces and run up a windowless shack with log walls, chinked against the wind. Chimneys were contrived of stones and mud and sticks. Bunks of rough-hewed timber flanked the fireplaces inside, and doors were hung on rawhide hinges. The huts were loosely grouped by regiments. The Texans were weather-tight in no time, although Hood and the West P'int inspectors grumbled continually that the shacks were out of dress.

Regimental duty was light; the brigade was in a support echelon of the Alexandria Line. Since the enemy was snug in winter quarters, too, no unpleasantness was anticipated before spring. The regiment did its turn on picket and grand guard, but the cavalry was having all the fun, or so the reports went; and the skeptical Texans, horse-riding folks to a man, began to hear stories about a fantastical cavalier called, amusingly, Jeb Stuart. Now and then they saw some bedraggled Yankee prisoners, plucked up by his troopers. But their only enemy, save winter and rough weather, was a regiment of New York Fire Zouaves which lived across the river on the Maryland shore; clear days, you could see the splash of color they made when they drilled, for they went gloriously in red and yellow.

It became the fashion for the men of the two commands to perpetrate small outrages on one another; venturous souls crossed the river by night in rowboats to this end, and now and then did not return. January, the river froze—the Potomac is a big river down there—and the thick ice ran out so far from each bank that men could approach to shouting distance and insult one another. The New Yorkers were easily first at such games; the provincials from the Trinity bottom could not approach the glib obscenities of the Bowery, and had to content themselves with promising to cover the earth with the ring-streaked and striped bodies of the Fire Zouaves, did they ever get a chance at them. Oddly enough, the Fifth Texas and the Zouaves came face to face along Young's Branch, about sunset the last day of Second Manassas, the August following, but that is another story, remembered more in Texas than in New York. Praxiteles deplored the presence of the New Yorkers, it made the men swear so.

If time in winter quarters fell heavy on the young soldiers—how wistfully, through three winters to come, some of them would look back upon that season when the war was new—the chaplains found sufficient employment. Praxiteles Swan jousted tirelessly at the devil of the camps, which is a particularly insidious devil, beguiling men with applejack and playing cards. Many of the war stories about him date from this time, and his journal gives further evidence to the effect that he was never idle. It was not in him to be idle.

My uncles had their narratives of these months: How he stopped a fight between two sergeants by plucking up the combatants and knocking their heads together. How he discouraged a blasphemer by immersing him in a horse trough, and then—it being freezing weather—conducting the man to his quarters and wrapping him in his own blankets while the fellow's clothes dried, Praxiteles admonishing him the while—that man was a talented swearer, but he always looked over his shoulder, afterward, before he expressed himself, and they say it spoiled his style—and the time he walked in on a game of brag, table stakes, blandly swept the money into his pockets, waited, from his great height, for objections, thanked the players for their charity, and turned the loot over to the brigade surgeon for hospital extras. In the army, also, he always was the material of which legend is made.

His own diary contains frank notes on people afterwards famous. Joseph E. Johnston, the commanding general in those parts, he considered a formalist; and he did not then nor later subscribe to the Old Army viewpoint which rated Joe Johnston at the top of the list. On Longstreet, he withheld his opinion, but came to regard him as a man who knew his business; and he never indulged in the hue and cry that clouded Longstreet's fame after the war. Brig. Gen. J. E. B. Stuart interested him because of his known piety; everybody knew Stuart, who seemed as ubiquitous as the wind, but Praxiteles held that he was too young and gay for responsibilities. Praxiteles never liked the cavalry. The officer most prominent in the Texas Brigade was Colonel Hood, the West Pointer who commanded the Fourth Texas and who, when General Wigfall discovered the atmosphere of the Confederate Senate more congenial to his talents than the tented field, was given the brigade.

This Hood was a great one for soldiering, and loved parades; had his men out in all weathers, tramping around. Praxiteles did not approve of him; he was by rumor a loose liver; a vessel, in fact, of wrath; and the chaplain of the Fifth considered his example terribly dangerous to the young men of his charge. Hood was a tall, high-shouldered Kentuckian, with long arms and legs and a big-boned frame, his face smothered in a straw-colored beard. There was a droop to the set of his pale blue eyes that gave him a curious, diffident, mournful look, like a regretful Viking, but never was an appearance more deceptive. Of him, Praxiteles would write more hereafter.

His journal tells, too, of the conference the chaplains of the brigade held to determine the proper station for a chaplain during battle—a question much debated by the Southern prelates. The doctrine of the Old Army held that the chaplain was a noncombatant, and might properly, at most, engage himself in the care of the wounded around the field hospitals, and with the ghostly consolation of those about to die. The Provisional Army of the Confederate States was, however, as little bound by doctrine as any ever mustered for war, and the militia soldiers looked with cold suspicion upon anything emanating from West Point. Thus numerous views were expounded.

A Brother Alpheus Murk, of a Cotton State brigade, stated that the presence of a chaplain among troops engaged in combat did the troops no good, and further, was exceedingly harmful to the health of the chaplain's soul. He had served with a volunteer regiment at Buena Vista in the Mexican War, and he related that the oaths and blasphemies of the soldiers were so appalling, he did not consider himself in a state of grace for at least eleven months thereafter, although he wore down the very springs of his knees with prayer. Several divines, present at First Manassas, were inclined to agree with Brother Murk. Praxiteles' contribution was that he'd never been in a battle and couldn't form an opinion until events brought him opportunity to observe. As affairs turned out, there were zealous brothers who, later on, would be catching up musket and cartridge box to pitch in with the boys, when battle joined. There were others who, for reasons cogent to themselves, would avoid violence and place themselves well to the rear of the army trains and the reserve artillery until the unpleasantness should be over, enduring with Christian fortitude the caustic comment of the uninstructed. And you would find padres at every station in between. The conference, after prolonged discussion, resolved that a chaplain's battle station was where his services were most needed. And matters stayed exactly where they were before. Deliberations were terminated by sudden orders to move south.

III

If you remember the records, the early spring of 1862 brought a great stirring throughout the armies. McClellan was accumulating a force in front of Washington, which, said the Federal city newspapers—sold daily to the Confederate outposts of the Alexandria Line, and read with much interest through the camps—would presently descend upon the Rebellion like the wolf on the fold. Praxiteles Swan, by the way, took this for his text on a Sunday about the first of March, and predicted that, did they come, their fate would be one with the Assyrian's. It was much admired in the Texas Brigade, to whom Elder Swan explained the allusion in detail. A little later, the scouts on the Potomac shore reported long columns of transports, blue with Yankees, filing downstream.

Gen. Joe Johnston, ever sensitive of his flanks, destroyed half a year's accumulation of stores between Manassas and Fredericksburg—a sin and a waste, inviting the rebuke of the Almighty, declared Praxiteles, watching a fine meat packery burn—and retired on Richmond. The Texans moved from their winter quarters the eighth of March, over hills sodden under a late fall of snow, and tramped to Fredericksburg, where they lay for a month, and had the grim news of Shiloh; there were many Texas regiments in the Western army. It was in Fredericksburg that there arose and clung to the Texas Brigade the reputation for chicken stealing, which, as other of its characteristics, became famous and is remembered to this day. There is something about it in the chaplain's diary; he mentions that the Lord blessed them with an abundance of nourishing food in the hospitable city on the Rappahannock, and adds: "Thou shalt not muzzle the ox when he treadeth out the corn." Nobody, then or afterward, was able to interest Praxiteles in the small peccadilloes of men on active service.

From Fredericksburg the brigade marched to Yorktown through rain and mud, only to march back up the Peninsula to Richmond, much bewildered by such tactics. They lay in reserve when Longstreet turned so savagely upon McClellan at Williamsburg, and only one of the regiments, the Fourth, was really engaged in the affair at Eltham's Landing, on the York, where they chased Franklin to his gunboats and saw their quartermaster struck dead off his horse by a stray bullet. So far, they had hardly seen a Yankee, save those incredible Zouaves, and the war was dull. Then they went up-country under General Whiting, with Law's Georgians, on a wild-goose chase toward the Valley of Virginia, where one Stonewall Jackson was shaking the bushes mightily, so that they had reason to anticipate real employment. But they did not so much as hear Jackson's bugles. Following fast, aimless marches and uneventful bivouacs, they turned east from the Blue Ridge, along roads suddenly heavy with strange troops, and proceeded by rail and by hard marching in the direction of Richmond. It was late June, and hot weather.

There was still enough of the circuit rider in Praxiteles Swan for him to note the direction and duration of each day's march, but he appears to have been thoroughly bored, and noted little more. You see known names about the end of June, '62: Gordonsville, Fredericks Hall, the Ashcake Road, Hanover Courthouse. The entry for the twenty-sixth says they lay near a church, Pole Green—or was it Hundley's Corner?—and a battle seemed to be going on, southward some miles. A little skirmishing for them on the Totopotomoy. Very hot weather; rumors of big events. He was writing his wife to dispatch, by first safe means available, his linen dusters! His uniform frock coat, with the crosses on the lapels, was oppressive. From the light of campfires in the sky that night, many troops were lying in the neighborhood of Richmond. A number of the men had asked for a discourse in the bivouac, and he talked on remission of sins and on the campaigns of Joshua.

If he had known it, that was the first of the Seven Days' Battle before Richmond; in the afternoon, Ambrose Hill's brigades had crossed the Chickahominy at Mechanicsville, and thrown themselves upon Fitz-John Porter's corps, while Lee prepared a major destruction for McClellan. But Jackson did not strike that day.

The morning of the twenty-seventh, the Texans gulped hasty coffee and half-seared dough cakes, then stood interminably in fours, and marched and countermarched vexatiously by blind wood roads in the heat and the dust, to stand again. Southward and to the right there was a lot of shooting, an angry sound of musketry that rose and fell, a continual growling of guns, and now and then a far faint yelling. Nobody knew anything; staff officers galloped with more than the usual air of mystery, to conceal the fact that they knew nothing, either; a dingy general officer rode by, men saying, "There goes old Jackson," and he was not cheered. Small insects bit and buzzed. Praxiteles' mare grew restive and hot, which concerned him. Midafternoon, the brigade moved again, closer to the noise; they could see smoke rising over a line of trees up the road; despondent walking wounded passed, and D. H. Hill's North Carolinians came from the south and went by with an air of going somewhere. Hill's regiments made a brave show, their flags uncased and their bayonets shining.

The Texans were all grumbling. General Hood rode along the column, and sat his horse near Praxiteles Swan, at the head of the Fifth, his eyes speculative on the smoke yonder. He had, Praxiteles considered, a fine appearance on a horse. Horses jingled on the road, horses well housed and in high condition—no jaded army nags, these—and Praxiteles Swan watched his brigadier trot to meet a neat iron-gray officer on a stout iron-gray gelding. Hood doffed his hat with a cavalier sweep, and the other general returned graceful salutation and spoke quietly and earnestly, pointing toward the lazy curling smoke above the trees. The battle grew louder as the day declined; it ran off for miles toward the south; it achieved something of a monstrous rhythm—wild yelling that pulsated through a staccato raving of musketry, on a steady underchord of cannon thunder. Up at this end, as the musketry fell a little, they could hear a deep, cadenced shouting; that would be the voice of the enemy. "They-uns don't jest open their throats and yell, like our boys. But they're gettin' mighty loud over there, ain't they?"

Balthis' Battery, well known to the brigade, waiting these hours down the road, trotted smartly out across the field and went into action, firing at something beyond the trees; the brigade watched with friendly interest. While Praxiteles craned his neck in that direction, and reassured his mare, orders pealed down from the head of the column. It went fours-left into line, flowed over the worm fence and obliqued across the field to the right of the guns, and through the screen of timber. Painfully thin timber, when you got into it. The regiments debouched in some disarray upon their first set battlefield. Just clear of the trees they halted and dressed their ranks, and while this was being meticulously accomplished by the officers, the regimental chaplain of the Fifth felt mighty solemn. He watched the color bearers strip the oilskin covers from the colors; the heavy red folds of the battle flags shook out, appeared to preen themselves as birds; and the color sergeant of the First Texas elevated higher than the rest, the fine state flag presented by the ladies of Brenham; the white and blue and red were as fresh as when the ladies cut them from their Sunday dresses last spring.

A zealot in the First yelled, "Ya-a-a-i-i-ih! Ya-a-a-i-i-ih! The Lone Star!" but he was firmly squelched by a duty-struck major.

Praxiteles felt a great surge of heat through all his bones. He broadened himself and sat erect on his mare. "Terrible as an army with banners—" Just then his regiment, the Fifth, faced to the right and departed at a trot, trailing arms. "We're going into it," he decided, and looked to the rear for a sapling, to tie his mare. Didn't want her hurt. Find a safe place for her, and catch up with the command on foot. Why, he reflected angrily, hadn't that question been decided, about the proper station of the chaplain in battle? He wanted to do what was right.

While he stood, undecided, flinching unconsciously from the noises in the air, Colonel Robertson's nigger trotted back, dragging at the bridle of the colonel's big flea-bitten gray. Praxiteles knew the boy, and flung him his reins, and, so to speak, girded up his loins to go after his regiment. But now the Fifth was out of sight in the woods, the brigade had taken ground to the right, and he was, he saw, behind the Fourth Texas Regiment—boys from the old Rutersville district of the East Texas Conference.

He halted to consider, and General Hood appeared from a flank on foot, his shadow reaching immensely before him in the low sun.

The general strode to the front and center of the Fourth, his sword flashed out in a bright curve, and he said, in that blunt carrying voice of his: "Fourth Texas! When I was your colonel, I promised that I would lead you in your first charge! I am keeping my promise!" He turned his head to the left, then to the right, as a hawk looks. "Brigade, attention! Right shoulder—shift!"

Every man could hear him, for the ripple of arms ran promptly down through Hampton's Legion, on the far left. That malignant could sway a camp meeting like an archangel's horn, thought Praxiteles, with envy.

"No man to fire until I give the order!" bayed Hood—the general had learned at Eltham's Landing that the Texans would not go into battle without loading and capping their pieces, no matter what orders he gave—"For-r-r-wa-a-rd!"

The brigade gave itself a jerk and lurched ahead, and Praxiteles followed, because he could think of nothing else to do. But a charge, now— and he a preacher with a family, and getting toward forty years— The men looked white under their tanned hides, and they leaned a little, as men lean against heavy rain. Almost at once the enemy was in view, on a hill across a valley, and Praxiteles, watching with concern the Yankee line, saw a purposeful agitation in the nearest part of it—a movement of gun teams and cannon.

Things howled in the air overhead, and the brigade bowed like wheat beneath the wind; explosions occurred in the immediate rear. The howling came again, and the set of fours in front of Praxiteles disintegrated violently. The air was full of hissing particles and a rank smell, and what looked like a bad sawmill accident littered the ground; there was some screaming, and officers and sergeants bawled angry exhortations. An ashen, frantic individual, his face drawn to a point, detached himself from the regiment and caromed into Praxiteles, leaping like a jack rabbit toward the rear. Praxiteles caught the soldier by the collar and shook him until his teeth rattled, thanking his Maker for the fortifying sight of a man more frightened than himself.

" 'The devil damn thee black, thou whey-faced loon!' " he quoted between his teeth—hadn't thought of Shakespeare for years—funny how apt the tag was. "You—" He recognized a notable card sharper of the Fourth Texas, a famous frequenter of the Dumfries stills. "Jim Hicks, get up in your place before I wring your neck!"

He administered two swinging slaps and a kick, and High Private Hicks, slobbering, sought safety in the ranks. To left and right, gray jackets were flung flat, or lay wriggling, in the trail of the regiment. There were spiteful singing sounds—musketry, personal shooting. But the line was going forward over the inequalities of an old field, and the flags had the appearance of brave swooping eagles. It came into his head: "Her young ones also suck up blood: and where the slain are, there is she," but he did not know that he roared from Habakkuk at the capacity of a pair of lungs as powerful as Hood's. "They are terrible and dreadful" —the words came to him, and a jet of arterial blood slopped against his chest, as a man, shot through the neck, spun against him; he eased the fellow down, started to kneel, and saw the line was going on without him. Boy from Big Sandy, in San Jacinto County—it seemed more important to keep up with that line. "Let the dead bury their dead—" He had to run.

Out in front, General Hood had faced about to the regiment; he held his saber lightly in both hands, at arm's length, level with his shoulders, and he walked backwards, chiding the Fourth: "The guide is left! . . . Dress on the colors, damn you to everlasting hell! . . . Up on the right there . . . up in the center!" He stepped unerringly backward, and his eye penetrated even to the file closers, where Praxiteles now marched.

A lot of men were getting hit; the brigade was at the bottom of the slope and began to climb. There was a line of men lying down in a dead space. They caught at the legs of the Texans and whined in the accents of the Deep South: "Betteh not go on up theh! It's hell an' damnation up theh!" but a young officer rose among them and waved his sword and screamed, "Fifteenth Alabama, will yo' let these heah Texicans go wheh yuh won't go?" and shouldered himself into the Texas line.

Again Hood's voice dominated. How had they come so close? Nearly in shotgun range among some shattered peach trees.

"Halt!" the general's sword made another flashing arc. "Fix . . . bayonets!" Most of the men did it. "Fire!" Hood must have capered sideways, for his voice came next out of the sudden smoke from the right of the regiment. Praxiteles reflected afterward that, once the advance started, he saw nothing and thought of nothing except what was directly in front of him. However, the regiment seemed to explode, and then the compelling voice blared. "Charge!" and all the bugles in the world rang in his word.

The men raised a high, thin, angry scream, and ran forward, only a few of them trying to bite cartridge and reload. They burst out of the fog of their own firing upon the raw earth of a fresh-dug trench, tenanted by crumpled dead men in dusty blue clothes. There was a confused blue mass in front of them—men in short jackets toiling at guns, men in frock coats waving silly swords and mouthing—more noise than Praxiteles had imagined in the world. One clump of blue stood solid and their Springfields spoke fierce and sharp in the ambiguous tumult; something caught at the skirt of Praxiteles' coat, and three men seemed to wind themselves around his legs. He sensed a suspension of movement; here were stanch Northern men standing firm to fight. But in a flicker of thought, Praxiteles knew that his personal antagonists, right there, were as men who had emptied their pieces into the head of a flock of geese—now they had to reload. How the musket came into his hand he did not notice, but it was there, and he broke a sergeant's skull with it. What followed after that, he never remembered clearly; there were some cavalry riding out of the smoke, who tumbled in hideous ruin at his very feet. He heard an officer, his leg under his fallen horse, say in clear disgusted tone, "But I'm Captain Chambliss, and we served together in the old Second, and he'll want to see me."

Himself, he was aware of fading light and of blue backs turned so that you couldn't see the buttons, and he shouted a supplication, "Sun, stand thou still upon Gibeon; and thou, Moon, in the valley of Ajalon!"

Over the plateau the flat rays of the sun made the smoke and dust all murky red. Beyond, the deep woods of the Chickahominy bottom invited fugitives and checked pursuit. The panting soldiers slowed down and stopped. One looted a knapsack; another went among the fallen, searching pockets; a third, with a tasseled meerschaum pipe in a shaking hand, asked every man he met for a smidgeon of tobacco. It was all confusion and "garments rolled in blood," as Isaiah put it; but it appeared to Praxiteles Swan that, anyway, his side had won. He leaned on the musket barrel and felt faint and empty. The sodden stain across his coat sickened him. How did the musket get broken? And the breech was smeared with what must be blood and brains from a towheaded man. Soldiers stopped to stare at him. General Hood, the light behind him, rode up, gigantic against the west, his horse stepping delicately, avoiding unspeakable things. He saw Praxiteles' gray frock coat.

He said, "You, there! You're an officer! Get these rapscallions into formation! Assemble your men, sir! No time for— Why!" His teeth showed in his beard, "It's the big parson! What you doing here, preacher?"

"Sir," Praxiteles told him, suddenly shaken, "may He of Galilee forgive me, but from this day henceforward, I serve the God of Battles, the greatest of commanders. Tell me what you want these young men to do and they will do it."

"Get them into line," Hood told him soberly. "Get them—get them, that is, straightened out, by companies. All the damned field officers seem to be shot. Do the best you can, Elder, and when I find an officer, I'll send him along."

Praxiteles Swan, sometime shepherd of the best-thought-of Methodist flocks in East Texas, inflated his chest and let out a roar. Men stopped what they were doing and listened. "All right, you scabrous sons of Belial! Cease from that grave robbing and come unto me! The curse of Achan on you, who turned aside to plunder! . . . You, young man—I mean you with the flag—stand right here and wave that flag! Come around here, you—" He tried to remember, but didn't, the commands in *Gilham's Manual*. "Huddle! Jehovah confound you, huddle! I would have you stay not, 'but pursue after your enemies, and smite the hindmost of them.'" He menaced them with the dreadful clotted musket barrel, and soldiers moved to assemble themselves, obedient. Even stray South Carolinians of Hampton's, high-chinned heroes from the proper side of Church Street, began to sort themselves into squads, well disposed and heedful.

General Hood gathered his horse; he wanted to find Whiting or D. H. Hill or Jackson, and get a pursuit started. "Elder," he said immensely pleased, "old Stonewall couldn't have put it better. 'Stay not . . . and smite the hindmost of them!' Go right ahead with what you're doing! You don't need any officer. And when I get my brigade headquarters set up, you come see me. I'm going to snatch that cross off your coat and put a star on it—well, captain's bars, anyway."

Again Praxiteles Swan felt that surge of heat along his bones. "General, I'll come," he said. And he added, to himself, "I'll be bound, Mrs. Swan will be right pleased when she hears about it!"

ANTIETAM

by JAMES BOYD

WEEKS AFTER, marching on as ever, marching as they always had since time began, as they always would till Judgment Day, lost souls doomed to stumble through a never-ending hell of weariness, James Fraser shifted his dust-blinded eyes from the back of the man ahead and stared without hope about him.

Low hills, dark green, which flanked a flat, slow river, hemmed them in, and seemed to look down, unmoved, on their laborious and futile haste. Futile it surely was. All day they had shuffled forward to the officers' refrain, "Close up . . . Close up," and still those wooded hills were just the same. A man might think that he and all that ghastly, tattered column were caught in the treadmill of some tormenting dream. Only the trampled dust crept by, ever so slowly, under foot. For the rest, they might be frantic imbeciles marking time throughout the ages, veiled by the gritty haze of their unending shuffle, drugged with the stench of their own ravaged bodies.

Ahead, the column, a close-packed mass of broken hats, of old gray caps, of long-haired, weather-beaten heads, all bobbing beneath the swing of rifle barrels, stretched out of sight, out of all guessing. Behind, the patter of hurrying bare feet, the muffled slap of brogans, followed them as far as they could hear. There was nothing for a man to do except to shuffle forward without ceasing in order to keep pace with the bobbing caps, to keep clear of the ghostly footsteps treading on his heels. Nothing else to do. That was the one necessity of all existence. Whatever happened a man must march, must struggle on through mud, through ruts, through heat and cold, through drought and dizziness and fits of vomiting. A man must march. Must drag one numb and wooden foot before the other, must set his meagre shoulder against the gnawing of his rifle, his mind against the maddening slap of the haversack across his thigh. A man must march. In all the universe that was the only thing that mattered.

And so much did it matter, so wholly had its grim compulsion mastered him, that James Fraser need no longer concern himself with it. His body, his very bones had long since learned the inexorable decree. They had, after many pains and tortures, acquiesced and now could be counted

From: *Marching On*. Copyright 1927. Charles Scribner's Sons.

on, without a thought from him, to move him forward as long as they could move at all. Twice of late he had gone to sleep while marching—like the fellows he used to hear about—and waked to find that his faithful, ravaged body still marched on. And when awake, as now, he could so to speak desert it, leave it to its misery, and wander among the scenes and fragmentary pictures that drifted through his mind.

Having looked at the mountains and seen that they did not change, he turned his thoughts loose, in hope that they would find something to feed on more satisfying than those forbidding hills. They flew at once to the last good food that he had eaten, long ago. He could see it as clearly as a painting on the wall, the big, thick slice of well-grained, ruddy ham with the smooth, white fringe of fat along the edges, the fat itself edged with a crust, brown, crumbling, sugary. On top of all the dab of tawny mustard. By shot! that ham and mustard hung right there before him, moved him to the depths of his pinched loins. His heart was almost trembling, his dusty, sour mouth watered with desire. Ham and mustard. He felt the firmness, the substance of the meat, tasted its sweetness through the salt, and the mustard's cheering bite. Ham and mustard. That was the stuff a man could march on, fight on. And hadn't he fought? He shifted his rifle and took a chew of slippery-elm bark. If he hadn't fought there was no such thing as fighting.

But that had been the day after the ham. The ham had been taken from the Yankee storehouses. The night he ate it they were camped in a wood above a railroad cut. As he went to sleep he had thought that maybe next day that railroad was to carry them back home. That was what he had thought. He almost laughed aloud. He was glad that no one had known his guileless notion. It would have made a grim, relentless jest for them. They would have called that next day "the train ride" maybe, have likely called him "passenger" till the day of his death. A day which might easily have come long before now.

But he was not grateful for past escape, or fearful of future extinction; he was only weary. Still he could think, could recall that day and many past events more clearly than ever. Yet without emotion. They were merely pictures to be looked at. Nothing was to be thought or felt about them.

Though he could feel surprise no longer, he could remember his surprise that morning, as looking across the railroad cut he had seen the long, blue, heavy-moving lines break from the distant woods below and creep up the meadow toward him. He had been startled. And yet it had not seemed real, did not seem real now. It had seemed queer, unearthly, strange, like an incredible and monstrous show. Behind him guns had begun to bump. Above him many shells were swishing. He and the others had gotten into the railroad cut and watched the meadows from the shelter of the further bank. The guns were grumbling. Among the blue lines, sprays of earth and white slow-curving smoke shot up like magic flowers bursting into bloom. Beneath the rain of flowers the blue lines melted away, flowed back in dots and streamers to the wood beyond the meadow. Nothing was left except thin veils of idle smoke and blue heaps inexplicably encumbering the ground.

All morning long the wide, blue lines had swayed up toward them and broken into fragments against the airy puffs of bursting shells. They came closer, close enough so that he and the rest had popped their rifles at them, adding a feeble crackle to the groaning of the guns.

Then a blue line had not turned back. It had come on in hurrying groups that stumbled forward clumsily, heads bowed against the blast of shells, of frantic rifle fire from the railroad cut. And though at the last they, too, had vanished, others followed. He had lain for ages, his breast pressed to the bank, ramming, firing, biting cartridges; he had cursed, had shrieked, had laughed—a dry blood-curdling cackle. Ramrods had jammed in red hot barrels, they had scrabbled for stones and hurled them at the ever climbing faces.

At last the faces climbed no more, the field in front of them was still as death, still as the mounds and strings of dark blue figures on the ground, still as the oddly tumbled heaps below his feet; the tumbled heaps of gray which gorged the bottom of the cut.

Before he had a chance to count or name those figures heaped behind him, far to the right the short, high Southern cheer cut through the trees. As far as eye could see, dingy lines, tipped by the sunset light, trundling long shadows ahead of them, swayed down the slope. He and the rest climbed out of the cut and, yelping from parched taut throats, tripping over the rigid lumps of blue, lumbered toward the dusk.

A man would think that day of victory would have been enough to last him for his life, enough to entitle him to ease and honor and plates of juicy meat. But it had only led to more relentless marching.

They marched further, faster every day. It was grotesque. Why did they do it? Why stand it? Their reward was that the wagon trains could not keep up. Horses foundered, faded away, even a yellow dog, a mascot who had joined them, broke down and must be carried. Without supplies, they shook the last dust of corn meal from their haversacks and thereafter lived as best they might by barter, begging, stealing, and twice, most sumptuously, on recent battle-fields, by scavenging among dead Yankees' knapsacks for bits of hardtack. Dead Yankees also yielded underclothes and socks and shoes and, for those who wanted them, money and rings and watches, provided of course the bodies were not already looted.

James Fraser himself took only hardtack and socks from them and he always cut the blood off the hardtack before he ate it. But many were not so particular. Once he had heard the Racker twins whispering together. A Yankee major was dying underneath an appletree. He had a big gold watch when first they saw him and they had figured how long he would likely last and had gotten back to him in good time. He was still alive. But the watch had gone. Their curses were low-pitched, filthy.

Yankee bodies could not always be found to supply rations. In fact they became scarce and so did all other sources of supply. In their hunger they pulled ears of half-ripe corn from the fields and ate them raw. That was a mistake. Diarrhœa followed, and cramps in their empty bellies. Foulness welled up within them, swirled around their brains. Seeping away, it drained them of strength and blood and courage, left them white-lipped, black-gummed, silver-skinned.

And still they marched beneath the morning stars, the noon-day sun, the dews of night. Their marching passed the bounds of credibility, the limits of human flesh; it became a vastly tortured fantasy performed by disembodied spirits. Nothing could change their fate—not even victory. Even death itself would be put to it to change them much from what they already were. And even after death no doubt they still would march on as now, would still, as now, fall down each evening in their tracks and lie there senseless, sweating with weakness and stinking to the heavens.

They could not quit. That was the curse that lay on them. Only a little while ago, sitting up stiffly in the dark, James Fraser watched the silhouette beside him tug with numb fingers at its shoes. It was Bill, the brakeman, and it seemed as though he could not move his hands. James reached down and tied the thongs.

"How you come on, Bill?"

"I started," Bill's dogged mutter answered, "and I'm bound to finish out." He turned his face. His eyes were black burnt pits. His cheek-bones shone sickly white beneath the stars. "But Gode damn me if I ever love another country!"

At the memory James started to chuckle weakly, but a dull gripe in his belly made him stop. He shifted his rifle to the left shoulder. With his right hand he held his pocket full of cartridges away from his body. They had long since discarded belts and cartridge boxes as so much extra weight. The only trouble was that a man got mighty weary of the heavy pocket flogging against his hip. He looked around. The mountains seemed a little lower. They ought to be; after all the marching he had done. They had come far that day, twenty-five miles he reckoned.

The night before he had huddled in his rags on a mountainside. At dawn the guns which had rumbled through his dreams were firing over him into a broad white lake of morning mist. From the mist, spires and roofs emerged, straight rows of houses and, last, a river curving around the crumbling town. Chimneys tilted and tumbled under the spatter of the guns, roofs burst into flames. In the streets little blue ants swarmed here and there distractedly.

No sooner had a horseman waving a white flag come out of the town than they were on the road again. They marched down through the streets where Yankee troops were stacking their surrendered arms. He had a chance to note them as he passed. They didn't look so bad. Maybe because they were fat, and for a long time he had seen only men who were thin. They were mostly just a lot of shamefaced boys who turned away from the passing column and looked down at the ground.

The column itself held straight on, did not pause even to gather in the spoils of war. And ever since, they had been toiling up the road beside the river.

A while back he had heard a man say, "What was that place wher' we caught all them Yankees this mo'nin'?"

For a time no one answered. James tried to think if he had heard the name. He couldn't remember. Anyhow, what difference did it make?

Now a voice was saying, "I tell you it *was* Harper's Ferry. Ain't I visited my aunt there in '44? And ain't this the Potomac River? And ain't that Maryland yonder on the other side?"

Harper's Ferry. He tried to think. Why, that was where the whole fuss started, where John Brown had been hung. If he'd known that, he'd have looked around more. As for the Potomac, which was always in the papers, it was here only a narrow stream, so small that, rounding a turn, he saw the column wading across it through the shallows. In a brief halt which followed, he and the others took off shoes and trousers and hung them on their rifles. Then their thin, white legs were pushing through the water, were fumbling on the bottom for a foothold. They lurched up the other bank and stopped a moment to put their trousers on again. A spire showed over the shoulder of a hill; the dust of the column headed toward it.

In the neat and peaceful little town through which they tramped citizens stared coldly, American flags hung over vineclad porches.

"My land!" cried a woman with contempt, "ain't they dirty!"

Beside James Fraser's shoulder Big Tom MacGruder, a hairy, flapping scarecrow, rallied to meet the thrust. "Lady," he took off his hat and bowed, "we always wear dirty clothes," his voice was sugary and mocking, "when we go to a Hog Killing."

By shot, thought James, the boys will remember Tom for that. He looked behind. No one spoke, but the men had turned to stare at the flushing citizens along the street and were showing their sorghum-blackened teeth in lean and wolflike grins.

That afternoon the marching stopped. Swinging off behind the other regiments through fields of trampled oats they halted in line behind a long, low, wooded crest. They had reached their journey's end. Without a word they dropped down on the sun-warmed grass and slept.

The wagons came up. They were given meal and bacon which they toasted feverishly before their fires and ate half-cooked till they grew sick and dizzy. Then they lay down again. But now they could not sleep; they were restless, jumpy, and harassed. In whispers they talked together to ease their minds.

"I wish I was back in Wilmington," said Bill; "I'd go down to Foretop's and get me a whiskey sour to settle my stomach."

"I reckon we all wish something different," said James. "If you could have one wish, Ance, what would it be?"

Ance reflected. "Well, since it don't cost nothin', I wish I was back in Bear Grass with my gal."

Big Tom MacGruder grunted in disdain. "I wish we may be in Washington by Thursday."

"I reckon we all do that," said James. He nodded at the switch-engine fireman. "What do you wish?"

The youth twisted his starved body inside his jacket.

"Come on," said James, "take a chance."

"I wish," he muttered, in a suffocated voice, "that my bowels was in order."

"Damn me," said Bill in high approval, "if that ain't the best wish for all of us."

By the light of campfires, they could see the veterans of the regiment next theirs tearing up scraps of paper and handing them around. Bill, the ever curious, wandered over. When he came back he sat down without speaking and stared into the embers.

"What are they doing, Bill?" James asked.

Bill did not raise his eyes. "They're writin' their names on scraps of paper," he muttered uneasily, "an' pinnin' them to their coats. Each man puts his name on hisse'f in case—" his voice trailed off.

A gripe seized James. All they had done, had suffered was not enough. The gripe stole upward, clutched his lungs, closed, cold and merciless, about his heart. "My Lord," he whispered to himself, "it looks like a rough time, sure enough."

☆

☆   ☆

THEIR SLEEP, when at last they slept, was broken by the rumble of caissons on the road, by the clink of trace-chains and the creak of harness, by lanterns swinging in the field behind them and shovels clicking against shale. At last James Fraser seemed to sink into a deep, small, breathless cavern of unconsciousness. Then, almost immediately it seemed, the morning sun was shining in his face. He started up, his mind a blank, burdened by some dim and nameless dread. Resting on his elbow he stared stupidly at the oat field in their rear. In trampled patches stood line after line of guns in battery; beneath them lay the huddled forms of sleeping cannoneers. Now he remembered. This was the day of battle. That other battle had caught him off his guard. Before he knew it he had been in action and even then he could hardly believe that it was so.

But this time the warnings, the portents were clear. They clustered round like buzzards. Shadowed by their wings, helpless beneath their ominous gathering, his thoughts drew back from all impending terrors and fled away to Stewart Prevost, fled away for one perhaps final gaze. He saw her graceful, swaying image, smiling, half amused, half tender, as it used to smile, and as, since the day her brother had been shot beside him, it would not smile again. He had carried the image in his mind so long, had become so used to gazing at it, with scarcely uttered hope, with weary and impotent desire, that he had come to look on the image and on his longing as for him the two unchanging features of the world. He knew, though still incredulous, that the day which had just dawned might mean the end of him and of them as well. And still it seemed impossible that, if he were to fall dead here in this field, in that same instant his dream of her would vanish. The very lightness, the airy, soft fragility of that dream should make it indestructible, keep it, whatever happened to himself, beyond the reach of bullets. But he knew it was not so. When he was ended, the dream would end. After a thrust of anguish he felt a sense of peace. Let the dream end—he had cherished it too long, too much in vain. He had grown weary. If he should go to-day, wherever dead men went, it would be all right, most likely. The dream would be ended, the struggle over and he would find release.

A piece of the paper which the veterans used the night before had drifted down not far from him. He slipped out of the blanket and captured it. He laid the paper on his canteen, fished out a stub of pencil from among his cartridges and wrote:

DEAR MISS STEWART:

We are going to have a battle today and though I hope everything will be all right, it may be that I will not have any more chances to write to you. There is nothing I have to say except that I have never loved anybody but you and ever since that day I came to see the Colonel at Beaumont, I have thought about you most all the time. If I should be killed it will be all right, I reckon, only I wish it could have been me instead of your brother, Charles.

I am going to put this letter in my pocket so if you get it you will know that it was found on me, and that when I went into the battle I was thinking about you with love.

Your friend,

JAMES FRASER.

While he wrote the other men were stirring. In camp the sight of a soldier writing had provoked them to gibes, to humorous messages of endearment; now they glanced at him, glanced quickly away, tried not to disturb him.

Drinking his coffee he looked back over the rise of ground on which they lay. A pasture field sloped to a little stream where water maples, already turning scarlet, half veiled the gray roofs and white spires of the town they had passed through the night before. Ahead of them the pasture sloped up to a long, dark wood and a white church cupola which stood out sharp against the eastern sky.

Along those woods, with slow, quiet bustle, other regiments in gray were forming. Feeling curiously detached and numb, James Fraser threw the dregs of his coffee on the ground and fell in with the others. He stood at ease facing toward the wooded crest. With restless eyes he searched the landscape for the enemy. No sign appeared, but behind him he heard a stir among the guns. Looking back he saw before each gun a cannoneer leaning on his ramrod; other men trudged up with round shot and bright red bags of powder. The cannoneers spun their ramrods and rammed the charges home.

Away to the left, with a dull bumping sound a gun went off, then two more. He saw a curl of thin pale smoke drift up above some locust trees. Before he could figure what those guns might mean, the guns in the oat field flashed yellow flames which dragged a curling ball of smoke behind them and cracked the air to shivers in his ears. The troops ahead tramped into the woods and were lost in the nervous rattle of musketry.

Still they did not move; just stood in ranks along the meadow—waiting. An officer galloped up the lane to their right, stared at them, galloped away. Beating his plowhorse into a canter, a farmer passed by in a wagon; his long white whiskers streamed behind, his eyes showed white with terror. A few small gray figures straggled out of the wood that stood so dark against the sky. Another little mannikin in a red sash ran up to one, pointed his hand at it. A puff of smoke came out of the hand. The other figure lay down.

"There's one deserter less," said Tom MacGruder.

Down the lane from the woods came an old man with a knapsack. He carried his rifle in his right hand, his left was clapped over his mouth. He swayed as he walked. James could see the twitching of his fingers above the tattered beard. Close by, where the lane turned toward the village, a guard stopped him. He levelled his bayonet at the old man's breast.

"Show blood," he said.

The old man took his hand down. Instead of a mouth there was only a monstrous, dripping hole. The guard raised his rifle. "Pass." The old man swayed on. Just before he would have gotten out of sight he fell down on his face. After hours, it seemed, two soldiers wearing white armbands came out of the village, knelt down beside him, stood up, crouched over him, rolled him into the ditch.

Other wounded came down the lane, limping, slinking, reeling, marching stolidly, chattering crazily. The guns in the oat field banged "one, two, three, four" without ceasing. The battle in the wood widened to right and left, swelled louder, died away.

Still they did not move. They lay down or squatted in ranks and watched the wounded drift back to the town, the gunners spin their ramrods, the cowed birds flutter soundlessly in the bushes by the road.

They chewed tobacco, slippery elm, and blades of grass. At noon they fished out bacon and hoe-cake from their greasy haversacks and ate it where they sat. Maybe it was the food which gave James Fraser peace of mind, but after eating he began to think that perhaps they would not get into the battle at all. He began to fear that the letter in his pocket might turn out to have been unnecessary. It might sound foolish, too. He wanted to read it, but with all the men around he did not dare.

There was a stir at the other end of the line. He could sense a feeling running toward him that something was afoot. Looking toward the lane he saw that one of those cursed aides, so neat and shiny, was standing by Clubby Jordan's long, gray horse and pointing toward the wood.

"Attention," the order passed from mouth to mouth.

"Fix bayonets." The dry metallic rattle ran along the company. Old Clubby trotted up, thumping his legs mechanically against the gray. He rubbed his knuckless on his scrubby chin.

"Right up the hill, boys, and into the woods yonder. Come up, horse!" He whacked his hickory-stick against the horse's rump. A cloud of dust flew up. The gray laid back an ear and started crab-wise up the hill.

"Don't you fuss, Clubby," said a strong, harsh voice. "We'll be ther'."

Abruptly the oat field behind them seemed to heave and rumble with a salvo from the guns; with a swift rustling sound the shells passed overhead. At once from way off yonder and now above their heads, with high-pitched swishing, the Yankee shells passed by. He heard them thudding into the soft earth of the oat field which they had left. Then he heard a crash, and a ripping crackle. "My Lord," he thought, "they must have hit a gun. I'm glad we're gone."

In the dark wood all was silent. James walked on cautiously, looking straight ahead but conscious of pale arms and faces showing among the shadows on the ground. No use to bother about them now. A man had better 'tend to business.

At the further edge he saw the backs of scattered men in gray who crouched and watched in silence the fields beyond. As he passed on, one, a meagre shrivelled boy, lifted his powder-blackened face and gave him a glance from red and deep-sunk eyes, a glance detached, hostile, as though James were a stranger from some despised and distant world.

Before them down the slope, post-and-rail fences followed a turnpike road. Old Clubby, buttoned to suffocation in his long frock coat, turned in the saddle stiffly, looked back in irritation. His eye paused.

"Hey, you red-headed fellow! Pull down them rails fo' me."

A gap was made. A whack— "Come up, horse!" The old gray floundered over the rails. He snorted, shied clumsily at a mound, all sprawling arms and legs, which lay along the road, then shuffled into a cornfield on the other side.

James Fraser's legs, as he threw them over the fence, felt cold and far away. The corn was tattered and trampled down. Not enough was left to cover the heaps of gray and blue which wound between the rows.

Once in the field beneath the tall still tassels, he stepped cautiously through the powdery loam, stepped cautiously over crooked gray arms and twisted feet. It was hot there in the narrow, faintly shaded lane. Lonely too. He could hardly see the rest, only hear them lightly rustling through the corn. In that cramped low tunnel under the stalks the air was close, was heavy with the odor of smoke, of sweat and blood. He would be glad when they got out of there, got where a man could see what he was doing and get a breath of air.

"Guide centre! Guide centre!" the officers kept calling. He heard the voice of Catlin Gregg, sounding very severe, as if the boys had done something wrong. Maybe Gregg was scared. Well, lots of folks were scared. But there was no use to talk that way.

Abruptly he emerged into the light; blinking his hot, dry eyes he saw with relief that the other men were coming out as well. Ahead a line of elderberries showed along a water-course and between two bushes Clubby was whacking his horse again to make him cross the stream. Three men ran forward and pushed against the big gray quarters while Clubby cursed them for their pains. "God's brimstone! Can't you puny weanlin's push? You push or I'll frail the everlasting gizzards out of you." The old horse teetered, slid down the bank and heaved out, grunting, on the other side.

The water smote James Fraser around the ankles as he waded through. He'd have given a heap to have kept dry shod. He had an idea that a man couldn't fight so good with wet feet.

They were in a stubble field on the other side and the officers again were calling "Guide centre! Close up! Close up!" Still they just walked along in line. He wished that they could charge and holler or shoot or something. But there was nothing to shoot at. A thought occurred to him. Maybe the Yankees would run away again. This time he would run after them until he got one. He would be all right if something happened, but he wished to God it would happen soon.

As he toiled up through the stubble field he warmed up a little and what with that and the sight of other long, gray lines and waving standards, surging slowly onward, by the time he reached the top he felt more like himself again.

And still there was nothing. Far off the guns worked steadily and shells were travelling overhead. Before them lay only a silent, motionless wood which dipped down into a ravine. They went straight into it. Now, by some instinct, they moved with caution, trod lightly. Not a sound was heard except the brush of branches across trouser legs, the light tap of twigs against canteens.

From the ravine, he could see daylight at the far edge of the woods. If they could get out into the open again he would feel easier in his mind. It was a mighty mean place here.

Above him he saw, standing motionless, a man in a blue coat, with a shining sword. For an instant he stared, then threw his rifle up. Before he could shoot, the world was overwhelmed, drowned out, by a roaring wave of musketry. He fired wildly through the roll of smoke which drifted down the hill. Around him men stumbled to their knees, crouched behind trees, stretched out flat on the ground and stared in stupefaction up the hill. He saw one start to run, heard Big Tom's voice, "Stop!" and the thud of a rifle butt against the coward's body. Standing behind a tree he glanced back. The man had dodged Tom and gotten clean away.

As he loaded his rifle he was conscious of Clubby Jordan squatting behind the dead body of the gray. He heard him holler, "Load your pieces, boys, we'll rush 'em next time." He heard a man sobbing "Ah—Ah—Ah," over and over again in a tearful, wondering voice. And just beyond him, in the oak leaves, Harry Horniblow lay on his back, his long, slim, fiddler's fingers stiffly curled, his meagre breast thrust upward in an arch of agony.

Now Clubby had his old wool hat on the end of his hickory-stick, now he was standing up, was trudging up the hill. The men hung back. Those trees and gnarled roots were mighty hard to leave. But Clubby's figure never paused nor turned to look behind. By shot, the old man was going there alone. They took long breaths, jumped out from hiding, and ran to catch him. They were closer to the summit this time. They could see bronzed, straining faces and blue caps just above the ground. They stopped to fire madly, then ran on. An answering volley met them like a wall. They pitched ahead, spun around, leapt high in air and fell down kicking. The woods were filled with their grotesque and dreadful posturings. They were stopped this time and no mistake. They made a snatch at the wounded and hurried down the hill.

Back in the ravine, James Fraser dropped to the ground the country boy he had been leading, and lay down close beside him. The sallow, stupid youth craned his head till he could see his legs.

"Will you look at that now?" he said with intense and reverent interest. "Will you look at that?" He gazed at the ooze of blood along his trousers as though it were a portentous and incredible phenomenon.

"Lie still," said James, "You ain't the only one."

He looked around to see what the rest were doing. They lay up and down the little ravine. Living and dead and wounded, indistinguishable, all hugged the friendly earth save where some fellow past all care of danger sat up to cough up blood or lying on his back swung his sharp knees unceasingly from side to side.

Crouching, Dougald Cameron stepped amongst them up the gully, matter of fact and serious. "Keep up a steady fire," he admonished. "We'll wear 'em down. We'll have somebody to look after these boys soon." He motioned toward the wounded with his pistol.

As James Fraser loaded his rifle, he got the idea from the sounds of scattered firing that the regiments on each side of them, veterans from Virginia, were also held up in the same ravine. This gave him boundless satisfaction. Their own crowd had not done so badly after all. Maybe in the end they would do as well as any one. But, my Lord, it was a mighty mean place! If there was just a chance to see what you were doing. Leaving the boy still staring at the bloodstains on his trousers, he crawled to the edge of the gully and found a spot where he could peep around a little hickory-tree. Once more the woods seemed empty. He shoved the rifle ahead of him, through the leaves, and waited, his eyes fixed on the crest above him. He saw the muzzle of a rifle moving slowly. He got ready. A blue cap showed behind it. He dropped his eye to the sight and fired. Two rifles beside him also spoke. Good, the boys were fighting back again. The distant rifle muzzle flopped down on the ground. Somebody must have hit him.

But as he lay there, watching intently, and firing from time to time, it was borne in on him that the Yankees would not give in too easily. They kept firing back, and every time they thought they reached a mark they shouted a heavy, deep-throated "Hurrah!" It was going to be a slow business. He was thirsty. He slid back into the ravine and took a pull at his canteen. The white face of Catlin Gregg turned toward him.

"Get out of here. This is for wounded men."

He crawled up to his tree again, his jaws locked tight with fury. But his anger sizzled, and for unnumbered hours afterward, it seemed, there was nothing to do except lie still and wait for a chance to shoot. His anger, his excitement, even his interest ebbed away. He grew dull and listless, indifferent to the firing. Tired of watching forever the wooded crest, he missed a chance or two to shoot and did not care. What was the use? They were getting nowhere.

The afternoon sun burned down on him through the branches. He was thirsty again. His lips were caked and his mouth tasted sour from biting the paper of the cartridges. But he would not slide back into the gully. He managed to draw his canteen up beside his face, uncorked it with his teeth and tilted it as best he could into the corner of his mouth. But he must have showed himself, for a couple of bullets flicked into the dead leaves beside him. He dropped the canteen, spilling water, and lay close behind his tree.

He had an uneasy sense that orders were travelling up the ravine. He heard the voices of Dougald Cameron and Catlin Gregg: "Load, and hold your fire."

"This time," said Dougald, "when we charge 'em, don't shoot till after their volley. Then fire and rush in at 'em."

Far to the left they heard the high-pitched Southern scream. They heard the sturdy "H-a-a-a-a" that Yankees gave. Both cheers were rolling down toward them like a great ball of mingled sound which grew and rumbled as it travelled. The regiment next to theirs was up and running. Clubby Jordan was out in front and Catlin Gregg, his face a white set mask, walked past James' tree. "By God, he's scared!" James thought. "But," he added in fairness, "he's goin' on." He rose up with the others and followed. A few were prodded and kicked from their hiding-places by the sergeants. Some moved up the hill, walking woodenly, jerking their knees like men in a trance. But most of them, their comic, powder-blackened mouths in pitiful contrast to their hunted eyes, stepped swiftly, cunningly from tree to tree.

Clubby waved his stick and broke into a run. They screeched and raced behind him.

As the Yankee volley smote them, James Fraser found a tree. Around him some went down, others stopped, turned to run. But their rifles still were loaded. The thought held them. The wavering ceased. They gripped their guns and dashed for the crest. A line of Yankees, hurriedly loading, showed behind a low stone wall. James Fraser halted, fired at an officer who stood back of them. The Yankees rose up. Some fired, some held their bayonets ready. They opened their mouths and shouted. They seemed not men but curious animals, dangerous and loathsome, who in fear and anger hooted at him. He gripped his rifle, screamed at them and ran.

An instantaneous shaft of flame—an engulfing roar—trees, men, grass shredded by a rake of canister; patches of clothing, branches, blood clots flew; the ground was littered with flayed bodies blown from the cannon's path. He ran the faster.

Here was the wall and here the hooting mouths. He knocked a bayonet aside and jumped up on the stones. Frantically he thrust at the upturned faces. Faster! Faster! His swinging bayonet cleared a circle. They crowded just beyond and thrust back at him, swung at his legs. Their eyes stared into his, their blackened mouths gaped at him. They thrust their bayonets. He fenced against them desperately.

A voice of thunder cried "Surrender!" Then in low tones, but dreadfully distinct it said: "Shoot him." He snatched a look along the wall. There was no one on it now but him. He leaped back, turning in the air, tripped over a gray arm on the ground and ran. His stinging eyes were blind with sweat. His lungs and throat were seared and raw with gasping. But he must make his dead legs travel until he reached safe cover. The flat crack of a pistol sounded from the wall, it seemed as though a splash of icy water struck his ankle. Two steps more and his leg curled up beneath him like a wet leaf. Steadying himself with his rifle he hopped behind an oak trunk and sank down.

His heart was trying to beat out through his roaring ears. His chest was bound with iron, his fingers fluttered. At last a long, deep breath flowed into him. He stretched out, relaxed and drifted on its tide.

When he came to himself he was still behind the tree, but though the fire from the wall had broken out again and down in the hollow scattered rifles answered it, he had no longer any fear. He raised his head to take stock of things. Below him dead figures, looking wonderfully flat and shrunken, lay among the leaves. He edged an eye around the trunk and looked up the slope. More figures lay before the wall and over a little heap of them hung Clubby Jordan's cowhide boots. He wondered why Clubby didn't pull his legs away. That was no way to lie, with your feet hanging over a couple of dead men. . . . Clubby was dead. Old Clubby with his hickory-stick, his horse-hair chair. The best Colonel anywhere at all. The heart within him died. He was sick. He was through. He never wanted to fight again. He did not want to march again or bivouac without that sturdy, homely figure to lead him on. Then he turned fierce. By shot! if he had known of Clubby he would have stayed on that wall and popped a skull or two before they got him. He could not bear to look at the yellow boots which hung there helpless. He drew his head behind the tree. He shut his eyes.

Some one was looking at him. In a clump of sumac bushes on his right lay a figure in an officer's red sash. The face which, half hidden by the leaves, peered fixedly at him, was the face of Catlin Gregg. Why in the nation didn't he crawl to cover! Anyhow, why didn't he say something if he wanted to, or else look another way. "Are you all right?" James called in a low, angry voice. Gregg did not answer, he merely kept his eyes, helpless and inquiring, fixed on James Fraser. He must be hurt bad. Maybe he couldn't speak. Maybe he was dead. He felt immediate relief. If Gregg was dead there was nothing to be done, he'd stay right there, behind this oak. There would be no question of venturing out there where stray bullets were spitting through the trees and where the Yankees would open fire at sight of him.

Then the full significance burst on him. By shot, Gregg was dead and he was alive! Just what poor Harry Horniblow had talked about. He had never thought of that. Now Dougald would be Captain and maybe he could get somewhere. He had done as well as any of them to-day. And if he came home with a good record, and maybe a commission, what would her father say to that? Instantly he saw that if Gregg were dead it was mighty important for him to come out of this place alive.

But still Gregg kept looking at him. A bullet struck near his pale, disdainful face and it seemed as though he winced; ever so slightly perhaps, but there seemed to be a movement. James Fraser looked hastily away. Why had he kept watching? If he had not he would not have seen. He stared obstinately at the bark of the trunk in front of his face. But the eyes, he knew, were still fixed on him. He looked back again. "Can't you hyear me?" he shouted angrily. "Do you want help?" The eyes still looked at him.

Black fury seized him. Christ! Why couldn't the ninny speak! His lips drawn back with rage, he started crawling toward the sumac bushes. One thought was in his mind. If he found that pup was able to speak, Captain or not, he'd give him something to remember.

Now the Yankees saw him. Bullets whipped around him. Dragging his wounded ankle he scuffled awkwardly but fast.

Even with his hand on Catlin's arm he could not tell. The arm was warm and limber but no sound came from the white, proud mouth. There was no time to lose. He pulled the arm across his shoulder and started back, dragging the body along beside him. He could only inch along. The Yankees would get him sure!

But no bullets came and as he reached the tree again he heard the Yankees call, "Hurrah for you, Johnny!" and give a cheer. Somehow that did not please him. They can afford to cheer, he reflected bitterly. They've not lost so many. He eased his burden to the ground and looked at it. There was no change. The eyes stared straight ahead. He put his hand on the wrist. Not a flicker. Even as he held it, he felt beneath his fingers the unmistakable chill and saw the gray-green leaden hue creep slowly to the face.

Through twilight and evening he lay there with the body. Night came.

The firing died away, ceased utterly. With swift, incredulous horror he realized that his regiment had gone.

A silent figure crept among the trees, squatted by bodies, fumbled hurriedly. It was coming toward him. He lay quite still. He threw up his rifle. The figure squeaked and vanished.

A lantern was coming down the hill. It paused, moved on, threw wandering shadows among the dead. A ruddy, red-faced man in blue looked down at him, dropped on one knee. "Well, Johnny," he slipped a stout, white-banded arm under James Fraser's shoulders. "How about some brandy?"

SHILOH

by T. S. STRIBLING

THE ARMY OF THE MISSISSIPPI marched out of Corinth. Endless ranks of gray infantry moved east with a frieze of bayonets glittering in the sun; cavalry pranced by with an interminable clanking of sabers and snub-nosed carbines; field guns rumbled onward with hooded snouts and rattling swabs and buckets.

To Miltiades Vaiden, as he stood hour after hour at the head of his company awaiting his turn to enter the line of march, this endless duplication of buckets and swabs on the gun carriages produced a queer smack of the domestic and the businesslike amid the high pageantry of war. The clanking buckets, the dust, the sweating faces of the marching men formed a dry, realistic comment on the pulse of drums, the shriek of fife, and the flaunt of Confederate flags.

The civilians of Corinth had turned out to see the departing hosts. The citizenry cheered as thousands and thousands of young men marched away to the glorious and multitudinous slaughter of war.

As Captain Vaiden watched, the first regiment of his own brigade, the Fifth Kentucky, fell into line; then the Third Kentucky, the Sixth Kentucky, the Fourth Alabama; presently the head of his own regiment started into motion. The movement of men flowed back to him, then he and his own company went forward as part of the endless lines of marching gray.

From: *The Forge*. Copyright, 1931, reprinted by permission from Doubleday, Doran and Company, Inc.

As the captain rode along, keeping his column dressed, he thought he distinguished a voice shouting his name in the tremendous cheering. Miltiades scanned the endless faces along the line of march. A man's voice halooed his name in overtones of amazement and urgency: "Miltiades! Miltiades Vaiden!"

But the captain could distinguish no acquaintance in the roadside full of waving arms. The voice fell to the rear and was lost. Miltiades peered backward as long as there was a possibility of seeing the man. He believed it must be Augustus. He had heard through a letter that Augustus was in Corinth. He had meant to look him up but he never did. Now, at the urgent affection in the faintly heard shout, self-reproach seized Miltiades.

"I'll be sure and look Augustus up when I get back from this campaign," he told himself.

Two roads led from Corinth across the gently rolling edge of the Mississippi Valley into the hills of Tennessee. Captain Vaiden's study of the map told him that his corps under General Breckenridge was following the river road through Monterey toward Hamburg on the Tennessee River. The road itself was pulverized by the regiments ahead of the Thirty-first Alabama.

The men were exuberant and marched forward cheering and singing during the morning. In the afternoon they went on more soberly but in good spirits. As his own company trudged along, an unaccustomed feeling of protectiveness toward them welled up in Miltiades.

None of these men had ever exhibited any friendliness toward him in Corinth, but now as he rode at their side they would glance at him with smiling, friendly expressions on their dusty faces.

For some reason a thought of Drusilla went through his mind. Something of the same spirit was stirred in him by the cheerful reliance of these men as would have been, he imagined, if Drusilla had trusted her life in his keeping. It was an odd emotion for Miltiades to feel toward any human being, much less for a company of men.

In the late afternoon Trabue's brigade entered the wooded hills of Tennessee. From the hill tops Miltiades caught, on the right, an occasional glimpse of the Tennessee River and the tree-crowned bluffs on the opposite shore. The creeks which lay across the line of march were marshy and spanned by rickety wooden bridges. At intervals the distant blowing of the steamers of the enemy sounded up the winding channel of the river.

At about a half an hour till sundown orders came for the men to be quiet. Later the column was halted on the road. The Thirty-first Alabama marched off at right angles and formed a line in the forest. Here Major Spearman sent orders to Captain Vaiden for absolute silence.

Miltiades moved his horse among the trees and saplings along the front of his company, enforcing silence in flatted, cautionary tones.

"Now men, keep quiet, no singing, no talking."

The excited men quieted. The river steamers filled the evening with melancholy reverberations. The gray line in the dense woods raked together piles of last year's leaves; the men sat down, opened their haversacks, and began eating after their long march.

As they ate, somewhere in the woods ahead of them came the notes of mess call blown on a bugle. This was repeated at greater and greater distances until it was barely audible.

One of the men mumbling his hard tack said he thought orders had been given for silence. A comrade said, "Them buglers don't take their orders from General Johnston to-day but they will to-morrow."

Night came with abruptness in the deep wood. There were no lights. The orderly hitched Captain Vaiden's horse to a sapling, raked his commanding officer a bed of leaves and spread a blanket over them. Such a bit of military routine always gratified something in Captain Vaiden. It was something to have another man rake up the leaves and spread the blanket.

Late that night music of a military band filled the forest. In the Federal encampment some regimental band was playing.

Captain Vaiden slept badly. It was his habit at about two o'clock every night to wake up. Then the details of his betrothal to and loss of Drusilla would move through his mind. He would tell himself that if she preferred any other man he did not want her. Then he would think over all the little incidents of their courtship, and what he might have done to keep her. He tried not to do this. He would repeat to himself an adage which he had heard his mother use years ago. He would say, "That which is without remedy should be without regard." But no sooner had he thought this than he would go back to replanning his courtship with Drusilla. . . . If he had devoted more time to her . . . if he had gone with some other girl to make her jealous . . . They were always simple thoughts which did not touch his spiritual loss of his betrothed. To-night the news that Drusilla Crowninshield had become the mother of a baby girl gave his reverie a strange and melancholy turn.

This tiny girl baby seemed somehow to reach back into his and Drusilla's past and inevitably to keep them apart from the first moment of their attraction for each other. The baby somehow obliterated any other path their lives could have taken. It deprived the captain even of his gray qualifying "if's." There were no "if's." His happiness, ironically, was lost from the day he saw its first promise in Drusilla Lacefield's eyes.

And this reminded him of the predestinarianism of his father's God; that brutal amoral focusing of omnipotence upon amoral ends; a spiritual mechanism destroying much and saving little; a symbol of simple materialism.

At half-past three o'clock in the morning a kind of faint milkiness formed in the tops of the trees. It was not light, but neither was it the blackness that still filled the undergrowth. A chill came into the air. From some barnyard a cock hallelujahed for the promise of another day.

The sleeping battle line stirred. It became light enough for Captain Vaiden to see the men nearest him sit up and take drinks from their canteens. One soldier looked up at the gray sky and asked what time it was. The men began stretching, standing up, taking out of their haversacks.

At half-past four the line began moving through the woods.

Miltiades Vaiden left his horse in the dense growth and dressed his company as best he could by walking ahead and in the open spaces, indicating the alignment with his sword. Each time he did so the men scrambled hurriedly into place, holding their muskets this way and that to get through the undergrowth.

A tension gradually keyed up the line. As it pushed forward through the dark-green obscurity, men would turn aside here and there to urinate out of nervousness. Suddenly a soldier near Miltiades jerked up his musket, pushed away some twigs. As he sighted, he jerked out, "Yonder's a damn Yankee," and fired.

The gun cracked loudly in the damp morning air. Came a silence, then the men heard three or four picket shots just ahead of them, and the bullets made a brief skittering through the leaves overhead.

The line moved more rapidly. Miltiades pushed out of some undergrowth and saw a picket post just ahead of him. The sentinels held their guns at attention and seemed about to challenge the oncomers when the whole battle line moved out of the brush. They discharged their pieces helter skelter, leaped behind bushes and were gone.

Some of the Confederates laughed. A few men started after the fugitives. Miltiades gesticulated with his sword and forced them back into line, with his attention fixed anxiously on keeping his company in formation.

The greatest confusion broke out in the woods ahead of the advancing army. A ghostly glint of tents appeared in the gray light. Men came running out of them half dressed. Drums burst into the long roll. Bugles brayed. The Federals, half asleep, pulled open their eyes to the sudden horror of long steady lines of gray slaughterers upon them.

Miltiades swung up his sword.

"Make ready! Aim! Fire!" he shouted.

The endless row of muskets gave a prolonged crash. Some of the half-garbed figures crumpled up; others went flying and limping in any direction. Officers barked to whip their surprised men into some sort of order. From the flying bluecoats came an occasional shot.

The Confederates charged ahead, loading and firing into the unresisting enemy. As they passed through the Federal tents numbers of the men broke ranks to dash inside for loot. Miltiades shouted and cursed and beat them back into line with the flat of his sword.

"Go on! Go on!" he yelled. "These tents are ours already!"

The men broke into a prolonged cheering. The wounded and dead Federals scattered about everywhere, the rabble that had fled before them filled the Confederates with the high ecstasy of multitudinous and organized homicide. Every man was a demigod who swept away resistance at a wave of his sword.

Whether the slight opposing fire had hurt any of his own men, Miltiades Vaiden did not know. He was shouting now to slow down the advance and keep his men in line with the general formation advancing through the woods. His own company ceased firing except for a snap shot at some wounded Yankee making a last effort to escape. To right and left sounded volleys of firing, now near, now remote on a two-and-a-half-mile front. The Thirty-first Alabama moved slowly into the woods again. Ahead of them innumerable bugles sounded a rally. Their confusion of sound sang and echoed in the dense forest.

A voice called in Miltiades' ear: "I think they are arranging a little reception committee for us out there, Captain."

Vaiden looked around and saw the long dark face of Captain Bloodgood filled with a new light.

"We've got 'em between the creek and the river," called Miltiades; "they can't cross either. They'll have to surrender."

The Kentuckian nodded.

"But the harder we press them the solider they'll get."

Miltiades suddenly broke out laughing.

"And the more we'll hit."

Bloodgood turned his head to listen to the growing confusion.

"Hear that—a battery of six-pounders turned loose."

"Are they our guns?"

"Just getting into action. We're warming up, Vaiden."

The use of his name by Bloodgood without his title filled Miltiades with pleasure. Such familiarity was usual among the other officers of the regiment, but up to that moment they had remained formal with Miltiades.

The line had halted now in an open glade. In front of them Miltiades could hear a persistent rifle fire, from the right hand came a fainter receding fusillade. By the time the sun was up this fainter firing seemed to come from behind a wooded acclivity which Miltiades could see toward the right.

Bloodgood nodded toward the nearer small arms.

"Whatever that is, it's holding up our center," he cried. "Our right flank is getting around . . ." He listened. "Can you tell what our left's doing?"

Miltiades paid attention in this new direction. In the persistent cannonading he could detect no movement.

"That's because a battery doesn't have to move often," explained Bloodgood nervously; "to pursue, they simply elevate their guns."

The Kentuckian's nervousness translated itself to Miltiades in a desire to act.

"I wish we'd get a chance at that center," he snapped; "they're holding up our whole advance."

They waited in growing impatience for upward of half an hour when Colonel Crowninshield came riding up the line through the open trees.

"Men!" he called out, "we're to move forward and stand ready to charge the enemy." He pointed his sword. "Clear that out and we'll drive the Yankees into the river!"

The men began shouting. Bloodgood turned back to the head of his company. A few minutes later the column moved forward again, flanking the sunlit hill. From their new position they would launch themselves against the obstinate center.

The line had advanced toward the rifle fire not more than a hundred yards when Miltiades saw horses and field guns dash up on the high wooded ground on the right. They were so far away that they looked like toy artillery among toy trees. The horses whirled the guns into place. Miltiades directed his attention to his own work.

As his line went forward the surrounding woods became more and more open. The rifle fire in front of his men developed into a sound like a continuous terrific tearing of cloth. The uproar tingled through Miltiades' nerves. He even heard distant cheers.

A queer sensation went over Miltiades, as if the whole line of his company were somehow a part of his own body. He felt an impulse to fling this extended self against the tearing gunfire ahead. Involuntarily he set the pace at the head of his column, increasing its tempo into a quick step.

Just then Colonel Crowinshield reappeared, barking an order at his subordinates.

Miltiades almost relayed the command into Forward Charge. The fire seemed just beyond a curtain of trees. Then he saw Crowinshield was making repressive gestures with his blade. He was halting the advance. Here was the position from which they must wait in reserve to strike. Captain Vaiden was in a quiver to go on. The whole Yankee thrust into middle Tennessee was there to be stopped and bagged. He wanted to sweep this resistance out of the way.

The enormous chessboard of war had concentrated itself on this one sharp salient of Federal resistance. Belmont, Paducah, Nashville, Fort Donelson—they were like wounds in the South and all could be cured by wiping out this salient and exterminating the enemy.

The Thirty-first Alabama had halted in a fairly open ground curtained by a heavy wood in front but commanded by the heights on the right.

As Captain Vaiden alternately stared at the skirt of woods and looked to his commander for the order to charge, he saw movement among the toy horses on the distant hill. The gunners worked with mechanical swiftness. A thought came to Miltiades that a Confederate battery was about to be trained on the resistant center. The next moment came a series of far-away flashes and puffs of smoke. Ten seconds later the sunlight overhead was filled with the whir of shells; blazes, smoke, and crashes shook the air. After the exploding shells had shaken into silence, Miltiades heard the heavy rumble of the guns on the distant elevation.

The crashing above the men's heads spread a feeling of indefinite destruction throughout the line. The first salvo had hurt no one, but all the men began watching the distant arillerists. More flashes broke forth; again sounded the crashing about the line and later the grumbling thunder of the cannon.

A fury against the distant cannoneers rose up in the captain. They were so safe, so utterly out of reach of his rifle fire; and to be working like miniature devils pouring thunder on his position!

A private shouted out, "Hell, Cap', le's charge them guns!"

The officer made no reply.

The cannon fire focused itself on the reserves. An explosion tore a hole in the ground not fifty feet from Miltiades. The next instant a dozen men were bowled over by dirt and débris. They struggled to their feet, some laughing, some frightened. Three men were wounded.

Presently the shells were dropping with a certain regularity. Every far-away flash became the signal for a tense motionless waiting; then a crash in air or earth and an occasional smashing of the line.

As Vaiden waited he cursed the withdrawn gunners. He wished furiously that his regiment stood under the foot of the distant hill.

Bloodgood came up to him again.

"This damn pounding will take a lot of fight out of our regiment." He stopped amid a renewed crashing.

At that moment the line about them burst into huzzahs. Vaiden looked and saw a line of antlike men charging the distant hill against the tiny battery. He could hear no reports of the far-away rifles, but he saw a string of smoke along the front of the hill and the sparkle of distant bayonets.

The Lilliputian cannoneers worked furiously at their guns. As the line of gray men crept up they were still loading their weapons. The gray line moved among the pieces. Then there were no gunners. They had fallen under the bayonets.

The fury of Captain Vaiden was suddenly appeased with the slaughter of the cannoneers. The shell fire stopped and his nerves were suddenly eased from an intense strain. They were all parts of a vastly complicated maze. The gray men on the hill died to relieve his own line. His own men in turn were about to advance toward some vast impersonal objective. . . .

A courier came dashing up from General Albert Sidney Johnston ordering the reserve corps to attack. A few minutes later the Thirty-first Alabama in Trabue's brigade moved into action.

The screen of woods also had been shelled by the guns on the hill. A mist of acrid smoke hung among the trees. As Captain Vaiden's company entered it, men appeared in the mist running or staggering or crawling toward them. Behind these wounded stragglers, still in line, retired the remnants of a brigade. Their numbers increased as Miltiades led his troops forward. It was like drawing near a swarm of bees.

Two hundred yards farther on, dimly discernible amid the pungent smoke, Miltiades saw the center of the lazar cluster. There was a pond among the trees. It was a red pond. Into it the wounded men waded to wash their wounds and fill their canteens. Soldiers who were whole carried water to the maimed who could not reach the bloody pond.

If the wounded groaned they could not be heard in the tearing musketry beyond the copse, but all walked or sat or lay in a kind of ghastly pantomime about the scarlet pond.

The advancing brigade moved in line through the trees and found themselves looking up a long gentle slope covered with dead men. At the top of the slope was a heavy tangle of undergrowth, trees and saplings. This was the obstacle that lay between the retreating Federals and annihilation.

The brigade formed its line just inside the copse. Miltiades heard the order to charge. He himself shouted:

"Come on, men, we'll take this hill!"

The whole line dashed out of the woods and up the slope. Their hobnailed shoes ran over the faces and mouths and eyes of wounded and dying men. A prolonged tearing set up on the rim of the hill. An enduring blaze burned there composed of momentary flashes. The air was filled with a multitudinous whining. Men reeled, pitched forward, slumped out of line, and helped resow the planted slope. Halfway up, the brigade fired into the abattis. The crashing string of fire burned on. Their second dash hesitated. Vaiden looked about for his colonel. He heard Bloodgood shouting through the din and smoke that Vaiden commanded the regiment. Miltiades leaned forward as if against an enormous gale.

"Come on—to the top! Charge to the top!"

The thinned line surged forward, hesitated, broke, and went scattering, running and staggering back down the slope of dead men.

Miltiades followed his flying men who dropped as they fled. He cursed them and the enemy. He himself was not touched, but as he went back down the great glacis he felt shattered. It was as if his company had been his own body. He had no feeling of sorrow for losing the men he had scattered up and down the hill, but a feeling of shock as if something of himself had been shot away.

In the edge of the copse he reformed his remnants. He suddenly understood what Bloodgood had shouted. He was the senior surviving officer.

He aligned the regiment as best he could and sent his wounded for what relief they could find at the ghastly pond.

Within about an hour a fresh brigade repeated the futile charge. Miltiades formed his men in this new line. The commanding officer asked who he was. He said:

"I am Captain Vaiden, acting colonel of the Thirty-first Alabama! That slope, sir, cannot be taken by a frontal attack! Come on, we'll help you take it!"

At three o'clock that afternoon the massed batteries of the entire Confederate army concentrated their fire on Prentiss' corps. A line of cannons a quarter of a mile long poured iron upon the acclivity of the Hornet's Nest.

From where he still held his battered line in the copse, Miltiades saw the dense abattis crowning the slope melt, explode into the air, catch fire. The storm of shells fired the leaves along the slope and their flames ran along among the wounded and the dead on the long natural glacis. Suddenly, amid the smoke and crash of the shells, a rout of blue coats leaped out of their untenable stronghold and dashed for the river. They were trying to cut through to the main body of Grant's retreating army. Captain Vaiden, with the remnants of half-a-dozen regiments charged up the hill at the exposed men. The Federals fled over the hill, but presently came huddling back. They were surrounded. From all sides rushed the gray lines. The Yankees who had covered the field with dead now withered among the men they had slain.

Suddenly Miltiades saw the stars and bars on top of the acclivity. The rifle fire slackened and finally hushed. An enormous cheering broke forth. It equaled the continuing thunder of the artillery. Presently the field guns also became silent; the enormous uproar of cheering armies persisted. Miltiades' own men added to the shouts and huzzahs; they dashed unresisted up the deadly glacis.

The Yankees had surrendered. The Confederates had captured the whole army corps. The battered gray lines dashed forward jubilating, brandishing muskets, flinging their caps in air. Every man thought complete victory had been won. They did not know that the Confederate enveloping movement had pinched out only a piece and had stopped. They did not know that two armies of reinforcements were even then double-quicking to the aid of the hard-pressed Grant.

In the midst of the rejoicing, news came that General Albert Sidney Johnston had been killed.

As Miltiades hurried toward the top of the slope, he glanced about where four hours before his regiment had been halted. Among the forms motionless on the ground he saw, here and there, a man he knew. Then, with a kind of stab, he recognized the cottony face of Emory Crowninshield. He ran to his commander and dropped beside him.

"Colonel! Colonel, we've taken the hill! We've captured Prentiss' army!"

The weak hand pulled at Miltiades, feebly drew his ear down to the bloodless lips.

"Captain Vaiden . . ." gasped the fading man . . . "won't you . . . take care of . . . Drusilla . . . and my little . . . baby . . . girl . . ."

WAR EXPERIENCES

by MARK TWAIN

THE LAST TIME I had the privilege of breaking bread with soldiers was some years ago, with the oldest military organization in England, the Ancient and Honorable Artillery Company of London, somewhere about its six hundredth anniversary; and now I have enjoyed this privilege with its eldest child, the oldest military organization in America, the Ancient and Honorable Artillery Company of Massachusetts, on this your two hundred and fortieth anniversary. Fine old stock, both of you,—and if you fight as well as you feed, God protect the enemy.

I did not assemble at the hotel parlors to-day to be received by a committee as a mere civilian guest; no, I assembled at the headquarters of the Putnam Phalanx and insisted upon my right to be escorted to this place as one of the military guests. For I, too, am a soldier! I am inured to war. I have a military history. I have been through a stirring campaign, and there is not even a mention of it in any history of the United States or of the Southern Confederacy,—to such length can the envy and malignity of the historian go! I will unbosom myself here, where I cannot but find sympathy; I will tell you about it, and appeal through you to justice.

In the earliest summer days of the war I slipped out of Hannibal, Missouri, by night, with a friend, and joined a detachment of the rebel Gen. Tom Harris's army (I find myself in a minority here), up a gorge behind an old barn in Rolls county. Col. Rolls swore us in. He made us swear to uphold the flag and constitution of the United States, and to destroy any other military organization that we caught doing the same

From a speech delivered at the 240th Meeting, Ancient and Honorable Artillery Company of Massachusetts.

thing. In other words, we were to repel invasion. Well, you see, this mixed us. We couldn't really tell which side we were on, but we went into camp and left it to the God of Battles (for that was the term then). I was made second lieutenant and chief mogul of a company of eleven men, for we had no captain. My friend, who was nineteen years old, six feet high, three feet wide, some distance through, and just out of the infant school, was made orderly sergeant. His name was Ben Tupper. He had a hard time. When he was mounted and on the march he used to go to sleep, and his horse would reach around and bite his leg, and then he would cry and curse, and want to go home. The other men pestered him a good deal, too. When they were dismounted they said they couldn't march in double file with him because his feet took up so much room. One night when we were around the camp fire, a fellow on the outside of the circuit said, "Ben Tupper, put down that newspaper; it casts a shadow like a blanket." Ben said, "I ain't got any newspaper." Then that other fellow said, "Oh, I see,—'twas your ear!" We all slept in a corn-crib, on the corn, and the rats were very thick. Ben Tupper had been rightly reared, and when he was ready for bed he would start to pray and a rat would bite him on the heel, and then he would sit up and swear all night and keep everybody awake. He was town-bred and did not seem to have any correct idea of military discipline. If I commanded him to shut up, he would say, "Who was your nigger last year?" One evening I ordered him to ride out on picket duty about three miles, to the beginning of a prairie. Said he, "What!—in the night!—and them blamed Union soldiers likely to be prowling around there any time!" So he wouldn't go. Next morning I ordered him again. Said he, "In the rain!—I think I see myself!" He didn't go. Next day I ordered him on picket duty once more. This time he looked hurt. Said he, "What! on Sunday?—you must be a damn fool!" Picketing was impracticable, so I dropped it from my military system.

We had a good enough time there at that barn, barring the rats and the mosquitoes and the rain. We levied on both parties impartially; and both parties hated us impartially. But one day we heard that the invader was approaching; so we had to pack up and move, of course. Inside of twenty-four hours he was coming again. So we moved again. Next day he was after us once more. We didn't like it much, but we moved rather than make trouble. This went on for a week or ten days, and we saw considerable scenery. Then Ben Tupper lost patience. Said he, "War aint what it's cracked up to be; I'm going home if I can't ever get a chance to sit down. Why do those people keep us a-humping around so? Blame their skins, do they think this is an excursion?" Some of the other town boys began to grumble; they complained that there was an insufficiency of umbrellas. So I sent around to the farmers and borrowed what I could. Then they complained that the Worcestershire sauce was out. There was mutiny and dissatisfaction all around, and of course here came the enemy pestering us again—as much as two hours before breakfast, too, when nobody wanted to turn out, of course. This was a little too much. The whole command felt insulted. I sent an aid to the brigadier, and asked him to assign us a district where there wasn't so much bother going on. The history of our campaign was laid before him, but instead of being touched by it, what did he do? He sent back an indignant message. He said, "You have had a dozen chances inside of two weeks to capture the enemy, and he is still at large. Feeling bad? Stay where you are this time, or I will court-martial and hang the whole of you." I submitted this rude message to my command, and asked their advice. Said the orderly sergeant, "If Tom Harris wants the enemy, let him come and get him; I aint got any use for my share. And who's Tom Harris, anyway, that's putting on so many frills? Why, I knew him when he wasn't nothing but a darn telegraph operator. Gentlemen, you can do as you choose; as for me I've got enough of this sashshaying around so's 't you can't get a chance to pray because the time's all required for cussing. So off goes my war-paint—you hear *me!*" The whole regiment said, "That's the talk for me!" So then and there my brigade disbanded itself and tramped off home, I at the tail of it. I hung up my sword and returned to the arts of peace. We were the first men that went into the service in Missouri; we were the first that went out of it anywhere. This, gentlemen, is the history of the part which my division took in the great rebellion, and such is the military record of its commander-in-chief. And this is the first time that the deeds of those eleven warriors have been brought officially to the notice of mankind. Treasure these things in your hearts, and so shall the detected and truculent historians of this land be brought to shame and confusion. I ask you to fill your glasses and drink with me to the reverent memory of the Orderly Sergeant and those other neglected and forgotten heroes, my foot-sore and travel-stained paladins, who were first in war, first in peace, and were not idle during the interval that lay between.

FREDERICKSBURG

by MARY JOHNSTON

SNOW LAY DEEP on the banks of the Rappahannock, in the forest, up and down the river, on the plain about the little city, on the bold heights of the northern shore, on the hills of the southern, commanding the plain. The snow was deep, but somewhat milder weather had set in. December the eleventh dawned still and foggy.

General Burnside with a hundred and twenty thousand blue troops appointed this day to pass the Rappahannock, a stream that flowed across the road to Richmond. He had been responsible for choosing this route to the keep of the fortress, and he must make good his reiterated, genial assurances of success. The Rappahannock, Fredericksburg, and a line of hills masked the onward-going road and its sign, *This way to Richmond.* "Well, the Rappahannock can be bridged! A brigade known to be occupying the town? Well, a hundred and forty guns admirably planted on Stafford Heights will drive out the rebel brigade! The line of hills, bleak and desolate with fir woods?—hares and snow birds are all the life over there! General Lee and Stonewall Jackson? Down the Rappahannock below Moss Neck. At least, undoubtedly, Stonewall Jackson's down there. The balloon people say so. General Lee's got an idea that Port Royal's our point of attack. The mass of his army's there. The gunboat people say so. Longstreet may be behind those hills. Well, we'll crush Longstreet! We'll build our bridges under cover of this fortunate fog, and go over and defeat Longstreet and be far down the road to Richmond before a man can say Jack Robinson!"

"Jack Robinson!" said the brigade from McLaws's division—Barksdale's Mississippians—drawn up on the water edge of Fredericksburg. They were tall men—Barksdale's Mississippians—playful bear-hunters from the cane brakes, young and powerfully made, and deadly shots. "Old Barksdale" knew how to handle them, and together they were a handful for any enemy whatsoever. Sixteen hundred born hunters and fighters, they opened fire on the bridge-builders, trying to build four bridges, three above, one below the town. Barksdale's men were somewhat sheltered by the houses on the river brink; the blue had the favourable fog with which to cover operations. It did not wholly help; the Mississippians had

From: *The Long Roll.* Copyright 1911. Houghton Mifflin Co.

keen eyes; the rifles blazed, blazed, blazed! Burnside's bridge-builders
were gallant men; beaten back from the river they came again and again,
but again and again the eyes of the swamp hunters ran along the gleaming barrels and a thousand bronzed fingers pulled a thousand triggers.
Past the middle of the day the fog lifted. The town lay defined and helpless beneath a pallid sky.

The artillery of the Army of the Potomac opened upon it. One hundred and forty heavy guns, set in tiers upon the heights to the north,
fired each into Fredericksburg fifty rounds. Under that terrible cover the
blue began to cross on pontoons.

A number of the women and children had been sent from the town
during the preceding days. Not all, however, were gone. Many had no
place to go to; some were ill and some were nursing the ill; many had
husbands, sons, brothers, there at hand in the Army of Northern Virginia and would not go. Now with the beginning of the bombardment
they must go. There were grey, imperative orders. "At once! at once!
Go *where*? God knows! but go."

They went, almost all, in the snow, beneath the pallid sky, with the
shells shrieking behind them. They carried the children, they half carried
the sick and the very old. They stumbled on, between the frozen hills
by the dark pointed cedars, over the bare white fields. Behind them home
was being destroyed; before them lay desolation, and all around was
winter. They had perhaps thought it out, and were headed—the various
forlorn lines—for this or that country house, but they looked lost, remnant
of a world become glacial, whirled with suddenness into the sidereal
cold, cold! and the loneliness of cold. The older children were very brave;
but there were babes, too, and these wailed and wailed. Their wailing made
a strange, futile sound beneath the thundering of the guns.

One of these parties came through the snow to a swollen creek on
which the ice cakes were floating. Cross!—yes, but how? The leaders consulted together, then went up the stream to find a possible ford, and
came in sight of a grey battery, waiting among the hills. "Oh, soldiers!—
oh, soldiers!—come and help!"

Down hastened a detachment, eager, respectful, a lieutenant directing,
the very battery horses looking anxious, responsible. A soldier in the saddle, a child in front, a child behind, the old steady horses planting their
feet carefully in the icy rushing stream, over went the children. Then the
women crossed, their hands resting on the grey-clad shoulders. All were
over; all thanked the soldiers. The soldiers took off their caps, wished
with all their hearts that they had at command fire-lit palaces and a ban-

quiet set! Having neither, being themselves without shelter or food and ordered not to build fires, they could only bare their heads and watch the other soldiers out of sight, carrying the children, half carrying the old and sick, stumbling through the snow, by the dark pointed cedars, and presently lost to view among the frozen hills.

The shells rained destruction into Fredericksburg. Houses were battered and broken; houses were set on fire. Through the smoke and uproar, the explosions and detonations and tongues of flame, the Mississippians beat back another attempt at the bridges and opened fire on boat after boat now pushing from the northern shore. But the boats came bravely on, bravely manned; hundreds might be driven from the bridge-building, but other hundreds sprang to take their places—and always from the heights came the rain of iron, smashing, shivering, setting afire, tearing up the streets, bringing down the walls, ruining, wounding, slaying! McLaws sent an order to Barksdale, Barksdale gave it to his brigade. "Evacuate!" said the Mississippians. "We're going to evacuate. What's that in English? 'Quit?'—What in hell should we quit for?"

Orders being orders, the disgust of the bear-hunters did not count. "Old Barksdale" was fairly deprecating. "Men, I can't help it! General McLaws says, 'General Barksdale, withdraw your men to Marye's Hill.' Well, I've got to do it, have n't I? General McLaws knows, now does n't he?—Yes,—just one more round. *Load! Kneel! Commence firing!*"

In the late afternoon the town was evacuated, Barksdale drawing off in good order across the stormed-upon open. He disappeared—the Mississippi brigade disappeared—from the Federal vision. The blue column, the 28th Massachusetts leading, entered Fredericksburg. "We'll get them all to-morrow—Longstreet certainly! Stonewall Jackson's from twelve to eighteen miles down the river. Well! this time Lee will find that he's divided his army once too often!"

By dark there were built six bridges, but the main army rested all night on the northern bank. December the twelfth dawned, another foggy day. The fog held hour after hour, very slow, still, muffled weather, through which, corps by corps, all day long, the army slowly crossed. In the afternoon there was a cavalry skirmish with Stuart, but nothing else happened. Thirty-six hours had been consumed in crossing and resting. The Rappahannock, however, *was* crossed, and the road to Richmond stretched plain between the hills.

But the grey army was not divided. Certain divisions had been down the river, but they were no longer down the river. The Army of Northern Virginia, a vibrant unit, intense, concentrated, gaunt, bronzed, and highly efficient, waited behind the hills south and west of the town. There was a creek running through a ravine, called Deep Run. On one side of Deep Run stood Longstreet and the 1st Corps, on the other, almost at right angles, Stonewall Jackson and the 2d. Before both the heavily timbered ridge sank to the open plain. In the woods had been thrown up certain breastworks.

Longstreet's left, Anderson's division, rested on the river. To Anderson's right were posted McLaws, Pickett, and Hood. He had his artillery on Marye's Hill and Willis Hill, and he had Ransom's infantry in line at the base of these hills behind a stone wall. Across Deep Run, on the wooded hills between the ravine and the Massaponax, was Stonewall Jackson. A. P. Hill's division with the brigades of Pender, Lane, Archer, Thomas, and Gregg made his first line of battle, the divisions of Taliaferro and Early his second, and D. H. Hill's division his reserve. His artillery held all favourable crests and headlands. Stuart's cavalry and Stuart's Horse Artillery were gathered by the Massaponax. Hills and forest hid them all, and over the plain and river rolled the fog.

It hid the North as it hid the South. Burnside's great force rested the night of the twelfth in and immediately about Fredericksburg—Hooker and Sumner and Franklin, one hundred and thirteen thousand men. "The balloon people" now reported that the hills south and west were held by a considerable rebel force—Longstreet evidently, Lee probably with him. Burnside repeated the infatuation of Pope and considered that Stonewall Jackson was absent from the field of operations. Undoubtedly he had been, but the shortest of time before, down the river by Port Royal. No one had seen him move. Jackson away, there was then only Longstreet—strongly posted, no doubt. Well! Form a great line of battle, advance in overwhelming strength across the plain, the guns on Stafford Heights supporting, and take the hills, and Longstreet on them! It sounded simple.

The fog, heavy, fleecy, white, persisted. The grey soldiers on the wooded hills, the grey artillery holding the bluff heads, the grey skirmishers holding embankment and cut of the Richmond, Fredericksburg and Potomac Railroad, the grey cavalry by the Massaponax, all stared into the white sea and could discern nothing. The ear was of no avail. Sound came muffled, but still it came. "The long roll—hear the long roll! My Lord! How many drums have they got, anyway?"—"Listen! If you listen right hard you can hear them shouting orders! Hush up, you infantry, down there! We want to hear."—"They're moving guns, too! Wish there'd come a little sympathizing earthquake and help them—'specially those siege guns on the heights over there!"—"No, no! I want to fight them.

Look! it's lifting a little! the fog's lifting a little! Look at the guns up in the air like that! It's closed again."—"Well, if that wasn't fantastic! Ten iron guns in a row, posted in space!"—"Hm! brass bands. My Lord! there must be one to a platoon!"—"Hear them marching! Saw lightning once run along the ground—now it's thunder. How many men has General Ambrose Everett Burnside got, anyhow?"—"Burnside's been to dances before in Fredericksburg! Some of the houses are burning now that he's danced in, and some of the women he has danced with are wandering over the snow. I hope he'll like the reel presently."—"He's a good fellow himself, though not much of a general! He can't help fighting here if he's put here to fight."—"I know that. I was just stating facts. Hear that music, music, music!"

Up from Deep Run, a little in the rear of the grey centre, rose a bold hill. Here in the clinging mist waited Lee on Traveller, his staff behind him, in front an ocean of vapour. Longstreet came from the left, Stonewall Jackson from the right. Lee and his two lieutenants talked together, three mounted figures looming large on the hilltop above Deep Run. With suddenness the fog parted, was upgathered with swiftness by the great golden sun.

That lifted curtain revealed a very great and martial picture,—War in a moment of vastness and grandeur, epic, sublime. The town was afire; smoke and flame went up to a sky not yet wholly azure, banded and barred with clouds from behind which the light came in rays fierce and bright, with an effect of threatening. There was a ruined house on a high hill. It gave the appearance of a grating in the firmament, a small dungeon grating. Beyond the burning town was the river, crossed now by six pontoon bridges. On each there were troops; one of the long sun rays caught the bayonets. From the river, to the north, rose the heights, and they had an iron crown from which already came lightnings and thunders. There were paths leading down to the river and these showed blue, moving streams, bright points which were flags moving with them. That for the far side of the Rappahannock, but on this side, over the plain that stretched south and west of the smoke-wreathed town, there moved a blue sea indeed. Eighty thousand men were on that plain. They moved here, they moved there, into battle formation, and they moved to the crash of music, to the horn and to the drum. The long rays that the sun was sending made a dazzle of bayonet steel, thousands and thousands and thousands of bayonets. The gleaming lines went here, went there, crossed, recrossed, formed angles, made a vast and glittering net. Out of it soared the flags, bright hovering birds, bright giant blossoms in the air. Batteries moved across the plain. Officers, couriers, galloped on fiery horses; some general officer passed from end to end of a forming line and was cheered. The earth shook to marching feet. The great brazen horns blared, the drums beat, the bugles rang. The gleaming net folded back on itself, made three pleats, made three great lines of battle.

The grey leaders on the hill to the south gazed in silence. Then said Lee, "It is well that war is so terrible. Were it not so, we should grow too fond of it." Longstreet, the "old war horse," stared at the tremendous pageant. "This wasn't a little quarrel. It's been brewing for seventy-five years—ever since the Bill-of-Rights day. Things that take so long in brewing can't be cooled by a breath. It's getting to be a huge war." Said Jackson, "Franklin holds their left. He seems to be advancing. I will return to Hamilton's Crossing, sir."

The guns on the Stafford Heights which had been firing slowly and singly now opened mouth together. The tornado, overpassing river and plain, burst on the southern hills. In the midst of the tempest, Burnside ordered Franklin to advance a single division, its mission the seizing the *unoccupied* ridge east of Deep Run. Franklin sent Meade with forty-five hundred Pennsylvania troops.

Meade's brigades advanced in three lines, skirmishers out, a band playing a quickstep, the stormy sunlight deepening the colours, making a gleaming of bayonets. His first line crossed the Richmond road. To the left was a tiny stream, beyond it a ragged bank topped by brushwood. Suddenly, from this coppice, opened two of Pelham's guns.

Beneath that flanking fire the first blue line faltered, gave ground. Meade brought up four batteries and sent for others. All these came fiercely into action. When they got his range, Pelham moved his two guns and began again a raking fire. Again the blue gunners found the range and again he moved with deliberate swiftness, and again he opened with a hot and raking fire. One gun was disabled; he fought with the other. He fought until the limber chests were empty and there came an imperious message from Jeb Stuart, "Get back from destruction, you infernal, gallant fool, John Pelham!"

The guns across the river and the blue field batteries steadily shelled for half an hour the heavily timbered slopes beyond the railroad. Except for the crack and crash of severed boughs the wood gave no sign. At the end of this period Meade resumed his advance.

On came the blue lines, staunch, determined troops, seasoned now as the grey were seasoned. They meant to take that empty line of hills, willy-nilly a few Confederate guns. That done, they would be in a position to flank Longstreet, already attacked in front by Sumner's Grand Division. On they came, with a martial front, steady, swinging. Uninterrupted, they marched to within a few hundred yards of Prospect Hill. Suddenly the woods that loomed before them so dark and quiet blazed and rang. Fifty guns were within that cover, and the fifty cast their thunderbolts full against the dark blue line. From either side the grey artillery burst the grey musketry, and above the crackling thunder rose the rebel yell. Stonewall Jackson was not down the river; Stonewall Jackson was here! Meade's Pennsylvanians were gallant fighters; but they broke beneath that withering fire,—they fell back in strong disorder.

Grey and blue, North and South, there were gathered upon and above the field of Fredericksburg four hundred guns. All came into action. Where earlier, there had been fog over the plain, fog wreathing the hillsides, there was now smoke. Dark and rolling it invaded the ruined town, it mantled the flowing Rappahannock, it surmounted the hills. Red flashes pierced it, and over and under and through roared the enormous sound. There came reinforcements to Meade, division after division. In the meantime Sumner was hurling brigades against Marye's Hill and Longstreet was hurling them back again.

The 2d Corps listened to the terrible musketry from this front. "Old Pete's surely giving them hell! There's a stone wall at the base of Marye's Hill. McLaws and Ransom are holding it—sorry for the Yanks in front." —"Never heard such hullabaloo as the great guns are making!"—"What're them Pennsylvanians down there doing? It's time for them to come on! They've got enough reinforcements—old friends, Gibbon and Doubleday." —"Good fighters."—"Yes, Lord! we're all good fighters now. Glad of it. Like to fight a good fighter. Feel real friendly toward him."—"A thirty-two-pounder Parrott in the battery on the hill over there exploded and raised hell. General Lee standing right by. He just spoke on, calm and imperturbable, and Traveller looked sideways."—"Look! Meade's moving. *Do you know, I think we ought to have occupied that tongue of land?*"

So, in sooth, thought others presently. It was a marshy, dense, and tangled coppice projecting like a sabre tooth between the brigades of Lane and Archer. So thick was the growth, so boggy the earth, that at the last it had been pronounced impenetrable and left unrazed. Now the mistake was paid for—in bloody coin.

Meade's line of battle rushed across the open, brushed the edge of the coppice, discovered that it was empty, and plunging in, found cover. The grey batteries could not reach them. Almost before the situation was realized, forth burst the blue from the thicket. Lane was flanked; in uproar

and confusion the grey gave way. Meade sent in another brigade. It left
the first to man-handle Lane, hurled itself on, and at the outskirt of the
wood, struck Archer's left, taking Archer by surprise and creating a demi-
rout. A third brigade entered on the path of the first and second. The latter, leaving Archer to this new strength, hurled itself across the military
road and upon a thick and tall wood held by Maxey Gregg and his South
Carolinians. Smoke, cloud, and forest growth—it was hard to distinguish
colours, hard to tell just what was happening! Gregg thought that the
smoke-wrapped line was Archer falling back. He withheld his fire. The
line came on and in a moment, amid shouts, struck his right. A bullet
brought down Gregg himself, mortally wounded. His troops broke, then
rallied. A grey battery near Bernard's Cabin brought its guns to bear upon
Gibbon, trying to follow the blue triumphant rush. Archer reformed.
Stonewall Jackson, standing on Prospect Hill, sent orders to his third line.
"Generals Taliaferro and Early, advance and clear the front with bayonets."

Yaaaiih! Yaaaiiih! Yaaaaihh! yelled Jubal Early's men, and did as they
were bid. *Yaaaaiiih! Yaaiiihhh! Yaaaaiiihhhh!* yelled the Stonewall Brigade and the rest of Taliaferro's, and did as they were bid. Back, back
were borne Meade's brigades. Darkness of smoke, denseness of forest
growth, treachery of swampy soil!—all order was lost, and there came no
support. Back went the blue—all who could go back. A. P. Hill's second
line was upon them now; Gibbon was attacked. The grey came down the
long slopes like a torrent loosed. Walker's guns joined in. The uproar was
infernal. The blue fought well and desperately—but there was no support.
Back they went, back across the Richmond Road—all who could get back.
They left behind in the marshy coppice, and on the wooded slopes and by
the embankment, four thousand dead and wounded. The Light Division,
Taliaferro and Early, now held the railroad embankment. Before them
was the open plain, and the backward surge to the river of the broken
foe. It was three o'clock of the afternoon. Burnside sent an order to Franklin to attack again, but Franklin disobeyed.

Upon the left Longstreet's battle now swelled to giant proportions.
Marye's Hill, girdled by that stone wall, crowned by the Washington
Artillery, loomed impregnable. Against it the North tossed to destruction
division after division. They marched across the bare and sullen plain, they
charged; the hill flashed into fire, a thunder rolled, the smoke cloud deepened. When it lifted the charge was seen to be broken, retreating, the plain
was seen to be strewed with dead. The blue soldiers were staunch and
steadfast. They saw that their case was hapless, yet on they came across the
shelterless plain. Ordered to charge, they charged; charged very gallantly,

receded with a stubborn slowness. They were good fighters, worthy foes, and the grey at Fredericksburg hailed them as such. Forty thousand men charged Marye's Hill—six great assaults—and forty thousand were repulsed. The winter day closed in. Twelve thousand men in blue lay dead or wounded at the foot of the southern hills, before Longstreet on the left and Stonewall Jackson on the right.

Five thousand was the grey loss. The Rockbridge Artillery had fought near the Horse Artillery by Hamilton's Crossing. All day the guns had been doggedly at work; horses and drivers and gunners and guns and caissons; there was death and wounds and wreckage. In the wintry, late afternoon, when the battle thunders were lessening, Major John Pelham came by and looked at Rockbridge. Much of Rockbridge lay on the ground, the rest stood at the guns. "Why, boys," said Pelham, "you stand killing better than any I ever saw!"

They stood it well, both blue and grey. It was stern fighting at Fredericksburg, and grey and blue they fought it sternly and well. The afternoon closed in, cold and still, with a red sun yet veiled by drifts of crape-like smoke. The Army of the Potomac, torn, decimated, rested huddled in Fredericksburg and on the river banks. The Army of Northern Virginia rested with few or no camp-fires on the southern hills. Between the two foes stretched the freezing plain, and on the plain lay thick the Federal dead and wounded. They lay thick, thick, before the stone wall. At hand, full target for the fire of either force, was a small, white house. In the house lived Mrs. Martha Stevens. She would not leave before the battle, though warned and warned again to do so. She said she had an idea that she could help. She stayed, and wounded men dragged themselves or were dragged upon her little porch, and within her doors. General Cobb of Georgia died there; wherever a man could be laid there were stretched the ghastly wounded. Past the house shrieked the shells; bullets imbedded themselves in its walls. To and fro went Martha Stevens, doing what she could, bandaging hurts till the bandages gave out. She tore into strips what cloth there was in the little meagre house—her sheets, her towels, her tablecloths, her poor wardrobe. When all was gone she tore her calico dress. When she saw from the open door a man who could not drag himself that far, she went and helped him, with as little reck as may be conceived of shell or minie.

The sun sank, a red ball, staining the snow with red. The dark came rapidly, a very cold dark night, with myriads of stars. The smoke slowly cleared. The great, opposed forces lay on their arms, the one closely drawn by the river, the other on the southern hills. Between was the plain, and the plain was a place of drear sound—oh, of drear sound! Neither army showed any lights; for all its antagonist knew either might be feverishly, in the darkness, preparing an attack. Grey and blue, the guns yet dominated that wide and mournful level over which, to leap upon the other, either foe must pass. Grey and blue, there was little sleeping. It was too cold, and there was need for watchfulness, and the plain was too unhappy —the plain was too unhappy.

The smoke vanished slowly from the air. The night lay sublimely still, fearfully clear and cold. About ten o'clock Nature provided a spectacle. The grey troops, huddled upon the hillsides, drew a quickened breath. A Florida regiment showed alarm. "What's that? Look at that light in the sky! Great shafts of light streaming up—look! opening like a fan! What's that, chaplain, what's that?—Don't reckon the Lord's tired of fighting, and it's the Judgment Day?"

"No, no, boys! It's an aurora borealis."

"Say it over, please. Oh, northern lights! Well, we've heard of them before, but we never saw them. Having a lot of experiences here in Virginia!"—"Well, it's beautiful, any way, and I think it's terrible. I wish those northern lights would do something for the northern wounded down there. Nothing else that's northern seems likely to do it."—"Look at them—look at them! pale red, and dancing! I've heard them called 'the merry dancers.' There's a shooting star! They say that every time a star shoots some one dies."—"That's not so. If it were, the whole sky would be full of falling stars to-night. Look at that red ray going up to the zenith. O God, make the plain stop groaning!"

The display in the heavens continued, luminous rays, faintly rose-coloured, shifting from east to west, streaming upward until they were lost in the starry vault. Elsewhere the sky was dark, intensely clear, the winter stars like diamonds. There was no wind. The wide, unsheltered plain across which had stormed, across which had receded, the Federal charges, was sown thick with soldiers who had dropped from the ranks. Many and many lay still, dead and cold, their marchings and their tentings and their battles over. They had fought well; they had died; they lay here now stark and pale, but in the vast, pictured web of the whole their threads are strong and their colour holds. But on the plain of Fredericksburg many and many and many were not dead and resting. Hundreds and hundreds they lay, and could not rest for mortal anguish. They writhed and tossed, they dragged themselves a little way and fell again, they idly waved a hat or sword or empty hand for help, they cried for aid, they cried for water. Those who could not lift their voices moaned,

moaned. Some had grown delirious, and upon that plain there was even laughter. All the various notes taken together blended into one long, dreary, weird, dull, and awful sound, steady as a wind in miles of frozen reeds. They were all blue soldiers, and they lay where they fell.

GETTYSBURG
by MacKinlay Kantor

He reached Middle street and found a mass of gray marching east, and could not understand why they were going in that direction, when peremptory gun-blasts kept summoning them to Zieglers' grove. He thought of Elijah . . . take them in the flank. That was one of the phrases Hud had always loved to roll on his tongue: a flank movement.

Undeniably he was a citizen in brown trousers and saffron shirt, but a hundred rebels were no more in uniform than he. He had a vision of a shrewd Federal watchman following him with the sights of a rifle . . . not that way, not just as I come toward them. He wanted blue. He found blue in the next yard; it sent him sprawling. A sturdy body swollen by summer, lying on its back beside a cistern, with a black blister for a face. Dan got up and came back; despite all horror he knew what he must do. The dusk sifted around him; he heard the regiments tramping toward the east. *Sorry,* came between his lips.

He unfastened the trouser-band that stretched so tight across the round abdomen. The legs were stiff as boards but the shoes were gone—some rebel had taken them— and it was that much easier to draw the cloth over puffy feet.

Huddled amid the rhubarb he worked savagely, kicking his own legs into the terrible trousers. They would do; they covered the brown pantaloons, and now a Federal sentry could not believe that he was shooting a rebel, even though Dan wore no blouse. I would have spared you this if I could, he wanted to say to the dead man . . . the wraith hustled beside him as he crossed the intersection diagonally at Baltimore street and sped east through back lots. Wait, it cried, explain, explain—I expected death at one time or another, but why should I have such indignity? I was a virgin, a German, a good wrestler, twenty years old: my name was Emil, my uncle said I was a reliable boy and cried when I went into the army, and now you leave me naked in the sight of a relentless world.

When he came abreast of the silent, quick-moving column the darkness had already claimed them. He heard soft voices muttering: *them Looss-wanna boys goes fust,* and he bent behind a stable wall for fear they would see him. The wall ended at an earthy ramp which led up to the barn door. A constant, muffled chafe of accoutrements sounded as the long files switched out into a field ahead, and when Bale lifted his face above the wall he could see clay-colored blots assuming formation beyond the fence. The village had fallen behind, a black quarry of rock houses bunched against the darkening west.

No smoking, the order whispered off across the pasture. Bayonets twisted around steel barrels; the same sound was ringing ahead; there were advanced masses of troops. Them Looswanna boys goes fust. Dan thought, if I can get across the road before anyone turns back. The dead man's pants made a tremendous brushing, swaddled over his own clothes as they were. He touched the rim of the wall: stones wedged firmly together, and not a one would slide. He squeezed across and crouched, holding his breath. A group of men loomed tall beside him, holding the sunset on their shoulders.

They did not see him. *"Oui,"* said one. It sounded as if he added: *Le too onsommell.* French, Dan thought. I don't know it; whatever it means. Them Looswanna boys. The men fanned past with an eager crunching. He ran across the road and lay down; there was a post fence directly ahead lining somebody's pasture-lot, and he hitched beneath the bottom rail. The grass lay thick, bent under a blanket of dust. *Forward,* came the mutter.

Another wall, a ruined one: it chased up the slope and continued as bushes. Dan came beside the ghostly line, and pressed ahead with them. They were far to the east and south of Gettysburg, swung half around the hump of the cemetery hill and now climbing toward it from a creek valley at the Culp farm. On the height ahead there was noise: hosts and horses dwelling among the rocks. A soldier began to cough. Stop that! and the man gagged in his effort to obey.

Gorilla loomed up, beyond the sultry breadth of bushes; gorilla walking slowly, taking a few steps backward, turning and marching forward again. He hissed at Dan, "Close up! They can't dress on you!" and Bale crowded close beside the hedge. On the opposite side another man was working his way ahead; the Cougher; he still made odd chucklings. You couldn't see buttons or buckles or the detailed shape of a weapon—only a smear, only smears trying to hold their breath and proceed as quietly as possible.

In front, surprisingly near, a man yelled: "Who's there? Lutz, have you got skirmishers out in front?" A solitary musket banged, farther on the right: *soor,* said the air. Fire! A thin command. Fire—at will! All the way from the side of the valley came the stutter of guns, little scraps of orange splitting out. The rebels started, ahhhhhhhhh, and now the line was running.

The hillside marred with rags of flame. Dan ran against fence rails: he wanted to cry, wait, hold on, I'm not one of them. He tumbled between the rails and landed in a trodden lane. The world began to come apart with spiteful luminosity, ahead and at his side . . . if they'll only stop that yell until I get past the lines. He plunged across an angular bowlder and a spray of dirt stung his face. Lie down, lie down until it stops. A freakish weight of human flesh fell upon him and smashed the air from his lungs. Bale drew up his legs, he could not sob, his chest was killing him, his arms flailing out on each side. The other man had picked himself up and was rattling on.

God damn, a monster roared amid the crackling orange.

Keep to that wall. *Lieber Gott,* keep to that—hold it, men, hold—And even in the anguish of empty lungs, Dan distinguished the individual report which wrapped itself around that voice and wiped it out. The noise picked up another combatant and hurled him among the stones; he suffered momentary pneumonia and died of it. Bale wrenched his head from side to side; now he felt clean air coming into his body, cold-water air, it was drowning him happily.

He wept, Well, had I known this would happen . . . the hill went up and down, trying to shake off the mange of rifle flashes and the yipping orders . . . well away from the wall, sir. Sky opened in one doomed, terrific split. Dan's eyes went shut and he felt the sides of his head twitching —felt the little membranes of his ears thrilling and lacerated, collapsing at last beneath the oppression put upon them.

Cannot stay here, cannot stay— She insists that I tell my lie.

He struggled up, on his elbows; a body was lying across his feet. He dragged one foot out and shoved with the other, and the limp weight rolled over into a depth beyond. Agonized nations squawked continually: *Don't lettum get those guns.* Now he had his ears again; he could hear. *Don't lettum get those guns.* In all the knife-thrusts of fire, he recognized that the vitality, the heart of it, breathed in the crags directly ahead. They made a thick barricade with their screeching, a dam through which other noises tried to cut. *Don't lettum whooooo don't lettum Rickett whooooo letum . . .* They were a circus of panthers let loose, and the flattened bullets squealed off every side. The frantic nations were throwing stones, breathing and sweating and hurling them as they howled, the stones cracking as they struck the lower bowlders. A blue spray went sky-high in front of Dan Bale; he felt the angry smart of a fist in his face. Got shot, said a stolid pronouncement, and he lay flat and listened to it.

☆

☆   ☆

Voice groaned, *gimme drink* . . . the sky widened again. He whispered, amid salty constellations: "Wish they'd stop that," and the blast went ringing among the rocks. He lifted a hand; thought it was somebody else's hand; it felt far away. By God, my own hand, and I don't recognize. Shot in the face—saw the sparks go.

He put his fingers into his hair . . . so very little blood. *Gimme drink.* The pale stars looked at him.

He touched his forehead. There was no hole: all a big lump. It seemed nonsensical, now that he was gossiping about it in his own mind, to have been struck by a stone when none of the bullets could find him. He planed his hand up and down, criss-cross, back around to each ear; it sensed the splitting ache inside his skull, but it could find no hole, no spring where blood and brains welled out. I didn't expect, he thought wisely.

Ow, men repeated off into the spinning curves of distance. Ow-*wo*. Bale began to repossess his own body again. It was difficult, when he had been away so long.

This hand. He moved again. He occupied himself with testing his feet, moving each foot on its ankle-joint, wriggling his hips, taking deep breaths of the sultry air. And feeling moonlight tint his face. No coolness in the world. The insects stewed above . . . mosquito hymns, wiry and annoying. Woe, woe, woe said a thousand quaint voices, interlarding their general complaint with names and mingled phrases. Where is this? There was a cemetery before.

Then the whole understanding occurred: where he was and why he was there, and the long day yonder. He sat up with his palms against his pounding temples. His vision cleared, and he saw the nearest bowlders looking cushiony in the moon-glow, and observed the ice of fallen musket barrels. Dim lumps lay along the wide bosom of the hill. Dan shifted his leg; a stone clattered down the incline. Some wide-spread life above seemed to catch its breath—the voiceless second of silence—then several muskets boomed in a merging report, and bullets spattered the granite beside him.

He burrowed flat, and dared not stand. The Confederates had retreated, he lay between the two opposing armies, and any further movement from him might provoke a fatal shower . . . Daylight, he thought. Then they can see my blue cloth. He slid his fingers down and touched the shoddy material, and tried to close his mind to the memory of how it was obtained.

Water and God and Melanie, the wounded men prayed. Who was Melanie? That person kept asking for her. Then he talked in French, and how could anyone know what he wanted? . . . They hooted like owls, all the way over toward Sulp's hill. The National army bustled, and chopped wood up past the cemetery.

Moon went higher, hour by hour; it was plastered by a close halo at times, and at other times washed out by a veiling of clouds; still it sent reflected heat against the white hillside and encouraged the mosquitoes. Far down the valley existed spots of light, and turning wheels and nickering horses, and the same sounds drifted over the brow of the hill: part of a background constructed of many thousand men, breathing and whispering and spying at the lower ground before them.

His headache dried up, and the skin stiffened and swelled around the welt at his hair-line. I will go all the way, he resolved, if they will kill me for it. I will spite them. . . . He even slept in snatches, huddled stiff on the hard soil, and conscious of the outcries beyond and the changing shadows made by the moon. Then he awoke, cooler than he had been, and found the world gray where it was black before. Every film of vapor evaporated from the sky; Dan stretched his neck and looked toward the east, and saw the wild beauty prepared in silver and blue without a semblance of war.

He slid out from between the caging rocks. In the dawn above him swelled a bulk of elms and evergreens and torn turf, with uniformed corpses spread in impossible positions. There was a low stone wall and a movement of life behind it. Dan got up. It was torture to move; he hobbled as he pushed up the hill. Behind, early rifles began to protest—the spraying lead clicked around him. "Take care," the officer said, "he's blue . . ." and the slim Springfields were pulled back over the wall. "Let him come in, men," and Dan had climbed across the barrier, and soldiers were staring suspiciously at him. Over on the other side of Culp's hill a storehouse of Chinese crackers began to be set off. The dawn was growing yellower and yellower.

☆
☆   ☆

THE BOY with the braided shoulder-straps said, "All right. Come on." They stepped over the legs of snoring men and across a low ditch; robins were singing in the cemetery and smoke came up from a dozen little fires along the road, gypsy saucers of glowing twigs where coffee steamed in tin cans. There was the friendly smell of scorched beef-fat: you thought of a kitchen where there were white curtains and geraniums at the window. The smoke of the Culp's hill muskets had already deadened the bright torrent of dawn. Ditch and roadside were banked with men and knapsacks and rolled blankets, edge to edge, knee to knee, covering the earth with a padded human carpet.

"*Was ist ein Gefängner,* Schmidt?" asked a tired voice.

The boy turned his stubbled face toward a group of men around a coffee can. "*Nein. Citizen. Wo ist der Über-Offizer?*"

"At the fence, Lieutenant."

Again Dan's guide said, "Come on." He halted at last before a pair of booted legs stuck out of a weedy tangle alongside the cemetery fence. The air smelled . . . my dead horse, Dan thought. No. It is at home. There must be more of them . . . Lieutenant Schmidt saluted the sprawling legs. "Colonel Yotes. Lieutenant Schmidt reporting, sir."

The legs moved reluctantly and a wan, bearded face pushed up out of the weeds. "Yes, Schmidt."

"This man just entered our lines. Says he's a civilian, sir."

Slowly the colonel turned his head. He blinked at Dan. Bale told him, My name's Bale, live in Gettysburg, I had to come inside the Union lines and this was the only way I could come.

"Why did you have to come?"

"It was necessary for me to see one of your officers."

"My—officers?" The colonel's jaws creaked.

Lieutenant Schmidt said, uninterestedly: "He says he's looking for the Seventy-second Pennsylvania Volunteers, sir."

"They're not in this corps, my man."

"I don't know. It's the Second Corps."

"What ails your forehead?"

"Someone threw a stone."

Colonel Yotes looked at Dan's legs. The robins yodeled behind him; in

the southeast the dawn kept crumbling among sodden powder-charges.
"Why are you wearing those pants?" he asked.

"I thought it would make it easier," Dan answered. "Your men came
near shooting me as it was. I was on the hillside all night."

The officer lay down suddenly; there was water in his eyes, and now
Dan saw that one sleeve of his blouse was black and sticky. He said
through a narcotic weariness, "Perhaps you are a spy. Deliver him to the
provost, Schmidt."

"Yes, *sir*," snapped the lieutenant. He saluted and left-faced as crisply
as if made of stiff paper. "This way," he ordered Dan. They went
through the gate into the graveyard; ahead loomed the barrels of cannon,
smooth surprises amid the acacias. Men were polishing out the big tubes
with greasy rags. The shod hoofs of tethered horses grated against grave-
stones. "Here," Lieutenant Schmidt cracked out, suddenly. He flung a
glance over his shoulder, and the rounded slope hid his regiment and his
commander. He looked Bale squarely in the eyes for the first time since
they had left the stone wall.

"His Congressman got this regiment for him three weeks ago. Spy!
Provost!" He laughed; his face was twenty years old, his eyes were forty,
and when he spoke it was with no discernible accent. "Get to hell out of
this, and don't come back. I want some breakfast. *Raus!*" He double-
quicked back down the incline, holding his scabbard with one hand and
hurdling trimly over a dead mule in his path.

Walked here before, Dan thought. He remembered his grandfather's
face, and in his mind it would be calm and resigned forever, no matter
what happened under the soil. That resignation bought of sorrow and
other battles long before Dan was born . . . hereabouts, he thought, hereabouts.

The Bearman lot. A lame horse teetered on three legs, eating grass from
a great-uncle's grave, and Adolph's new mound was trampled. You didn't
think they'd follow you here, did you? . . . Faces went by, going about
their jibes and their tasks; faces eating crackers. There were ammunition
carts crowded beside the brick gate-house where the sexton had lived, and
Dan could smell onions frying, somewhere. The odor slit through him.
I must eat—I *must*. Keep alive until I see Fanning . . . Culp's hill
crackled like a burning woodpile, but none of these men seemed as concerned as he should have seemed.

"Where's the Second Corps?" Dan demanded of curly red whiskers.
Ich haben none speak.

"'Way over to the left and forward," someone called. Damnation, sold-

ier, you're a long ways from home. This is K Battery, First Ohio. He ain't
a soldier, muttered someone else. Another said, He must be a sutler. Sutler,
you got a wagon back there? What's the chances of—Their petitions followed him, but most of the artillerymen slept on, lumps as motionless as
the graves they lay among.

Telitha F., devoted wife of Pentland Bale. Here his family waited for
him. The tombstones got up, breaking their roots, and whirled like
dervishes. Dan walked on: the cemetery and the sprawled blue colonies,
the guns shining in smoky sunlight, interlocking shadows, hot dawn, all
flowed past him. A fluent stealth to their passing . . . where in time is
the Seventy-second Pennsylvania?

A row of stacked muskets before him. The tired young dead were aris-
ing; Culp's hill was the trumpet sounding behind them, and this became
the morning of the day of judgment with a million waking tramps past
the graveyard, far beyond the green cornfield and woods, far into the torn
wheat. Bayonet poked viciously. For Christ sake, don't walk on Captain—
He'll wake up and kick the stuffing out of you. What you say? . . This
the Ninety-fourth New York. Well, Christ sake, if you want the Second
Corps get down past the road toward those woods. That's Hays's Division.

Want the Seventy-second Pennsylvania. If I walk the whole length of
the army.

Through Zieglers' grove a few rifles were pattering, all porcelain sun-
rises forgotten. . . . They must think I'm a straggler rejoining my regiment: keep away from officers, for they will call a provost guard . . .
Naw, this is the Fourteenth Connecticut. (This man, too old to be in a
war. He is older than John Burns, but from his eyes you know that he has
seen a lot of wars.) This is the Twelfth New Jezzy. "I own property in
New Jersey," Dan said, and left the soldier staring after him, scratching
his beard.

Again the odor of onions. Faces were more numerous, now, and more
and more of them were waking faces with eyes in them. This, said a clear
voice, is the First Delaware. He looked down into the satiny eyes. "You're
a girl!" he blurted, and the eyes were suddenly wide with an admitted
terror. Afterward, he didn't know how he was so certain. Her voice—so
like a young boy's voice . . . she ran, scooting over the rocks, lugging
her drum with her. The pecking rifles were directly ahead.

Men lay flat here in the lower woods; even the officers crouched behind
whatever cover offered. Dan heard the m-sounds, the same as yesterday,
they would always be the same. This regiment was not sleeping; it lay be-

hind boards and rails and was about a very serious business. Halt, came the command, and he knew enough to obey.

"Well, get down." A big man rose up, resting on his elbow, and glared bitterly at Dan. Bale dropped to his knees. The m's above. "I know," he said, "sharp-shooters."

"What's your regiment?"

He told his story. The man still had the scowl between his eyes, but he nodded as Dan talked. "That's Webb's brigade you want. Got the California regiment in it. I know them well. Wait here." Dan lay back and closed his eyes; the perpetual shooting moved far up into the freshening sky. He heard the officer go crawling away, pebbles scraping. "I'm sick of this, Gibson!" he ranted, some distance beyond. "Take skirmishers—a company, anyhow—and clean out that barn over there. Take Company D; that ought to be enough. I'll answer for it." Tired reply: Yes-sir. Orders began to click along the woods' edge.

"That'll stop 'em, perhaps," growled the big man when he returned. Bale sat up. "What?" he asked. The officer wagged his swarthy head. "Rebs in a barn out there beyond that road—they've been raising sin with us." His scornful gaze pried close. "Here," he said, "have you breakfasted?"

Don't know . . . ate something . . . when— The major told him: "I'm finished. You're welcome to this." He offered a handful of crackers, a chunk of cold sausage and a whiskey bottle in which muddy coffee splashed like tar. "If you can handle it," he added.

"God," Bale said.

The thick coffee ate into his stomach. His jaws were sore; kept chewing and chewing; he was ravenous, but it hurt to swallow. "I know how it goes," sneered the major. He was beetle-browed, and his sneer had been designed for him when he was a child. "But you'd better join the army. If you're going to be shot at you might as well get greenbacks for it. Now you'll have to excuse me, my friend; I've got a war to fight. You'll find Webb's brigade over to the left—we extend Gibbon at the edge of these trees, and Webb's in Gibbon's Division." He peered past the oak trees ahead and over the board fence bounding them. Dan followed his gaze. A crowd of soldiers raced toward the Emmetsburg road, and a few hundred yards beyond was the Bloss's barn with rapid streaks of smoke springing from haymow and windows. "Goodbye." The officer rose. He added, gruffly, "Leave that coffee bottle there in the rocks; I need it. Don't forget. Webb's brigade of Gibbon's Division."

"It's the Second Corps," Bale said.

The officer's angry face exploded. *"This is* the Second Corps!" He went sliding away between the trees, revolver holster swinging against his leg.

Dan picked his way south. There were no more bullets sighing across from the Bliss barn, but around the barn lifted a rally of howls, the rapid spanking of shots, and everywhere men were standing up to watch the action on their front. . . . He asked again. They said the something-or-other New York. Then he came out past the trees. There were no buzzards in the sky but an odor washed up through the dry daisy field, over sweltering hay and fencevines; something dead, over by Codoris', and God knows it's no calf. The climbing sun made a gold rinse on the western ridge and the ridge was quartz—myriad little sparkles of metal over there. That's what the rebels look like to an enemy; now I am almost an enemy; they are not men who sing *oh let not my own love,* men named English, men eating bacon at a kitchen table. Now I know why the buzzards were here.

Sweat came out all over him. They *knew.* He cried it again in his mind. Even Tyler knew. . . . Heads turning; a lounging rim of rifle-stocks and soiled suspenders and brass buttons within the boundary of the board fence. What is this? Something-or-other New York. Still New York. There was the rock-oak copse; blue men were picnicking around it, the little field frothed with people watching the toy battle at Bliss's barn. All these soldiers had cloverleaves on their caps, and suddenly the color had changed.

Flint eyes questioned him. He croaked, "No, I'm not a soldier. Citizen—" What in hell? the boy said.

Those clover-leaves on your caps. A minute ago they were all blue—back through the woods. Now they are all white.

The boy grinned, a wistful grin in spite of the stony eyes. "Oh, that was the Third Division. Hays'. This is the Second. The first is different too—red. I don't know what you want here, but have you got any tobacco?"

"Yes," Dan said, and gave him the Winnebago-beaded pouch which he had brought from the West. Where is Gibbon's Division? Now the boy knew that he talked like a madman. This is it—Seventy-first Pennsylvania. . . . They lay at ease along the wall, and again they were munching crackers.

I want Webb's brigade. Yah, this is it. I want the Seventy-second Pennsylvania. And then the soldier had had all he could endure. He went toward a slight man with a dirty white havelock hanging to his shoulders, who stood gazing at the Bliss barn through his glass.

"Captain Ballou, sir—"

The man snapped, "It can wait, Private!" He went on looking through the glass for centuries. At last his hand dropped, and his eyes skewered the youth beside him, and went past him to look at Dan. The officer's goatee helped a chin which was frail and childish, but there was a kind of poison in his eyes.

"Well, Grimes?"

"He wants the Fire Zouaves, sir."

Bale said, "I've been through a lot to find them. It is most imperative that I communicate with Captain Tyler Fanning. I am a civilian and have come through the lines for that purpose."

"Who larruped you on the pate?"

"I was caught in a fight, last night."

Mm, said the officer. "You know Fanning?"

"Yes."

"How are his children?"

"He has none."

"And his father's legal practice. What of it?"

It's a shoe factory, Dan said. He felt his teeth baring; what was this? . . . The captain's shallow face relaxed. I wondered whether you knew him, that's all. I am well acquainted with Captain Fanning. But I am sorry to say that the Seventy-second has been detached from this position at the moment. They may be up presently.

I'll go. Where—

"Oh, no. You shan't stir. . . . Captain Ballou laughed tinnily. . . . I marvel that you got this far. They'd gather you up and hustle you to the rear so fast it would make your head swim. Excuse me, but you are a walking corpse—with that bruise, and all. Lie down here behind the stones out of harm's way, and wait your chance. I will aid you insofar as possible, but I ought to report you to brigade headquarters. However, you may not have to wait long. Your message would appear to be most urgent. I trust—his family—

They're well, Dan said. It—it is something.

He lay in the grass at the corner of the field. The wall went west some eighty yards, then angled to the south. The whole enclosure was full of troops, and there was gleaming field artillery ranged not far behind. Bale closed his eyes: Captain Ballou, he thought. I am becoming acquainted with many of them . . . Close at hand men were gabbling. Look at them Butternuts go out of there—looks like a rat hunt—they ought to burn that barn. Jehosaphat, they won't let us burn nothing.

And God knew what might be happening to the Niedes, on the next farm. Dan's forehead throbbed. Seventy-second Pennsylvania, and where are they?

She sat by this wall. She wasn't wearing hoops. That day I spoke of Another Field, and she knew what I meant. Tyler was asleep, and it was not a picnic; they had nothing to eat. But the buzzards sensed the strange picnic which was to come, and here it is today.

Far beyond the Taneytown road, over near Rock Creek, guns were slackening their savagery, and there was an echoing whimper of cheering. Dan could feel the sun at work, thawing stiffness from his muscles. *Lie in the grass and let the sun pound me.* Again he closed his eyes. Who's that feller over there? He was talking to old Ballou.

"He's not old," Dan thought of yelling. "Young, and his chin is weak, but that signifies nothing." Then the scorch of sun claimed him, and he slept forever, and the Seventy-second P.V. did not come, ho, to the wars.

☆

☆   ☆

THERE WAS A DEAD HUSH when he awakened. No more guns rang from the east. The sun had him: he was a cricket in the trough of the country-side, and the sun had impaled him on its broad, brass blade. He opened his eyes and saw flattened weeds and corn-sprouts and the stones of the wall; a boy said, Well, I got two jacks. Dan turned his wet head. They were playing cards on a jacket spread open a few feet away. Blue uniforms made a plump inner lining for the whole, jutting field. The sun burned out Bale's eyes, seeping in sweat, helpless as he was . . . other insects clucked in the grass near his head. He wondered how the sun had ever climbed to that imposing height.

The youth with the gray flint eyes grinned at him. "You looked to have died, mister." He was chewing something, and so were the other men.

Dan's head swam away and then came back. "Are they here, yet?"

The boy shook his head. "They're still back behind the ridge."

"I'll go," Dan told him. He thought that he was stronger than he had been in days; he was strong enough to freeze his face as he talked with Tyler. But he hated his body nevertheless—hated the worms in his brain and the sore tendons lacing him together. "I gave you that tobacco pouch," he said. "Now you've got to give me some food."

The boy tossed a roll of damp newspaper across the grass. Inside was a wad of crushed cherries and gingerbread. The soldier turned back to his card game. Fill up my floosh, somebody else demanded. The dealer said:

How's a diamond, Stemson? The ridge toward the west was still pimpled with its armies; animals crept among the trees, hauling guns. The sounds of their journeying came in a faint discussion—all echoes flat and baked by the high heat of noon, and the mile of grain baking in between.

The cherries and soaked gingerbread were vile enough; Dan ate as the starving eat. The man on his right had an open cartridge-pouch between his legs and was counting paper cartridges into it, and he kept declaring to a sergeant while he counted: No, their powder tests better than ours. Try it—that's all I got to say—try it. You know well enough ours is half dirt and too much charcoal, and them that make it are setting on their fat asses, getting rich.

Captain Ballou arrived with an officious rattle of equipment, swinging past the angle of the wall to where Dan sat. Ballou had taken off his blouse and now wore his sword-belt over a wet flannel shirt. "You'll have to come with me to headquarters," he announced. "I've been talking to Colonel Baker about it. We can't have a civilian sitting at the line with us; I have orders to evacuate you to the rear."

Bale stood up. He wiped the soggy crumbs from his hands. "I must see Fanning," he said.

There were deep pencil-lines between the young officer's pale eyes. "You should be thankful that I permitted you to lie down and sleep, sir. Now will you come along, please." The nearby men had fallen silent; they were watching.

"Wait," Bale cried. He felt for his watch. The chain hung loose, its links shorn in two.

The captain shook out the folds of his dirty havelock. "Some of our burglars attended you, I see," and the card players bent closer over their game. "Well," Ballou nodded, "General Hancock once said that he wouldn't give a damn for a man who was issued half enough food and couldn't steal the other half. They rob the dead: God help the living." He seemed rather proud of his burglars.

"I won't go to the rear unless it's to reach Fanning's company," Bale said with cold defiance. He unfastened the watch chain and slipped it into his hip pocket. It was the first time he had put his hand inside. The dead man had owned a black handkerchief and an onion and a tin box of salve. Dan threw them over the wall, and in the silence of watching men he could hear the articles pelt softly into the grass.

Ballou put his heels together. "If you are ready, sir, follow along."

Dan folded his arms.

Ballou took a deep breath. "I don't know why I was so lax in the first place. Possibly because we were all weary from our long march." He called over his shoulder: "Grimes. Lennihan. You—other fellow—" They were all leaping to attention, saluting, the cards fluttered away and there was a heap of copper and paper currency on the jacket. "If this civilian will not accompany me of his own will, you are to fetch him." His heel dug into the sod as he swung on it.

A sharp sound rapped across from the tip of Oak Ridge, and everyone turned to look. There was new smoke among the trees and a dull, mechanical whirring screeched toward them. "Whitworth!" exclaimed the captain. North, a few rods away, came a grating crash and a column of dirt and stubble flew high. Somebody cried, what the hell's that for? All the men were standing up and looking. Just imagine—them Whitworths load at the breech.

Well, began Ballou. The western ridge divided itself into booming segments of eruption. The landscape looked funny . . . there was something. Now Dan understood: the Bliss barn was gone—a smoking rubble lay where it had been. Burned it, he whispered to himself, and I slept through it all. Nest of wool flew apart, alongside the little grove of oaks. "Ballou," yelled a commanding spirit, "take charge of your company!" and a horse fled past as men tumbled out of its way. The fold of earth south of the seminary was become a round crest of organic smoke, and the hammers came down all around. By God, yelped the Counter of Cartridges, so that's what they were kiting around for. The soldiers of this regiment began to clatter their ramrods; they had loaded their guns, they were all worming close to the wall, and hugging the board fence which leaned away to the right.

Ballou had gone ducking toward the front of the angle, gesticulating at heads which bobbed up on each side of the wall. Another spout of earth, back by the Taneytown road, another, another, and Dan Bale sensed the horse-cry which had started its life on Wednesday morning and would exist on these farms until the end of time. Hammers stung against his skull.

The world beyond the valley farms was ballasted with smoke, shot through with colorless jabs of light, evasive pinks and reds which faded on the instant of their inception. The trees of the little copse began to pull apart, their leaves ripped loose and spattering wide. *Get down,* somebody yelled in Bale's ear, *for the lova* . . . He dropped to his knees, and the earth jiggled with that ugliness of underground avalanches.

Why don't we open up? they were all hooting. Get busy, Mister Hunt! came a bawdy cheer. Did he say *Hunt?* . . they laughed, the west was a long bulge of lightning and tropical spume. Must have a hundred guns over there. Two hundred going at once, they estimated. Heavier than Fredericksburg if they keep this up.

Through the mutilation a stampede came from the rear: people scuttled to shelter, gun after gun lurched in from the Taneytown road, lining beside the cannon which had been squatting in that upper field since daylight The gunners tore the harness apart, bounding like fleas, pushing the thick pieces into position, hauling and leaning against the wheels. They straddled the slanting trails, screwing away at tiny wheels beneath each breech. All Dan could think was: how'll I get back? Seventy-second. I can't run toward those guns if they're shooting. He got to his feet and the air was bumped close beside him. A bushel of stones flew from the wall. One of the card-players stood up and screamed. He beat his chest with open hands, shaking his head and rolling his eyes until the whites puffed out and glistened. Hands pulled him down, but he fought with them. The bent pastures seemed wearing away beneath this incessant crash of bursting iron.

Between two swinging mauls of sound a distant voice called flatly: Load . . . watch your fuses and . . . The cannoneers were perked by wires; you heard the rammerheads driving in. A short-legged man was standing on the nearest caisson—above him a splinter of white bit into the sky. He bent down and scratched his knee, then straightened again . . . faintly through the devouring noise: Number One, Fire. The concussion leveled the infantrymen by the wall; fingers of flame singed at them. Number Two, Fire. Dan heard somebody laughing—he was in the grass, and Captain Ballou was crawling across his chest, knees and sword and all . . . *more than* . . . *bargained for*. Ballou looked down at him with eyes as bright as a squirrel's. He crawled on around the corner with his sword dragging behind. Number One, Fire. The Milky Way came down and flung itself up again.

Bale's ears made a wet sound within his head. He grew against the old stones of the wall foundation, became a legal part of them. Where's Tyler Fanning, he thought. Fire Zouaves . . . the wars. Number Two, Fire. A man screeched. "Son of a bitch if they're not concentrating on us!" Yah, we're focal. Captain Ballou came along the line again; his mouth was wrinkling above his cornsilk goatee. I should say we'll get it presently. Voice said, a whisper born in the ruction: *Thy Kingdom come, Thy will be done, on earth as it is in*— There goes Perkins, praying again. You let him be, Scut—if he dies 'twon't be with no oaths on his— Ballou screamed back at Dan: "You can't go to the rear now. They're shortening on our guns—stay where you are until this stops!" Torpedoes blew with every stroke of the mallets: you couldn't see the world over by Bliss's and Pitzers' any more. Horses squirmed, dotted all the way back to the road, heads arching and squealing, high out of the dust they were stirring around themselves. Number Three, Fire . . . how long, Dan thought. Twenty minutes. He didn't know. The flint-eyed neighbor spat out a stream of blood and tobacco juice. He had been chewing the linings of his cheeks, and the diluted saliva trickled over his hard little lip. Wish I was out in front, he said. Skirmishers. They're not getting much of this.

Ready. Between the shivering anvils. *By piece. At will. Fire.* Nearer reports merged together, separated again; there was no longer any Number One or Number Two or number anything. Some round object was squeezed into Bale's hand; he looked; it was his watch. The boy grinned eerily at him. Then he squirmed nearer, to howl, "I thought I'd like to have that! But I think I'm going to glory this time. I had a feeling. Can't take no watch along with me." He choked in the smoke, and hitched away. Bale looked at the watch, then it seemed that the roof of his head had flown apart, and a mist of blood was in his eyes. The men were all gagging, blinded by that sound, that splintering crash which blew a hole fairly through the sky.

He managed to turn his head. Red still wiggled across the salty landscape, but when the smoke thinned he could see that the caisson where the officer had stood was gone—forever vanished, and there existed only a tangled sprawl of cloth and earth and dripping spokes, with one cannon barrel up-ended at the side. Chariot of fire . . . forty-five minutes. An hour. An hour of days, with the fields blowing up like crops of geysers, and the whole insane asylum of horses telling their Creator what he had done to them.

All the way across, Dan thought, all the way across Pennsylvania. A thousand miles, from the Round Top Hills to the cemetery. The dead will get up out of the grave-yard and work the guns when the cannoneers are killed: stiff and ghastly in their grave-clothes, they will push the black rammers and pull them out again. He looked toward the higher ground in the north and east—the Ever Green, the Baby Rest Darling place. There was nothing but one rain-cloud of smoke and crawling flame.

ALL PERSONS FOUND USING FIREARMS IN THESE GROUNDS
WILL BE PROSECUTED WITH THE UTMOST VIGOR OF THE LAW.

He screeched with laughter, but he couldn't hear his own laugh. A new sound came from the south, past the mound of saplings: the blue huddlers were lifting their heads, craning their necks; they held their guns ready in efficient hands. A lot of horsemen were coming through the smoke, and a sound trotted alongside them. It's him? What in the devil. Yah, it's him. What's he want?

A large man rode through the mist on a big-boned horse. He was a man with a hard face modeled in an iron grin. The men began to stand up; dimly under the roar you could hear the clank of their rifles as they waved them aloft. A boy's voice shrilled: *Prrresent . . . hahm!* The general had his hat in his hand, flapping it limply; his blouse was buttoned at the throat but hung gaping on each side of his round blue belly; the howl came through the copse and around the walled angle of the little field. *Han-cock,* they were all yelling. Three cheers for *Han-cock . . .* the guns blotted them, they poured in stronger again, a wrenching exultation which mingled with the thunder all around: rrrah . . . rrrah . . . rrrah. We'll show 'em, Winfield, came a screech. He rode past the corner, his staff fighting their rearing horses, and looking very pale. A pin-wheel crackled above the wall and men staggered back. Hancock kept the metal grin on his jaws, his mustaches sticking out above it. Hold fast, gentlemen. Give them what Paddy gave the drum. They'll be coming across, he bellowed, and make them like it when they get here *. . . Han-cock! Han-cock! Han-cock! . . .* the vapor whirled behind him.

Nobody knew how long. An hour. Two hours. Maybe a day. There wasn't any time in creation. The smoke was thinning gradually and guns were falling silent all along this highland, and you could hear parched throats squawking: Shake ass, cut that harness, get that three-incher outa there. Mist weighted the mild slopes, falling thickly into the valley, and the infantry wasn't crouching down behind the barricade any more. They were spreading rows of cartridges on the rocks in front of them and as the firing slackened you could hear the squeak of leather; they dug eagerly into their cartridge boxes.

A lone man was racking the whole county with his scream, back where the battery of rifled guns had stood: a man who lay amid the broken wheels and smoking harness, and he had been there all the time but you couldn't hear him until the guns stopped. One of Henry Niede's straw-stacks was burning, near the barn, its tiny sparks squirting up in a thick purge of flame. . . . The scream in the rear continued; it stopped; the last haze fell away, and a man in citizen's clothes was there in the wreckage.

Dan croaked, "Doctor Duffey," but nobody looked at him. This seemed a most grotesque fabrication, it was a more violent lie than any he would tell to Tyler. The fat man grew there, on his knees in the hot mess of the exploded caisson. The final crush of Confederate artillery had lightened, and troubled waters gushed in everyone's ears. It was impossible to realize that such thunder might ever have an end.

Bale made his way slowly up the pasture, stepping over the men who lay there. Duffey was a cartoon of the Duffey whom Bale had known once. He possessed fish eyes and a seamed, baggy face; he had been floundering in blood; the cups of his hands were brown and sticky. "I was back by the stables, back at General Meade's house," he roared. "This man has been shot to bits. I thought I would be doing something for him, but he was shot to bits. It's a marvel he could yell about it, being shot to bits." Only two rebel guns still fired—distinct reports—you could tell them. A sulphur bolster swelled up a mile and a half wide, God knew how long or how thick. The silver sun tried to get through it.

Dan cried again, Doc! . . . Well? . . . Duffey seemed to say: I know you, you were once my friend, once I was a man and had friends, we are both here, what does it matter? His enormous voice blurbed: "Cut off. I was cut off, that day, with old Salt and the carryall. I've been here— since—"

Dan said, *I came* . . . seized Duffey's arm and hurled himself backward, and together they fell out from under a scurry of horse-legs. Here were more guns, different guns, they came down across the field over the dead and the living, cracking outstretched legs with their bounding wheels. Order, wiry and high, a hawk-voice from the heat overhead: Will you get your Napoleons in line at once, Lieutenant Cushing? Yes, sirrrrr . . . all the rebel cannon had stopped, and the smoke was spreading wider; the sun burned it away with fast-recovering strength. The orders talked like neighborhood gossip along the twice-bent wall. Across the valley, the flat extension of Oak Ridge seemed to grow and wiggle. Codoris' house and barns were out in front, still, the Niede place was there and the Emmetsburg road, but something queer was happening beyond.

Bale said, Look. Everybody said the same thing. Look at. There's a plentiful number of them . . . a generous wedge of dirt color, dotted with spikes of pale red, crawling steadily out of the trees more than a mile away. Duffey went down on one knee, then rose again: he staggered and put his hand on Dan's shoulder. He mumbled thickly: What—doing here —Daniel— Bale cried, "I had to see—" and the activity of the batteries covered his words. The cannoneers were drenched in lamp-black, faces, hands, bare chests, ragged pants. Lieutenant told them, coolly enough: Load. Cannister. Double.

Duffey's head seemed to come loose on his thick neck. He bowed, shaking it, and pushing his sticky hands up over the mat of gray hair. "I've men back there by the barns," he said, "men to see after. Will you be with me?"

"I can't," Bale told him. "Got to wait here for Seventy-second Pennsylvania, don't know where they are, they must be coming down here soon." Be sure and let the skirmishers under your range before you fire, a lot of aggrieved people were saying. The men began to squat down, all along the stone wall. Doctor Duffey went back toward the crest of the ridge, going rather blindly. He stooped above one man, got up and went on.

The western face of the flat valley was shifting, a brown sand that turned itself over and over, and now the pale red spikes became flags. Plentiful number. Bet a paper dollar they don't get to this wall. Take you, Charlie; sure as hell they will. Dan looked into the face of Captain Ballou. "Oh, great God in heaven," the captain howled, "now I know you're crazy! Get to the rear, man, while you've a chance!"

Mounted officers poked up out of the advancing mass, lone and remote. There was a faint scattering of fire down along the Emmetsburg road— from Codoris' and Niedes' yards. Bale thought. That can't be Uncle Otto shooting at them; probably the whole family's run away. They should have . . . little blue morsels behind every rock and fence corner, and toy puffs of smoke marking them. The dirt color fell wider, wider, spreading, spreading, you could see lines: three immense billows of dust and steel-shine, filling the dish of the valley from Sherfys' all the way up past the Bliss place.

They'll get it on the left. Naw, it's coming this way. The devil you say —it's coming all along. Must be their whole army. Suddenly a man wheeled away from the wall and started toward the rear, his gun hung loosely from his hand. He kept looking over his shoulder. "Come on back," several voices yelled. Captain Ballou sprinted after the man. He cried. "What do you mean?" The soldier began to sob . . . only a youngster, someone grunted. . . . He crouched, whirled, and raced back to the wall once more. Over by the copse they were crying, Get some rails on top of that wall. Pile it up, Appleton, pile it up . . . brown swarm had legs; it was all men as it flowed toward the road, but you would never have known it before.

Blue morsels oozed in retreat, firing back as they came up the field from the highway. The last dirty wave was well out of the groves across the valley. Anxious cannon started in to the right and left: *Gom—g-g-gom*, and bursts of white and gold appeared in the middle of the swarm. They came on, seriously and steadily. A tiny, mounted figure fell from its horse, the horse stood motionless, the sea came past, vermillion flags and all. They began to make a sound. That Noise, Bale said. His finger-nails bent against the stones where he stood, watching. It was a wind, a gusty sighing that gained volume and shrillness as it trampled ahead. The colored flags, blue and rosy alike, bowed and nodded. The dust of exploding shells was thicker across them. *Whoooooooo.*

The rifled guns by the cemetery were clanging, and all the way along the upper ridge, when you turned you could see the stubby fingers of metal bounding between their wheels, and sizzling vapor got in the way. Well, Bale said, I'm damned if I stay here and be killed. Seventy-second. I don't hate these brown men, they ate in my kitchen, they slept in my house— I don't give a good God damn what Elijah said about them. . . . He swung around and started toward the Taneytown road, his head bent beneath the explosions and the howl running up the fields behind him. He reached the first fence. A voice he'd never heard before cried, "You cowardly bastard!" and something struck him across the shoulders.

He whirled, doubling his fists. A boy with a set, greenish face confronted him. "I'm not a soldier!" Dan cried. The youth shook his head; he couldn't hear, now that the guns were going without a pause; he dropped his sword and ripped out his revolver in one quick motion. He motioned Dan toward the wall at the front of the field beside the copse.

Well, Bale thought, be killed one way or another. The boy officer found a gun in the weeds, and picked it up and put it in Dan's hands. It was set at full cock—a Vincennes musket—Lucas Mite had one, during the Indian uprising. . . . The boy came behind, revolver shaking in his hand. The brown mass was at the Emmetsburg road, split by the Codoris buildings, and fence rails rolled or waved high as they came over. Dan reached the wall. There's twice that many on the right, a man said. Lookit. Behind them echoed a livid blat: *Ready. By Piece. At Will. Fire.* The family of brass guns flamed.

The Confederates began to lie down on the ground. They lay down rapidly, sideways, forward, blotted flat in tumbled crops . . . *whoooooo* . . . wrench of sparks, along the whole front of them, and splinters flew from rails atop the stone wall, and the man who had said Lookit stood up and lay down across the rails with his hands dangling. Lettergo at will, boys. The wall uttered a sundering cough.

God, they're dressing. Lookit that—dressing—crazy as—Anyway, that's prettiest movement ever saw executed under fire. The ramrods clattered. Gray nations straightened out and swung to the right, arching in toward the slope. The nest of guns gave out their bile, spurt by spurt. Bale said aloud, Something dead, over by Codoris'—must be a calf. Persons found using firearms will be prosecuted utmost vigor. The yell went tussling along the dusty tribes; rapidly they began to have faces. Most of them were lugging their rifles at their sides and working the rods with their right hands as they came. Crust of smoke sped out to meet them.

They kept roaring, every throat wide open with sound. The Nationals were standing up, man by man, standing up and falling down and standing up and falling down. Pink flag dodged forward; the smoke shredded and let it through, and a struggling clay torrent screeched behind. The front runners kept flinging out their hands and sprawling forward, and others tumbled over them to do the same thing. The flag bobbed closer, supported by a tight-locked mass of bare arms. Squarely in front of the rolling haze, a row of men came out and knelt; their muskets flamed, but you couldn't hear the sound any more. There lived a single ocean of pulsation and wail, a bursting rattle which knit all solitary explosions together. A man in a green jacket ran forward and put both hands on the wall beside Dan—he didn't have a gun or anything. A rifle-butt swung, and the green jacket was spattered.

Gray bodies: they smelled of sweat and chemicals; the red flags wavered, bunched together, there were a dozen of them in front of the trees. That ain't milishy, looky them clovahs, came a discordant howl. Dan felt people pressing him back, staggering over rocks and outflung arms and legs, and always that rim of wolf-faces pushing him. A black-nailed hand tore the sleeve from his shirt. He still had the gun—he didn't know what to do except go back with the others. Through the mist before the wall, a block of blue soldiers tumbled out at the left of the copse, striking toward the side of the shrieking swarm. Ahead of them ran a young man with a contorted face; he swung a hatchet over his head. The guns in the rear had ceased firing. The nearer world was too unsupported, though ghosts of detonations still made the ground heave, it would be jelly forever. Bale felt a metal-tired wheel strike his back, and he slid around it. Back this far, he thought. Face poked up beside him and said, Get outa the way. *Nuther shot.* Claw hauling at a string. A stem of flame crushed the wolf-heads, crushed everyone's eyes and ears as the cannon went off. Dan slipped, his feet were tangled in something slimy. Felt like ropes: good God, they weren't ropes.

Here's Fire Zouaves. New yell rose up in the rear. They yelled, *Raaaa* as they came swarming past. Dan saw a man with wooden face and narrow eyes; he was coughing as he ran. Dan yelled, "Ty—for——*Ty.*" The reserves smashed past the single, silent gun; Tyler swung around, he was announcing something, his face looked like no face he had ever worn before. "Be killed," Bale said in his brain. He couldn't hear anything Ty was saying, and Ty couldn't hear him. Thinks she's damned if he dies before I talk to him. More important than that—

He swung up the muzzle of the gun in his hand and knocked two snarling wrestlers aside. *Ty,* he screamed. There was a bald man in a gray jacket—he was middle-aged, he held a sword high above his head and he was crying aloud. Again Fanning turned to halloo at the blue froth beside him—he had lost his hat, and his hair was all tousled and childish. Sword glitter . . . bald head, you cannot do that . . . Dan pulled the trigger. The middle-aged man stumbled. His hand grabbed at the big barrel of the brass cannon, it was steaming, he coughed and said something about cold steel, and went down under a stampede. Dan dropped the musket.

Once he saw the tops of little oak trees trembling as the bodies pushed against them. There was a remarkable and increasing patter of shots on the right and the left; pink flag came down, and its staff glanced off the cannon barrel. Lonely outcry, *Ah Surrendah* . . . the stubborn clay washed back and disappeared, the musket rattle lessened, increased, and lessened again. Go to the rear, people were calling. Oh-my-God-oh-my-God-oh-God-kill-me-oh-God-quit-it-oh-God-stop-it-oh . . . *go to the rear.* Lay down them guns, Johnny. The crush thinned and distorted itself; men were sliding down on their hands and knees. A red and black image fell against Dan Bale, the arms convulsed around him and then turned to dough and collapsed.

You could see a soapy gray remnant sliding back toward Codoris', guns still popping, but most of the mass had lain down or gone staggering to the rear. Ty, Bale said. Where in damnation. He can't be dead. He started to look around. Guns near at hand had all stopped their crackling. He yelled, "Fanning! Fanning!" and there came some kind of a responsive drooling. He climbed across the retching, gargling pile. Tyler leaned back, his face chalky, his shoulders against the cannon wheel. Here, he whined. He saw Dan and blinked at him. The devil, he said at last, and then lifted his wet hands and made a foolish gesture—he had been caressing his thigh and it was all soaked and purple.

Dan got down beside him. Was going to tell him something, he thought: what? I had to see you . . the distant, stubborn volleys fought to take his words away from him. Tyler rolled his eyes this way and that . . . what-you-doing-in-the-army, ahhh, he said.

I came through the lines to see you. I was here—

The pale eyes went around again. Had to tell you, Dan railed at him—

it's not true. You see, it's not true. That letter. . . . Tyler said, *Bluhhh,* and his lips went away from his teeth . . . that letter, Ty, it's not true, not a word of it, it was all a fabrication, I was here and killed somebody—he was middle-aged—I shot a man, just to tell you—I tell you, I shot him— you God damn dirty son of a bitch, do you hear, do you hear, do you hear?

Fanning slid lower and began to vomit; his lips were fish-gills. He mourned, Tell me what's not true . . . *Bluhhh.*

Your wife. Fanning opened his eyes, and closed them, and opened, and closed. Aw, he sighed with the yellow dripping from his chin. Aw, that.

Do you believe me? I killed a man just to—

What? Yes. Of course, I— Leg . . . aw . . . aw, my Christ.

There were some officers bending over a man just ahead. National officers—one of them was spitting blood but he seemed strong enough; the other man was naked to the waist, but you could tell he was an officer. They lifted a limp, baldheaded figure in shabby gray, and their eyes met as they raised him up. Yes, one declared, we must take him back to the stretcher-bearers. Did you hear? Yes, said the other, I heard. *He has called for help as the son of a widow.*

The hospitals were back in the valley of Rock Creek. Darkness came on, stinking and thick. Dan found a surgeon kneeling in the middle of a moaning waste of straw and wet rags.

"Who?" the surgeon asked. "He was mainly bald, and had stars on his jacket collar? Ah, yes." He nodded sadly. "You refer to General Armistead of Virginia. He was mortally wounded."

KENESAW MOUNTAIN

by AMBROSE BIERCE

JEROME SEARING, a private soldier of General Sherman's army, then confronting the enemy at and about Kenesaw Mountain, Georgia, turned his back upon a small group of officers with whom he had been talking in low tones, stepped across a light line of earthworks, and disappeared in a forest. None of the men in line behind the works had said a word to him, nor had he so much as nodded to them in passing, but all who saw

From: *In the Midst of Life.* Copyright 1909. Albert & Charles Boni, Inc.

understood that this brave man had been intrusted with some perilous duty. Jerome Searing, though a private, did not serve in the ranks; he was detailed for service at division headquarters, being borne upon the rolls as an orderly. "Orderly" is a word covering a multitude of duties. An orderly may be a messenger, a clerk, an officer's servant—anything. He may perform services for which no provision is made in orders and army regulations. Their nature may depend upon his aptitude, upon favor, upon accident. Private Searing, an incomparable marksman, young, hardy, intelligent and insensible to fear, was a scout. The general commanding his division was not content to obey orders blindly without knowing what was in his front, even when his command was not on detached service, but formed a fraction of the line of the army; nor was he satisfied to receive his knowledge of his *vis-à-vis* through the customary channels; he wanted to know more than he was apprised of by the corps commander and the collisions of pickets and skirmishers. Hence Jerome Searing, with his extraordinary daring, his woodcraft, his sharp eyes, and truthful tongue. On this occasion his instructions were simple: to get as near the enemy's lines as possible and learn all that he could.

In a few moments he had arrived at the picket-line, the men on duty there lying in groups of two and four behind litle banks of earth scooped out of the slight depression in which they lay, their rifles protruding from the green boughs with which they had masked their small defenses. The forest extended without a break toward the front, so solemn and silent that only by an effort of the imagination could it be conceived as populous with armed men, alert and vigilant—a forest formidable with possibilities of battle. Pausing a moment in one of these rifle-pits to apprise the men of his intention Searing crept stealthily forward on his hands and knees and was soon lost to view in a dense thicket of underbrush.

"That is the last of him," said one of the men; "I wish I had his rifle; those fellows will hurt some of us with it."

Searing crept on, taking advantage of every accident of ground and growth to give himself better cover. His eyes penetrated everywhere, his ears took note of every sound. He stilled his breathing, and at the cracking of a twig beneath his knee stopped his progress and hugged the earth. It was slow work, but not tedious; the danger made it exciting, but by no physical signs was the excitement manifest. His pulse was as regular, his nerves were as steady as if he were trying to trap a sparrow.

"It seems a long time," he thought, "but I cannot have come very far; I am still alive."

He smiled at his own method of estimating distance, and crept forward. A moment later he suddenly flattened himself upon the earth and lay motionless, minute after minute. Through a narrow opening in the bushes he had caught sight of a small mound of yellow clay—one of the enemy's rifle-pits. After some little time he cautiously raised his head, inch by inch, then his body upon his hands, spread out on each side of him, all the while intently regarding the hillock of clay. In another moment he was upon his feet, rifle in hand, striding rapidly forward with little attempt at concealment. He had rightly interpreted the signs, whatever they were; the enemy was gone.

To assure himself beyond a doubt before going back to report upon so important a matter, Searing pushed forward across the line of abandoned pits, running from cover to cover in the more open forest, his eyes vigilant to discover possible stragglers. He came to the edge of a plantation—one of those forlorn, deserted homesteads of the last years of the war, upgrown with brambles, ugly with broken fences and desolate with vacant buildings having blank apertures in place of doors and windows. After a keen reconnaissance from the safe seclusion of a clump of young pines Searing ran lightly across a field and through an orchard to a small structure which stood apart from the other farm buildings, on a slight elevation. This he thought would enable him to overlook a large scope of country in the direction that he supposed the enemy to have taken in withdrawing. This building, which had originally consisted of a single room elevated upon four posts about ten feet high, was now little more than a roof; the floor had fallen away, the joists and planks loosely piled on the ground below or resting on end at various angles, not wholly torn from their fastenings above. The supporting posts were themselves no longer vertical. It looked as if the whole edifice would go down at the touch of a finger.

Concealing himself in the débris of joists and flooring Searing looked across the open ground between his point of view and a spur of Kenesaw Mountain, a half-mile away. A road leading up and across this spur was crowded with troops—the rear-guard of the retiring enemy, their gun-barrels gleaming in the morning sunlight.

Searing had now learned all that he could hope to know. It was his duty to return to his own command with all possible speed and report his discovery. But the gray column of Confederates toiling up the mountain road was singularly tempting. His rifle—an ordinary "Springfield," but fitted with a globe sight and hair-trigger—would easily send its ounce and a quarter of lead hissing into their midst. That would probably not affect the duration and result of the war, but it is the business

of a soldier to kill. It is also his habit if he is a good soldier. Searing
cocked his rifle and "set" the trigger.

But it was decreed from the beginning of time that Private Searing
was not to murder anybody that bright summer morning, nor was the
Confederate retreat to be announced by him. For countless ages events
had been so matching themselves together in that wondrous mosaic to
some parts of which, dimly discernible, we give the name of history, that
the acts which he had in will would have marred the harmony of the
pattern. Some twenty-five years previously the Power charged with the
execution of the work according to the design had provided against that
mischance by causing the birth of a certain male child in a little village
at the foot of the Carpathian Mountains, had carefully reared it, supervised its education, directed its desires into a military channel, and in due
time made it an officer of artillery. By the concurrence of an infinite number of favoring influences and their preponderance over an infinite number of opposing ones, this officer of artillery had been made to commit
a breach of discipline and flee from his native country to avoid punishment. He had been directed to New Orleans (instead of New York),
where a recruiting officer awaited him on the wharf. He was enlisted and
promoted, and things were so ordered that he now commanded a Confederate battery some two miles along the line from where Jerome Searing, the Federal scout, stood cocking his rifle. Nothing had been
neglected—at every step in the progress of both these men's lives, and
in the lives of their contemporaries and ancestors, and in the lives of the
contemporaries of their ancestors, the right thing had been done to bring
about the desired result. Had anything in all this vast concatenation been
overlooked Private Searing might have fired on the retreating Confederates that morning, and would perhaps have missed. As it fell out, a
Confederate captain of artillery, having nothing better to do while awaiting his turn to pull out and be off, amused himself by sighting a field-
piece obliquely to his right at what he mistook for some Federal officers
on the crest of a hill, and discharged it. The shot flew high of its mark.

As Jerome Searing drew back the hammer of his rifle and with his
eyes upon the distant Confederates considered where he could plant his
shot with the best hope of making a widow or an orphan or a childless
mother,—perhaps all three, for Private Searing, although he had repeat-
edly refused promotion, was not without a certain kind of ambition,—
he heard a rushing sound in the air, like that made by the wings of a
great bird swooping down upon its prey. More quickly than he could
apprehend the gradation, it increased to a hoarse and horrible roar, as

the missile that made it sprang at him out of the sky, striking with a deafening impact one of the posts supporting the confusion of timbers above him, smashing it into matchwood, and bringing down the crazy edifice with a loud clatter, in clouds of blinding dust!

When Jerome Searing recovered consciousness he did not at once understand what had occurred. It was, indeed, some time before he opened his eyes. For a while he believed that he had died and been buried, and he tried to recall some portions of the burial service. He thought that his wife was kneeling upon his grave, adding her weight to that of the earth upon his breast. The two of them, widow and earth, had crushed his coffin. Unless the children should persuade her to go home he would not much longer be able to breathe. He felt a sense of wrong. "I cannot speak to her," he thought; "the dead have no voice; and if I open my eyes I shall get them full of earth."

He opened his eyes. A great expanse of blue sky, rising from a fringe of the tops of trees. In the foreground, shutting out some of the trees, a high, dun mound, angular in outline and crossed by an intricate, patternless system of straight lines; the whole an immeasurable distance away—a distance so inconceivably great that it fatigued him, and he closed his eyes. The moment that he did so he was conscious of an insufferable light. A sound was in his ears like the low, rhythmic thunder of a distant sea breaking in successive waves upon the beach, and out of this noise, seeming a part of it, or possibly coming from beyond it, and intermingled with its ceaseless undertone, came the articulate words: "Jerome Searing, you are caught like a rat in a trap—in a trap, trap, trap."

Suddenly there fell a great silence, a black darkness, an infinite tranquillity, and Jerome Searing, perfectly conscious of his rathood, and well assured of the trap that he was in, remembering all and nowise alarmed, again opened his eyes to reconnoitre, to note the strength of his enemy, to plan his defense.

He was caught in a reclining posture, his back firmly supported by a solid beam. Another lay across his breast, but he had been able to shrink a little away from it so that it no longer oppressed him, though it was immovable. A brace joining it at an angle had wedged him against a pile of boards on his left, fastening the arm on that side. His legs, slightly parted and straight along the ground, were covered upward to the knees with a mass of débris which towered above his narrow horizon. His head was as rigidly fixed as in a vise; he could move his eyes, his chin—no more. Only his right arm was partly free. "You must help us out of this," he said to it. But he could not get it from under the heavy timber athwart his chest, nor move it outward more than six inches at the elbow.

Searing was not seriously injured, nor did he suffer pain. A smart rap on the head from a flying fragment of the splintered post, incurred simultaneously with the frightfully sudden shock to the nervous system, had momentarily dazed him. His term of unconsciousness, including the period of recovery, during which he had had the strange fancies, had probably not exceeded a few seconds, for the dust of the wreck had not wholly cleared away as he began an intelligent survey of the situation.

With his partly free right hand he now tried to get hold of the beam that lay across, but not quite against, his breast. In no way could he do so. He was unable to depress the shoulder so as to push the elbow beyond that edge of the timber which was nearest his knees; failing in that, he could not raise the forearm and hand to grasp the beam. The brace that made an angle with it downward and backward prevented him from doing anything in that direction, and between it and his body the space was not half so wide as the length of his forearm. Obviously he could not get his hand under the beam nor over it; the hand could not, in fact, touch it at all. Having demonstrated his inability, he desisted, and began to think whether he could reach any of the débris piled upon his legs.

In surveying the mass with a view to determining that point, his attention was arrested by what seemed to be a ring of shining metal immediately in front of his eyes. It appeared to him at first to surround some perfectly black substance, and it was somewhat more than a half-inch in diameter. It suddenly occurred to his mind that the blackness was simply shadow and that the ring was in fact the muzzle of his rifle protruding from the pile of débris. He was not long in satisfying himself that this was so—if it was a satisfaction. By closing either eye he could look a little way along the barrel—to the point where it was hidden by the rubbish that held it. He could see the one side, with the corresponding eye, at apparently the same angle as the other side with the other eye. Looking with the right eye, the weapon seemed to be directed at a point to the left of his head, and *vice versa*. He was unable to see the upper surface of the barrel, but could see the under surface of the stock at a slight angle. The piece was, in fact, aimed at the exact centre of his forehead.

In the perception of this circumstance, in the recollection that just previously to the mischance of which this uncomfortable situation was the result he had cocked the rifle and set the trigger so that a touch would discharge it, Private Searing was affected with a feeling of uneasiness. But that was as far as possible from fear; he was a brave man, somewhat familiar with the aspect of rifles from that point of view, and of cannon too. And now he recalled, with something like amusement, an incident of his experience at the storming of Missionary Ridge, where, walking up to one of the enemy's embrasures from which he had seen a heavy gun throw charge after charge of grape among the assailants he had thought for a moment that the piece had been withdrawn; he could see nothing in the opening but a brazen circle. What that was he had understood just in time to step aside as it pitched another peck of iron down that swarming slope. To face firearms is one of the commonest incidents in a soldier's life—firearms, too, with malevolent eyes blazing behind them. That is what a soldier is for. Still, Private Searing did not altogether relish the situation, and turned away his eyes.

After groping, aimless, with his right hand for a time he made an ineffectual attempt to release his left. Then he tried to disengage his head, the fixity of which was the more annoying from his ignorance of what held it. Next he tried to free his feet, but while exerting the powerful muscles of his legs for that purpose it occurred to him that a disturbance of the rubbish which held them might discharge the rifle; how it could have endured what had already befallen it he could not understand, although memory assisted him with several instances in point. One in particular he recalled, in which in a moment of mental abstraction he had clubbed his rifle and beaten out another gentleman's brains, observing afterward that the weapon which he had been diligently swinging by the muzzle was loaded, capped, and at full cock—knowledge of which circumstance would doubtless have cheered his antagonist to longer endurance. He had always smiled in recalling that blunder of his "green and salad days" as a soldier, but now he did not smile. He turned his eyes again to the muzzle of the rifle and for a moment fancied that it had moved; it seemed somewhat nearer.

Again he looked away. The tops of the distant trees beyond the bounds of the plantation interested him: he had not before observed how light and feathery they were, nor how darkly blue the sky was, even among their branches, where they somewhat paled it with their green; above him it appeared almost black. "It will be uncomfortably hot here," he thought, "as the day advances. I wonder which way I am looking."

Judging by such shadows as he could see, he decided that his face was due north; he would at least not have the sun in his eyes, and north—well, that was toward his wife and children.

"Bah!" he exclaimed aloud, "what have they to do with it?"

He closed his eyes. "As I can't get out I may as well go to sleep. The

rebels are gone and some of our fellows are sure to stray out here foraging. They'll find me."

But he did not sleep. Gradually he became sensible of a pain in his
forehead—a dull ache, hardly perceptible at first, but growing more and
more uncomfortable. He opened his eyes and it was gone—closed them
and it returned. "The devil!" he said, irrelevantly, and stared again at
the sky. He heard the singing of birds, the strange metallic note of the
meadow lark, suggesting the clash of vibrant blades. He fell into pleasant
memories of his childhood, played again with his brother and sister,
raced across the fields, shouting to alarm the sedentary larks, entered the
sombre forest beyond and with timid steps followed the faint path to
Ghost Rock, standing at last with audible heart-throbs before the Dead
Man's Cave and seeking to penetrate its awful mystery. For the first
time he observed that the opening of the haunted cavern was encircled
by a ring of metal. Then all else vanished and left him gazing into the
barrel of his rifle as before. But whereas before it had seemed nearer, it
now seemed an inconceivable distance away, and all the more sinister for
that. He cried out and, startled by something in his own voice—the note
of fear—lied to himself in denial: "If I don't sing out I may stay here
till I die."

He now made no further attempt to evade the menacing stare of the
gun barrel. If he turned away his eyes an instant it was to look for assistance (although he could not see the ground on either side the ruin), and
he permitted them to return, obedient to the imperative fascination. If
he closed them it was from weariness, and instantly the poignant pain
in his forehead—the prophecy and menace of the bullet—forced him to
reopen them.

The tension of nerve and brain was too severe; nature came to his relief with intervals of unconsciousness. Reviving from one of these he
became sensible of a sharp, smarting pain in his right hand, and when
he worked his fingers together, or rubbed his palm with them, he could
feel that they were wet and slippery. He could not see the hand, but he
knew the sensation; it was running blood. In his delirium he had beaten
it against the jagged fragments of the wreck, had clutched it full of
splinters. He resolved that he would meet his fate more manly. He was
a plain, common soldier, had no religion and not much philosophy; he
could not die like a hero, with great and wise last words, even if there
had been some one to hear them, but he could die "game," and he would.
But if he could only know when to expect the shot!

Some rats which had probably inhabited the shed came sneaking and scampering about. One of them mounted the pile of débris that held the rifle; another followed and another. Searing regarded them at first with indifference, then with friendly interest; then, as the thought flashed into his bewildered mind that they might touch the trigger of his rifle, he cursed them and ordered them to go away. "It is no business of yours," he cried.

The creatures went away; they would return later, attack his face, gnaw away his nose, cut his throat—he knew that, but he hoped by that time to be dead.

Nothing could now unfix his gaze from the little ring of metal with its black interior. The pain in his forehead was fierce and incessant. He felt it gradually penetrating the brain more and more deeply, until at last its progress was arrested by the wood at the back of his head. It grew momentarily more insufferable: he began wantonly beating his lacerated hand against the splinters again to counteract that horrible ache. It seemed to throb with a slow, regular recurrence, each pulsation sharper than the preceding, and sometimes he cried out, thinking he felt the fatal bullet. No thoughts of home, of wife and children, of country, of glory. The whole record of memory was effaced. The world had passed away—not a vestige remained. Here in this confusion of timbers and boards is the sole universe. Here is immortality in time—each pain an everlasting life. The throbs tick off eternities.

Jerome Searing, the man of courage, the formidable enemy, the strong, resolute warrior, was as pale as a ghost. His jaw was fallen; his eyes protruded; he trembled in every fibre; a cold sweat bathed his entire body; he screamed with fear. He was not insane—he was terrified.

In groping about with his torn and bleeding hand he seized at last a strip of board, and, pulling, felt it give way. It lay parallel with his body, and by bending his elbow as much as the contracted space would permit, he could draw it a few inches at a time. Finally it was altogether loosened from the wreckage covering his legs; he could lift it clear of the ground its whole length. A great hope came into his mind: perhaps he could work it upward, that is to say backward, far enough to lift the end and push aside the rifle; or, if that were too tightly wedged, so place the strip of board as to deflect the bullet. With this object he passed it backward inch by inch, hardly daring to breathe lest that act somehow defeat his intent, and more than ever unable to remove his eyes from the rifle, which might perhaps now hasten to improve its waning opportunity. Something at least had been gained: in the occupation of his mind in this attempt at self-defense he was less sensible of the pain in his head and had ceased to wince. But he was still dreadfully frightened and his teeth rattled like castanets.

The strip of board ceased to move to the suasion of his hand. He tugged at it with all his strength, changed the direction of its length all he could, but it had met some extended obstruction behind him and the end in front was still too far away to clear the pile of débris and reach the muzzle of the gun. It extended, indeed, nearly as far as the trigger guard, which, uncovered by the rubbish, he could imperfectly see with his right eye. He tried to break the strip with his hand, but had no leverage. In his defeat, all his terror returned, augmented tenfold. The black aperture of the rifle appeared to threaten a sharper and more imminent death in punishment of his rebellion. The track of the bullet through his head ached with an intenser anguish. He began to tremble again.

Suddenly he became composed. His tremor subsided. He clenched his teeth and drew down his eyebrows. He had not exhausted his means of defense; a new design had shaped itself in his mind—another plan of battle. Raising the front end of the strip of board, he carefully pushed it forward through the wreckage at the side of the rifle until it pressed against the trigger guard. Then he moved the end slowly outward until he could feel that it had cleared it, then, closing his eyes, thrust it against the trigger with all his strength! There was no explosion; the rifle had been discharged as it dropped from his hand when the building fell. But it did its work.

Lieutenant Adrian Searing, in command of the picket-guard on that part of the line through which his brother Jerome had passed on his mission, sat with attentive ears in his breastwork behind the line. Not the faintest sound escaped him; the cry of a bird, the barking of a squirrel, the noise of the wind among the pines—all were anxiously noted by his overstrained sense. Suddenly, directly in front of his line, he heard a faint, confused rumble, like the clatter of a falling building translated by distance. The lieutenant mechanically looked at his watch. Six o'clock and eighteen minutes. At the same moment an officer approached him on foot from the rear and saluted.

"Lieutenant," said the officer, "the colonel directs you to move forward your line and feel the enemy if you find him. If not, continue the advance until directed to halt. There is reason to think that the enemy has retreated."

The lieutenant nodded and said nothing; the other officer retired. In a moment the men, apprised of their duty by the non-commissioned officers in low tones, had deployed from their rifle-pits and were moving forward in skirmishing order, with set teeth and beating hearts.

This line of skirmishers sweeps across the plantation toward the mountain. They pass on both sides of the wrecked building, observing nothing. At a short distance in their rear their commander comes. He casts his eyes curiously upon the ruin and sees a dead body half buried in boards and timbers. It is so covered with dust that its clothing is Confederate gray. Its face is yellowish white; the cheeks are fallen in, the temples sunken, too, with sharp ridges about them, making the forehead forbiddingly narrow; the upper lip, slightly lifted, shows the white teeth, rigidly clenched. The hair is heavy with moisture, the face as wet as the dewy grass all about. From his point of view the officer does not observe the rifle; the man was apparently killed by the fall of the building.

"Dead a week," said the officer curtly, moving on and absently pulling out his watch as if to verify his estimate of time. Six o'clock and forty minutes.

☆

☆ ☆

THE FIGHTING had been hard and continuous; that was attested by all the senses. The very taste of battle was in the air. All was now over; it remained only to succor the wounded and bury the dead—to "tidy up a bit," as the humorist of a burial squad put it. A good deal of "tidying up" was required. As far as one could see through the forest, among the splintered trees, lay wrecks of men and horses. Among them moved the stretcher-bearers, gathering and carrying away the few who showed signs of life. Most of the wounded had died of neglect while the right to minister to their wants was in dispute. It is an army regulation that the wounded must wait; the best way to care for them is to win the battle. It must be confessed that victory is a distinct advantage to a man requiring attention, but many do not live to avail themselves of it.

The dead were collected in groups of a dozen or a score and laid side by side in rows while the trenches were dug to receive them. Some, found at too great a distance from these rallying points, were buried where they lay. There was little attempt at identification, though in most cases, the burial parties being detailed to glean the same ground which they has assisted to reap, the names of the victorious dead were known and listed. The enemy's fallen had to be content with counting. But of that they got enough: many of them were counted several times, and the total, as given afterward in the official report of the victorious commander, denoted rather a hope than a result.

At some little distance from the spot where one of the burial parties had established its "bivouac of the dead," a man in the uniform of a Federal officer stood leaning against a tree. From his feet upward to his neck his attitude was that of weariness reposing; but he turned his head uneasily from side to side; his mind was apparently not at rest. He was perhaps uncertain in which direction to go; he was not likely to remain long where he was, for already the level rays of the setting sun straggled redly through the open spaces of the wood and the weary soldiers were quitting their task for the day. He would hardly make a night of it alone there among the dead. Nine men in ten whom you meet after a battle inquire the way to some fraction of the army—as if any one could know. Doubtless this officer was lost. After resting himself a moment he would presumably follow one of the retiring burial squads.

When all were gone he walked straight away into the forest toward the red west, its light staining his face like blood. The air of confidence with which he now strode along showed that he was on familiar ground; he had recovered his bearings. The dead on his right and on his left were unregarded as he passed. An occasional low moan from some sorely-stricken wretch whom the relief-parties had not reached, and who would have to pass a comfortless night beneath the stars with his thirst to keep him company, was equally unheeded. What, indeed, could the officer have done, being no surgeon and having no water?

At the head of a shallow ravine, a mere depression of the ground, lay a small group of bodies. He saw, and swerving suddenly from his course walked rapidly toward them. Scanning each one sharply as he passed, he stopped at last above one which lay at a slight remove from the others, near a clump of small trees. He looked at it narrowly. It seemed to stir. He stooped and laid his hand upon its face. It screamed.

The officer was Captain Downing Madwell, of a Massachusetts regiment of infantry, a daring and intelligent soldier, an honorable man.

In the regiment were two brothers named Halcrow—Caffal and Creede Halcrow. Caffal Halcrow was a sergeant in Captain Madwell's company, and these two men, the sergeant and the captain, were devoted friends. In so far as disparity of rank, difference in duties and considerations of military discipline would permit they were commonly together. They had, indeed, grown up together from childhood. A habit of the heart is not easily broken off. Caffal Halcrow had nothing military in his taste nor disposition, but the thought of separation from his friend was disagreeable; he enlisted in the company in which Madwell was second-lieutenant. Each had taken two steps upward in rank, but between the highest non-commissioned and the lowest commissioned officer the gulf is deep and wide and the old relation was maintained with difficulty and a difference.

Creede Halcrow, the brother of Caffal, was the major of the regiment —a cynical, saturnine man, between whom and Captain Madwell there was a natural antipathy which circumstances had nourished and strengthened to an active animosity. But for the restraining influence of their mutual relation to Caffal these two patriots would doubtless have endeavored to deprive their country of each other's services.

At the opening of the battle that morning the regiment was performing outpost duty a mile away from the main army. It was attacked and nearly surrounded in the forest, but stubbornly held its ground. During a lull in the fighting, Major Halcrow came to Captain Madwell. The two exchanged formal salutes, and the major said: "Captain, the colonel directs that you push your company to the head of this ravine and hold your place there until recalled. I need hardly apprise you of the dangerous character of the movement, but if you wish, you can, I suppose, turn over the command to your first-lieutenant. I was not, however, directed to authorize the substitution; it is merely a suggestion of my own, unofficially made."

To this deadly insult Captain Madwell coolly replied:

"Sir, I invite you to accompany the movement. A mounted officer would be a conspicuous mark, and I have long held the opinion that it would be better if you were dead."

The art of repartee was cultivated in military circles as early as 1862.

A half-hour later Captain Madwell's company was driven from its position at the head of the ravine, with a loss of one-third its number. Among the fallen was Sergeant Halcrow. The regiment was soon afterward forced back to the main line, and at the close of the battle was miles away. The captain was now standing at the side of his subordinate and friend.

Sergeant Halcrow was mortally hurt. His clothing was deranged; it seemed to have been violently torn apart, exposing the abdomen. Some of the buttons of his jacket had been pulled off and lay on the ground beside him and fragments of his other garments were strewn about. His leather belt was parted and had apparently been dragged from beneath him as he lay. There had been no great effusion of blood. The only visible wound was a wide, ragged opening in the abdomen. It was defiled with earth and dead leaves. Protruding from it was a loop of small intestine. In all his experience Captain Madwell had not seen a wound like this. He could neither conjecture how it was made nor explain the attendant circumstances—the strangely torn clothing, the parted belt, the besmirching of the white skin. He knelt and made a closer examination. When he rose to his feet, he turned his eyes in different directions as if looking for an enemy. Fifty yards away, on the crest of a low, thinly wooded hill, he saw several dark objects moving about among the fallen men—a herd of swine. One stood with its back to him, its shoulders sharply elevated. Its forefeet were upon a human body, its head was depressed and invisible. The bristly ridge of its chine showed black against the red west. Captain Madwell drew away his eyes and fixed them again upon the thing which had been his friend.

The man who had suffered these monstrous mutilations was alive. At intervals he moved his limbs; he moaned at every breath. He stared blankly into the face of his friend and if touched screamed. In his giant agony he had torn up the ground on which he lay; his clenched hands were full of leaves and twigs and earth. Articulate speech was beyond his power; it was impossible to know if he were sensible to anything but pain. The expression of his face was an appeal; his eyes were full of prayer. For what?

There was no misreading that look; the captain had too frequently seen it in eyes of those whose lips had still the power to formulate it by an entreaty for death. Consciously or unconsciously, this writhing fragment of humanity, this type and example of acute sensation, this handiwork of man and beast, this humble, unheroic Prometheus, was imploring everything, all, the whole non-ego, for the boon of oblivion. To the earth and the sky alike, to the trees, to the man, to whatever took form in sense or consciousness, this incarnate suffering addressed that silent plea.

For what, indeed? For that which we accord to even the meanest creature without sense to demand it, denying it only to the wretched of our own race: for the blessed release, the rite of uttermost compassion, the *coup de grâce*.

Captain Madwell spoke the name of his friend. He repeated it over and over without effect until emotion choked his utterance. His tears plashed upon the livid face beneath his own and blinded himself. He saw nothing but a blurred and moving object, but the moans were more distinct than ever, interrupted at briefer intervals by sharper shrieks. He turned away, struck his hand upon his forehead, and strode from the spot. The swine, catching sight of him, threw up their crimson muzzles, regarding him suspiciously a second, and then with a gruff, concerted grunt, raced away out of sight. A horse, its foreleg splintered by a cannon-shot, lifted its head sidewise from the ground and neighed piteously. Madwell stepped forward, drew his revolver and shot the poor beast between the eyes, narrowly observing its death-struggle, which, contrary to his expectation, was violent and long; but at last it lay still. The tense muscles of its lips, which had uncovered the teeth in a horrible grin, relaxed; the sharp, clean-cut profile took on a look of profound peace and rest.

Along the distant, thinly wooded crest to westward the fringe of sunset fire had now nearly burned itself out. The light upon the trunks of the trees had faded to a tender gray; shadows were in their tops, like great dark birds aperch. Night was coming and there were miles of haunted forest between Captain Madwell and camp. Yet he stood there at the side of the dead animal, apparently lost to all sense of his surroundings. His eyes were bent upon the earth at his feet; his left hand hung loosely at his side, his right still held the pistol. Presently he lifted his face, turned it toward his dying friend and walked rapidly back to his side. He knelt upon one knee, cocked the weapon, placed the muzzle against the man's forehead, and turning away his eyes pulled the trigger. There was no report. He had used his last cartridge for the horse.

The sufferer moaned and his lips moved convulsively. The froth that ran from them had a tinge of blood.

Captain Madwell rose to his feet and drew his sword from the scabbard. He passed the fingers of his left hand along the edge from hilt to point. He held it out straight before him, as if to test his nerves. There was no visible tremor of the blade; the ray of bleak skylight that it reflected was steady and true. He stooped and with his left hand tore away the dying man's shirt, rose and placed the point of the sword just over the heart. This time he did not withdraw his eyes. Grasping the hilt with both hands, he thrust downward with all his strength and weight. The blade sank into the man's body—through his body into the earth; Captain Madwell came near falling forward upon his work. The dying man drew up his knees and at the same time threw his right arm across his breast and grasped the steel so tightly that the knuckles of the hand visibly whitened. By a violent but vain effort to withdraw the blade the wound was enlarged; a rill of blood escaped, running sinuously down into the deranged clothing. At that moment three men stepped silently forward from behind the clump of young trees which had concealed their approach. Two were hospital attendants and carried a stretcher.

The third was Major Creede Halcrow.

THE SHENANDOAH

by HERVEY ALLEN

YOU WILL NOT FIND it in the books called history. There are only two old men alive who still remember it. In a war of colossally grisly battles, with staggering losses even in minor engagements, so small an affair was not worth the chronicling. Its statistics were simply lumped with a larger whole, for to the official military mind it was merely one phase of a long-drawn-out cavalry skirmish that extended up the South Fork of the Shenandoah from Luray to the Danville Railroad. It was all over in a few minutes—all but the grief and the suffering. Even the survivors, when they met afterwards, always spoke of it casually as "that action at Aquila" or "the cavalry brush south of Luray." What was that, if you had been at Manassas; at Antietam and Gettysburg?

"But do you remember?" they would sometimes say, do you remember—

"when Early's men who lived in the Valley tried to come back home? Some of them were what was left of Jackson's veterans. They were the backbone of that attack. They thought of their ruined farms. It was hard to stop them from coming home. The rest were just the last sweepings of the draft, boys or old clerks from the sidewalks of Richmond and Petersburg. But even they fought well. They were desperate. Much depended upon them. And they knew it."

That is what one used to hear. Actually—

General Early was preparing to move the bulk of his forces out of the Valley of Virginia. The dying Confederacy was shrinking its life-blood back to its heart. The Virginia Central was busy bringing empties west to take Early's men back towards Richmond. A raid northward into the Valley to cut, if possible, that important federal artery, the Manassas Gap

From: *Action at Aquila.* Copyright 1938, by Hervey Allen, and reprinted by permission of Farrar & Rinehart, Inc.

Railroad, would create a diversion; screen the withdrawal to Richmond. It might even fool Sheridan long enough to put him on the defensive again. And time was precious then, even more precious than men.

For his purpose, a purely strategic one, the Confederate general picked his men carefully. Many of them were natives of the Valley, old volunteers, Stonewall's veterans who could be depended upon to fight their way back home. They were to leaven the lump of the new, drafted men and the raw, young recruits. Early was prepared to sacrifice them if necessary, and there wasn't much time to organize.

There was one regiment of Lomax's cavalry, commanded by a captain, and remounted on newly-captured federal horses. They were mostly veterans and would carry through. There were several provisional battalions of infantry sketchily organized for the occasion; doubtful, but the best available. There was no artillery, because there was none to spare. Cannon were almost as scarce as capable officers. Daring must be the substitute for both. So the command was placed in the hands of a fearless, but wild, Mississippian by the name of LaTouche, Major Mathis LaTouche.

LaTouche specialized in forlorn hopes. "Christ help the foremost" was his motto, and he always led his own men. Also he told one funny story in Cajun dialect of which General Early was very, very tired. Perhaps he told it once too often? Anyway, he was given a general's responsibility with a major's rank. "Nothing matters to dead men," the general muttered, when he was once asked about it long afterwards.

LaTouche and his men, about twenty-five hundred in all, got off the cars at a little siding on the Virginia Central just west of Waynesboro. They could ride no farther. The iron bridge over the Shenandoah at Waynesboro had been destroyed some weeks before by Torbert's Union cavalry. The Confederates hurried rapidly down the Valley, the infantry in bad shoes and bare feet.

They passed through ruined Staunton and Port Republic, also lately visited by General Torbert. Consequently, they kept gathering in a good many "independents" and "volunteers" along the way; lean, bearded men who came out of hiding from the woods and ravines, rifle in hand and grim determination at heart. They had nothing to lose now but their lives.

So far LaTouche had seen nothing of the federal forces except their benign handiwork. By the time he reached Rockingham on the South Fork his column numbered over three thousand by "natural accretion," and he was greatly encouraged. It looked as though he might get far enough down the Valley by midnight to strike at the railroad next day.

That would be magnificent! Early might have to make him a colonel yet.

So he kept pushing his one well-organized and veteran unit, the cavalry regiment, far ahead of his limping infantry, hoping to occupy Luray after nightfall. All was going merrily—when his scouts struck the vedettes of the 6th Pennsylvania Cavalry posted along the river south of Felix Run and in the gorge above Aquila.

Although it was now pitch dark, the Confederate cavalry still made a determined attempt to push on. The skirmish along the river road grew fast and furious. But the volume of fire from the breech-loading carbines used by the Federals convinced the Confederates that the gorge must be quite heavily occupied, and they fell back up the Valley to await the arrival of their infantry still many miles behind.

It was the last of this skirmish in the gorge that Colonel Franklin had heard from the porch at Coiner's Retreat. In less than no time he was back in camp and had the situation in hand. Farfar returned to camp a few minutes after him. The firing by then had died away. Evidently the Confederates were not going to risk a night attack before their main body came up to support them.

Colonel Franklin could have asked for nothing better than a delay. He took every precaution against a surprise, but permitted the bulk of his men to sleep under arms. Meanwhile, he summoned the force at Luray to join him, and sent couriers to Front Royal with the news of the threatened raid, to be transmitted to headquarters.

The night passed peacefully. Shortly before sunrise the 23rd Illinois Infantry and the Rhode Island Artillery marched in up the Luray road, quietly, as they had been instructed. By dawn they were posted. Before that time the colonel felt sure that his message must have been relayed by the signal corps at Front Royal to General Sheridan at Winchester.

The sun rose through a bank of fog. At the lower end of the Valley a lowering, black cloud, which extended from one mountain wall to the other, lingered like a patch of night, moving imperceptibly southward. It was the first major threat of a break in the weather for many weeks. At Aquila, of course, no one paid any attention to it. It was still miles away, and few in that vicinity on that particular morning had their heads in the clouds.

It seemed obvious to everyone that a clash would take place immediately between the opposing forces gathering about Aquila; that is, as soon as it should be light enough for effective fighting to begin. Men and officers strained, looking into the thinning fog and shadows before them, and as the visibility increased the tension grew.

It was found that during the night the Confederates had advanced through the gorge. Their infantry had worked along both sides of the river in small parties, filtering through the woods and over the "impassable" hills. Morning found them in full possession of all but the lower end of the little pass.

Colonel Franklin had expected that. He had slowly withdrawn his cavalry pickets rather than sacrifice them uselessly. Except for a sharp interchange of rifle fire just before daylight, when the massed Union outposts finally withdrew from the gorge to fall back on their main body, there had been no serious resistance.

It was during this brief outbreak of firing that the infantry and artillery from Luray had arrived on the field. As the senior officer present, Colonel Franklin then found himself in command of a combined force of about eighteen hundred splendidly-equipped veterans from the three major arms of the service, and he made his dispositions accordingly.

In spite of the efficiency of his little force, he must, until reinforcements arrived, play a waiting and defensive game. Both his orders and the situation made it imperative to do so rather than to waste his strength in a doubtful offensive. He had Sheridan's own instructions to "hold the bottle neck at Aquila" until help arrived, and to send word of any movement to the south of him. The latter he had done, and the former he determined to do if possible. But he was outnumbered by about two to one, and reports from his scouts led him to believe that the Confederates were in even greater numbers. He might, then, be forced back. Yet, if he were, it must only be after he had so crippled the Confederates that they would fall an easy prey to the federal reinforcements coming up the Valley—or, in any event, find themselves too enfeebled to reach the Manassas Gap Railroad.

Colonel Franklin's task was therefore "to dam" the Valley with the force at his disposal against twice his numbers; that of the Confederates, to overflow him and smash through. Time would be the deciding element. The "dam" necessarily consisted of a defendable line across the narrow part of the Valley just below where the river broke through the hills. Roughly, that line stretched along Aquila Creek from the ruined village itself to the river. There were dense forests and tumbled foothills on either flank.

The colonel put Aquila Creek behind him. It was fordable if he did have to fall back down the Valley, and it might offer in that case an excellent second line of defence. He posted the 23rd Illinois Infantry on the left. The extreme left battalion of that regiment occupied the thin woods and some of the heavy-walled buildings in the ruined village of Aquila. The artillery, a crack battery of six rifled, steel field-pieces, he posted in the centre, supported by sharpshooters composed of some of his cavalrymen and the Illinois Irish, twenty-two in all. He held the right of the line with his own regiment, his right flank resting on the river, where Dr. Holtz-maier also set up his field hospital in Mr. Felix Mann's canteen. The empty camp lay a quarter of a mile behind him in charge of a few in-valids and musicians. There were no reserves. It was the best he could do. The line was too long, but it was concave to the enemy and concentrated fire.

The line was crescent-shaped because it followed roughly the rim of a shallow bowl of meadows several square miles in extent. The hay on them had been cut some weeks before, so there were now perfectly-clear manœuvring for cavalry and unimpeded shooting for artillery and rifle-men. The Confederates would have to advance over those clean, cropped fields for nearly a mile before they struck the Union troops. At the present they were debouching from the gorge and taking up position in a tangle of unbroken forest just opposite, woods that stretched from the Blue Ridge to the river.

Success in action frequently depends upon apparently quite minor features in the terrain. Such was the case at Aquila. Both sides were quick to take advantage of them. If the Confederates lay fully concealed in the woods along the south side of the meadows and in the river gorge itself, the Federals were equally well-protected by the little valley of Aquila Creek. It made a gradual, a scarcely noticeable, swale in the fields where it flowed down to the river. That wide-sweeping, grassy dip, nevertheless, was deep enough to conceal a mounted man so that his head would not show above the sky line.

It was within this hollow in the fields that Colonel Franklin placed the artillery and his own regiment of cavalry, massed and ready. Over the crest towards the enemy there was nothing but a thin line of skirmishers lying down in the short grass with their rifles and carbines beside them. That was all that Major LaTouche could see there when he examined the Union line with field-glasses, shortly after sunrise, while wisps of fog were still curling through the pines.

It was plain to the major that the Union left was strongly held by a regiment of Zouave infantry. He could see their red trousers and white leggings gleaming through the open woods in that direction and in the ruins of the village, which would, with its sturdy brick buildings, be a hard nut to crack. In the fields nearer the river, however, there seemed to be nothing but a thin line of dismounted cavalry. Hence, the major decided to attack there at once.

He generally felt impetuous just after breakfast and the five cups of eye-opening, black New Orleans coffee which his darky orderly brewed him every morning. The cherished coffee and nine Mexican silver dollars were all that remained of the major's estate. But even that was too much. Seeing only as clearly as he did, despite the coffee, he had no idea that in a slant of the fields, that looked level through the field-glasses, a battery of artillery and a regiment of cavalry lay concealed. There was, in fact, no immediate way of his finding this out, unless he had ordered one of his men to climb a tree and look over. It did occur to him to give such an order, but he felt that it would be thought eccentric, and he refrained.

What is described by clerkly historians as an "inexplicable delay" now took place. That is, killing on a large scale did not begin as soon as might logically be expected. The whole morning passed with only desultory firing by sharpshooters on both sides. It was nearly noon before the impetuous, and by now impatient, Major LaTouche was able to deliver his first thrust. His infantry illogically insisted upon having something to eat before they started to die. Most of them had been marching all night. They had few shoes and many sore feet. They sat down and made flapjacks and cooled their feet in the river. They picked their way slowly along the rocky gorge road, and it took several hours to get them deployed through the woods facing the Federals and reorganized for attack. The "volunteers" picked up along the route were particularly troublesome. They insisted upon sticking together in neighbourhood gangs.

Among them was a party of Valley men, veterans of many a fight, who had joined up at Waynesboro. And in that group was a peaked-looking youngster with his left arm in a sling.

Paul Crittendon had got no farther than Waynesboro when he ran away from Coiner's Retreat. There he had been ill again. His chance to get back to the army had seemed heaven-sent when LaTouche's column came through. Since he could not use a rifle, he had been given a six-shooter and assigned to a colour guard. He said he didn't care whether he was killed or not, and he thought he meant it. Flags were always carried into battle, although they were unnecessary. Paul's flag had been at Gettysburg, and all up and down the Valley with Early. It was shot full of holes and tattered by the weather until it looked like old lace. It had the fatal property of acting like a "magnet" for lead.

Colonel Franklin did not let his artillery shell the woods where he knew the Confederates were assembling. He was saving the guns as a surprise. Nor would he permit the lieutenant-colonel commanding the 23rd Illinios to attack and "clean out" the country in front of him, although the wild Irish were eager to advance and kept up a constant peppering fire. "Wait," said the colonel, "wait and save your ammunition."

So they waited, all through the morning. The colonel finally fed his men and horses. On the left, the little springhouse at Aquila was full of Zouave Irishmen from Chicago filling their canteens to a constant clinking of cans. The men lay low and ate their rations. It looked like a big picnic through the woods while they munched their hardtack and cold beans. Smoke rose from the chimney of one of the deserted houses where the staff made coffee. On the right the cavalry and artillery broke out nosebags for the horses, ready to snatch them away. Details carried buckets of water, slung on poles, across the fields. A few skulkers sneaked back to camp.

At the end of the line near the river Surgeon Holtzmaier laid out his instruments and cleared the counters of Mr. Mann's canteen for operating tables. The stone farmhouse, where the store had been situated, offered a welcome protection from stray bullets, and extra hospital space. A dozen or so wounded from the skirmish of the night before had been treated there. Already four dead men were laid out on the river-bank behind. The tents of the deserted camp lay farther down the stream, still and gleaming, with the forgotten headquarters flag flopping idly on its staff as the wind gradually shifted from south to north.

A chill crept into the air. The cloud down the Valley began to draw perceptibly nearer. It slowly threatened to shut half the world from sunlight like a vast, sliding lid.

But on the bright pastures where men waited for battle Indian summer still lingered, gilding the meadows with a wide, empty yellow light. The slanting sunlight twinkled on weapons scattered through the woods and fields; glittered on the polished steel barrels of the six rifled cannons of the "Star Battery" from Providence, Rhode Island.

Lieutenant Lyman de Wolf Dorr, the dandy, young officer in charge, beat the dust out of his gauntlets against his saddle-bow, and wished to God the fun would begin and be got over with. He was twenty-three and this was his thirteenth battle. He listened with professional appraisal to the distant "howling" in the woods held by the Confederates. It seemed to him the enemy was trying to keep up his own courage rather than express defiance. Certainly those yells were nothing like the rebel yells of earlier in the war; not to be compared with the noise when they were closing in on McClellan on the Peninsula. He wondered idly how soon the war would be over. The annual subscription dances must be beginning at home now. To have missed three seasons! He whistled his favourite waltz of 1861, listening to invisible fiddles. A bullet droned over the crest and smacked into an apple tree on the knoll near by. A branch with a withered fruit bent and fell. There was no reply. The Union lines lay silent. Waiting, waiting. My God, that was what wore you out—waiting!

A courier with an exhausted and sobbing horse came stumbling up from the river road and asked for Colonel Franklin. The lieutenant pointed him out sitting on the little knoll on the crest among the bare apple trees, where he had been observing since ten o'clock. He watched the courier hand the colonel his dispatch. At that moment the entire Union picket line on the other side of the crest burst into a fury of fire.

The lieutenant never forgot the next few seconds. He kept his eyes on the colonel. He thought the man would never get through reading that dispatch:

Hold hard. Merritt's and Averell's cavalry divisions left Winchester at 4 A. M.

S.

That was all.

The colonel tucked the paper in his pocket, turned, looked over the field, and made a signal to Lieutenant Dorr.

Instantly, men, horses, and guns leaped forward, animated by a single will. The battery raced for the crest, opening fanwise, each gun heading for its appointed place already prepared hours before. The static tension was resolved into violent action.

To the line of Confederates some eight hundred strong, advancing across the fields through a hail of droning bullets from the Union riflemen, the heads of the artillery, men and horses, the outlines of the flying caissons and cannons appeared abruptly above the low sky line ahead, like a sinister apparition materializing out of the solid green earth of the meadows themselves.

The guns unlimbered. The horses trotted back over the crest.

There was a moment of frantic activity about the battery, and then a great wall of pallid, yellow smoke seemed to be pushed out against and to be rushing down upon the oncoming Southerners. The wall cracked and bellowed with thunder. Streaks of red light leaped out of its heart, followed by the howlings and hummings of the invisible things that fell upon that line of advancing men like bundles of whirling knives; that cut them, sliced them, filled them full of fine steel needles which pierced to the bone.

The line continued to advance. The distant yelling of men came nearer, heard faintly above the bellows of the volcano on the knoll. Somehow there were not so many in the line now. The yelling grew fainter. Then suddenly—no one could tell just exactly when—the advancing line was going the other way, turned back as if by command.

But it was no longer a line. It was lonely individuals converging upon one another, rushing into bunches and groups. They went tearing back into the woods they had left only a few minutes before, to lie down white, exhausted, and panting. To each man it seemed as though the guns should have ceased when he turned back. The terrible thing was that those cannons had continued to kill every foot of the way, coming and going.

Finally they ceased.

And now from the fields, dotted with motionless and squirming bundles, came a low wailing, and a high, tearing screaming that did not cease in that vicinity until early the following morning. Lieutenant Dorr had been firing alternate but continuous salvos of shrapnel and canister. The wind drifted the acrid powder smoke sinuously through the woods where the Confederates now lay silent. Silence hung over the Union lines. The battery was cooling its guns.

Someone out on the field kept calling for "William Anderson" in a hoarse, agonized voice and ceased not to do so. Curiously enough, several others finally took up the refrain. Then, as if in answer, the guns began again.

One of them tolled like a bell, the others barked and bellowed. Each had a different voice. It was like a monster with six heads roaring. They were plunging round shot into the Confederate woods. These whined and smashed through the trees, scattering branches and splinters as though lightning had struck. On the knoll the battery was once more enveloped in a dense cloud of yellow smoke. The explosions gradually grew more deliberate. Afterwhile they stopped. The battery seemed to have run down like a clock. Doubtless they were winding it up again. In the woods men lifted pale, strained faces from their arms and stood upright once more.

Major LaTouche determined to have those guns. They were stopping him. It had been a mistake—he could see it now—to attack with only part of his infantry. He should have used every available man and broken through. Now he would hurl his regiment of cavalry on the battery and follow up with all his infantry. Horsemen could get across the field to the guns before they were all killed getting there. That was the gist of it. He still regarded his men as invincible, once they arrived. Also, he was a cavalryman. Having made a terrible mistake, he determined to wipe out either his error or himself by leading the cavalry in person. He tugged his long moustache thoughtfully. That damn' Yankee battery was the best he had ever seen. "Well, suh, let's go over an' call on 'em," said he, as he put himself at the head of his cavalry massed in an open glade. He issued orders for the infantry to follow "instantly."

LaTouche may have been mad or just from Mississippi, either or both. Anyway, he rode a large cream-coloured stallion that actually tossed his mane. He also carried a fine repeater hunting watch. He now took this out of his pocket and held it up to his ear. All those sitting near him on their horses in the silent forest heard its faint chime. A slightly elfin look flitted over the major's face. "It is exactly two and a half o'clock," said he, and looked about him. No one disputed the fact. It was his last irrational action save one. He next gave the command to take the guns.

The guns were not very cool yet. "The trouble with these damned steel babies," said Lieutenant Dorr, "is that they heat up like hell over a brief affair. Look at number one there, her breeches are still hot as a hoar's!" He spat on the metal, and the saliva cracked back at him.

"Give the slut a chance, sir!" exclaimed a young gunner who was proud of number one. "*I'll* cool her off"—and before anyone could stop him he dumped a bucket of cold spring water over the breech. A torrent of oaths and a hail of kicks on his behind rewarded him. Someone started to laugh, when from an opening in the woods opposite a regiment of Confederate cavalry led by a man on a cream-coloured horse emerged at a rapid trot. It was a full half-mile away. The battery went into action immediately.

"Shrapnel!" roared the lieutenant, and started to move over to number two gun, which was slow in fire.

Just then number one burst with a crack like a tight earthquake, and the caisson behind it went up with red fire and a volcanic roar. Men, horses, wheels, and metal fragments were spewed all over the meadows, and the blast carried havoc through the rest of the battery. The man who had poured cold water over the breech was blown spread-eagled up into an apple tree to hang there with his bowels streaming out while he made noises like a sick rooster.

Lieutenant Dorr could not hear him, though, nor the rebel trumpets sounding the charge. He never heard anything again. He stood dazed, watching the battery trying to reassemble itself. There were only enough men left to man four guns. For a while they were clear out of action.

For several minutes the lieutenant was out too. All he could do was to lean against a shattered tree and watch things unroll before him in a stunned dream. Time seemed to have slowed up as if only the intervals of a dismal music were being played long drawn out. Yet he could see; he still knew what was going on.

Across the half-mile of meadow before him, one to the left and one to the right, two columns of cavalry, moving on parallel lines but in opposite directions, rode flashing into the afternoon sunlight. There was not quite a mile of perfectly smooth meadow between them. The Confederates were making for the guns. The Federals seemed to be heading for the line of woods opposite. The lieutenant saw this. It seemed to him to be happening slowly. He saw the man on the cream-coloured horse throw up his hands and slowly fall off backward. He saw the column of Union cavalry swing into line and start to sweep down the field, slowly. The Confederates had turned to meet them. The two lines would meet directly in front of the guns. The lieutenant could not move. Something was wrong with him. He knew he ought to move. He had forgotten how. The trouble was in his head. He groaned. Nightmare had become a reality.

Colonel Franklin on Black Girl had halted exactly half-way across the fields with his trumpeter beside him. A crackle of rifle fire came from the woods towards which his column was heading. The bullets tore up the turf about him. Black Girl danced as though she were in a swarm of bees. Half the column galloped past the colonel. The trumpet sounded. The troopers swung left into line, stretching well across the meadows, and halted. Here and there a man dropped from the saddle and a horse galloped away. But most of the empty saddles stayed in line.

History does not remember the name of the young officer who commanded the regiment of Confederate cavalry at Aquila after LaTouche fell—only that he was a captain from New Bern, North Carolina. Nevertheless, he was probably the best soldier on the field. The instant Major LaTouche was killed, he stopped the charge on the battery and brought his men into line to face the 6th Pennsylvania Cavalry that seemed to have sprung from the earth. And he never stopped galloping. He simply swung his squadrons like so many doors on hinges and swept on up the field.

It was now that Colonel Franklin made the mistake of his life. He had behind him a splendid machine for firing carbines. He used it as a sword. He might have kept his men sitting their horses in line, while they crashed volley after volley into the long front of the Confederate cavalry sweeping down upon him. He might have emptied half their saddles before they struck him. That would have been the calm, approved tactics of it.

But Colonel Franklin also was a cavalryman. He had been born in 1821 and brought up on Napoleon, Sir Walter Scott, and Balaklava. The clear field before him, the line of horsemen speeding towards him over the grass, his own regiment lined up spick, span, and ready behind him— that was the moment and the situation he had been dreaming of, living and drilling for, for years.

He gave the order to charge.

All fire from either side had ceased. It was as though that bowl of meadows full of sunlight was nothing more than a prepared field for the greatest of human spectacles. Infantrymen stood up in the woods and craned their necks. On the knoll the artillerymen waited. The lines of cavalry would meet directly in front of the battery. To fire would be to slaughter friend and foe alike. Lieutenant Dorr threw his arms behind him to grasp the tree. His vision was clearing now, dizzily. He heard nothing.

But a rolling storm of hoofs that sounded like subterranean thunder came faster and nearer from either side. Like the crest of two floods the lines of horses with manes curling backward in the wind swept forward. Men leaned low in the saddles with their sabres flashing before them. The sound of the desperate breathing of a thousand beasts, snorting, and the creaking of leather approached like a whirlwind. Fifty yards from each other a long blast of withering fire swept from one end to the other of either line. Powder smoke floated away like spume drift as though the two waves had broken—as they had. For to a storm of hoarse cheering and a screaming rebel yell the lines met directly before the lieutenant standing on the knoll.

Men threw up their hands and fell backward, men pitched forward. Horses reared and plunged. Frantic beasts, kicking and screaming, rolled over and over. Lieutenant Dorr could look down upon and clear across a quarter of a mile of furious slaughter. It was fortunate that he could not hear. Swords are really great knives. Men were chopping one another out of the saddle like so much meat on the block. The haze of pistol smoke grew denser. The sun dazzled on tossing crests of steel. Here and there groups broke through and wheeled back again into the mêlée. Horses shot through the lungs, with purple foam spurting from their nostrils, plunged, bucked, and rolled, bashing the brains and bowels out of their masters, trampling them flat. Dismounted men hewed and shot at each other. For something over two hundred seconds this went on.

Yet in the silent, dazed world of Lieutenant Dorr, where impressions still registered themselves slowly, the events before him seemed to be prolonged and delayed. A sabre fell deliberately upon the blue sleeve of a Union trooper who had thrown his carbine up to ward off the blow. A flash of crimson spray followed the severed arm and the carbine as they curved free through the air. Two officers rode around each other shooting. A hole appeared in the forehead of one and he closed his eyes, falling. A couple of horses reared straight upward, their riders slashing. One horse fell upon his rider backward, the other sank slowly upon his haunches, trembling, his backbone cut behind the saddle. A cascade of yellow water spurted from his tail. A swirl of maddened blue-coats led by their colonel passed over the beast's body, sweeping everything before them. The lieutenant closed his eyes. When he opened them again the fight had passed on. He was looking at what was left behind.

Immediately before him, the horse with the severed spine was struggling to rise on its forelegs. It seemed to be trying to crawl someplace where men could never come. Its head reared up strangely with staring eyes and open jaws. There was something lizardlike about it. Its long, smooth neck and body swept serpentwise back into its dead haunches. It looked like one of the horses of Pluto, emerging from the ground. The lieutenant turned away sickened, pressing his hands to his head that now throbbed in a returning tide of feeling with a ruinous, internal agony. The man on number two gun was just about to pull the lanyard. The lieutenant fell on him with cries out of nowhere only in time to prevent his firing into his own men. In an utterly silent world the young officer stood trying to hear himself groan, left entirely alone with his pain.

The furious confusion of the cavalry action swirled on up the field to the left. The Confederates had been forced back. From the woods their infantry, which had at last received its orders to advance, swept out to support them.

From the little knoll on the crest, where Lieutenant Dorr was standing by with what remained of his guns, the field presented a scene of disastrous confusion. The Confederate cavalry had finally broken and had been forced back, with the Federals pressing them hard, almost to the border of the woods. There they met the solid lines of their own infantry emerging from the underbrush and rushing impetuously forward. While some of the Confederate cavalry was received through intervals and thus found shelter behind the line of their advancing infantry, most of the mounted men, both Confederates and Federals, were now rolled back again towards the Union position, a seething, swirling mass of men and animals locked in confused conflict.

As seen from the Union lines, the whole advancing, bayonet-flashing front of the Confederate infantry was now masked and curtained by this cavalry mêlée of inextricably-mixed friend and foe; by patches of squadrons that still held some semblance of formation; by riderless horses galloping aimlessly up and down; by distracted men still fighting or attempting to flee—and behind them a hedge of bayonets that advanced relentlessly.

The Union lines perforce remained silent. The advance had not yet come within effective range of the 23rd Illinois rifles on the left, and Lieutenant Dorr was now faced with the dilemma either of permitting his guns to remain idle, until his battery was overwhelmed by the approaching flood, or of firing upon the ranks of the enemy through the living bodies of his friends of the 6th Pennsylvania still scattered all along the Confederate front. There was no alternative. He must either fire—or not fire, and be captured.

The pain in his head was, he thought, driving him mad. A white-hot bar of metal seemed to be extending through the back of his skull from ear to ear. Someone else, he felt, finally forced the word "canister" through his lips and kept giving orders like an automaton. The four guns burst into a frenzy of continuous drumfire. The lieutenant could not hear them, their sound for him was transmuted into vibrations of pure pain. The brain of the young officer seemed to be catching afire internally, and he rolled on the grass holding his head and moaning.

The small affair at Aquila had now reached its crisis. But it was a senseless crisis. There was no general leadership left on either side. The main attack of the Confederates had been launched, in obedience to the command of a dead man, and was sweeping across the fields towards the Union line. The unfortunate cavalry being brushed before it was merely so much living chaff caught between two millstones about to engage each other. That was the situation when Lieutenant Dorr's guns began to vomit canister.

Gaps, aisles, and vacant intervals began to appear in that portion of the onrolling mass immediately facing the battery. A process as of the rapid melting of a solid appeared to be taking place. Some of the survivors of the Union cavalry rode in through the smoke, and throwing themselves on the ground, opened fire on the approaching enemy. The gunners serving the four pieces attained their physical maximum of speed. There was a moment when the knoll upon which the battery stood was involved in a continuum of explosion.

The Confederates facing the guns wavered, rallied, came on again—and then suddenly darted back. A small portion of them who came racing up onto the knoll were literally clubbed to death by the now frantic remnant of the Union cavalry that had gathered about the guns. There was something peculiarly terrible about this last fight about the still flashing and tolling cannons. There was no quarter. The sounds were ferocious. Suddenly the cannons stopped and the gunners were heard roaring hoarsely for ammunition.

When the smoke cleared, it was seen that the attack on the Union right had been halted. The field was piled with dead and wounded. Stragglers were melting away into the woods. Lieutenant Dorr was shrieking for someone to put a bullet through his head.

But it was not over yet.

A half-mile up the field to the left the 23rd Illinois Infantry was advancing out into the meadows and extending its intervals to cover the front of the oncoming Confederates. The Union regiment, trained to machinelike precision by Zouave tactics, moved as though on parade. It was "guide centre" on the colours, with the drums beating and the fifes squealing:

"The Union forever, hurrah, boys, hurrah."

The shrill, distant defiance of the fifes sounded pitiful, the drums ominous. The effect upon the Confederates was electric. They gave a long, defiant rebel yell, emptied their rifles at the blocks of blue-coats before them, and rushed forward with the bayonet.

The files of the 23rd Illinois closed up where men had fallen. The regiment halted. At a distance of two hundred yards it began to fire volleys by alternate platoons. Behind the ranks the lieutenants and sergeants counted. The rifles were loaded in six counts. The effect was precise, mechanical, and inhuman. For nearly two minutes an unbroken series of volleys continued to flash along the front of the regiment from right to left. Billows of powder smoke rolled before the line, through which crashed sheets of flame. The Confederate centre, upon which this fire was concentrated, parted, seemed to dissolve in the smoky air. The slaughter at that point was the worst on the field. But the attack flowed around the flanks of the blue-coats. Groups of desperate, bearded men with haggard faces began to throw themselves on the lines of the clockwork regiment from the rear. The volleys ceased. A fusillade petered out into pistol-shots. Then men rolled about with each other on the ground. The Chicago Irish clubbed muskets against the bayonets. This was the kind of riot they best understood. The field dissolved into a swirling mass of inextricable confusion.

Scattered over it, and under the feet of those who still fought there, were the dead, the dying, and the wounded.

NEAR APPOMATTOX

by LAURENCE STALLINGS

WHEN THEY FOUND those old embroidery scissors under that stump to-day, I went a long way back in memory. To memories of blue. I remember how blue their uniforms were.

In those days the lane from the steps here to the clay road seemed about a mile long. It is no more than two hundred feet, but it bisected a universe for me. My mother had her flower garden in a little square which was fenced off with white pickets, and it was there, after my brothers went away, that I played.

I was playing store when the Yankees rode by the house down the Appomattox road and pulled in their horses at our gate. I can remember best how blue the cloth of their uniforms was, and how it glinted in the sun.

I had heard talk of Yankees before that, but they were the first we ever saw here. My father and brothers rode away in butternut gray, with nothing blue about them. Amos held me aloft to throw kisses to Jim when his time came to ride away to Virginia's battle line. Jim was, next to me, the youngest of mother's boys. He was well turned sixteen when he left. I seem to recollect his plaguing mother for some time to go, but I paid no attention to it. I was playing store mostly. I used to pretend I had a little store under that oak there. . . . No, that's a white oak. I forget the old one's down. My mother sometimes gave me things for my store. Empty tins and bits of harness catches, and an occasional spool for an extra clerk. My chief decoration was a broken conch shell with a picture of Vesuvius set in a little mirror in its bell. My Great-Uncle Randolph had brought it home with him after squandering his fortune abroad in the 40's.

They pulled in their horses, these men in blue. There must have been a dozen of them as they sat their horses and talked down at the gate by the clay road. I watched them a moment in wonder, but without fear. I did not at first understand that they were Yankees. They were men in blue—the most surprising blue. I watched them for a moment without fear. Then I understood that they were Yankees. Fear seized me, and I crept along the box bushes and ran around the house to the brick kitchen, calling for mother.

"Yankees!" I cried. "The Yankees have come to steal Spotsylvania Court House." My father had brought the pony home the year before, when he was on furlough. I don't recollect now what moved me, but the moment I saw the pony I said: "I'm going to call him Spotsylvania Court House." I did not know what it meant, or where it came from, but the name must have been in my mind, for that's what I called him. It seemed a very gallant name. "Yankees!" I yelled. "They've come to steal him!"

"Nonsense!" my mother said sharply. "Nonsense! No grown man wants to ride your pony."

In those days there were no stoves. Our cooking was done over an open fireplace, and I can remember the Negroes around the hearth that day. There must have been about twenty Negroes who lived around the house. Yard niggers. My mother often complained about so many being around, but we couldn't drive them off. They were from the carriage house, and from the loom house where mother supervised the spinning. There was a cobbler's shop and a smokehouse; but they're gone, too, all of them. They were of whitewashed logs and they made up a town square for us. The kitchen was in a turmoil when I said "Yankees."

Amos was our butler and coachman. He was putting fresh logs on the fire when I ran into the kitchen. He dropped the wood.

"You want yo' gun, Mis' Sarah?"

My mother was the calmest woman I ever saw. "Bring me my rifle, Amos," she said.

I held her skirt and started crying. It was a print of gray woolen with little, fine, red flowers and green leaves dotting it. I can remember the pattern.

"Stop crying, everybody," she said. "Stop it!"

Amos brought the gun. My mother took my hand and walked through the brick passage to the house, and went to the front door. Amos walked behind her. Amos had a hat with a cockade. He never wore it that I ever knew, unless for the Sundays when the bishop came to Amelia to preach and then home to dinner with us. Amos wore his hat with the cockade now.

I stopped crying just to see that cockade. It was a badge of distinction, a thing that rendered us immune from ordinary things such as Yankees. I know that his hat, which he put on miraculously, dried my tears before we reached the front door. Amos opened the door for mother to pass to the front porch. We all went outside—my mother in her print dress and kitchen cap, with her long light rifle which my father had given her on their silver anniversary, and I with my storekeeper's paper cap, and Amos with the hat. My mother could bark a squirrel with her rifle. Many a time I had seen her do it.

I doubt that more than a minute had passed since I ran to the kitchen. They were still down on the road; and just as I had said, they were Yankees. My mother's hand tightened over mine when she saw them. You can't imagine how far that road seemed to me, a little child, that day.

"Be mighty careful, Mis' Sarah," I heard Amos saying. Then he began mumbling to one of the slaves, who was whimpering inside the door. "Go lead de stallion away," he was saying sharply under his breath. "Go lead de stallion away down to de ice house, and git inside and stay wid him."

Our ice house was double-planked, with sawdust filling, and was three-quarters sunk in the earth anyway. It was soundproof. I knew Amos was placing big Logan where he wouldn't neigh and be heard.

I could hear Rupe's trembling answer, "Dey'd kill me. Dey'd kill me."

Amos was looking over my mother's shoulder at the men in blue down on the road. "Ise going to kill you as soon as dey leave, if dey don't," he said. "Go take de stallion down to de ice house."

There wasn't a Negro on our place who would have shut himself in the icehouse with Logan. Except, of course, Amos. He and the stallion understood each other. Amos gave the stallion a pint of corn whiskey every Sunday morning. I know my father allowed Amos a quart of whiskey every week for his rheumatism, and the yard niggers said he gave half of it to Logan as regularly as he got it.

"It keeps him proud like me," Amos said. It was generally believed that Logan, when he heard the big meeting bell ringing over at Amelia every Sunday morning, would come to the bars and neigh until Amos brought him his whiskey. I know that every Sunday morning he would tear up the turf of his pasture, throwing his heels and charging even the least bit of grass or a butterfly, galloping in short circles from the gate to his stall.

Our stallion's name was Logan, I said. My father had two. But Logan killed the other one fighting in the snow, when a field hand left the gate open the winter before. I remember how my mother said she hated to write my father that the little stallion was dead. "Your father has enough worry with that regiment of no-accounts," she had said.

Two of the Yankees were detaching themselves from the main group on the road. One of them dismounted at the main gate and opened it.

"Stop trembling," my mother said to me. "Keep cool, Amos."

Amos narrowed his eyes and set the cockade hat at an angle. "Ise got de li'l' one-shot pistol," he said simply.

The Yankee who spurred forward through the gate is still in my vision. The picket fence has gone and the road is infinitely nearer, and one exaggerates childhood estimates; I am sure the Yankee's horse stood seventeen and a half hands at the shoulder. The Yankee simply lifted that big gray horse over the picket-fence gate, keeping to the gravel walk between the little, old-fashioned, button-chrysanthemum bushes.

I can never get the blue of his uniform jacket from my eyes. Not the yellow stripes or the brass buttons, nor the insignia at shoulder and cap are remembered vividly now. It is that powerful, flashing blue. It seemed immensely superior to the gray of my father and brothers. My father used to say "once in a blue moon" a lot when I was a child. Somehow, the blue of that smart jacket, under which the man's muscles moved and made it glint alive, seemed to have belonged to the man in the moon. That Yankee—the first I had ever seen—was a moon man. A blue—an intensely blue—moon man.

He pulled his horse in at the steps. These very steps. My mother waited for him to speak. Amos did not move. Amos must have looked a fine figure to that Yankee. For Yankees think that some of the colored people are handsome. Amos must have been a very handsome man. He was very tall, with a peaked forehead and tightly wound hair that grew down almost to his eyebrows, and his head was as round as an acorn. His head was not unlike an acorn from a black-oak tree, for it was of dark, polished shell with a close-fitting top of black.

I heard Amos sigh as the Yankee lifted his own hard little cap in a sweep and by some trick of leg brought the horse low at his right shoulder, as he swept his cap along its withers to the ground. Both horse and man in the gravel path managed a bow that made my face tingle.

The Yankee was very grave as he eyed the rifle and the group of us. "We hate to disturb you, madam," he said, "but we'd like to trouble you for some fire to light our pipes." That was all he said.

"Amos," said my mother gently, "take a shovel of fire down to those gentlemen by the big gate." I could not take my eyes from his blue, though I heard Amos going back through the hall. "For I am sure," my mother was saying, "that they are gentlemen."

The Yankee smiled at this, his big, strong teeth flashing above his brown beard. "A lady is never uncertain in matters of this distinction," he said, smiling. "We thank you for the fire." He wheeled his horse sharply and gathered up the bridle for a run at the fence gate, holding the gray's head high and thrusting his feet home in the stirrups. I always rode Spotsylvania with box stirrups.

"Wait," my mother called sharply. "Are your men hungry?"

The Yankee turned his horse again, the blue of his back changing to the brass and blue of his front. "We could only eat, madam," he said, "if you have plenty to spare."

"Bread and butter," I said. "That's all we have now."

"What is better?" mother asked me.

"I don't know of anything," the Yankee said seriously.

"She never asked you," I said.

"Ask the gentleman to excuse you," mother told me. In our family, if someone said something rude to another, he was always excused to go to his room until evening prayers.

"Excuse me," I said. But I couldn't let go mother's hand to leave.

"There's no offense," said the man in blue. "I've a little boy in New Hampshire just like you. I'd want him to give your father a call-down under similar circumstances."

"I had thought better of New Hampshire," my mother said, leaning against a column. . . . That column there.

Amos came by the side gate with a shovelful of smoking coals, and carrying a big twist of our bright tobacco. He had put his hat away and was wearing the cook's white cap, one freshly starched. I knew that he did not believe the men at the gate were gentlemen, whatever my mother said. But there was something about the man on the gray that made me feel Amos would have worn the cockade to offer him fire. His jacket was of a blue more brilliant than the others.

"Amos doesn't want to be free," I said, hostile.

"No one does," the Yankee said, showing his teeth again.

"Nobody is," my mother said. She turned to the doorway, still holding my hand. "Will you ask your men to come around to the kitchen?" She opened the door. "And will you please come in, sir?" she said, leaving the door open.

Mother held my hand, walking the long hall, but she set her rifle in the corner by the clock. We went into the kitchen. The people there were silent. "How much hot bread is there?" she asked old Lizzie.

Lizzie made our bread because she knew where to hide the silver coins and how many fern leaves to put into the conjure bag when it failed to rise.

" 'Bout six pans," she said.

Mother looked them all over. "We're going to feed some soldiers," she said. "They are just like other soldiers."

"They have on very blue coats," I said.

"That's their only difference from our men," she said. "I don't want any weeping and wailing and carrying on when they ride up. Do you all hear me?"

They all heard, because they didn't say anything. When they "yes, sir," and "I sho will" and "I declare I truly did hear you," it means that they have been thinking of something else and have not heard. They haven't changed much since they were sold into slavery here, and I doubt that they ever will, whether this is good or bad for us or for them.

The Yankees did not ride around to the kitchen. They left their horses, with a picket, around by the gate, and they walked in their long boots slowly to the kitchen door. How blue their coats were when they came in! Not quite so blue as the first Yankee's on the gray, but terrifyingly so. I think the people in the kitchen felt as I did at first about their being men from the moon.

I sat on Amos' knee as they were fed, and marked with satisfaction how the hot butter, when they bit into the cut squares of the hot bread, dripped down onto the blue of their jackets. One of them put his hand on my head and called me "Bub," but I twisted away from it and they let me alone. The short one with big yellow slashes on his arms said that this house sat on a hill, so they could hold it just as they were against a hundred men. They ate the bread as fast as Lizzie cut it and buttered it, and they drank gourds of water from the big bucket. Suddenly I missed mother.

I began to cry. I ran into the hall and to the porch. The man at the picket line was eating bread, just as the rest were. I don't know how he got it. I went into the dining room. The Yankee was there at the table, eating bread with a knife and fork, and drinking buttermilk from one of the tumblers mother used when the bishop came to preach.

Mother sat at the other end of the table, but her bread was hardly touched. The dining room was always in half darkness, because mother said sunlight would fade the painted paper of the ceiling and peel the varnish on the wainscot. The Yankee's buttons were reflected on the table. He seemed to give off a blue light. I went to mother's side and stood by her.

"Here," she said, giving me small mouthfuls. "Mind the rug."

"They'll be coming home, then?" she said to the Yankee.

I could feel deep down that mother wanted to cry. It was the way she did when she wouldn't cry the time they brought the news that Great-Uncle Randolph had killed Mr. Harrison's eldest son; when they had a fight with shotguns over the ownership of one of great-uncle's yard niggers. Mother didn't cry until they left her, but I know that afterward she went upstairs and sank down by her bed and held on to one of the posts and cried.

There was something about what this Yankee was saying that made her want to cry. I could tell the way she put her arm about me when she fed me the bread.

"It will be over by tomorrow or next day," the Yankee was saying. "We're Sheridan's men. All of us are back of him, and he can't possibly get out."

"Back of father?" I asked, frightened.

"Back of General Lee," mother said. "Your father's all right."

"My father's the best one of General Lee's men," I said.

"He's a wonderful man then," the Yankee said. He had finished his bread. "We must go on," he said. "We might bring something down upon this house, remaining here." He got up from the table, and he bowed, and remained bowing until mother left the dining room holding my hand. "We are deeply grateful," he said.

As we came into the hall, Amos was standing there. I knew he had been watching. The Yankee spoke to him. "God knows I wish we were to be the last to trouble you."

"Just let mine come home to me," mother said. "It is all that I ask."

"We shall," the Yankee said. "It isn't that they'll come home. It's the thousands who will follow them that I regret."

Outside, the men were on the picket lines again, each holding his own horse. They swung into saddles when the big man came to the door with us, only one of them remaining on the ground to hold the big gray.

"May my little boy send yours a present from New Hampshire?" the Yankee asked. "Does he like maple sugar? Blocks of it?"

"We've never discovered a sugar he doesn't like," mother said.

The kitchen people were at the entrance to the brick hall. They were all peering around the door. "He's a damned Yankee," I said, "but he won't hurt you."

The big Yankee half shut his eyes then and sighed. As he straightened up and clicked his heels together sharply, I heard the people scamper back down the hall to the kitchen. He bent low and kissed mother's hand. He turned then and walked slowly down the steps and along the gravel walk of the garden, never looking back, his cap in his hand. Then he opened the little picket gate he had jumped when he first rode up, and he continued slowly, taking the gray's bridle and swinging himself into the saddle as though he was too tired to mount and ride again.

One of his soldiers, who rode up by him, had a small flag on a long staff which he carried with its butt in a saddle sling. The big Yankee took this pennon, which was red and yellow with a big "8" and a little "F" and rode over to our main gate, where he drove it with a hard thrust into the soft soil that is always there in the clay when the spring rains have swept the yard of the winter's dust. They fell in behind him, the others on their horses, and they rode away leaving the pennon on our gate. At the turn in the road where the cornfield is now—there used to be a grove of hickories there—all of them stood in the stirrups and their swords flashed in the sun as they waved back to us. Then they cantered around the trees and out of sight.

My mother stood looking after them a long time. She reached into her pocket then and brought out her small embroidery scissors with the filigree handles.

"Here," she said. "You can sell some scissors in your store today."

The scissors were forbidden property. I was never to touch them, for mother said the Lord only knew whenever she would get any more.

"But you'll need them," I said, "with your hoops and your embroidery."

"We are done embroidering," she said.

I didn't want to take them, but with mother ready to cry any minute, I had to. I resolved to hide them in the moss walls of my little store and give them back to her someday. I started into the flower garden. But there was a sound of many guns firing up the road.

When father used to let the Negroes all take muzzle-loaders out for the rabbit hunting around Christmastime guns would be popping that way, for everyone shot quickly whenever the dogs jumped a cottontail. Father would never let me go if there was more than one gun, which Amos carried. At times when Amos carried me, he always looked to see where I was before he shot at a rabbit. But the firing up the road was heavier than we would hear on Christmas Eve.

I ran to my mother and held to her skirts, and she held me closely as we stood there, the popping coming nearer all the time. Amos came out again in his cockade and led mother back into the house and up the stairs. Then he ran to the front door and locked it and drew the curtain tight.

Upstairs we could hear the uproar from the kitchen. Mother ran out upon the sewing porch upstairs, for it overlooked the road. Presently the Yankees came in sight again. They were galloping, but each man would turn occasionally and rise in his stirrups and fire his short rifle—one not half as long as mother's—at something we could not see. I could see their blue coats sometimes over the trees and then between the branches as they streamed back down the road.

The last man to ride into view was the very blue one on the big gray. Mother caught me and sobbed when she saw him round the bend of the hickories that my father had to sell for timber later when he sent me off to the military academy. As they came back along the clay they bunched together at our gate and one of them tried to open it from horseback. His horse was fretting so that he had trouble seizing the catch. I knew anyway that he couldn't open it without dismounting. My brother Jim could do it, but that was because he practiced so hard. The latch was a bar that fell into a tongue catch, and there was a little iron trip which fell over it when it shot home.

The shots were coming nearer when the man on the gray rode into the men at the gate, waving his sword and beating them with the flat of it, trying to make them go farther down the road. He flashed his sword and got them off flying again, seizing the pennon out of the ground and thrusting it to the man with the yellow sleeves. They spurred up and started toward the bend going toward Amelia. There weren't so many of them as we had fed in the kitchen.

My mother gasped, and I could see over the trees more riders coming in great bunches, galloping hard. They were in gray, and their coat tails fluttered behind them in long ribbons, but their horses weren't so fast as the Yankee horses.

The big Yankee at our gate waited until they turned the bend and then began firing from a pistol. I think it shot four times before he threw it away. The gray riders were firing back at him now, galloping by the stable turnout. Father had said never to gallop a horse up to the stables, because that way gave the horse his will, which you should never give him if you wanted a good horse. But they weren't turning in at the stable.

"Run!" my mother screamed. "Run!"

I don't know if the big Yankee heard her. But he did just what he had done when he jumped our gate. He made a sweeping bow, horse and rider, and then turned and dashed off after his men.

There was a place up the road that father never could pack hard enough. No matter how many slaves worked on it, it was either mud or dust. It was a cloud of dust now from the stir the other Yankees made when they rode into it. The gray horse rode into it, the men in flying coat tails about a hundred yards back of him, from the stable gate to the bend there. The big Yankee fell from his horse just as the gray entered the dust.

I saw his blue jacket rolling as the other men galloped over him and into the dust after the others. Group and group of them came racing down our road and into the cloud of dust. I held to the banisters of the sewing porch, watching the clouds go past—clouds of yellow dust with figures, mostly hats and swords, rolling on the crest of them.

When it began to clear and they were all past, I discovered that Amos and mother had left me. They were down on the road, bending over the man in blue. The big gray stood there occasionally tripping over his bridle, waiting by them. Amos wanted to save his cockade from the dust, for he took it off and held it beneath his arm. Then he gave it to mother.

While she held the gray he picked up the Yankee and, folding him over the saddle, they came slowly up to the gate he had not let his men open. Mother carried the cockade and the little flat cap the Yankee had worn, and Amos led the gray. His jacket wasn't blue any more, for it was covered with dust, but just as they opened the gate I could see patches of it beneath his arms, shining as it had when he first put his gray over our picket fence and swept his cap along its withers in a bow from both man and horse. I went into mother's bedroom and cried on a post.

Amos took me over to Uncle Billy's to spend the afternoon, for he had sent word that the wood violets were out for the spring in the bowl of rocks we called the Wolf's Den. They say wolves used to live there. I stayed two days with Uncle Billy, and we spent many hours picking wood violets and shooting at a mark with his old gun. And I had a fine time playing store with two little black boys named Roy and Troy. When I came back home father and the boys were there. But they stayed in the back of the house all the time. It was so dusty on the porches, for the blue riders streamed by all day long.

When they found the embroidery scissors under that old stump today, it made me think of all this. I still remember how blue his jacket was when he lifted the gray over the picket fence and came down the gravel walk between those little button chrysanthemums.

WAR WITH SPAIN
1898

WAR WITH SPAIN
1898

As a reaction from the exhausting and bitter tension of the Civil War, the United States Government, to all intents and purposes, sold our fleet and disbanded our Army while our people applied themselves to money-making jobs both as an art and as a profession. If ever it could be said that our military and naval establishment entered into a period of dry rot, it was through the years 1868-1898.

Western Indian Wars of local significance occupied those officers and men of the Army who had courage and ambition, but schooled them in nothing but small-scale, irregular fighting, consequently, our invasion of Cuba revealed the Army in a confusion unknown since the sad, bad days of 1812.

It is odd that the inept campaigns of this war found so many scribes more than worthy of them, such as the clear, visual talent of Stephen Crane and the bitter satire of "Mr. Dooley."

One finds next to nothing in the mawkish, sentimental fiction typical of the times and none of the reporting by the yellow press of that era deserves reprinting.

Characteristic of the scandalous unpreparedness which distinguished the War Department, of that day—especially its Medical Department—is the fact that fever deaths far exceeded all other casualties. Richard Harding Davis' tale unhappily is an example of this war's aftermath.

SANTIAGO—THE PRICE OF THE HARNESS

by STEPHEN CRANE

TWENTY-FIVE MEN were making a road out of a path up the hillside. The light batteries in the rear were impatient to advance, but first must be done all that digging and smoothing which gains no encrusted medals from war. The men worked like gardeners, and a road was growing from the old pack-animal trail.

Trees arched from a field of guinea-grass which resembled young wild corn. The day was still and dry. The men working were dressed in the consistent blue of United States regulars. They looked indifferent, almost stolid, despite the heat and the labour. There was little talking. From time to time a Government pack-train, led by a sleek-sided tender bell-mare, came from one way or the other way, and the men stood aside as the strong, hard, black-and-tan animals crowded eagerly after their curious little feminine leader.

A volunteer staff-officer appeared, and, sitting on his horse in the middle of the work, asked the sergeant in command some questions which were apparently not relevant to any military business. Men straggling along on various duties almost invariably spun some kind of a joke as they passed.

A corporal and four men were guarding boxes of spare ammunition at the top of the hill, and one of the number often went to the foot of the hill swinging canteens.

The day wore down to the Cuban dusk, in which the shadows are all grim and of ghostly shape. The men began to lift their eyes from the shovels and picks, and glance in the direction of their camp. The sun threw his last lance through the foliage. The steep mountain-range on the right turned blue and as without detail as a curtain. The tiny ruby of light ahead meant that the ammunition-guard were cooking their supper. From somewhere in the world came a single rifle-shot.

Figures appeared, dim in the shadow of the trees. A murmur, a sigh of quiet relief, arose from the working party. Later, they swung up the hill in an unformed formation, beings always like soldiers, and unable

Reprinted from: *Wounds in the Rain,* by Stephen Crane, by permission of and special arrangement with Alfred A. Knopf, Inc.

even to carry a spade save like United States regular soldiers. As they passed through some fields, the bland white light of the end of the day feebly touched each hard bronze profile.

"Wonder if we'll git anythin' to eat," said Watkins, in a low voice.

"Should think so," said Nolan, in the same tone. They betrayed no impatience; they seemed to feel a kind of awe of the situation.

The sergeant turned. One could see the cool grey eye flashing under the brim of the campaign hat. "What in hell you fellers kickin' about?" he asked. They made no reply, understanding that they were being suppressed.

As they moved on, a murmur arose from the tall grass on either hand. It was the noise from the bivouac of ten thousand men, although one saw practically nothing from the low-cart roadway. The sergeant led his party up a wet clay bank and into a trampled field. Here were scattered tiny white shelter tents, and in the darkness they were luminous like the rearing stones in a graveyard. A few fires burned blood-red, and the shadowy figures of men moved with no more expression of detail than there is in the swaying of foliage on a windy night.

The working party felt their way to where their tents were pitched. A man suddenly cursed; he had mislaid something, and he knew he was not going to find it that night. Watkins spoke again with the monotony of a clock, "Wonder if we'll git anythin' to eat."

Martin, with eyes turned pensively to the stars, began a treatise. "Them Spaniards——"

"Oh, quit it," cried Nolan. "What th' piper do you know about th' Spaniards, you fat-headed Dutchman? Better think of your belly, you blunderin' swine, an' what you're goin' to put in it, grass or dirt."

A laugh, a sort of a deep growl, arose from the prostrate men. In the meantime the sergeant had reappeared and was standing over them. "No rations to-night," he said gruffly, and turning on his heel, walked away.

This announcement was received in silence. But Watkins had flung himself face downward, and putting his lips close to a tuft of grass, he formulated oaths. Martin arose and, going to his shelter, crawled in sulkily. After a long interval Nolan said aloud, "Hell!" Grierson, enlisted for the war, raised a querulous voice. "Well, I wonder when we *will* git fed?"

From the ground about him came a low chuckle, full of ironical comment upon Grierson's lack of certain qualities which the other men felt themselves to possess.

II

In the cold light of dawn the men were on their knees, packing, strapping, and buckling. The comic toy hamlet of shelter-tents had been wiped out as if by a cyclone. Through the trees could be seen the crimson of a light battery's blankets, and the wheels creaked like the sound of a musketry fight. Nolan, well gripped by his shelter tent, his blanket, and his cartridge-belt, and bearing his rifle, advanced upon a small group of men who were hastily finishing a can of coffee.

"Say, give us a drink, will yeh?" he asked, wistfully. He was as sad-eyed as an orphan beggar.

Every man in the group turned to look him straight in the face. He had asked for the principal ruby out of each one's crown. There was a grim silence. Then one said, "What fer?" Nolan cast his glance to the ground, and went away abashed.

But he espied Watkins and Martin surrounding Grierson, who had gained three pieces of hard-tack by mere force of his audacious inexperience. Grierson was fending his comrades off tearfully.

"Now, don't be damn pigs," he cried. "Hold on a minute." Here Nolan asserted a claim. Grierson groaned. Kneeling piously, he divided the hard-tack with minute care into four portions. The men, who had had their heads together like players watching a wheel of fortune, arose suddenly, each chewing. Nolan interpolated a drink of water, and sighed contentedly.

The whole forest seemed to be moving. From the field on the other side of the road a column of men in blue was slowly pouring; the battery had creaked on ahead; from the rear came a hum of advancing regiments. Then from a mile away rang the noise of a shot; then another shot; in a moment the rifles there were drumming, drumming, drumming. The artillery boomed out suddenly. A day of battle was begun.

The men made no exclamations. They rolled their eyes in the direction of the sound, and then swept with a calm glance the forests and the hills which surrounded them, implacably mysterious forests and hills which lent to every rifle-shot the ominous quality which belongs to secret assassination. The whole scene would have spoken to the private soldiers of ambushes, sudden flank attacks, terrible disasters, if it were not for those cool gentlemen with shoulder-straps and swords who, the private soldiers knew, were of another world and omnipotent for the business.

The battalions moved out into the mud and began a leisurely march in the damp shade of the trees. The advance of two batteries had churned the black soil into a formidable paste. The brown leggings of the men, stained with mud of other days, took on a deeper colour. Perspiration broke gently out on the reddish faces. With his heavy roll of blanket and the half of a shelter-tent crossing his right shoulder and under his left arm, each man presented the appearance of being clasped from behind, wrestler fashion, by a pair of thick white arms.

There was something distinctive in the way they carried their rifles. There was the grace of an old hunter somewhere in it, the grace of a man whose rifle has become absolutely a part of himself. Furthermore, almost every blue shirt sleeve was rolled to the elbow, disclosing fore-arms of almost incredible brawn. The rifles seemed light, almost fragile, in the hands that were at the end of these arms, never fat but always with rolling muscles and veins that seemed on the point of bursting. And another thing was the silence and the marvellous impassivity of the faces as the column made its slow way toward where the whole forest splut-tered and fluttered with battle.

Opportunely, the battalion was halted a-straddle of a stream, and before it again moved, most of the men had filled their canteens. The firing increased. Ahead and to the left a battery was booming at method-ical intervals, while the infantry racket was that continual drumming which, after all, often sounds like rain on a roof. Directly ahead one could hear the deep voices of field-pieces.

Some wounded Cubans were carried by in litters improvised from hammocks swung on poles. One had a ghastly cut in the throat, probably from a fragment of shell, and his head was turned as if Providence particularly wished to display this wide and lapping gash to the long column that was winding toward the front. And another Cuban, shot through the groin, kept up a continual wail as he swung from the tread of his bearers. "Ay—ee! Ay—ee! Madre mia! Madre mia!" He sang this bitter ballad into the ears of at least three thousand men as they slowly made way for his bearers on the narrow woodpath. These wounded in-surgents were, then, to a large part of the advancing army, the visible messengers of bloodshed and death, and the men regarded them with thoughtful awe. This doleful sobbing cry—"Madre mia"—was a tangible consequent misery of all that firing on in front into which the men knew they were soon to be plunged. Some of them wished to inquire of the bearers the details of what had happened; but they could not speak Spanish, and so it was as if fate had intentionally sealed the lips of all in order that even meagre information might not leak out concerning this mystery—battle. On the other hand, many unversed private soldiers looked upon the unfortunate as men who had seen thousands maimed and bleeding, and absolutely could not conjure any further interest in such scenes.

A young staff-officer passed on horseback. The vocal Cuban was always wailing, but the officer wheeled past the bearers without heeding anything. And yet he never before had seen such a sight. His case was different from that of the private soldiers. He heeded nothing because he was busy—immensely busy and hurried with a multitude of reasons and desires for doing his duty perfectly. His whole life had been a mere period of preliminary reflection for this situation, and he had no clear idea of anything save his obligation as an officer. A man of this kind might be stupid; it is conceivable that in remote cases certain bumps on his head might be composed entirely of wood; but those traditions of fidelity and courage which have been handed to him from generation to generation, and which he has tenaciously preserved despite the persecution of legislators and the indifference of his country, make it incredible that in battle he should ever fail to give his best blood and his best thought for his general, for his men, and for himself. And so this young officer in the shapeless hat and the torn and dirty shirt failed to heed the wails of the wounded man, even as the pilgrim fails to heed the world as he raises his illumined face toward his purpose—rightly or wrongly, his purpose—his sky of the ideal of duty; and the wonderful part of it is, that he is guided by an ideal which he has himself created, and has alone protected from attack. The young man was merely an officer in the United States regular army.

The column swung across a shallow ford and took a road which passed the right flank of one of the American batteries. On a hill it was booming and belching great clouds of white smoke. The infantry looked up with interest. Arrayed below the hill and behind the battery were the horses and limbers, the riders checking their pawing mounts, and behind each rider a red blanket flamed against the fervent green of the bushes. As the infantry moved along the road, some of the battery horses turned at the noise of the trampling feet and surveyed the men with eyes as deep as wells, serene, mournful, generous eyes, lit heart-breakingly with something that was akin to a philosophy, a religion of self-sacrifice—oh, gallant, gallant horses!

"I know a feller in that battery," said Nolan, musingly. "A driver."

"Dam sight rather be a gunner," said Martin.

"Why would ye?" said Nolan, opposingly.

"Well, I'd take my chances as a gunner b'fore I'd sit way up in th' air on a raw-boned plug an' git shot at."

"Aw——" began Nolan.

"They've had some losses t'-day all right," interrupted Grierson.

"Horses?" asked Watkins.

"Horses and men too," said Grierson.

"How d'yeh know?"

"A feller told me there by the ford."

They kept only a part of their minds bearing on this discussion because they could already hear high in the air the wire-string note of the enemy's bullets.

III

The road taken by this battalion as it followed other battalions is something less than a mile long in its journey across a heavily-wooded plain. It is greatly changed now—in fact it was metamorphosed in two days; but at that time it was a mere track through dense shrubbery, from which rose great dignified arching trees. It was, in fact, a path through a jungle.

The battalion had no sooner left the battery in rear when bullets began to drive overhead. They made several different sounds, but as these were mainly high shots it was usual for them to make the faint note of a vibrant string, touched elusively, half-dreamily.

The military balloon, a fat, wavering, yellow thing, was leading the advance like some new conception of war-god. Its bloated mass shone above the trees, and served incidentally to indicate to the men at the rear that comrades were in advance. The track itself exhibited for all its visible length a closely-knit procession of soldiers in blue with breasts crossed with white shelter-tents. The first ominous order of battle came down the line. "Use the cut-off. Don't use the magazine until you're ordered." Non-commissioned officers repeated the command gruffly. A sound of clicking locks rattled along the columns. All men knew that the time had come.

The front had burst out with a roar like a brushfire. The balloon was dying, dying a gigantic and public death before the eyes of two armies. It quivered, sank, faded into the trees amid the flurry of a battle that was suddenly and tremendously like a storm.

The American battery thundered behind the men with a shock that seemed likely to tear the backs of their heads off. The Spanish shrapnel fled on a line to their left, swirling and swishing in supernatural velocity. The noise of the rifle bullets broke in their faces like the noise of so many lamp-chimneys or sped overhead in swift cruel spitting. And at the front the battle-sound, as if it were simply music, was beginning to swell and swell until the volleys rolled like a surf.

The officers shouted hoarsely, "Come on, men! Hurry up, boys! Come on now! Hurry up!" The soldiers, running heavily in their accoutrements, dashed forward. A baggage guard was swiftly detailed; the men tore their rolls from their shoulders as if the things were afire. The battalion, stripped for action, again dashed forward.

"Come on, men! Come on!" To them the battle was as yet merely a road through the woods crowded with troops, who lowered their heads anxiously as the bullets fled high. But a moment later the column wheeled abruptly to the left and entered a field of tall green grass. The line scattered to a skirmish formation. In front was a series of knolls treed sparsely like orchards; and although no enemy was visible, these knolls were all popping and spitting with rifle-fire. In some places there were to be seen long grey lines of dirt, intrenchments. The American shells were kicking up reddish clouds of dust from the brow of one of the knolls, where stood a pagoda-like house. It was not much like a battle with men; it was a battle with a bit of charming scenery, enigmatically potent for death.

Nolan knew that Martin had suddenly fallen. "What——" he began. "They've hit me," said Martin.

"Jesus!" said Nolan.

Martin lay on the ground, clutching his left forearm just below the elbow with all the strength of his right hand. His lips were pursed ruefully. He did not seem to know what to do. He continued to stare at his arm.

Then suddenly the bullets drove at them low and hard. The men flung themselves face downward in the grass. Nolan lost all thought of his friend. Oddly enough, he felt somewhat like a man hiding under a bed, and he was just as sure that he could not raise his head high without being shot as a man hiding under a bed is sure that he cannot raise his head without bumping it.

A lieutenant was seated in the grass just behind him. He was in the careless and yet rigid pose of a man balancing a loaded plate on his knee at a picnic. He was talking in soothing paternal tones.

"Now, don't get rattled. We're all right here. Just as safe as being in church. . . . They're all going high. Don't mind them. . . . Don't mind them. . . . They're all going high. We've got them rattled and they can't shoot straight. Don't mind them."

The sun burned down steadily from a pale blue sky upon the crackling woods and knolls and fields. From the roar of musketry it might have been that the celestial heat was frying this part of the world.

Nolan snuggled close to the grass. He watched a grey line of intrenchments, above which floated the veriest gossamer of smoke. A flag lolled on a staff behind it. The men in the trench volleyed whenever an American shell exploded near them. It was some kind of infantile defiance. Frequently a bullet came from the woods directly behind Nolan and his comrades. They thought at the time that these bullets were from the rifle of some incompetent soldier of their own side.

There was no cheering. The men would have looked about them, wondering where was the army, if it were not that the crash of the fighting for the distance of a mile denoted plainly enough where was the army.

Officially, the battalion had not yet fired a shot; there had been merely some irreponsible popping by men on the extreme left flank. But it was known that the lieutenant-colonel who had been in command was dead—shot through the heart—and that the captains were thinned down to two. At the rear went on a long tragedy, in which men, bent and hasty, hurried to shelter with other men, helpless, dazed, and bloody. Nolan knew of it all from the hoarse and affrighted voices which he heard as he lay flattened in the grass. There came to him a sense of exultation. Here, then, was one of those dread and lurid situations, which in a nation's history stand out in crimson letters, becoming a tale of blood to stir generation after generation. And he was in it, and unharmed. If he lived through the battle, he would be a hero of the desperate fight at ——; and here he wondered for a second what fate would be pleased to bestow as a name for this battle.

But it is quite sure that hardly another man in the battalion was engaged in any thoughts concerning the historic. On the contrary, they deemed it ill that they were being badly cut up on a most unimportant occasion. It would have benefited the conduct of whoever were weak if they had known that they were engaged in a battle that would be famous for ever.

IV

Martin had picked himself up from where the bullet had knocked him and addressed the lieutenant. "I'm hit, sir," he said.

The lieutenant was very busy. "All right, all right," he said, just heeding the man enough to learn where he was wounded. "Go over that way. You ought to see a dressing-station under those trees."

Martin found himself dizzy and sick. The sensation in his arm was distinctly galvanic. The feeling was so strange that he could wonder at times if a wound was really what ailed him. Once, in this dazed way, he examined his arm; he saw the hole. Yes, he was shot; that was it. And more than in any other way it affected him with a profound sadness.

As directed by the lieutenant, he went to the clump of trees, but he found no dressing-station there. He found only a dead soldier lying with his face buried in his arms and with his shoulders humped high as if he were convulsively sobbing. Martin decided to make his way to the road, deeming that he thus would better his chances of getting to a surgeon. But he suddenly found his way blocked by a fence of barbed wire. Such was his mental condition that he brought up at a rigid halt before this fence, and stared stupidly at it. It did not seem to him possible that this obstacle could be defeated by any means. The fence was there, and it stopped his progress. He could not go in that direction.

But as he turned he espied that procession of wounded men, strange pilgrims, that had already worn a path in the tall grass. They were passing through a gap in the fence. Martin joined them. The bullets were flying over them in sheets, but many of them bore themselves as men who had now exacted from fate a singular immunity. Generally there were no outcries, no kicking, no talk at all. They too, like Martin, seemed buried in a vague but profound melancholy.

But there was one who cried out loudly. A man shot in the head was being carried arduously by four comrades, and he continually yelled one word that was terrible, in its primitive strength,—"Bread! Bread! Bread!" Following him and his bearers were a limping crowd of men less cruelly wounded, who kept their eyes always fixed on him, as if they gained from his extreme agony some balm for their own sufferings.

"Bread! Give me bread!"

Martin plucked a man by the sleeve. The man had been shot in the foot, and was making his way with the help of a curved, incompetent stick. It is an axiom of war that wounded men can never find straight sticks.

"What's the matter with that feller?" asked Martin.

"Nutty," said the man.

"Why is he?"

"Shot in th' head," answered the other, impatiently.

The wail of the sufferer arose in the field amid the swift rasp of bullets and the boom and shatter of shrapnel. "Bread! Bread! Oh, God, can't you give me bread? Bread!" The bearers of him were suffering exquisite

agony, and often they exchanged glances which exhibited their despair
of ever getting free of this tragedy. It seemed endless.

"Bread! Bread! Bread!"

But despite the fact that there was always in the way of this crowd
a wistful melancholy, one must know that there were plenty of men who
laughed, laughed at their wounds whimsically, quaintly inventing odd
humours concerning bicycles and cabs, extracting from this shedding of
their blood a wonderful amount of material for cheerful badinage, and,
with their faces twisted from pain as they stepped, they often joked like
music-hall stars. And perhaps this was the most tearful part of all.

They trudged along a road until they reached a ford. Here under the
eave of the bank lay a dismal company. In the mud and in the damp
shade of some bushes were a half-hundred pale-faced men prostrate. Two
or three surgeons were working there. Also, there was a chaplain, grim-
mouthed, resolute, his surtout discarded. Overhead always was that incessant maddening wail of bullets.

Martin was standing gazing drowsily at the scene when a surgeon
grabbed him. "Here, what's the matter with you?" Martin was daunted.
He wondered what he had done that the surgeon should be so angry
with him.

"In the arm," he muttered, half-shamefacedly.

After the surgeon had hastily and irritably bandaged the injured
member he glared at Martin and said, "You can walk all right, can't
you?"

"Yes, sir," said Martin.

"Well, now, you just make tracks down that road."

"Yes, sir." Martin went meekly off. The doctor had seemed exasperated
almost to the point of madness.

The road was at this time swept with the fire of a body of Spanish
sharpshooters who had come cunningly around the flanks of the American
army, and were now hidden in the dense foliage that lined both sides
of the road. They were shooting at everything. The road was as crowded
as a street in a city, and at an absurdly short range they emptied their
rifles at the passing people. They were aided always by the over-sweep
from the regular Spanish line of battle.

Martin was sleepy from his wound. He saw tragedy follow tragedy,
but they created in him no feeling of horror.

A man with a red cross on his arm was leaning against a great tree.
Suddenly he tumbled to the ground, and writhed for a moment in the
way of a child oppressed with colic. A comrade immediately began to

bustle importantly. "Here," he called to Martin, "help me carry this man, will you?"

Martin looked at him with dull scorn. "I'll be damned if I do," he said. "Can't carry myself, let alone somebody else."

This answer, which rings now so inhuman, pitiless, did not affect the other man. "Well, all right," he said. "Here comes some other fellers." The wounded man had now turned blue-grey; his eyes were closed; his body shook in a gentle, persistent chill.

Occasionally Martin came upon dead horses, their limbs sticking out and up like stakes. One beast mortally shot, was beseiged by three or four men who were trying to push it into the bushes, where it could live its brief time of anguish without thrashing to death any of the wounded men in the gloomy procession.

The mule train, with extra ammunition, charged toward the front, still led by the tinkling bellmare.

An ambulance was stuck momentarily in the mud, and above the crack of battle one could hear the familiar objurgations of the driver as he whirled his lash.

Two privates were having a hard time with a wounded captain, whom they were supporting to the rear. He was half cursing, half wailing out the information that he not only would not go another step toward the rear, but that he was certainly going to return at once to the front. They begged, pleaded at great length as they continually headed him off. They were not unlike two nurses with an exceptionally bad and headstrong little duke.

The wounded soldiers paused to look impassively upon this struggle. They were always like men who could not be aroused by anything further.

The visible hospital was mainly straggling thickets intersected with narrow paths, the ground being covered with men. Martin saw a busy person with a book and a pencil, but he did not approach him to become officially a member of the hospital. All he desired was rest and immunity from nagging. He took seat painfully under a bush and leaned his back upon the trunk. There he remained thinking, his face wooden.

v

"My Gawd," said Nolan, squirming on his belly in the grass, "I can't stand this much longer."

Then suddenly every rifle in the firing line seemed to go off of its own accord. It was the result of an order, but few men heard the order; in the main they had fired because they heard others fire, and their sense was so quick that the volley did not sound too ragged. These marksmen had been lying for nearly an hour in stony silence, their sights adjusted, their fingers fondling their rifles, their eyes staring at the intrenchments of the enemy. The battalion had suffered heavy losses, and these losses had been hard to bear, for a soldier always reasons that men lost during a period of inaction are men badly lost.

The line now sounded like a great machine set to running frantically in the open air, the bright sunshine of a green field. To the prut of the magazine rifles was added the under-chorus of the clicking mechanism, steady and swift, as if the hand of one operator was controlling it all. It reminds one always of a loom, a great grand steel loom, clinking, clanking, plunking, plinking, to weave a woof of thin red threads, the cloth of death. By the men's shoulders under their eager hands dropped continually the yellow empty shells, spinning into the crushed grass blades to remain there and mark for the belated eye the line of a battalion's fight.

All impatience, all rebellious feeling, had passed out of the men as soon as they had been allowed to use their weapons against the enemy. They now were absorbed in this business of hitting something, and all the long training at the rifle ranges, all the pride of the marksman which had been so long alive in them, made them forget for the time everything but shooting. They were as deliberate and exact as so many watchmakers.

A new sense of safety was rightfully upon them. They knew that those mysterious men in the high far trenches in front were having the bullets sping in their faces with relentless and remarkable precision; they knew, in fact, that they were now doing the thing which they had been trained endlessly to do, and they knew they were doing it well. Nolan, for instance, was overjoyed. "Plug 'em," he said: "Plug 'em." He laid his face to his rifle as if it were his mistress. He was aiming under the shadow of a certain portico of a fortified house: there he could faintly see a long black line which he knew to be a loop-hole cut for riflemen, and he knew that every shot of his was going there under the portico, mayhap through the loop-hole to the brain of another man like himself. He loaded the awkward magazine of his rifle again and again. He was so intent that he did not know of new orders until he saw the men about him scrambling to their feet and running forward, crouching low as they ran.

He heard a shout. "Come on, boys! We can't be last! We're going up! We're going up." He sprang to his feet and, stooping, ran with the others.

Something fine, soft, gentle, touched his heart as he ran. He had loved the regiment, the army, because the regiment, the army, was his life,—he had no other outlook; and now these men, his comrades, were performing his dream-scenes for him; they were doing as he had ordained in his visions. It is curious that in this charge he considered himself as rather unworthy. Although he himself was in the assault with the rest of them, it seemed to him that his comrades were dazzlingly courageous. His part, to his mind, was merely that of a man who was going along with the crowd.

He saw Grierson biting madly with his pincers at a barbed-wire fence. They were half-way up the beautiful sylvan slope; there was no enemy to be seen, and yet the landscape rained bullets. Somebody punched him violently in the stomach. He thought dully to lie down and rest, but instead he fell with a crash.

The sparse line of men in blue shirts and dirty slouch hats swept on up the hill. He decided to shut his eyes for a moment because he felt very dreamy and peaceful. It seemed only a minute before he heard a voice say, "There he is." Grierson and Watkins had come to look for him. He searched their faces at once and keenly, for he had a thought that the line might be driven down the hill and leave him in Spanish hands. But he saw that everything was secure, and he prepared no questions.

"Nolan," said Grierson clumsily, "do you know me?"

The man on the ground smiled softly. "Of course I know you, you chowder-faced monkey. Why wouldn't I know you?"

Watkins knelt beside him. "Where did they plug you, old boy?"

Nolan was somewhat dubious. "It ain't much. I don't think but it's somewheres there." He laid a finger on the pit of his stomach. They lifted his shirt, and then privately they exchanged a glance of horror.

"Does it hurt, Jimmie?" said Grierson, hoarsely.

"No," said Nolan, "it don't hurt any, but I feel sort of dead-to-the-world and numb all over. I don't think it's very bad."

"Oh, it's all right," said Watkins.

"What I need is a drink," said Nolan, grinning at them. "I'm chilly—lying on this damp ground."

"It ain't very damp, Jimmie," said Grierson.

"Well, it is damp," said Nolan, with sudden irritability. "I can feel it. I'm wet, I tell you—wet through—just from lying here."

They answered hastily. "Yes, that's so, Jimmie. It *is* damp. That's so."

"Just put your hand under my back and see how wet the ground is," he said.

"No," they answered. "That's all right, Jimmie. We know it's wet."

"Well, put your hand under and see," he cried, stubbornly.

"Oh, never mind, Jimmie."

"No," he said, in a temper. "See for yourself." Grierson seemed to be afraid of Nolan's agitation, and so he slipped a hand under the prostrate man, and presently withdrew it covered with blood. "Yes," he said, hiding his hand carefully from Nolan's eyes, "you were right, Jimmie."

"Of course I was," said Nolan, contendedly closing his eyes. "This hillside holds water like a swamp." After a moment he said, "Guess I ought to know. I'm flat here on it, and you fellers are standing up."

He did not know he was dying. He thought he was holding an argument on the condition of the turf.

VI

"Cover his face," said Grierson, in a low and husky voice afterwards.

"What'll I cover it with?" said Watkins.

They looked at themselves. They stood in their shirts, trousers, leggings, shoes; they had nothing.

"Oh," said Grierson, "here's his hat." He brought it and laid it on the face of the dead man. They stood for a time. It was apparent that they thought it essential and decent to say or do something. Finally Watkins said in a broken voice, "Aw, it's a damn shame." They moved slowly off toward the firing line.

In the blue gloom of evening, in one of the fever-tents, the two rows of still figures became hideous, charnel. The languid movement of a hand was surrounded with spectral mystery, and the occasional painful twisting of a body under a blanket was terrifying, as if dead men were moving in their graves under the sod. A heavy odour of sickness and medicine hung in the air.

"What regiment are you in?" said a feeble voice.

"Twenty-ninth Infantry," answered another voice.

"Twenty-ninth! Why, the man on the other side of me is in the Twenty-ninth."

"He is? . . . Hey, there, partner, are you in the Twenty-ninth?"

A third voice merely answered wearily. "Martin of C Company."

"What? Jack, is that you?"

"It's part of me. . . . Who are you?"

"Grierson, you fat-head. I thought you were wounded."

There was the noise of a man gulping a great drink of water, and at its conclusion Martin said, "I am."

"Well, what you doin' in the fever-place, then?"

Martin replied with drowsy impatience. "Got the fever too."

"Gee!" said Grierson.

Thereafter there was silence in the fever-tent, save for the noise made by a man over in a corner—a kind of man always found in an American crowd—a heroic, implacable comedian and patriot, of a humour that has bitterness and ferocity and love in it, and he was wringing from the situation a grim meaning by singing the "Star-Spangled Banner" with all the ardour which could be procured from his fever-stricken body.

"Billie," called Martin in a low voice, "where's Jimmie Nolan?"

"He's dead," said Grierson.

A triangle of raw gold light shone on a side of the tent. Somewhere in the valley an engine's bell was ringing, and it sounded of peace and home as if it hung on a cow's neck.

"And where's Ike Watkins?"

"Well, he ain't dead, but he got shot through the lungs. They say he ain't got much show."

Through the clouded odours of sickness and medicine rang the dauntless voice of the man in the corner.

SANTIAGO—VIRTUE IN WAR

by STEPHEN CRANE

GATES HAD LEFT the regular army in 1890, those parts of him which had not been frozen having been well fried. He took with him nothing but an oaken constitution and a knowledge of the plains and the best wishes of his fellow-officers. The Standard Oil Company differs from the United States Government in that it understands the value of the loyal and intelligent services of good men and is almost certain to reward them at the

Reprinted from: Wounds in the Rain, by Stephen Crane, by permission of and special arrangement with Alfred A. Knopf, Inc.

expense of incapable men. This curious practice emanates from no benef-
icent emotion of the Standard Oil Company, on whose feelings you
could not make a scar with a hammer and chisel. It is simply that the
Standard Oil Company knows more than the United States Government
and makes use of virtue whenever virtue is to its advantage. In 1890
Gates really felt in his bones that, if he lived a rigorously correct life and
several score of his class-mates and intimate friends died off, he would get
command of a troop of horse by the time he was unfitted by age to be
an active cavalry leader. He left the service of the United States and
entered the service of the Standard Oil Company. In the course of time
he knew that, if he lived a rigorously correct life, his position and income
would develop strictly in parallel with the worth of his wisdom and
experience, and he would not have to walk on the corpses of his friends.

But he was not happier. Part of his heart was in a barracks, and it was
not enough to discourse of the old regiment over the port and cigars to
ears which were polite enough to betray a languid ignorance. Finally
came the year 1898, and Gates dropped the Standard Oil Company as if
it were hot. He hit the steel trail to Washington and there fought the first
serious action of the war. Like most Americans, he had a native State,
and one morning he found himself major in a volunteer infantry regiment whose voice had a peculiar sharp twang to it which he could
remember from childhood. The colonel welcomed the West Pointer with
loud cries of joy; the lieutenant-colonel looked at him with the pebbly eye
of distrust; and the senior major, having had up to this time the best
battalion in the regiment, strongly disapproved of him. There were only
two majors, so the lieutenant-colonel commanded the first battalion,
which gave him an occupation. Lieutenant-colonels under the new rules
do not always have occupations. Gates got the third battalion—four companies commanded by intelligent officers who could gauge the opinions
of their men at two thousand yards and govern themselves accordingly.
The battalion was immensely interested in the new major. It thought
it ought to develop views about him. It thought it was its blankety-blank
business to find out immediately if it liked him personally. In the company streets the talk was nothing else. Among the non-commissioned
officers there were eleven old soldiers of the regular army, and they
knew—and cared—that Gates had held commission in the "Sixteenth
Cavalry"—as *Harper's Weekly* says. Over this fact they rejoiced and were
glad, and they stood by to jump lively when he took command. He would
know his work and he would know *their* work, and then in battle there

would be killed only what men were absolutely necessary and the sick list would be comparatively free of fools.

The commander of the second battalion had been called by an Atlanta paper, "Major Rickets C. Carmony, the commander of the second battalion of the 307th ——, is when at home one of the biggest wholesale hardware dealers in his State. Last evening he had ice-cream, at his own expense, served out at the regular mess of the battalion, and after dinner the men gathered about his tent where three hearty cheers for the popular major were given." Carmony had bought twelve copies of this newspaper and mailed them home to his friends.

In Gates's battalion there were more kicks than ice-cream, and there was no ice-cream at all. Indignation ran high at the rapid manner in which he proceeded to make soldiers of them. Some of his officers hinted finally that the men wouldn't stand it. They were saying that they had enlisted to fight for their country—yes, but they weren't going to be bullied day in and day out by a perfect stranger. They were patriots, they were, and just as good men as ever stepped—just as good as Gates or anybody like him. But, gradually, despite itself, the battalion progressed. The men were not altogether conscious of it. They evolved rather blindly. Presently there were fights with Carmony's crowd as to which was the better battalion at drills, and at last there was no argument. It was generally admitted that Gates commanded the crack battalion. The men, believing that the beginning and the end of all soldiering was in these drills of precision, were somewhat reconciled to their major when they began to understand more of what he was trying to do for them, but they were still fiery untamed patriots of lofty pride and they resented his manner toward them. It was abrupt and sharp.

The time came when everybody knew that the Fifth Army Corps was the corps designated for the first active service in Cuba. The officers and men of the 307th observed with despair that their regiment was not in the Fifth Army Corps. The colonel was a strategist. He understood everything in a flash. Without a moment's hesitation he obtained leave and mounted the night express for Washington. There he drove Senators and Congressmen in span, tandem and four-in-hand. With the telegraph he stirred so deeply the governor, the people and the newspapers of his State that whenever on a quiet night the President put his head out of the White House he could hear the distant vast commonwealth humming with indignation. And as it is well known that the Chief Executive listens to the voice of the people, the 307th was transferred to the Fifth Army Corps. It was sent at once to Tampa, where it was brigaded with two dusty regiments of regulars, who looked at it calmly and said nothing. The brigade commander happened to be no less a person than Gates's old colonel in the "Sixteenth Cavalry"—as *Harper's Weekly* says—and Gates was cheered. The old man's rather solemn look brightened when he saw Gates in the 307th. There was a great deal of battering and pounding and banging for the 307th at Tampa, but the men stood it more in wonder than in anger. The two regular regiments carried them along when they could, and when they couldn't waited impatiently for them to come up. Undoubtedly the regulars wished the volunteers were in garrison at Sitka, but they said practically nothing. They minded their own regiments. The colonel was an invaluable man in a telegraph office. When came the scramble for transports the colonel retired to a telegraph office and talked so ably to Washington that the authorities pushed a number of corps aside and made way for the 307th, as if on it depended everything. The regiment got one of the best transports, and after a series of delays and some starts, and an equal number of returns, they finally sailed for Cuba.

II

Now Gates had a singular adventure on the second morning after his arrival at Atlanta to take his post as a major in the 307th.

He was in his tent, writing, when suddenly the flap was flung away and a tall young private stepped inside.

"Well, Maje," said the newcomer, genially, "how goes it?"

The major's head flashed up, but he spoke without heat.

"Come to attention and salute."

"Huh!" said the private.

"Come to attention and salute."

The private looked at him in resentful amazement, and then inquired:

"Ye ain't mad, are ye? Ain't nothin' to get huffy about, is there?"

"I— Come to attention and salute."

"Well," drawled the private, as he stared, "seein' as ye are so darn perticular, I don't care if I do—if it'll make yer meals set on yer stomick any better."

Drawing a long breath and grinning ironically, he lazily pulled his heels together and saluted with a flourish.

"There," he said, with a return to his earlier genial manner. "How's that suit ye, Maje?"

There was a silence which to an impartial observer would have seemed pregnant with dynamite and bloody death. Then the major cleared his throat and coldly said:

"And now, what is your business?"

"Who—me?" asked the private. "Oh, I just sorter dropped in." With a deeper meaning he added: "Sorter dropped in in a friendly way, thinkin' ye was mebbe a different kind of a feller from what ye be."

The inference was clearly marked.

It was now Gates's turn to stare, and stare he unfeignedly did.

"Go back to your quarters," he said at length.

The volunteer became very angry.

"Oh, ye needn't be so up-in-th'-air, need ye? Don't know's I'm dead anxious to inflict my company on yer since I've had a good look at ye. There may be men in this here battalion what's had just as much edjewca-tion as you have, and I'm damned if they ain't got better *manners*. Good-mornin'," he said, with dignity; and, passing out of the tent, he flung the flap back in place with an air of slamming is as if it had been a door. He made his way back to his company street, striding high. He was furious. He met a large crowd of his comrades.

"What's the matter, Lige?" asked one, who noted his temper.

"Oh, nothin'," answered Lige, with terrible feeling. "Nothin'. I jest been lookin' over the new major—that's all."

"What's he like?" asked another.

"Like?" cried Lige. "He's like nothin'. He ain't out'n the same kittle as us. No. Gawd made him all by himself—sep'rate. He's a speshul produc', he is, an' he won't have no truck with jest common—*men,* like you be."

He made a venomous gesture which included them all.

"Did he set on ye?" asked a soldier.

"Set on me? No," replied Lige, with contempt. "I set on *him*. I sized 'im up in a minute. 'Oh, I don't know,' I says, as I was comin' out; 'guess you ain't the only man in the world,' I says."

For a time Lige Wigram was quite a hero. He endlessly repeated the tale of his adventure, and men admired him for so soon taking the conceit out of the new officer. Lige was proud to think of himself as a plain and simple patriot who had refused to endure any high-soaring nonsense.

But he came to believe that he had not disturbed the singular com-posure of the major, and this concreted his hatred. He hated Gates, not as a soldier sometimes hates an officer, a hatred half of fear. Lige hated as man to man. And he was enraged to see that so far from gaining any hatred in return, he seemed incapable of making Gates have any thought of him save as a unit in a body of three hundred men. Lige might just as well have gone and grimaced at the obelisk in Central Park.

When the battalion became the best in the regiment he had no part in the pride of the companies. He was sorry when men began to speak well of Gates. He was really a very consistent hater.

III

The transport occupied by the 307th was commanded by some sort of a Scandinavian, who was afraid of the shadows of his own topmasts. He would have run his steamer away from a floating Gainsborough hat, and, in fact, he ran her away from less on some occasions. The officers, wishing to arrive with the other transports, sometimes remonstrated, and to them he talked of his owners. Every officer in the convoying warships loathed him, for in case any hostile vessel should appear they did not see how they were going to protect this rabbit, who would probably manage during a fight to be in about a hundred places on the broad, broad sea, and all of them offensive to the navy's plan. When he was not talking of his owners he was remarking to the officers of the regiment that a steamer really was not like a valise, and that he was unable to take his ship under his arm and climb trees with it. He further said that "them naval fellows" were not near so smart as they thought they were.

From an indigo sea arose the lonely shore of Cuba. Ultimately, the fleet was near Santiago, and most of the transports were bidden to wait a minute while the leaders found out their minds. The skipper, to whom the 307th were prisoners, waited for thirty hours half way between Jamaica and Cuba. He explained that the Spanish fleet might emerge from Santiago Harbour at any time, and he did not propose to be caught. His owners—— Whereupon the colonel arose as one having nine hundred men at his back, and he passed up to the bridge and he spake with the captain. He explained indirectly that each individual of his nine hundred men had decided to be the first American soldier to land for this campaign, and that in order to accomplish the marvel it was necessary for the transport to be nearer than forty-five miles from the Cuban coast. If the skipper would only land the regiment the colonel would consent to his then taking his interesting old ship and going to h—— with it. And the skipper spake with the colonel. He pointed out that as far as he officially was concerned, the United States Government did not exist. He was responsible solely to his owners. The colonel pondered these sayings. He perceived that the skipper meant that he was running his ship as he deemed best, in consideration of the capital invested by his owners, and that he was not at all concerned with the feelings of a certain American military expedition to Cuba. He was a free son of the sea—he was a sovereign citizen of the republic of the waves. He was like Lige.

However, the skipper ultimately incurred the danger of taking his ship under the terrible guns of the *New York, Iowa, Oregon, Massachusetts, Indiana, Brooklyn, Texas* and a score of cruisers and gunboats. It was a brave act for the captain of a United States transport, and he was visibly nervous until he could again get to sea, where he offered praises that the accursed 307th was no longer sitting on his head. For almost a week he rambled at his cheerful will over the adjacent high seas, having in his hold a great quantity of military stores as successfully secreted as if they had been buried in a copper box in the cornerstone of a new public building in Boston. He had had his master's certificate for twenty-one years, and those people couldn't tell a marlin-spike from the starboard side of the ship.

The 307th was landed in Cuba, but to their disgust they found that about ten thousand regulars were ahead of them. They got immediate orders to move out from the base on the road to Santiago. Gates was interested to note that the only delay was caused by the fact that many men of the other battalions strayed off sight-seeing. In time the long regiment wound slowly among hills that shut them from sight of the sea.

For the men to admire, there were palm-trees, little brown huts, passive, uninterested Cuban soldiers much worn from carrying American rations inside and outside. The weather was not oppressively warm, and the journey was said to be only about seven miles. There were no rumours save that there had been one short fight and the army had advanced to within sight of Santiago. Having a peculiar faculty for the derision of the romantic, the 307th began to laugh. Actually there was not *anything* in the world which turned out to be as books describe it. Here they had landed from the transport expecting to be at once flung into line of battle and sent on some kind of furious charge, and now they were trudging along a quiet trail lined with somnolent trees and grass. The whole business so far struck them as being a highly tedious burlesque.

After a time they came to where the camps of regular regiments marked the sides of the road—little villages of tents no higher than a man's waist. The colonel found his brigade commander and the 307th was sent off into a field of long grass, where the men grew suddenly solemn with the importance of getting their supper.

In the early evening some regulars told one of Gates's companies that at daybreak this division would move to an attack upon something.

"How d'you know?" said the company, deeply awed.

"Heard it."

"Well, what are we to attack?"

"Dunno."

The 307th was not at all afraid, but each man began to imagine the morrow. The regulars seemed to have as much interest in the morrow as they did in the last Christmas. It was none of their affair, apparently.

"Look here," said Lige Wigram, to a man in the 17th Regular Infantry, "whereabouts are we goin' ter-morrow an' who do we run up against—do ye know?"

The 17th soldier replied, truculently: "If I ketch th' ——— ——— ——— what stole my terbaccer, I'll whirl in an' break every ——— ——— bone in his body."

Gates's friends in the regular regiments asked him numerous questions as to the reliability of his organisation. Would the 307th stand the racket? They were certainly not contemptuous; they simply did not seem to consider it important whether the 307th would or whether it would not.

"Well," said Gates, "they won't run the length of a tent-peg if they can gain any idea of what they're fighting; they won't bunch if they've about six acres of open ground to move in; they won't get rattled at all if they see you fellows taking it easy, and they'll fight like the devil as long as they thoroughly, completely, absolutely, satisfactorily, exhaustively understand what the business is. They're lawyers. All excepting my battalion."

IV

Lige awakened into a world obscured by blue fog. Somebody was gently shaking him. "Git up; we're going to move." The regiment was buckling up itself. From the trail came the loud creak of a light battery moving ahead. The tones of all men were low; the faces of the officers were composed, serious. The regiment found itself moving along behind the battery before it had time to ask itself more than a hundred questions. The trail wound through a dense tall jungle, dark, heavy with dew.

The battle broke with a snap—far ahead. Presently Lige heard from the air above him a faint low note as if somebody were blowing softly in the mouth of a bottle. It was a stray bullet which had wandered a mile to tell him that war was before him. He nearly broke his neck looking upward. "Did ye hear that?" But the men were fretting to get out of this gloomy jungle. They wanted to see something. The faint rup-rup-rrrrup-rup on in the front told them that the fight had begun; death was abroad, and so the mystery of this wilderness excited them. This wilderness was portentously still and dark.

They passed the battery aligned on a hill above the trail, and they had not gone far when the gruff guns began to roar and they could hear the rocket-like swish of the flying shells. Presently everybody must have called out for the assistance of the 307th. Aides and couriers came flying back to them.

"Is this the 307th? Hurry up your men, please, Colonel. You're needed more every minute."

Oh, they were, were they? Then the regulars were not going to do *all* the fighting? The old 307th was bitterly proud or proudly bitter. They left their blanket rolls under the guard of God and pushed on, which is one of the reasons why the Cubans of that part of the country were, later, so well equipped. There began to appear fields, hot, golden-green in the sun. On some palm-dotted knolls before them they could see little lines of black dots—the American advance. A few men fell, struck down by other men who, perhaps half a mile away, were aiming at somebody else. The loss was wholly in Carmony's battalion, which immediately bunched and backed away, coming with a shock against Gates's advance company. This shock sent a tremor through all of Gates's battalion until men in the very last files cried out nervously, "Well, what in hell is up now?" There came an order to deploy and advance. An occasional hoarse yell from the regulars could be heard. The deploying made Gates's heart bleed for the colonel. The old man stood there directing the movement, straight, fearless, sombrely defiant of—everything. Carmony's four companies were like four herds. And all the time the bullets from no living man knows where kept pecking at them and pecking at them. Gates, the excellent Gates, the highly educated and strictly military Gates, grew rankly insubordinate. He knew that the regiment was suffering from nothing but the deadly range and oversweep of the modern rifle, of which many proud and confident nations know nothing save that they have killed savages with it, which is the least of all informations.

Gates rushed upon Carmony.

"—— —— it, man, if you can't get your people to deploy, for —— sake give me a chance! I'm stuck in the woods!"

Carmony gave nothing, but Gates took all he could get and his battalion deployed and advanced like men. The old colonel almost burst into tears, and he cast one quick glance of gratitude at Gates, which the younger officer wore on his heart like a secret decoration.

There was a wild scramble up hill, down dale, through thorny thickets. Death smote them with a kind of slow rhythm, leisurely taking a man now here, now there, but the cat-spit sound of the bullets was always. A large number of the men of Carmony's battalion came on with Gates. They were willing to do anything, anything. They had no real fault, unless it was that early conclusion that any brave high-minded youth was necessarily a good soldier immediately, from the beginning. In them had been born a swift feeling that the unpopular Gates knew everything, and they followed the trained soldier.

If they followed him, he certainly took them into it. As they swung heavily up one steep hill, like so many wind-blown horses, they came suddenly out into the real advance. Little blue groups of men were making frantic rushes forward and then flopping down on their bellies to fire volleys while other groups made rushes. Ahead they could see a heavy house-like fort which was inadequate to explain from whence came the myriad bullets. The remainder of the scene was landscape. Pale men, yellow men, blue men came out of this landscape quiet and sad-eyed with wounds. Often they were grimly facetious. There is nothing in the American regular so amazing as his conduct when he is wounded—his apologetic limp, his deprecatory arm-sling, his embarrassed and ashamed shot-hole through the lungs. The men of the 307th looked at calm creatures who had divers punctures and they were made better. These men told them that it was only necessary to keep a-going. They of the 307th lay on their bellies, red, sweating and panting, and heeded the voice of the elder brother.

Gates walked back of his line, very white of face, but hard and stern past anything his men knew of him. After they had violently adjured him to lie down and he had given weak backs a cold, stiff touch, the 307th charged by rushes. The hatless colonel made frenzied speech, but the man of the time was Gates. The men seemed to feel that this was his business. Some of the regular officers said afterward that the advance of the 307th was very respectable indeed. They were rather surprised, they said. At least five of the crack regiments of the regular army were in this division, and the 307th could win no more than a feeling of kindly appreciation.

Yes, it was very good, very good indeed, but did you notice what was being done at the same moment by the 12th, the 17th, the 7th, the 8th, the 25th, the——

Gates felt that his charge was being a success. He was carrying out a successful function. Two captains fell bang on the grass and a lieutenant slumped quietly down with a death wound. Many men sprawled suddenly. Gates was keeping his men almost even with the regulars, who were charging on his flanks. Suddenly he thought that he must have come close to the fort and that a Spaniard had tumbled a great stone block down upon his leg. Twelve hands reached out to help him, but he cried:

"No—d—— your souls—go on—go on!"

He closed his eyes for a moment, and it really was only for a moment. When he opened them he found himself alone with Lige Wigram, who lay on the ground near him.

"Maje," said Lige, "yer a good man. I've been a-follerin' ye all day an' I want to say yer a good man."

The major turned a coldly scornful eye upon the private.

"Where are you wounded? Can you walk? Well, if you can, go to the rear and leave me alone. I'm bleeding to death, and you bother me."

Lige, despite the pain in his wounded shoulder, grew indignant.

"Well," he mumbled, "you and me have been on th' outs fer a long time, an' I only wanted to tell ye that what I seen of ye t'day has made me feel mighty different."

"Go to the rear—if you can walk," said the major.

"Now, Maje, look here. A little thing like that——"

"Go to the rear."

Lige gulped with sobs.

"Maje, I know I didn't understand ye at first, but ruther'n let a little thing like that come between us, I'd—I'd——"

"Go to the rear."

In this reiteration Lige discovered a resemblance to that first old offensive phrase, "Come to attention and salute." He pondered over the resemblance and he saw that nothing had changed. The man bleeding to death was the same man to whom he had once paid a friendly visit with unfriendly results. He thought now that he perceived a certain hopeless gulf, a gulf which is real or unreal, according to circumstances. Sometimes all men are equal; occasionally they are not. If Gates had ever criticised Lige's manipulation of a hay fork on the farm at home, Lige would have furiously disdained his hate or blame. He saw now that he must not openly approve the major's conduct in war. The major's pride was in his business, and his, Lige's congratulations, were beyond all enduring.

The place where they were lying suddenly fell under a new heavy rain of bullets. They sputtered about the men, making the noise of large grasshoppers.

"Major!" cried Lige. "Major Gates! It won't do for ye to be left here, sir. Ye'll be killed."

"But you can't help it, lad. You take care of yourself."

"I'm damned if I do," said the private, vehemently. "If I can't git *you* out, I'll stay and wait."

The officer gazed at his man with that same icy, contemptuous gaze. "I'm—I'm a dead man anyhow. You go to the rear, do you hear?"

"No."

The dying major drew his revolver, cocked it and aimed it unsteadily at Lige's head.

"Will you obey orders?"

"No."

"One?"

"No."

"Two?"

"No."

Gates weakly dropped his revolver.

"Go to the devil, then. You're no soldier, but——" He tried to add something, "But——" He heaved a long moan. "But—you— —you— oh, I'm so-o-o tired."

v

After the battle, three correspondents happened to meet on the trail. They were hot, dusty, weary, hungry and thirsty, and they repaired to the shade of a mango tree and sprawled luxuriously. Among them they mustered twoscore friends who on that day had gone to the far shore of the hereafter, but their senses were no longer resonant. Shackles was babbling plaintively about mint-juleps, and the others were bidding him to have done.

"By-the-way," said one, at last, "it's too bad about poor old Gates of the 307th. He bled to death. His men were crazy. They were blubbering and cursing around there like wild people. It seems that when they got back there to look for him they found him just about gone, and another wounded man was trying to stop the flow with his hat! His hat, mind you. Poor old Gatesie!"

"Oh, no, Shackles!" said the third man of the party. "Oh, no, you're wrong. The best mint-juleps in the world are made right in New York, Philadelphia or Boston. That Kentucky idea is only a tradition."

A wounded man approached them. He had been shot through the shoulder and his shirt had been diagonally cut away, leaving much bare skin. Over the bullet's point of entry there was a kind of a white spider, shaped from pieces of adhesive plaster. Over the point of departure there was a bloody bulb of cotton strapped to the flesh by other pieces of adhesive plaster. His eyes were dreamy, wistful, sad. "Say, gents, have any of ye got a bottle?" he asked.

A correspondent raised himself suddenly and looked with bright eyes at the soldier.

"Well, you have got a nerve," he said grinning. "Have we got a bottle, eh! Who in h—— do you think we are? If we had a bottle of good licker, do you suppose we could let the whole army drink out of it? You have too much faith in the generosity of men, my friend!"

The soldier stared, ox-like, and finally said, "Huh?"

"I say," continued the correspondent, somewhat more loudly, "that if we had had a bottle we would have probably finished it ourselves by this time."

"But," said the other, dazed, "I *meant* an empty bottle. I didn't mean no *full* bottle."

The correspondent was humorously irascible.

"An empty bottle! You must be crazy! Who ever heard of a man looking for an empty bottle? It isn't sense! I've seen a million men looking for full bottles, but you're the first man I ever saw who insisted on the bottle's being empty. What in the world do you want it for?"

"Well, ye see, mister," explained Lige, slowly, "our major he was killed this mornin' an' we're jes' goin' to bury him, an' I thought I'd jest take a look 'round an' see if I couldn't borry an empty bottle, an' then I'd take an' write his name an' reg'ment on a paper an' put it in th' bottle an' bury it with him, so's when they come fer to dig him up sometime an' take him home, there sure wouldn't be no mistake."

"Oh!"

PORTO RICO

by FINLEY PETER DUNNE

"DEAR, OH, DEAR," said Mr. Dooley, "I'd give five dollars—an' I'd kill a man f'r three—if I was out iv this Sixth Wa-ard to-night, an' down with Gin'ral Miles' gran' picnic an' moonlight excursion in Porther Ricky. 'Tis no comfort in bein' a cow'rd whin ye think iv thim br-rave la-ads facin' death be suffication in bokays an' dyin' iv waltzin' with th' pretty girls iv Porther Ricky.

"I dinnaw whether Gin'ral Miles picked out th' job or whether 'twas picked out f'r him. But, annyhow, whin he got to Sandago de Cubia an' looked ar-round him, he says to his frind Gin'ral Shafter, 'Gin'ral,' says he, 'ye have done well so far,' he says. ' 'Tis not f'r me to take th' lorls fr'm th' steamin' brow iv a thrue hero,' he says. 'I lave ye here,' he says, 'f'r to complete th' victhry ye have so nobly begun,' he says. 'F'r you,' he says, 'th' wallop in th' eye fr'm th' newspaper rayporther, th' r-round robbing, an' th' sunstroke,' he says, 'f'r me th' hardship iv th' battlefield, th' late dinner, th' theayter party, an' th' sickenin' polky,' he says. 'Gather,' he says, 'th' fruits iv ye'er bravery,' he says. 'Return,' he says, 'to ye'er native land, an' receive anny gratichood th' Sicrety iv War can spare fr'm his own fam'ly,' he says, 'F'r me,' he says, 'there is no way but f'r to tur-rn me back upon this festive scene,' he says, 'an' go where jooty calls me,' he says. 'Ordherly,' he says, 'put a bottle on th' ice, an' see that me goold pants that I wear with th' pale blue vest with th' di'mon buttons is irned out,' he says. An' with a haggard face he walked aboord th' excursion steamer, an' wint away.

"I'd hate to tell ye iv th' thriles iv th' expedition, Hinnissy. Whin th' picnic got as far as Punch, on th' southern coast iv Porther Ricky, Gin'ral Miles gazes out, an' says he, 'This looks like a good place to hang th' hammicks, an' have lunch,' says he. 'Forward, brave men,' says he, 'where ye see me di'mon's sparkle,' says he. 'Forward, an' plant th' crokay arrches iv our beloved counthry,' he says. An' in they wint, like inthrepid warryors that they ar-re. On th' beach they was met be a diligation fr'm th' town of Punch, con-sistin' iv th' mayor, th' common council, th' polis an' fire departments, th' Gr-rand Ar-rmy iv th' Raypublic, an' prominent citizens in carredges. Gin'ral Miles, makin' a hasty tielet, advanced

From: *Mr. Dooley in Peace and War.*

onflinchingly to meet thim. 'Gintlemen,' says he, 'what can I do f'r ye?' he says. 'We come,' says th' chairman iv th' comity, 'f'r to offer ye,' he says, 'th' r-run iv th' town,' he says. 'We have held out,' he says, 'as long as we cud,' he says. 'But,' he says, 'they'se a limit to human endurance,' he says. 'We can withstand ye no longer,' he says. 'We surrinder. Take us prisoners, an' rayceive us into ye'er gloryous an' well-fed raypublic,' he says. 'Br-rave men,' says Gin'ral Miles, 'I congratulate ye,' he says, 'on th' heeroism iv yer definse,' he says. 'Ye stuck manfully to yer colors, whativer they ar-re,' he says. 'I on'y wondher that ye waited f'r me to come befure surrindhrin,' he says. 'I welcome ye into th' Union,' he says. 'I don't know how th' Union'll feel about it, but that's no business iv mine,' he says. 'Ye will get ye'er wur-rkin-cards fr'm th' walkin' diligate,' he says; 'an' ye'll be entitled,' he says, 'to pay ye'er share iv th' taxes an' to live awhile an' die whin ye get r-ready,' he says, 'jus' th' same as if ye was bor-rn at home,' he says. 'I don't know th' names iv ye; but I'll call ye all Casey, f'r short,' he says. 'Put ye'er bokays in th' hammick,' he says, 'an' return to Punch,' he says; 'an' freeze somethin' f'r me,' he says, 'f'r me thrawt is parched with th' labors iv th' day,' he says. Th' r-rest iv th' avenin' was spint in dancin', music, an' boat-r-ridin'; an' an inj'yable time was had.

"Th' nex' day th' army moved on Punch; an' Gin'ral Miles marched into th' ill-fated city, preceded be flower-girls sthrewin' r-roses an' geranyums befure him. In th' afthernoon they was a lawn tinnis party, an' at night the gin'ral attinded a banket at th' Gran' Palace Hotel. At midnight he was serenaded be th' Raymimber th' Maine Banjo an' Mandolin Club. Th' entire popylace attinded, with pork chops in their buttonholes to show their pathreetism. Th' nex' day, afther breakfastin' with Mayor Casey, he set out on his weary march over th' r-rough, flower-strewn paths f'r San Joon. He has been in gr-reat purl fr'm a witherin' fire iv bokays, an' he has met an' overpowered some iv th' mos' savage orators in Porther Ricky; but, whin I las' heerd iv him, he had pitched his tents an' ice-cream freezers near the inimy's wall, an' was grajually silencin' thim with proclamations."

"They'll kill him with kindness if he don't look out," said Mr. Hennessy.

"I dinnaw about that," said Mr. Dooley; "but I know this, that there's th' makin' iv gr-reat statesmen in Porther Ricky. A proud people that can switch as quick as thim la-ads have nawthin' to larn in th' way iv what Hogan calls th' signs iv gover'mint, even fr'm th' Supreme Court."

AFTERMATH—THE FEVER SHIP

by Richard Harding Davis

There were four rails around the ship's sides, the three lower ones of iron and the one on top of wood, and as he looked between them from the canvas cot he recognized them as the prison-bars which held him in. Outside his prison lay a stretch of blinding blue water which ended in a line of breakers and a yellow coast with ragged palms. Beyond that again rose a range of mountain-peaks, and, stuck upon the loftiest peak of all, a tiny block-house. It rested on the brow of the mountain against the naked sky as impudently as a cracker-box set upon the dome of a great cathedral.

As the transport rode on her anchor-chains, the iron bars around her sides rose and sank and divided the landscape with parallel lines. From his cot the officer followed this phenomenon with severe, painstaking interest. Sometimes the wooden rail swept up to the very block-house itself, and for a second of time blotted it from sight. And again it sank to the level of the line of breakers, and wiped them out of the picture as though they were a line of chalk.

The soldier on the cot promised himself that the next swell of the sea would send the lowest rail climbing to the very top of the palm-trees or, even higher, to the base of the mountains; and when it failed to reach even the palm-trees he felt a distinct sense of ill use, of having been wronged by some one. There was no other reason for submitting to this existence save these tricks upon the wearisome, glaring landscape; and now, whoever it was who was working them did not seem to be making this effort to entertain him with any heartiness.

It was most cruel. Indeed, he decided hotly, it was not to be endured; he would bear it no longer, he would make his escape. But he knew that this move, which could be conceived in a moment's desperation, could only be carried to success with great strategy, secrecy, and careful cunning. So he fell back upon his pillow and closed his eyes, as though he were asleep, and then opening them again, turned cautiously, and spied upon his keeper. As usual, his keeper sat at the foot of the cot turning the pages of a huge paper filled with pictures of the war printed in daubs of tawdry colors. His keeper was a hard-faced boy without human pity or consideration, a very devil of obstinacy and fiendish cruelty. To make it worse, the fiend was a person without a collar, in a suit of soiled khaki, with a curious red cross bound by a safety-pin to his left arm. He was intent upon the paper in his hands; he was holding it between his eyes and his prisoner. His vigilance had relaxed, and the moment seemed propitious. With a sudden plunge of arms and legs, the prisoner swept the bed-sheet from him, and sprang at the wooden rail and grasped the iron stanchion beside it. He had his knee pressed against the top bar and his bare toes on the iron rail beneath it. Below him the blue water waited for him. It was cool and dark and gentle and deep. It would certainly put out the fire in his bones, he thought; it might even shut out the glare of the sun which scorched his eyeballs.

But as he balanced for the leap, a swift weakness and nausea swept over him, a weight seized upon his body and limbs. He could not lift the lower foot from the iron rail, and he swayed dizzily and trembled. He trembled. He who had raced his men and beaten them up the hot hill to the trenches of San Juan. But now he was a baby in the hands of a giant, who caught him by the wrist and with an iron arm clasped him around his waist and pulled him down, and shouted, brutally, "Help, some of youse, quick! he's at it again. I can't hold him."

More giants grasped him by the arms and by the legs. One of them took the hand that clung to the stanchion in both of his, and pulled back the fingers one by one, saying, "Easy now, Lieutenant—easy."

The ragged palms and the sea and block-house were swallowed up in a black fog, and his body touched the canvas cot again with a sense of home-coming and relief and rest. He wondered how he could have cared to escape from it. He found it so good to be back again that for a long time he wept quite happily, until the fiery pillow was moist and cool.

The world outside of the iron bars was like a scene in a theater set for some great event, but the actors were never ready. He remembered confusedly a play he had once witnessed before that same scene. Indeed, he believed he had played some small part in it; but he remembered it dimly, and all trace of the men who had appeared with him in it was gone. He had reasoned it out that they were up there behind the range of mountains, because great heavy wagons and ambulances and cannon were emptied from the ships at the wharf above and were drawn away in long lines behind the ragged palms, moving always toward the passes between the peaks. At times he was disturbed by the thought that he should be up and after them, that some tradition of duty made his presence with them imperative. There was much to be done back of the mountains. Some event of momentous import was being carried forward there, in which he held a part; but the doubt soon passed from him, and he was content to lie and watch the iron bars rising and falling between the block-house and the white surf.

If they had been only humanely kind, his lot would have been bearable, but they starved him and held him down when he wished to rise; and they would not put out the fire in the pillow, which they might easily have done by the simple expedient of throwing it over the ship's side into the sea. He himself had done this twice, but the keeper had immediately brought a fresh pillow already heated for the torture and forced it under his head.

His pleasures were very simple, and so few he could not understand why they robbed him of them so jealously. One was to watch a green cluster of bananas that hung above him from the awning, twirling on a string. He could count as many of them as five before the bunch turned and swung lazily back again, when he could count as high as twelve; sometimes when the ship rolled heavily he could count to twenty. It was a most fascinating game, and contented him for many hours. But when they found this out they sent for the cook to come and cut them down, and the cook carried them away to his galley.

Then, one day, a man came out from the shore, swimming through the blue water with great splashes. He was a most charming man, who spluttered and dove and twisted and lay on his back and kicked his legs in an excess of content and delight. It was a real pleasure to watch him; not for days had anything so amusing appeared on the other side of the prison-bars. But as soon as the keeper saw that the man in the water was amusing his prisoner, he leaned over the ship's side and shouted, "Sa-ay, you, don't you know there's sharks in there?"

And the swimming man raced back to the shore like a porpoise with great lashing of the water, and ran up the beach half-way to the palms before he was satisfied to stop. Then the prisoner wept again. It was so disappointing. Life was robbed of everything now. He remembered that in a previous existence soldiers who cried were laughed at and mocked. But that was so far away and it was such an absurd superstition that he had no patience with it. For what could be more comforting to a man when he is treated cruelly than to cry. It was so obvious an exercise, and when one is so feeble that one cannot vault a four-railed barrier it is something to feel that at least one is strong enough to cry.

He escaped occasionally, traversing space with marvelous rapidity and to great distances, but never to any successful purpose; and his flight inevitably ended in ignominious recapture and a sudden awakening in bed. At these moments the familiar and hated palms, the peaks, and the block-house were more hideous in their reality than the most terrifying of his nightmares.

These excursions afield were always predatory; he went forth always to seek food. With all the beautiful world from which to elect and choose, he sought out only those places where eating was studied and elevated to an art. These visits were much more vivid in their detail than any he had ever before made to these same resorts. They invariably began in a carriage, which carried him swiftly over smooth asphalt. One route brought him across a great and beautiful square, radiating with rows and rows of flickering lights; two fountains splashed in the center of the square, and six women of stone guarded its approaches. One of the women was hung with wreaths of mourning. Ahead of him the late twilight darkened behind a great arch, which seemed to rise on the horizon of the world, a great window into the heavens beyond. At either side strings of white and colored globes hung among the trees, and the sound of music came joyfully from theaters in the open air. He knew the restaurant under the trees to which he was now hastening, and the fountain beside it, and the very sparrows balancing on the fountain's edge; he knew every waiter at each of the tables, he felt again the gravel crunching under his feet, he saw the *maître d'hôtel* coming forward smiling to receive his command, and the waiter in the green apron bowing at his elbow, deferential and important, presenting the list of wines. But his adventure never passed that point, for he was captured again and once more bound to his cot with a close burning sheet.

Or else, he drove more sedately through the London streets in the late evening twilight, leaning expectantly across the doors of the hansom and pulling carefully at his white gloves. Other hansoms flashed past him, the occupant of each with his mind fixed on one idea—dinner. He was one of a million of people who were about to dine, or who had dined, or who were deep in dining. He was so famished, so weak for food of any quality, that the galloping horse in the hansom seemed to crawl. The lights of the Embankment passed like the lamps of a railroad station as seen from the window of an express; and while his mind was still torn between the choice of a thin or thick soup or an immediate attack upon cold beef, he was at the door, and the *chasseur* touched his cap, and the little *chasseur* put the wicker guard over the hansom's wheel. As he jumped out he said, "Give him half-a-crown," and the driver called after him, "Thank you, sir."

It was a beautiful world, this world outside of the iron bars. Everyone in it contributed to his pleasure and to his comfort. In this world he was not starved nor manhandled. He thought of this joyfully as he leaped up the stairs, where young men with grave faces and with their hands held negligently behind their backs bowed to him in polite surprise at his speed. But they had not been starved on condensed milk. He threw his coat and hat at one of them, and came down the hall fearfully and quite weak with dread lest it should not be real. His voice was shaking when he asked Ellis if he had reserved a table. The place was all so real, it must be true this time. The way Ellis turned and ran his finger down the list showed it was real, because Ellis always did that, even when he knew there would not be an empty table for an hour. The room was crowded with beautiful women; under the light of the red shades they looked kind and approachable, and there was food on every table, and iced drinks in silver buckets. It was with the joy of great relief that he heard Ellis say to his underling, *"Numéro cinq, sur la terrace, un couvert."* It was real at last. Outside, the Thames lay a great gray shadow. The lights of the Embankment flashed and twinkled across it, the tower of the House of Commons rose against the sky, and here, inside, the waiter was hurrying toward him carrying a smoking plate of rich soup with a pungent, intoxicating odor.

And then the ragged palms, the glaring sun, the immovable peaks, and the white surf stood again before him. The iron rails swept up and sank again, the fever sucked at his bones, and the pillow scorched his cheek.

One morning for a brief moment he came back to real life again and lay quite still, seeing everything about him with clear eyes and for the first time, as though he had but just that instant been lifted over the ship's side. His keeper, glancing up, found the prisoner's eyes considering him curiously, and recognized the change. The instinct of discipline brought him to his feet with his fingers at his sides.

"Is the Lieutenant feeling better?"

The Lieutenant surveyed him gravely.

"You are one of our hospital stewards."

"Yes, Lieutenant."

"Why aren't you with the regiment?"

"I was wounded, too, sir. I got it same time you did, Lieutenant."

"Am I wounded? Of course, I remember. Is this a hospital ship?"

The steward shrugged his shoulders. "She's one of the transports. They have turned her over to the fever cases."

The Lieutenant opened his lips to ask another question; but his own body answered that one, and for a moment he lay silent.

"Do they know up North that I—that I'm all right?"

"Oh, yes, the papers had it in—there were pictures of the Lieutenant in some of them."

"Then I've been ill some time?"

"Oh, about eight days."

The soldier moved uneasily, and the nurse in him became uppermost.

"I guess the Lieutenant hadn't better talk any more," he said. It was his voice now which held authority.

The Lieutenant looked out at the palms and the silent gloomy mountains and the empty coastline, where the same wave was rising and falling with weary persistence.

"Eight days," he said. His eyes shut quickly, as though with a sudden touch of pain. He turned his head and sought for the figure at the foot of the cot. Already the figure had grown faint and was receding and swaying.

"Has anyone written or cabled?" the Lieutenant spoke, hurriedly. He was fearful lest the figure should disappear altogether before he could obtain his answer. "Has anyone come?"

"Why, they couldn't get here, Lieutenant, not yet."

The voice came very faintly. "You go to sleep now, and I'll run and fetch some letters and telegrams. When you wake up, maybe I'll have a lot for you."

But the Lieutenant caught the nurse by the wrist, and crushed his hand in his own thin fingers. They were hot, and left the steward's skin wet with perspiration. The Lieutenant laughed gayly.

"You see, Doctor," he said, briskly, "that you can't kill me. I can't die. I've got to live, you understand. Because, sir, she said she would come. She said if I was wounded, or if I was ill, she would come to me. She didn't care what people thought. She would come anyway and nurse me— well, she will come."

"So, Doctor—old man—" He plucked at the steward's sleeve, and stroked his hand eagerly, "old man—" he began again, beseechingly, "you'll not let me die until she comes, will you? What? No, I know I won't die. Nothing made by man can kill me. No, not until she comes. Then, after that—eight days, she'll be here soon, any moment? What? You think so, too? Don't you? Surely, yes, any moment. Yes, I'll go to sleep now, and when you see her rowing out from shore you wake me.

You'll know her; you can't make a mistake. She is like—no, there is no one like her—but you can't make a mistake."

That day strange figures began to mount the sides of the ship, and to occupy its every turn and angle of space. Some of them fell on their knees and slapped the bare deck with their hands, and laughed and cried out, "Thank God, I'll see God's country again!" Some of them were regulars, bound in bandages; some were volunteers, dirty and hollow-eyed, with long beards on boys' faces. Some came on crutches; others with their arms around the shoulders of their comrades, staring ahead of them with a fixed smile, their lips drawn back and their teeth protruding. At every second step they stumbled, and the face of each was swept by swift ripples of pain.

They lay on cots so close together that the nurses could not walk between them. They lay on the wet decks, in the scuppers and along the transoms and hatches. They were like shipwrecked mariners clinging to a raft, and they asked nothing more than that the ship's bow be turned toward home. Once satisfied as to that, they relaxed into a state of self-pity and miserable oblivion to their environment, from which hunger nor nausea nor aching bones could shake them.

The hospital steward touched the Lieutenant lightly on the shoulder. "We are going North, sir," he said. "The transport's ordered North to New York, with these volunteers and the sick and the wounded. Do you hear me, sir?"

The Lieutenant opened his eyes. "Has she come?" he asked.

"Gee!" exclaimed the hospital steward. He glanced impatiently at the blue mountains and the yellow coast, from which the transport was rapidly drawing away.

"Well, I can't see her coming just now," he said. "But she will," he added.

"You let me know at once when she comes."

"Why, cert'nly, of course," said the steward.

Three trained nurses came over the side just before the transport started North. One was a large, motherly looking woman, with a German accent. She had been a trained nurse, first in Berlin, and later in London Hospital in Whitechapel, and at Bellevue. The nurse was dressed in white, and wore a little silver medal at her throat; and she was strong enough to lift a volunteer out of his cot and hold him easily in her arms, while one of the convalescents pulled his cot out of the rain. Some of the men called her "nurse"; others, who wore scapulars around their necks, called her "Sister"; and the officers of the medical staff addressed her as Miss Bergen.

Miss Bergen halted beside the cot of the Lieutenant and asked, "Is this the fever case you spoke about, Doctor—the one you want moved to the officers' ward?" She slipped her hand up under his sleeve and felt his wrist.

"His pulse is very high," she said to the steward. "When did you take his temperature?" She drew a little morocco case from her pocket and from that took a clinical thermometer, which she shook up and down, eying the patient meanwhile with a calm, impersonal scrutiny. The Lieutenant raised his head and stared up at the white figure beside his cot. His eyes opened and then shut quickly, with a startled look, in which doubt struggled with wonderful happiness. His hand stole out fearfully and warily until it touched her apron, and then, finding it was real, he clutched it desperately, and twisting his face and body toward her, pulled her down, clasping her hands in both of his, and pressing them close to his face and eyes and lips. He put them from him for an instant, and looked at her through his tears.

"Sweetheart," he whispered, "sweetheart, I knew you'd come."

As the nurse knelt on the deck beside him, her thermometer slipped from her fingers and broke, and she gave an exclamation of annoyance. The young Doctor picked up the pieces and tossed them overboard. Neither of them spoke, but they smiled appreciatively. The Lieutenant was looking at the nurse with the wonder and hope and hunger of soul in his eyes with which a dying man looks at the cross the priest holds up before him. What he saw where the German nurse was kneeling was a tall, fair girl with great bands and masses of hair, with a head rising like a lily from a firm, white throat, set on broad shoulders above a straight back and sloping breast—a tall, beautiful creature, half-girl, half-woman, who looked back at him shyly, but steadily.

"Listen," he said.

The voice of the sick man was so sure and so sane that the young Doctor started, and moved nearer to the head of the cot. "Listen, dearest," the Lieutenant whispered. "I wanted to tell you before I came South. But I did not dare; and then I was afraid something might happen to me, and I could never tell you, and you would never know. So I wrote it to you in the will I made at Daiquiri, the night before the landing. If you hadn't come now, you would have learned it in that way. You would have read there that there never was anyone but you; the rest were all dream people, foolish, silly—mad. There is no one else in the world but you; you have been the only thing in life that has counted. I thought I might do something down here that would make you care. But I got shot going up a hill, and after that I wasn't able to do anything. It was very hot, and the hills were on fire; and they took me prisoner, and kept me tied down here, burning on these coals. I can't live much longer, but now that I've told you I can have peace. They tried to kill me before you came; but they didn't know I loved you, they didn't know that men who love you can't die. They tried to starve my love for you, to burn it out of me; they tried to reach it with their knives. But my love for you is my soul, and they can't kill a man's soul. Dear heart, I have lived because you lived. Now that you know—now that you understand—what does it matter?"

Miss Bergen shook her head with great vigor. "Nonsense," she said, cheerfully. "You are not going to die. As soon as we move you out of this rain, and some food cook——"

"Good God!" cried the young Doctor, savagely. "Do you want to kill him?"

When she spoke, the patient had thrown his arms heavily across his face, and had fallen back, lying rigid on the pillow.

The Doctor led the way across the prostrate bodies, apologizing as he went. "I am sorry I spoke so quickly," he said, "but he thought you were real. I mean he thought you were some one he really knew——"

"He was just delirious," said the German nurse, calmly.

The Doctor mixed himself a Scotch and soda and drank it with a single gesture.

"Ugh!" he said to the ward-room. "I feel as though I'd been opening another man's letters."

The transport drove through the empty seas with heavy, clumsy upheavals, rolling like a buoy. Having been originally intended for the freight-carrying trade, she had no sympathy with hearts that beat for a sight of their native land, or for lives that counted their remaining minutes by the throbbing of her engines. Occasionally, without apparent reason, she was thrown violently from her course; but it was invariably the case that when her stern went to starboard, something splashed in the water on her port side and drifted past her, until, when it had cleared the blades of her propeller, a voice cried out, and she was swung back on her home-bound track again.

The Lieutenant missed the familiar palms and the tiny block-house; and seeing nothing beyond the iron rails but great wastes of gray water, he decided he was on board a prison-ship, or that he had been strapped to a raft and cast adrift. People came for hours at a time and stood at the foot of his cot, and talked with him and he to them—people he had loved and people he had long forgotten, some of whom he had thought were dead. One of them he could have sworn he had seen buried in a deep trench, and covered with branches of palmetto. He had heard the bugler, with tears choking him, sound "taps"; and with his own hand he had placed the dead man's campaign hat on the mound of fresh earth above the grave. Yet here he was still alive, and he came with other men of his troop to speak to him; but when he reached out to them they were gone —the real and the unreal, the dead and the living—and even She disappeared whenever he tried to take her hand, and sometimes the hospital steward drove her away.

"Did that young lady say when she was coming back again?" he asked the steward.

"The young lady! What young lady?" asked the steward, wearily.

"The one who has been sitting there," he answered. He pointed with his gaunt hand at the man in the next cot.

"Oh, that young lady. Yes, she's coming back. She's just gone below to fetch you some hard-tack."

The young volunteer in the next cot whined grievously.

"That crazy man gives me the creeps," he groaned. "He's always waking me up, and looking at me as though he was going to eat me."

"Shut your head," said the steward. "He's a better man crazy than you'll ever be with the little sense you've got. And he has two Mauser holes in him. Crazy, eh? It's a good thing for you that there was about four thousand of us regulars just as crazy as him, or you'd never seen the top of the hill."

One morning there was a great commotion on deck, and all the convalescents balanced themselves on the rail, shivering in their pajamas, and pointed one way. The transport was moving swiftly and smoothly through water as flat as a lake, and making a great noise with her steam-whistle. The noise was echoed by many more steam-whistles; and the ghosts of out-bound ships and tugs and excursion steamers ran past her out of the mist and disappeared, saluting joyously. All of the excursion steamers had a heavy list to the side nearest the transport, and the ghosts on them crowded to that rail and waved handkerchiefs and cheered. The fog lifted suddenly, and between the iron rails the Lieutenant saw high green hills on either side of a great harbor. Houses and trees and thousands of masts swept past like a panorama; and beyond was a mirage of three cities, with curling smoke-wreaths, and sky-reaching buildings, and a great swinging bridge, and a giant statue of a woman waving a welcome home.

The Lieutenant surveyed the spectacle with cynical disbelief. He was far too wise and far too cunning to be bewitched by it. In his heart he pitied the men about him, who laughed wildly, and shouted, and climbed recklessly to the rails and ratlines. He had been deceived too often not to know that it was not real. He knew from cruel experience that in a few moments the tall buildings would crumble away, the thousands of columns of white smoke that flashed like snow in the sun, the busy, shrieking tug-boats, and the great statue would vanish into the sea, leaving it gray and bare. He closed his eyes and shut the vision out. It was so beautiful that it tempted him; but he would not be mocked, and he buried his face in his hands. They were carrying the farce too far, he thought. It was really too absurd; for now they were at a wharf which was so real that, had he not known by previous suffering, he would have been utterly deceived by it. And there were great crowds of smiling, cheering people, and a waiting guard of honor in fresh uniforms, and rows of police pushing the people this way and that; and these men about him were taking it all quite seriously and making ready to disembark, carrying their blanket-rolls and rifles with them.

A band was playing joyously, and the man in the next cot, who was being lifted to a stretcher, said, "There's the Governor and his staff; that's him in the high hat." It was really very well done. The Custom-house and the Elevated Railroad and Castle Garden were as like to life as a photograph, and the crowd was as well handled as a mob in a play. His heart ached for it so that he could not bear the pain, and he turned his back on it. It was cruel to keep it up so long. His keeper lifted him in his arms, and pulled him into a dirty uniform which had belonged, apparently, to a much larger man—a man who had been killed probably, for there were dark-brown marks of blood on the tunic and breeches. When he tried to stand on his feet, Castle Garden and the Battery disappeared in a black cloud of night, just as he knew they would; but when he opened his eyes from the stretcher, they had returned again. It was a most remarkably vivid vision. They kept it up so well. Now the young Doctor and the hospital steward were pretending to carry him down a gangplank and into an open space; and he saw quite close to him a long line of policemen, and behind them thousands of faces, some of them women's faces—women who pointed at him and then shook their heads and cried, and pressed their hands to their cheeks, still looking at him. He wondered why they cried. He did not know them, nor did they know him. No one knew him; these people were only ghosts.

There was a quick parting in the crowd. A man he had once known shoved two of the policemen to one side, and he heard a girl's voice speaking his name, like a sob; and She came running out across the open space and fell on her knees beside the stretcher, and bent down over him, and he was clasped in two young, firm arms.

"Of course it is not real, of course it is not She," he assured himself. "Because She would not do such a thing. Before all these people She would not do it."

But he trembled and his heart throbbed so cruelly that he could not bear the pain.

She was pretending to cry.

"They wired us you had started for Tampa on the hospital ship," She was saying, "and Aunt and I went all the way there before we heard you had been sent North. We have been on the cars a week. That is why I missed you. Do you understand? It was not my fault. I tried to come. Indeed, I tried to come."

She turned her head and looked up fearfully at the young Doctor.

"Tell me, why does he look at me like that?" she asked. "He doesn't know me. Is he very ill? Tell me the truth." She drew in her breath quickly. "Of course you will tell me the truth."

When she asked the question he felt her arms draw tight about his shoulders. It was as though she was holding him to herself, and from someone who had reached out for him. In his trouble he turned to his old friend and keeper. His voice was hoarse and very low.

"Is this the same young lady who was on the transport—the one you used to drive away?"

In his embarrassment, the hospital steward blushed under his tan, and stammered.

"Of course it's the same young lady," the Doctor answered, briskly. "And I won't let them drive her away." He turned to her, smiling gravely. "I think his condition has ceased to be dangerous, Madam," he said.

People who, in a former existence, had been his friends, and Her brother, gathered about his stretcher and bore him through the crowd and lifted him into a carriage filled with cushions, among which he sank lower and lower. Then She sat beside him, and he heard Her brother say to the coachman, "Home, and drive slowly and keep on the asphalt."

The carriage moved forward, and She put her arm about him, and his head fell on her shoulder, and neither of them spoke. The vision had lasted so long now that he was torn with the joy that after all it might be real. But he could not bear the awakening if it were not, so he raised his head fearfully and looked up into the beautiful eyes above him. His brows were knit, and he struggled with a great doubt and an awful joy.

"Dearest," he said, "is it real?"

"Is it real?" she repeated.

Even as a dream, it was so wonderfully beautiful that he was satisfied if it could only continue so, if but for a little while.

"Do you think," he begged again, trembling, "that it is going to last much longer?"

She smiled, and bending her head slowly, kissed him.

"It is going to last—always," she said.

WORLD WAR I

1917–1918

WORLD WAR I

1917-1918

Although the United States Army, through no fault of its own, was caught off base in 1917 nearly as badly as in the Spanish War, the scope of things to come had loomed on its horizon. The nation then made its first gigantic military effort since Appomattox, started building a national Army from the ground up.

Wisely, it ended for good and all the pernicious militia, or State-owned, -armed and -equipped troop, system. It established dozens of R.O.T.C. courses in our leading universities, the National Guard became permanently Federalized, and the exercise of initiative in military thinking was not only fostered but rewarded.

Though evidences of resentment against authority yet lingered in the breast of the American soldier of 1917, he was far more amenable to regimentation than either his father or grandfather. Contact with the well-drilled armies of his Allies helped to demonstrate the inevitable while the amazing efficiency of his German enemies added a final convincing argument that team-work triumphs over individual effort.

Had World War I lasted another year the world might well have beheld the finest fighting machine of all time; as it was, the conflict ended before the A.E.F. was scarcely more than blooded. Once again the nation returned to the folly of its idealistic dreams of eternal peace and let the Army weaken and dwindle.

In this section the anthologist has attempted to present as many A.E.F. types as is consistent with the space at his command.

There is the typical doughboy slogging doggedly along, doing the best he can; there is the idealistic crusader; the tradition-ridden general who wants to fight without frills and finds himself dismayed by the clever, smiling young Harvard and Yale men who make up his staff. Then there is the hard-boiled soldier of whom Sergeant Flagg is the prototype. There is no glamour about him—he just grouses, fights and dies.

For a great majority of the men who were enrolled during World War I there was little actual fighting. For many of them the war proved a happy escape from monotony, from responsibility and from domestic unhappiness. This army as a whole never really settled down to the deadly business of fighting, never really understood war for what it really is.

For every soldier who suffered in the trenches there were hundreds to whom the war meant nothing but souvenirs, sandy roads at a cantonment and a grand time for the gang. This spirit has been reflected in countless get-togethers and rallies of various veterans' organizations. One imagines that there will be less light-heartedness, less of the "hinkey, dinkey, parley-voo" spirit among the survivors of World War II.

"GOOD-MORNING, MAJOR!"

by J. P. Marquand

Surely Billy Langwell, in spite of a certain polite indifference toward things which he considered of no importance, had been with brigade headquarters long enough to know that the General was not a funny man. Surely Billy must have known that the General hated all of us, for anyone could have read uncomplimentary sentiments in the General's harsh green eyes and in the way his hard lips, straight as a disciplined platoon, moved when he spoke to the young gentlemen. Perhaps, in part, it was the natural dislike and contempt of a disciplined old man who had spent his life in the service for *parvenus* like us, but anyone could tell there was something else.

"Young gentlemen" was what he used to call us. It is easy still to recall his voice those times he came into the mess-room late for breakfast, when all the young gentlemen stood up hastily to attention. It was not a pleasant voice, General Swinnerton's—slightly thick, and of a suppressed timbre that made you wonder how it would sound when he was angry. Down in the mess-room one can imagine him walking still, heavy but straight as a post, and aggressively shaven in that way peculiar to old soldiers risen from the ranks, that way no civilian can imitate—so closely shaven that you would think his epidermis must have been removed by the razor's edge, revealing a pinker, thinner skin beneath. Without a word he would walk to his place at the table, while the young gentlemen listened to his boot-heels hit the floor. Snap they went, as inevitable as Regulations. Snap—and then a pause, a military pause, and it was up to me to say: "Good-morning, General." It was my part of the drill that he had taught me.

"Good-morning, Major," he would answer, and we would shake hands there in the mess-room, stiffly, like pugilists posing for the Sunday supplements.

"Good-morning, Major," he would say, and sometimes there seemed to be a note in his voice of a lonely man, and sometimes it seemed like the voice of a man slightly puzzled by a changing world.

Then he would pause, and then his heavy neck would move deliberately within the circumference of his stiff white collar—you could almost hear it grate—as he stared down the mess-hall. Of course, all the over-night Lieutenants would be watching him, stiffly trying to look military and knowing that they could not. They were so young, without a trace in their faces of any blow from life. They were so fearless, so serenely sure of themselves. Was that what General Swinnerton could not understand and what he resented most? There was Billy Langwell in his whipcords, much more expensive than the General's—one of those nice New York Langwell's, slender and almost delicate—with his yellow hair still moist from his morning bath, and smiling at the General. Billy was always smil-ing as though he had encountered some amusing private thought. And then there was—what was his name? sometimes faces are so clear and names so hard to remember—Edwin Bryce, the General's other aide, one of the Philadelphia Bryces, with a gentle voice, but always with a look that was slightly supercilious. Then there were those other ones, faces new and pleasant voices. Sometimes in our mess-hall you might have thought it was a college house-party, and not a brigade about to sail for France.

As the General looked at those faces before he pulled back his chair, his own face would assume a slightly peculiar expression, almost of be-wilderment, you would sometimes think, and then he would speak, pre-cisely still, but somewhat differently:

"Good-morning. Sit down, young gentlemen. You won't get any ra-tions like this a month from now."

Then he would seat himself stiffly and raise his coffee cup with exag-gerated ease, and grasp his spoon in his awkward fingers. What was he thinking of as he raised his cup and stared slightly above its brim? Was he envious or sad? Was he thinking that he was not and never would be quite like the rest? Was he thinking that we knew it? I wonder —— Perhaps he always thought that we were laughing.

What strange intuition or trick of caste made Billy spot the General for what he was? The first time Billy's eyes met the General's eyes he knew, and the General knew he knew.

Of course I can remember—anyone can remember—those first days when uniforms were new, when Camp Abraham Hicks was just begin-ning to rise out of its wilderness of yellow pine, a hideous checker-board of order, when the first men of the draft were herded in, in cheap baggy clothes which they took off, never to wear again.

Those were the days when brigade headquarters seemed a place of mystery—a veritable religious shrine, in which one could imagine strange rites marching in the night. Headquarters was almost the only wooden house in Camp Abraham Hicks in those days. Typewriters were clicking through the half-open windows; an orderly was standing at the door, one of those jaded Regular Army orderlies, passive yet sneering, whom the War Department doled out, one to each of our companies.

In front of that wooden shack the stumps of yellow pine still obtruded themselves, making you stumble in your new boots. And a set of awkward men in olive drab were grubbing at those roots, while a young Second Lieutenant, who had been a Lieutenant no longer than they had been soldiers, kept saying: "Now, fellows, make it snappy! Make it snappy!"

The orderly at the door had a reason to grin sourly. It was probably the first time in his life that he had heard enlisted men addressed as "fellows." He was still grinning when I saw him.

"Yes, sir," he said, "the General's expecting you. He'll see you in a minute." Then he stopped grinning and stared wearily beyond me and wearily saluted, and then I heard a voice behind me that I knew. It was Billy Langwell, hopping adroitly over the pine stumps, and only stumbling once over an upthrust root.

"Oh, now, George," he said, "are you here too? How did you pull it? By writing to your Congressman?"

"I don't know," I answered. The Army ways were as strange to me then as they are to-day. "I just got an order and came here to report." Billy grinned and flicked at his boot with a swagger stick that he twirled self-consciously, in nervous, knowing arcs.

"Now don't be so up-stagy just because you have those what-you-may-call-'ems on your shoulders," he suggested. "They got you because you can ride, of course. I bet we're the only people in this place that can mount without a ladder. It's just as well. I don't want to be a nurse to those East Side criminals in my outfit, and anyhow, the family wanted me to be an aide."

The orderly interrupted us, saluting languidly. "The General sends his compliments and says he'll see you now."

"Both of us?" I asked.

A round solid mass of something moved in the orderly's beefy cheek. "Yeh," he said, "both of you, sir."

As we entered, from the corner of my eye I saw the orderly expectorate furtively. It was my first experience with the Regular enlisted personnel, and still I do not know how some of them chew tobacco and yet appear not to chew it.

The General was standing in a stuffy little room, with a table, two chairs, and a map, showing the squared barrenness of the future Camp Abraham Hicks, pasted on the cardboard-composition wall. He wore the marching shoes of an enlisted man—broad and dusty, like two solid corner-stones, necessarily large to support his weight. His leather leggings, of an inferior type, were also covered with the camp's red dust, and over his heart was that curious array of ribbons and bits of masonic jewellery that we were even then beginning to stare at with fascination, not to say with envy. They began with the Indian War ribbon and ran the whole gamut of ribbons—Spanish War, the Philippines, and Boxer. Also hanging among them was a silver medal and a pair of crossed rifles. But you needed no service badges to spot him. You could read his service on his face. His jaw and his mouth, without speaking, fairly shouted Regular Army. His eyes were the eyes of the Regular Army, typical and peculiarly like the eyes of the orderly who sinned in secret by chewing tobacco at the door.

"When you come into my room," said the General, "take off your hats. Good-morning, Major." And he held out a stubby hand to me and looked me in the eye.

"Good-morning, sir," I answered.

He stood motionless, still looking at me. "Say 'Good-morning, General,'" he replied. "I consider it better etiquette."

Then, precisely as a machine-gun turns on a pivot, his head veered, rising from his white collar, to Billy Langwell.

"Lieutenant," inquired the General, "what's that in your hand?"

"A swagger stick, sir," said Billy.

There was no expression of contempt, no change in the General's face. "Throw it out the window," he said.

Without moving from where he was standing, Billy threw it. It made a little whistling arc through the room and was gone.

"Who told you," asked the General, "to carry one of those things?"

"Why, no one—" began Billy.

"Sir," said the General.

"Sir," said Billy.

The General folded his hands behind his back and rocked backward and forward from his toes to his heels. "Now listen to me, both of you," he said. "Where did you go to school?"

"To Harvard," I answered.

The General's lips contracted. "Sir," he said.

"Sir," I said hastily.

You could tell what the General was thinking. Like a machine-gun on a pivot, his eyes again met those of Billy Langwell, who began to smile.

"I am just as effete as he is, sir. I came from Harvard, too, sir."

"Yes?" said the General. "Well, it's no joke being effete, young man, not when there's a war. Now listen to me, both of you."

He paused, and once again rocked from his toes to his heels, as though the rocking might give impetus to his thoughts.

"You won't like me," he said. "Neither of you will like me, but that makes no difference in the service. In '75 I was a private in Arizona, before either of you was born. There used to be real fighting in '75, and the service used to be a real service. I got my corporal's stripes when I pulled Chief Three Horns off his pony and choked him, back in the Navaho War. I got my majority for going out ahead of my detachment and killing three brown brothers with a bayonet in Mindanao. I'd rather have a bayonet in my hands now than this confounded job. But as long as I'm a General I'll be a soldier's General"—he scowled slightly, and his voice began to sharpen—"and not one of those boot-licking, dancing-party Generals with a pull back in the War Department. And the men on my staff will be soldiers and they'll act as soldiers, and not like military attachés. I haven't been to Harvard. I haven't been anywhere except to military schools. That's why you won't like me. But you'll be soldiers just the same. That's all. Sit down at that table, Major, and go over those reports. And you, Mr. —— I've forgotten your name."

It was a new experience to Billy to have anyone forget his name once it had been mentioned.

"Langwell, sir," he said—"William Langwell."

The General looked at him for a moment in silence. Then for the first time I became aware of that curious, baffled expression in his eyes—half puzzled, almost diffident.

"Langwell? There used to be—where was it?—back in the 65th a shave-tail named Langwell. Mr. Langwell, go out and tell that low-lived no-account orderly that he'll be making little ones out of big ones if I see him chewing tobacco again the way he's chewing it now. If he'd been in cavalry in '75 he'd know how to stow it in the back of his jaw when he's on duty. Little ones out of big ones—he'll understand if you don't. And then go to the stables and get my horse and one for yourself. And, by the way, Major, you'd better go out with him and see that he speaks properly to the enlisted men. There's nothing more important than speaking properly to enlisted men. Salute when you go out. And right-about! One! Two!"

Then we were outdoors again, where the men were grubbing at the pine stumps, and Billy was speaking to the orderly.

"My boy," he said, "the General has just sent me out to tell you he'll have you making little ones out of big ones if he sees you chewing tobacco. Personally, I can't perceive that you're chewing. But just as a friend—strictly as a friend—I'd advise you to cut it—or shall I say spit it out?—because you didn't serve in the cavalry back in '75."

I seized Billy by the arm and pulled him out of earshot.

"Don't make an ass of yourself," I hissed. "Can't you watch your step?"

Billy smiled at me and blinked. "Tut-tut, George," he said. "Now don't be so continually up-stagy because you've got those fig or maple leaves on you. Can't we be boys together once in a while? All right; I'll promise not to do it again. All right; but I somehow couldn't—— George" —his smile grew broader and he patted me softly on the arm—"do you know what I perceived? Really, my perception has grown remarkably keen since I embarked on this military business. I perceived, or it seemed to me I perceived"—his voice grew lower, but was very careless, very playful—"I actually perceived that the General isn't quite a gentleman."

And there you have it—that stupid, inexorable conventionality we all of us have when we are young. Billy Langwell was too young, always too young, to have perceived that a man could be a man and still not quite a gentleman.

Billy was smiling at the tree stumps, but you could see that he was thinking, for his eyes had a curious distant look, and suddenly he tapped my arm again. "George, my boy," he said, "the more I think of it—do you know what I think? Seriously, George, I've got a mission to perform."

"What sort of a mission?" Somehow you could not help but be amused, for he was never more than half serious even at his worst.

"I feel it devolves upon me," said Billy, and tapped my arm again, "as a representative—I'm hanged if I know of what, but—well, I feel it devolves on me, under the circumstances, to put the General in his place."

"To what?" I gasped.

"To put the General in his place," repeated Billy. "Oh, not crudely —of course, not crudely; but watch me. I'll find a way."

The egotism of it! It's the sort of thing that always rather shocks you, but Billy Langwell did it. There was that unyielding, curious sense of pride, of decency, or position, or something of the sort. It took Billy Langwell four months, but just the same he did it, and nicely—oh, so nicely.

It was an afternoon when the thick mud of Camp Abraham Hicks was baking into the clay of spring. You remember those afternoons, dreary as a misspent life, with the weight of badly cooked dinner resting like a sin upon the conscience. The General was at his table in the orderly room, licking his thumbs the better to turn the papers before him. His blunt thumbs went snap with grim steadiness; his hair was like a grey rat's nest; his coat was unbuttoned at the collar and his eyes were slightly protruding. At the sound of a gentle tap on the door, he muttered something beneath his breath and sighed. It was Billy Langwell in his whip-cords, walking delicately in his new custom-made riding-boots and silver spurs, with his garrison cap pulled smartly over his eyes as he had seen in pictures.

The General cleared his throat, and Billy spoke at once with his inevitable slight smile: "Excuse me, sir."

The General looked at him coldly for a moment before he answered. "Mr. Langwell," he said at length, "when you come into the orderly room, take off your cap."

The slight smile did not leave Billy's lips. His cap was instantly in his hand.

"Certainly, sir. But the General said——"

Of course the General interrupted him at once, but not unpleasantly—rather with a sort of triumph. "Don't argue. I can appreciate the way you feel, but don't argue. I won't make pets of Second Lieutenants because they're aides of mine. Do you remember I told you that?"

"Yes, sir." Billy had not moved from attention, and his voice was perfectly respectful. "But the General said——"

"Well, what did I say?"

"The General told us to keep our hats on when we carried side arms."

Of course the General had not noticed. There was a moment's pause, and you could almost feel sorry for the General. Of course it was a little thing, but Billy Langwell had the General right on the hip, the way he said he would.

"Side arms?" The General cleared his throat. "Who told you to put on side arms?"

Yes, he had put the General in his place. Billy's face had the innocent triumph of youth and something more—that indefinable expression that made the General know what Billy thought.

"The General," he replied, "told me to report at three with side arms."

Right on the hip—that was where Billy had him. The General pushed back his chair, but did not rise. The chair creaked and grated beneath his weight, and you could have laughed almost to see his embarrassment. He had made a mistake, and he knew he had made one. It might seem little, but not to a Regular Army man.

"Then why"—his voice was thicker—"then why didn't you tell me in the first place, without all this confounded argument?"

Against the thickness of the General's voice came Billy's answer, pleasant and conventional, devoid of any emotion. He did it nicely, very nicely. "I tried to, sir," he said.

"Well," said the General, "you didn't try hard enough."

"No, sir," said Billy. It was almost sad to watch them. Why could the General not have left it there? Billy was speaking so quietly, leading the General slowly beyond his depth. It was childish, so absurd you could almost laugh, though the pulses were beating in the General's temples.

"Well, you should have," said the General. "See here—you put your hand over your holster. You hid it. Did you try to make a fool of me on purpose?"

Billy's answer came at once, perfectly certain, perfectly controlled, and that eternal trace of a smile still flickered on his lips. "I'm sure I beg the General's pardon," he replied. "If the General thinks——"

General Swinnerton rose slowly from his chair. His voice was chilly, his hand trembling. Something within him, the thing that was always there, broke bounds for a moment before he could stop it. "Can't you speak to me like a man?" he roared.

Why is it that youth is so obtuse and can never understand?

That very evening Billy came into my tent with a stiff parody of a walk and held out his hand.

"Good-morning, Major," he said softly, and giggled beneath his breath.

"Stop it!" I whispered. "Don't be such a fool!"

Billy giggled again. He always had a most engaging way when his friends fell out. "Don't be such a fool yourself. Just because you've got those fig leaves, or whatever they are, on you—you can't forget we used to go on parties. Oh, I know we're in the Army now, but maybe I didn't have the General dead to right. What? Didn't I?"

"You ought to be ashamed of yourself——" I began; but he stopped me with a delicate shrugging gesture.

"Why the deuce should I be ashamed?" he demanded. "Do you think I'm going to sit still and have the life ragged out of me, my boy? Do you remember what I told you? He isn't a gentleman, George, my boy. I said he wasn't—remember?"

"If you aren't a West Pointer"—I can still hear the General's voice as

he paced about the orderly room one evening when we were there alone—
"if you're not a West Pointer, young man, or if you haven't come from
the ranks like me, there isn't any hope for you. You don't know what the
Army is, that's all."

And I suppose in a hundred other barracks, a hundred other old men
with ribbons on their chests were holding forth in the same grim strain.
Of course you can't understand; no civilian can fathom the eccentricity
of the military mind. That ridiculous affair of the garrison cap and the
side arms did something to General Swinnerton.

It has occurred to me sometimes that a monk's life and a soldier's life
are really quite the same, for they both have their eternal round of order
in which the smallest thing that moves against the methodical current
becomes great enough to shatter all existence.

If anyone had come to Camp Merritt to see the General off, it might
have been a better thing, because I think he would have liked a kindly
word; but no one came. No one sent him a box of cigars or candy. No one
but the camp commandant said good-bye.

He was a short, asthmatic little man, too old to go across, who could
only sit and watch others go. He took us down to the Fort Lee Ferry himself, and shook the General's hand. It was what the General had said—you
couldn't understand the Army unless you were an Army man.

"Good-bye, Swinnerton," he said. "Give 'em hell."

Billy Langwell was opening the automobile door.

"So long," said General Swinnerton. "Don't drink yourself to death.
You needn't help me, Mr. Langwell. I'm still young enough to walk. Run
aboard there and give the Colonel my compliments, and tell him to see
his men below and stop their singing. This isn't a Y.M.C.A. social. It's a
war."

And that was all the General said as he left his native shores. Yet he
seemed to want to talk that night. He called the young gentlemen to his
cabin on the boat deck after dinner, where all the port-holes were battened
tight, and gave them a short lecture.

"Now don't forget," he ended—and for once that day he seemed to be
almost happy—"don't forget we are through with *thés dansants,* or however you say it, and pink teas and kissing the girls good-bye at those
hostess houses, or whatever you call them. Don't forget we're going to
a war. Don't forget that to-morrow morning or a month from now we
may all be dead." Then he paused, and looked a little puzzled at the young
gentlemen. Of course he could not understand the way they took it, and
his voice grew louder. "You don't believe me, do you? You think you've

got a return ticket because you're on the staff. What do you find to smile at, Mr. Langwell?"

There was a slight sound of shifting feet above the churning of the engines, and we looked at Billy Langwell. He was standing in the centre of the cabin. He was scarcely smiling; certainly not broadly enough to merit a rebuke. And he answered at once, without embarrassment, as he always did: "I'm sure I beg the General's pardon. I wasn't smiling at the General."

"Then what the devil are you smiling at?" General Swinnerton demanded. "Tell us, Mr. Langwell, if it's funny."

If Billy Langwell had only blushed or stammered! but he neither blushed nor stammered, and he answered right away: "It's not exactly funny, sir, but I was only thinking——"

"Go ahead," said the General. "It's obvious that you're thinking."

"I was only thinking," said Billy, "that the General's room used to be the bridal suite not so many months ago."

The General looked at the brass bedstead and at the velvet hangings before the port-holes, already tawdry from the Army, reeking with stale cigar smoke.

"Major," he said, "send my compliments to the gunnery officer, and tell him my aides will be on submarine lookout with the other young men from the regiments. Tell him to put them in the bow. Good-evening, young gentlemen."

The General was alone when I returned. He was pacing up and down the bridal suite, and in spite of the slight pitching of the boat his step was as accurate as ever. His boots were pit-pat on the heavy carpet. In his right cheek was a slight spherical bulge which he caused to disappear when I came in, in the manner of a good cavalryman back in '75.

"I don't understand them," he said. "I'm damned if I understand. Young men didn't used to be like that when I was young. Don't they ever think of anything serious?"

I tried to pass it off lightly. Somehow I knew he was oppressed and lonely, and suspected his dinner was not setting right that first night at sea.

"It's their tradition, General," I said. "They don't mean anything by it; they're only following the tradition—being *toujours gai.*"

But the General stood stock-still and folded his arms behind him. "*Two joor?*" he inquired. "What does *two joor* mean? Oh, it means always, does it?" He coughed and moved his jaw hastily, and continued his walk about the bridal suite.

I moved toward the door, was just about to say good-night, when he said the most peculiar thing that made me stop and look at him.

"Just a minute, Major." Was it possible that his voice sounded diffident? "Would you mind—have you got time—— Here, I wish you'd read this letter. It's written to my son."

It was the first time that I knew—the first time that any of us knew—that General Swinnerton had a son. And why he told me of it then I never could understand. Perhaps he was thinking of his farewell from Merritt that morning.

Perhaps he knew that among us all he was a being apart, and for a moment did not want to be.

He handed me a sheet of foolscap paper from a field clerk's box that was set upon a rosewood writing-table.

"Dear Earl," I read. Now you might have known his name would have been Earl!

"DEAR EARL,

"The old man has got off in a cloud of dust. I am sitting in a bridal suite surrounded by a lot of college boys and a Y.M.C.A. secretary, with a bunch of city boys in the steerage who don't know how to wear their O.D. breeches. God knows how we can ever fight a war with a lot of college boys and city boys who think they're soldiers. I'm glad you're not a college boy. See if you can't be a soldier even if you are a half-baked shave-tail. Do what they tell you and don't grin about it. So long, Earl. I wish I was going with you to the front line, where there isn't all this damn funny business. Remember what I said—always keep two biscuits and a clean pair of socks, old army issue if you can get them, in your back breeches pocket. And be sure to take along a .45 revolver. Good-night, Earl.

"YOUR OLD MAN."

I handed the letter back. What was there to say? What could I possibly have said?

The General looked at me curiously, trying to read my comment in my face.

"You think it's a bum letter, don't you?" he inquired. "But you see the way I feel."

"I don't blame you," I said. I forgot to call him sir.

"Good-night, Major," said the General. "Go round the decks before you turn in, and if you find anybody smoking a cigarette or showing a light outside, take his name for a special court. That's all. Good-night."

As I turned to close the door I had a glimpse of him standing alone in the bridal suite, staring at the curtains, and I never told anyone about the letter. Somehow I could never even smile about it. If it was not a letter from Lord Chesterfield to his son, at least it was a letter from an Army man.

As one thinks of it, it becomes inevitable that Billy Langwell should have laughed at General Swinnerton. And yet it's so hidden now that one can scarcely recall all those little things leading to that end.

Take the history of the Umpty-something Brigade, for instance. You know those stories, printed on smooth, shiny paper by some local printer and pathetic from their sheer inadequacy. There is only a sentence in it that brings a picture back.

"On the evening of September 8," it read, "the Umpty-something Brigade was carried in trucks to Je Ne Sais Quoi and marched on foot to Ça Ne Fait Rien, where it relieved the Umpty-something-else Brigade of the Fig Leaf Division at 10.40, occupying a front extending east from and including the town of Quelque Chose, along the line of the Quelque Chose highway, through the farm of Petites Chausettes and thence to the woods and Je Ne Sais Quoi." There it is, in black and white, written with all that singular lack of imagination which is characteristic of all things military.

And yet it brings back pictures—a dark, startled obscurity, and noise as constant as silence to the ears; muddy columns of men; sweating, startled horses; and a grim shape riding on his horse in silence, without a hat.

It was like the General to throw his tin helmet away. "If they get me they get me," he said. "What's the use of all this funny business?"

Those are the sort of things that those pedantic words bring back— even to the shadows of the town of Quelque Chose.

When we took over the brigade P.C. and the front line, of course the enemy specialised on the town of Quelque Chose. You could see its houses two miles off, as it stood there on the hill. They had only to say a number, that was all, and let the guns turn loose.

You should have heard the General swear when those first shells went by. It was enough to have made you laugh, if it had been a time for laughing. You should have been seen him scramble in the mud among the wounded horses and have heard his voice, not frightened, only angry, as he shouted to a runner from the Umpty-something Division: "Where are we? This is a hell of a place!"

"We're just getting in, sir. It's Quelque Chose," said the runner. But he was a green man. He had a catch in his voice. "Damn their hides!

Them Jerries know we're moving out to-night. You might 'a' knowed those Blanks 'ud know it."

Then the General's voice came out of the dark. It really was a funny thing he said, and I felt Billy nudge me in the ribs as the General said it. "Damn your own hide!" roared General Swinnerton. "Cut out that swearing!"

We were stumbling over a heap of rubbish that had once been a street. Billy Langwell tripped and grasped instinctively at the General's arm to keep his balance, and I heard him draw a sharp, quick breath.

"What is it, Mr. Langwell?" said the General. "Can't you keep your feet?"

"A man," said Billy. His voice was a little high. "General, I stepped on a man."

You would have known the General was a soldier even in the dark. "Did you hear Mr. Langwell, young gentlemen?" he inquired. "Mr. Langwell stepped on a dead man. Don't be surprised. There are always dead men in a war."

"Here we are, sir," said the orderly. "Mind the step, sir. It's in a cellar. Lord! what's that?"

"A heavy gun, you ass," said the General.

And we were in the headquarters of the town of Quelque Chose. I can still hear the General's voice. It goes with candlelight and the damp and reeking smell of night. "Give me a map. Where the devil is that map? Are the telephones installed?" And then it is all a nightmare, nothing more.

Quelque Chose I called the town. It isn't its real name, but every town was Quelque Chose in the stretches of those nights. Every town was something that makes you sit up still and stare into the black. As a matter of fact, it was Ouchy or Coulchy-sur-the-Something-or-Other. The way the old General spluttered and coughed as he pronounced it was enough to make you laugh. It's not so long ago since I saw the place, but though eight years or more have passed, there is a shocked silence, and you can almost think it was the day before yesterday, the time those names meant nothing.

I can remember the General glaring at the French artillery map. The rest is dim, but that part of it seems almost the day before yesterday. There were two candles in that cellar-hole where headquarter P.C. were located, shining mellowly upon his face and making the silver stars glitter on his shoulders. And the yellow light gave his face a most peculiar reddish tint which was almost like old copper.

He was in the centre of that cellar, quite calm, standing in a welter of equipment that had not been cleared away, between the box where the field telephones were already going and the muddy curtain of blankets by the door. The mud from the road—that strange grey mud of France—came off his stubby fingers on the map he was holding. He was staring at the map with reddish eyes, running his forefinger slowly across it.

"What the devil's the name of this place?" he inquired, looking up for a moment. The young gentlemen were standing around trying to look perfectly calm. "Oozy—Coozy? What the devil is it? And what the devil are those little gimcracks up ahead?"

It was not peculiar. Maps of all kinds always annoyed the General. He did not have time to get an answer, for the telephone operator interrupted him.

"Call from the division, sir," he said.

"Confound the division!" said the General. "Can't they leave a man alone?" And he sat down by the instrument.

His two aides were just behind him, straight and quiet—Billy Langwell, a little paler than usual, and Edwin Bryce, playing at his belt with his long fingers.

"Stop that noise!" said the General. He seemed to forget that no one could stop that noise until the war was over.

"Hello! Is this what? Is this what? What? Brewery One? Are you crazy? What do you mean by Brewery One? This is General Swinnerton speaking. Headquarters of the Umpty-umph Brigade."

Billy Langwell looked at me and winked. The colour had returned to his cheeks.

"Oh! it's a code word, is it? The Germans will hear me, will they? How many peanuts have I got. What do you mean by peanuts? . . . Oh! Every man has got a hundred rounds, if the fools know how to fire them. . . . What's that? The Germans will hear me? Don't make me laugh, sir. You used to talk sense before you got those two stars on you. A hell of a mess? Of course it's a mess. They're turning on everything they've got. Have I got my front line located? No. How can I be sure when all the wires are out? Well, hold the wire."

The General tossed the instrument to the telegraph orderly and seized the map again. Of course he knew we were all watching him. Of course we knew he was in a strange position, not knowing where the front line was, not knowing anything—just stumbling in the dark.

"What the devil's the name of this place?" he repeated. "Oozy? Coozy? Why the devil can't they make sense? And what's that little gimcrack?

That's where the Umpty-umph ought to be, isn't it? No, not that. That's a brook. That little square thing. La Ferme? What the devil's a *ferme*? I came here to fight a war, not to learn French. Confound this light! La Ferme de la Sainte?" The map crumpled beneath the General's fingers.

He looked around at the young gentlemen almost stupidly, with his mouth half open. "That's a deuce of a name to call anything! It isn't a name at all. It's like a piece of underwear. It's like one of those things women put on themselves when they don't wear corsets."

There was a moment's silence. The word "corsets" in that place seemed to have a magic sound. The orderly at the telephone looked up. The runners at the door with red bands on their sleeves looked up. And all the rest of us looked at him helplessly as we listened to the noise outside. Then there came the most incongruous sound. The General's head flew up. Billy Langwell had not meant to laugh. You could see it on his face. It was a reflex of strained nerves, when everyone's nerves were strained. But General Swinnerton heard him. For an instant his face went scarlet and his lips moved without a sound. For an instant even the noise outside seemed to lessen. And then the General spoke, quietly—much more quietly than he had spoken all that night. "You're laughing, Mr. Langwell?" he inquired.

It was the first time I ever saw Billy startled. In spite of the shadow his helmet cast over his face, his whole face looked drawn and startled.

"I beg the General's pardon," he said hastily. Even then he did not forget the etiquette he had been taught.

"Well, what were you laughing at?" The General's voice was louder. "You're laughing at me, Mr. Langwell. You've always been laughing at me. Now tell me what's so funny."

"I beg the General's pardon," began Billy again.

General Swinnerton stared at him. He seemed to have forgotten everything—even the noise outside. "Don't be so damned polite," he said. "You're always laughing. Now tell me what's so funny."

Billy's answer came quickly. He wasn't frightened exactly, but he was embarrassed. "I'm awfully sorry, sir. I had no business to laugh. I—I don't know why I did, except what you said about the name—the corsets. I——"

Billy stammered and stopped, and the General nodded. "I understand," he said. "You like to see the old man make a fool of himself."

You couldn't help but be sorry for Billy Langwell then. Just to see the colour in the General's face and the glazed look in his eyes was enough to make you sorry.

For the end of everything was there or the ultimate result. All that had gone before—the little things, memories of sly glances and half smiles, everything which was hidden beneath courtesy and manners—flashed into the General's cheeks and forehead, as though some unseen caldron had boiled over and had completely spilled its reddish-purple contents even over the General's nose. He blushed and stammered, as though he was fighting against something that had grown too strong at last.

"You second-chop shave-tail!"—you would hardly have known it was the General, his face had grown so dark—"did you think I haven't watched you? Do you flatter yourself I haven't seen you and the lot of you sneering at me because I can't hold a fork? Don't lie to me about it! You think I am a mucker, don't you? you damned dude! I may be a mucker, but I've got eyes and ears. Don't think I am fit to order you! You don't think I'm a gentleman, do you? I've seen the bunch of you whispering at Hicks and on the boat. You don't think I'm one, do you? Answer me—you! D'you hear?"

The words poured out of him suddenly as the colour had poured into his face, just as ugly and as horrid, and with them came all the pain and the resentment he must always have harboured, for he was not under control. No one was under control unless it was Billy Langwell. I saw Edwin Bryce's face flush and his lip curl angrily, but Billy Langwell maintained the most irritating poise—that poise which the General had always hated—and stared at the General placidly.

"The General," he said, "has me at a disadvantage. I can't say what I think—what I should have to say—without going under anew. Perhaps some other time——"

The General interrupted him as though the sound of Billy's voice was more than he could bear. "Say what you mean for once in your life—to my face—like a man, you snivelling coward!"

He was not a snivelling coward. The General ought to have seen that from the way that Billy stood and answered.

"You want me to?" he inquired. Everyone must have wanted to catch him, to pull him away; but no one did, and his voice continued meticulously distinct. "You want me to? All right, then. I've stood enough. I think you're a bully and a windbag. Stop it! Put down your hand!"

There was no doubt the General was not himself. Edwin Bryce sprang in front of him just in time, and you could almost have been proud of Edwin.

"There, sir," he said "we'll apologise, of course. But let me remind you——The division is on the wire. They want the co-ordinates for the front line."

"The division is still on the wire, sir."

The General looked at Edwin Bryce and then back at Billy Langwell. His hand trembled so that the map moved uncertainly in his fingers, and his voice was as unpleasant as I had ever heard it.

"You know everything, don't you?" he remarked, "you two young men? Orderly, tell headquarters that I'm sending runners up, and I'll telephone the co-ordinates when I get them. And now, Mr. Langwell, do you know that word? Can you read it for us?"

Billy leaned over the map. His voice trembled slightly. "Certainly, sir. It's La Ferme de la St.-Hilaire."

"De la St.-Hilaire," mimicked the General, suddenly grotesque and terrible. "Is it now? And can't you read all these other names, Mr. Langwell?"

Billy looked at the General. Billy no longer looked exactly nonplussed. He took a corner of the map in his thumb and forefinger. "Certainly—easily," he answered; "in fact, without trouble at all."

The General made no comment. He looked at Edwin Bryce. "And you, Mr. Bryce?" he inquired, with that same unpleasant parody. "Of course you can read them, Mr. Bryce?"

"Of course," said Edwin shortly.

And then Billy said something that finished it. Although he was perfectly cool, you could see he was angry—as angry as the General.

"The General must remember," he said gently, "that we haven't had—the benefits of an Army education."

The fool! What a fool he was! The coldness and the silence of the General were what made it terrible. He looked at them both with that slightly puzzled expression which changed into something else, and swayed back and forth from his toes to his heels before he finally spoke.

"How fortunate," said the General, and swayed again from his toes to his heels, "we've got someone who can locate the front line. Rise and shine, young gentlemen." They didn't understand him. None of us exactly understood. "Do you hear me?" The colour of the General's face seemed to choke his voice. "Get out with you both, if you know so much. Go up and find that farm. Go up and see if the line is in front of it, behind it, or in it. And come back and let me know."

And he knew what he was doing. That was what made it worse. He was sending them up to the front line in the dark, under heavy shelling, on the first night that they had ever heard a shell go off—in the dark, without their ever having known the road. Was there any wonder Billy Langwell looked a little sick?

"Of course you'll send us a runner who knows the way?" he said.

"Knows the way?" said the General. "Can't you see the way—on that road past the little gimcrack and by the thingumajig? What are you standing arguing about? Go up and find that front line, and come back and report. Do you think you're any more valuable than anyone else because you're on the staff? My aides are expendable. Go out with you! Forward, march!"

Even as the General spoke he must have known how he appeared, from the way that Billy Langwell looked. For Billy Langwell was the better man just then—much the better man.

He gave a slight pull to the gas-mask on his chest and nodded to Edwin Bryce. "Let's go out of this," he said.

They walked straight to the door, while the General stared at their backs. Once I thought he was going to speak. Once he cleared his throat.

But at the door Billy Langwell turned and smiled at the General in a most annoying way. "Will the General excuse me if I don't take off my hat?" he said. "I may need it on outside."

Before the General could answer they were gone. For a moment he stared at the swaying blankets by the door, almost forgetful of where he was.

"Major," he said at length, "make a note on Mr. Langwell's record tomorrow morning—that his manner is insolent toward his superior officers. Send out two more men from the detail with my compliments to the signal officer, and ask him why he cannot mend his wires."

Then he hesitated, still standing in the centre of the room. You see, he was a soldier—too good a soldier to let his anger carry him away for any length of time. He swayed for a moment from his toes to his heels.

"Is there any runner here who knows the way to that farm?" he asked suddenly. And somehow the tension in everyone relaxed, soundlessly yet definitely.

"Yes, sir." It was the single Regular orderly from Camp Abraham Hicks who spoke. "I've been there, sir."

"Is it hard to find?" The General looked relieved. At last he was speaking to someone he understood.

"No, sir. You gotta go in the fields, though. They're shelling hell out of the roads."

"Then you better——" began the General. The orderly was moving automatically toward the door, but the General did not have time to finish.

"The regimental wire's in, sir!" cried the telephone orderly.

"GOOD-MORNING, MAJOR!"   637

The General whirled about. "Which regimental line?" he cried. "Give me the telephone. . . . Hello! Who are you? Baggage? How can you get artillery support if you don't send back your co-ordinates? Well, send another man back. Send two more. Now read them before you go out again. Write 'em down, Major, as I say 'em—23 point. I've got that. Two-three point." There was a silence. The General set down the instrument and swore.

"The damn thing's out again," he said. "Orderly, go out and give those Lieutenants my compliments, and say you'll take one to the farm and send the other back. And the rest of you clean up this mess in here and give me a chair to sit on."

But when he got the chair the General would not sit down. He began pacing up and down instead, listening to the noise outside. And you could tell what he was thinking. He was wishing he was up there. He understood better than any of us his present uselessness. It was making him restless. It was wearing down his nerves. Once he looked at his wrist watch. It was two o'clock in the morning, and you could tell he was wishing it was light.

The suspense—the uncertainty of everything—was enough to get on anybody's nerves. The telephone orderly sat rigid, fingering the plugs on his board with tense fingers. The orderlies by the door sat with their shoulders slouched forward, looking at their hands.

But the General's shoulders were the ones that should have sagged. Everything was resting on them, and he knew it. But he still kept walking up and down. He was the first one who heard a noise in the passage— a scraping, hesitating step.

"Pull back those blankets!" he cried. "Here comes a message!" We all saw it at the same time.

"What——" began the General. "What——"

A private entered—a stupid, red-headed farmer's boy—carrying an officer like a bag of meal across his shoulder.

The General was the first person who spoke, for, you see, he was an Army man. "Lay him down," he said. "Don't stand there looking at me! Lay him down and put something under his head." Without surprise, without contrition—quite methodically, the General spoke. And he knew who it was. You could tell by the useless spurs and the whipcords and the exquisite Sam Browne belt, even before you saw his face.

"Break out a first-aid kit, one of you!" he said. "What are you looking at? Haven't you seen any blood before? One of you orderlies go out and call a stretcher."

The red-haired private was scrambling to his feet. His shoulder was wet and dripping. "There was two of 'em," he said. "They was walking up the road just like—just like——"

The General stopped him. His voice was enough to stop anything just then. "And where's the other one?" he said.

The soldier blinked. He was very stupid and startled—almost dazed. "Dead," he answered. And then his voice became querulous and wild. He was seeking relief in words. "I seen him and he yelled at me," he said. "He was coming from here, poor kid, and I was coming here."

"What's that again?" The General's voice stopped his flow of words. "You were coming here? Where from?"

The orderly was still dazed. He had difficulty to think. "From head-quarters of the Umpteenth up to that farm with a message."

"Well, why didn't you say so in the first place?" The General took a step toward him. "Where is your message?"

That poor red-headed boy was a stupid sight. He blinked, he swallowed, he fumbled at his belt. "I—I can't remember, sir."

"Can't remember?" roared the General.

"I—I must have dropped it, sir, when I picked him up."

General Swinnerton's fingers closed on his palm and opened. Before he even spoke that red-headed boy cowered away from him. But we never heard what he had to say.

"Don't jump him, sir." It was Billy Langwell, speaking in a curious, dreamy way as he turned his head on his blanket pillow. "The poor boy did the best he could. We"—he moved slightly and caught his breath— "we can't all be in the cavalry back in '75."

The General turned toward him and bent down. Perhaps it was because the candles were flickering that his face looked grey, and that he looked older than he had before—much older.

"Don't talk, Mr. Langwell," he said. "Are you in pain?"

Someone was applying a rude tourniquet to Billy Langwell's leg. Another was cutting open his whipcord jacket and trying to pull off his Sam Browne belt. But Billy Langwell hardly seemed to notice. He was in that state, you see, where pain has ceased to mean anything or where pain itself brought its own peculiar peace. As he stared at the General, he seemed peculiarly delicate, fragile, as fine as a tenuous thought which a word or a gesture might send away. It was not what he said to the General that made the General's face grow grey and still. It was something in his eyes, rather, and the way he moved his lips.

"Don't bother about me, thank you, sir," he answered. "I'm all right—perfectly all right."

The General turned to the telephone operator. His face had become like a stone—as hard and quite as grey. "Get the division," he said, "and ask why those casual officers they were sending have not come up." And then he turned and looked at me.

Except for Billy Langwell, we were the only officers in the cellar then, for the signal officer was out, the intelligence officer was out, so was the detachment commander. And of course he saw the way I felt. But he was kind about it—surprisingly kind. He put his hand quite gently on my shoulder.

"Don't look so sick, Major," he said. "It's the war, that's all; and the next Lieutenant that comes in to report will go out the same way if the telephones are working."

He was not exactly justifying himself, for he thought it was duty, straight duty. Two stretcher-bearers had come in, and the two were working over Billy Langwell, talking in low voices. That constant inflow and outflow of people which is a part of any headquarters was beginning again, like a part of the same vague dream.

Some newcomers had appeared, seemingly from nowhere, as people often did in those vague nights. They stood, blinking and looking about them until one of them spoke. "Beg pardon, sir. Is this brigade headquarters?"

For some reason I was startled. They were officers—Second Lieutenants—those casual officers of which the General had spoken. The one in front saluted, holding the salute for exactly the right length of time, almost like a Regular officer.

"Sir," he said, "Lieutenant Swinnerton reports for duty with the detail."

The theatre—always the theatre! Even up there we had those close-cut banal phrases. Lieutenant Swinnerton! You would have known he was the General's son without any intuition to make you feel it. He had the same heavy shoulders, the same uncompromising head, and he looked from me to the General without showing any recognition. He knew the old man was a soldier. He knew what the old man wanted, and you had to hand it to the General then, for the thing he did was not what he wished to do. I heard him draw a quick breath, but he spoke at once. He could not hesitate, because he was an Army man; and if he had not been, how could he have hesitated, with Billy Langwell lying on the floor?

Billy Langwell had not lost consciousness. You could see he was listening and taking a detached interest, as men sometimes do in spite of pain.

"Mr. Swinnerton," said the General—and once again Billy Langwell had him, though perhaps the General never knew it or never thought— "Mr. Swinnerton, do you see that thingumajig on the map—the Ferme-something-or-other? We can't pronounce it now since Mr. Langwell's got laid out. Well, get up there to the Umpteenth Regiment. Give the Colonel my compliments, and tell him to give you the co-ordinates of the front line, and tell him to send every man he can spare to lay out another wire. That's all."

The Lieutenant saluted. He must have known the old man well enough not to argue, and yet he asked a question: "Can you let me have a runner, sir, who knows the way?"

There was a slight tremor in the General's voice, but very slight. "The last one's out, and he hasn't come back yet. But you don't mind a thing like that. You were raised in an Army post."

They were lifting Billy Langwell to the stretcher, they were moving with him to the blankets by the door, when the General noticed. "Are you comfortable, Mr. Langwell?" he inquired, and Billy opened his eyes.

"Thank you sir," he said.

And then there was an embarrassing moment. The stretcher-bearers did not know whether to move on or stop, because the General made no sign.

"You don't feel——" The General cleared his throat and seemed to have difficulty with his words. "I hope you don't feel you've been dis-criminated against in any way?"

Billy Langwell twisted his lips upward. He was quite himself in that last moment and careless, but not so careless as we had sometimes seen him.

"Lord, no, sir," he said. "It's funny what an idiot I was. I thought you couldn't be real, you know. But now I've seen you working out——" without finishing his thought he waved his hand slightly in a curious, airy way. "George, give me a cigarette, will you? Now I've seen you working out—— Good-morning, General. I don't mean to be rude, sir. It's just a way I have." He had ceased waving his hand, and added the truest thing he ever said: "We're just a different breed of cats—that's all." What else was there to say—now that he had definitely, completely, put General Swinnerton in his place and himself in his place as well?

When did that regimental wire come in? It might have been an hour or less, although it was impossible to think of time in hours or minutes. The General was seated when they called him, staring at the floor, and no one wished to interrupt him. He might have been asleep, for his chin was sunk on his chest, and his campaign ribbons moved with a regular, easy motion. As the telephone orderly spoke, however, General Swinnerton started and seized the instrument.

"Have you heard?" he began. "Is there——" you could tell what he wanted to say, but he stopped himself. "Well, it's time you hooked up. This has been a hell of a mess. And those signal officers will get a court for it, or I'll know the reason why. What can I expect? Didn't you get any messages? Didn't?"

The General's shoulder moved forward and he cleared his throat. "Didn't a Lieutenant report to you with my message? Yes, a new one. His name's Swinnerton. Can't you hear me? Swinnerton. Yes, he's my son, as a matter of fact. But what's that got to do with it? What's that?"

The General's shoulders moved suddenly. He sat up very straight. And suddenly his voice was choked and queer. "Thanks. Thanks. . . . But there's no use saying that. There are others who have caught it. Lots of others. Thanks. Now keep in the wire."

There was a noise. The telephone orderly stooped down hastily. The General had dropped the telephone headpiece on the floor and was standing up.

"Major"—his voice was still queer but perfectly controlled—"when you get after the morning report, add on Lieutenant Swinnerton. He—he's dead. I—I think I'll turn in now."

Now what was there to say? What was there to do? Absolutely nothing, for, you see, he was an Army man. No one said a word, and he stood by himself in the light of the guttering candles—alone, as he had always been alone. And why I did it I do not know, but suddenly I found myself holding his hand, trying to say something, anything at all. But still he was an Army man, though I felt his fingers close on mine.

"Don't be a damned fool," he said. "What time is it? Three o'clock? Well, I'm turning in till six. Good-night, or, rather, good-morning, Major."

FEAR

by JAMES WARNER BELLAH

IT WAS A LITTLE SPOT, that fear, but it had ached in his heart for months—ever since his first solo flight at Upavon Aerodrome. It had come suddenly one morning like the clean pink hole of a steel-jacketed bullet—a wound to be ashamed of, a wound to fight against, a wound that never quite healed. Always it was there to throb and to pinch like the first faint gnawing of cancer. It came with him to the theatre and rankled his mind: "Enjoy this—it may be your last play." It crept into his throat at meals sometimes, and took away the poor savour that was left to the foods of wartime.

The fear of the men who fly. Sometimes he pictured it as an imp—an imp that sat eternally on his top plane and questioned him on the strength of rudder wires, pointed to imaginary flaws in struts, suggested that petrol was low in the tank, that the engine would die on the next climbing turn.

It was with him now as the tender that was to take him up to his squadron jolted and bounced its way across the *pavé* on the outskirts of Amiens. The squadron was the last place he had to go to. All the months that were gone had led up to this. These were the wars at last. This was the place he would cop it, if he was to cop it at all.

He shrugged. Anyway, he had had his four days in London and his ten days idling at Pilot's Pool before the squadron sent for him. He braced one shoulder against the rattling seat and reached in his tunic pocket for a cigarette. Mechanically he offered one to the driver. The man took it with a grubby finger.

"Thankee, sor-r."

He nodded and lighted both cigarettes with the smudge of his pocket lighter. Anyway, he was not flying up to 44. That was one flight saved. Funny, that fear—how it came and went like the throb of a nerve in an open tooth. Sometimes the spot was large, and filled his whole being; then again it would shrink to a dull ache, just enough to take the edge from the beauty of the sunrise and the sparkle from the wine of the moon.

There had been a time when it had jumped in every fibre of his soul. He had been a cadet officer then, with only twelve solo hours in the air, under the old rough-and-tumble system of learning to fly. Spinning at

Reprinted by permission of the author.

that time was an unsolved mystery to him, a ghastly mystery that had meant quick death in a welter of blood, flecked with splinters. Fred Mc-Cloud had gone that way, and Johnny Archamboult. For weeks afterward, Johnny's screams had rung in his ears like a stab of pain, until the mere smell of petrol and fabric dope made the fear crawl into his throat and strangle him. Somehow he had kept on with the rest, under the merciless scourge that lashed one on to fly—and the worst fear of seeing cold scorn in the eyes of the men who taught the lore of thin cloud miles.

The tender twisted and dodged along the hard mud ribbon that ran like a badly healed cicatrix across the pock-scarred face of the fields. Gnarled and bleak, they were fields that had held the weight of blood-crazed men—still held them in unmarked graves, where they had fallen the year before under the steel flail. He had heard stories from his older brother about those fields—the laughing brother who had gone away one day and returned months later without his laugh, only to go away again, not to come back. He had seen pictures in the magazines—— But somehow no one had caught their utter bleakness as he saw it now.

The riven boles of two obscene trees crouched and argued about it on the lead-grey horizon, tossing their splintered arms and shrieking, he fancied, like quarreling old women in the lesser streets of a village. Close to the roadway, there were a torn shoe and a tin hat flattened like a crushed derby. Poor relics that even salvage could see no further use in. Farther off, a splintered caisson pointed three spokes of a shattered wheel to the sky, like a mutilated hand thrown out in agony. He was seeing it for himself now.

No one could smile at the cleanness of his uniform again and say: "Wait till you get out. When I was in France——" He was out himself now. In a day or so he would go over the line with loaded guns. His instructors at the training 'drome—thin-jawed men with soiled ribbons under their wings—had done no more, and some of them had done less. The thought braced him somewhat. They had seemed so different—so impossible to imitate—those men. Their war had always been a different one from his; a war peopled with vague, fearless men like Rhodes-Moorehouse and Albert Ball and Bishop, the Canadian; men who flew without a thought for themselves.

It occurred to him with a start that theirs was the same war as his now. Twenty-five miles ahead of him, buried somewhere in rat runs, between Bapaume and Cambrai, it went on and on, waiting for him to come—waiting to claw and maim and snuff him out when he did come. It had seemed so far away from him in England. When he was at ground school he had seen it as a place where one did glorious things—he was young, pitifully young—a place that one came back from with ribbons under one's wings, with nice clean scratches decently bandaged. And he had been slightly offended at his brother's attitude—at the things his brother had said of the staff. Then he had gone to Upavon to learn to fly. He had soloed for the first time, and the spot of fear had crawled into his own heart.

They were rattling into the broken streets of a tottering town—a town that leered at them and grimaced through blackened gaps in its once white walls. There was a patched-up estaminet with a tattered yellow awning that tried bravely to smile.

"Albert," said the driver.

The new pilot nodded. Some sapper officers were loitering in the doorways of the café. Their uniforms were faded to a rusty brown and reinforced with leather at the cuffs and elbows. Their buttons were leather, too, to save polishing, and their badges were a dull bronze. He looked down at his white bedford-cord breeches and the spotless skirts of his fur-collared British warm—privileges of the flying corps that men envied. Baths, clean clothing, and better food. The P.B.I.'s idea of heaven. They called flyers lucky for their privileges and cursed them a little bit for their dry beds and the wines they had in their messes, miles behind the line.

The new pilot wondered if they knew what it meant to be alone in the stabbing cold with no one to talk to, no one to help you, nothing between you and the ground save a thin, trembling fabric of cloth and wire and twenty thousand feet of emptiness. That was his fear—emptiness—nothingness—solitude. Those men under the awning could die in company. Not so himself—alone, screaming into the cloud voids, with no one to hear, no one to help, staring with glazed eyes and foam-flecked lips at the emptiness into which one hurtled to death miles below. The price one paid for a bath! He remembered seeing Grahame-White fly at Southport before the War. People had called him an intrepid aviator. The new pilot laughed harshly inside his throat and stared out across the bare fields.

The car topped a slight rise and turned sharply to the left. The driver pointed his grubby finger. "They be comin' in from affernoon patrol," he said. "Yonder is aerodrome."

There were three flat canvas hangars painted a dull brown, and a straggling line of rusty tin huts facing them from across the narrow landing space—like a deserted mining village, shabby and unkempt. As he watched, he saw the last machine of the afternoon patrol bank at a hundred and fifty feet and side-slip down for its landing. In his heart he could hear the metal scream of wind in the flying wires. A puff of black smoke squirted out in a torn stream as the pilot blipped on his engine for one more second before he came into the wind and landed. By the time the tender rolled up to the dilapidated squadron office, the machine had taxied into the row of hangars and the pilot was out, fumbling for a cigarette with his ungloved hands. A thin acrid smell of petrol and carbonised castor oil still hung in the quiet air between the shabby huts. Snow in large wet flakes commenced to fall slowly, steadily.

The new pilot climbed down from the tender, tossed his shoulder haversack beside his kit-bag, and pushed open the door of the squadron office. The Adjutant was sitting on his desk top, smoking and talking to someone in a black leather flying coat and helmet—someone with an oil-streaked face and fingers still blue and clumsy from the cold.

"Paterson, sir, G. K., Second Lieutenant, reporting in from Pilot's Pool for duty with the 44th."

The Adjutant raised a careless finger in acknowledgment. "Oh yes. How do? Bring your log books?"

"Yes, sir."

"Chuck 'em down. D'ye mind?"

Paterson laid them upon the desk top, still standing to attention. The Adjutant smiled. "Break off," he said. "We're careless here. This isn't cadet school."

The new pilot smiled and relaxed. "Very good, sir."

"That's better," said the Adjutant; "makes me feel more comfortable. Just give me a note of yourself now." He reached for a slip of paper. "G. K. Paterson, Two Lt. Next of kin?" Paterson gave his father's name. "Age?"

"Eighteen and four-twelfths."

"Good!" said the Adjutant. "You'll find an empty cubicle in B Block —that's the middle line of huts. You're lucky. Roof only leaks in three places. I'll have your duffel trekked over shortly."

The man in the flying coat blew upon his numbed fingers and smiled. "I'm Hoyt," he said. "Skipper of C Flight. I'm going to take you now, before A gets after you." He turned to the Adjutant. "That's all right, isn't it, Charlie? Tell 'em I intimidated you." He grinned.

The Adjutant shrugged. "Right-o!"

"Come on," said Hoyt. "I'm in your hut block. I'll show you your hole."

They went out into the snow flurry. Mechanics were fussing in little knots around the five tiny machines that had just landed, lining them up, refilling them, and trundling them into the brown musty hangars.

"Le Rhône Camels," said Hoyt. "We've just been over around Cambrai taking a look-see."

Inside one of the hangars, as they passed, Paterson saw something that drew a thin, wet gauze across his eyeballs. On a rough bench just beside the open flap sat a man with his eyes closed and his lips drawn tightly into a straight bluish line. His flying coat was rolled up behind his head for a pillow, and his tunic had been unbuttoned and cut away from his left shoulder. The white of his flesh showed weirdly in the gloom, like the belly of a dead fish. Just below the shoulder, the white was crumpled and reddened as if a clawed paw had been drawn across it. One man was holding his other hand, while another probed and cleaned and dabbed with little puffs of snowy cotton that turned quickly to pink and then to a deep brown.

Hoyt shrugged. "Lucky man. That's Mallory. He was Number Four this afternoon. We never saw a thing. Just happened. Funny." And he smiled. "That's why I was so keen to get you. Can't tell how long it will be before Mallory gets around again, and I've got one vacancy in the flight already." He shrugged. "You'll see a lot of that here—get used to it. It doesn't mean a thing as long as you get back alive."

Paterson looked at him sharply. He wanted to ask him how many didn't get back alive. He wanted to know what had caused the other vacancy in the flight. But people didn't ask those things. People merely nodded casually and went on.

"I suppose not," he said. They tramped on across the aerodrome.

"Here we are," said Hoyt. He kicked open the hut door and groped down the dark passageway, with Paterson after him. Presently he pushed back another door and yanked at a tattered window curtain.

The new pilot saw a tiny room, with two washstands, a cot, a folding chair, and a cracked mirror. In a corner were his kit-bag and haversack. He pulled out his own cot and chair and set them up; meanwhile Hoyt threw himself down on the other cot and let his cigarette smoke dribble straight upward into the gloom of the pine-rafted roof. Presently he spoke.

"This is a queer war," he said; "full of queer things, and the queerest of these is charity." He laughed in the darkness, and the tip of his cigarette became suddenly pink as he drew the smoke into his lungs. "What was your school?"

"Winchester," said Paterson.

"Right," said Hoyt. "Remember your first day? This is it over again. They've fed you up on poobah at your training 'drome and down at the Pool. They always do. It's part of the system. Just take it for what it is worth and forget the rest. If you want to know anything, come to me and I'll tell you as well as I can. I've been here three months. When I came, I came just as you did to-day, pucka green and afraid to the marrow—afraid of uncertainty. You get over that shortly.

"Our job is a funny one, and we're not here for ourselves, and we're not here to be heroes or to get in the newspapers. The V.C.s are few and far between." He raised himself upon his elbow. "I'm not preaching self-abasement and a greater loyalty to a cause that is right, mind you. I don't know anything about causes or who started the War or why, and I don't care. I'm preaching C Flight and the lives of five men.

"You saw Mallory over at the hangar. It was teamwork that put him there in his own M.O.'s hands. Not much, perhaps"—the cigarette described a quick arc in the darkness—"just a slight closing in of the formation—a wave of somebody's hand—somebody else dropping back and climbing above him to protect his tail from any stray Huns that might've waylaid him on the way home. That's what I mean. *Esprit de corps* is a cold, hard phrase. Call it what you like. It's the greatest lesson you learn. Never give up a man." Hoyt laughed. "They call me an old woman. Perhaps I am. Take it or leave it.

"Slick up a bit and come into my hutch while I scrape off the outer layer of silt. Dinner in half a tick and I'm as filthy as a pig." He vaulted up from the cot and punched his cigarette out against the sole of his foot. At the door he paused for a moment.

"Ever have wind up?" he asked casually.

Paterson stiffened against the question and the small spot of fear danced within him. "No," he said firmly. Hoyt shrugged. "Lucky man." And he went out into the passage-way.

At dinner he met the rest of the squadron and the other men in C Flight. Mallory, very pale, with his arm slung in a soft pad of bandages, sat beside him. They were coming for him later to take him down to the base hospital. Phelps-Barrington sat on the other side of Mallory, mourning the fact that the wound was not his that he might get the inevitable leave to follow. Phelps-Barrington took Paterson's hand with a shrug and asked how Marguerite was in Amiens. "What? You didn't meet Marguerite on your way through? 'Struth!" MacClintock sat across the table beside Hoyt—MacClintock, too young to grow a moustache, but a deep burr that smelled of the heather in the Highlands and huge pink knees under his Seaforth kilts, muscles like the corded roots of an oak. The other man in the flight, Trent, was down with mild flu. He was due back in a week or so from hospital.

There was a wild argument on about the dawn patrol the next morning. Paterson listened to the fragments of talk that flew like sabre cuts across the glasses:

"He's in a red tripe. I don't give a damn for Intelligence. Saw him this morning myself. Same machine Mac and I had that brush with down at Péronne."

"The next time they'll get an idea for us to strafe a road clear to Cologne for them. What are we—street cleaners?"

"So I let go a covey of Coopers and turned for home. They had it spotted for a battery over at 119 Squadron. I saw the pictures. Right pictures, but wrong map squares as usual. That crowd can't tell a battery from a Chinese labour-corps inclosure. I'd rather be a staff officer than a two-seater pilot."

"Steward, a whisky-soda for Mr. MacClintock and myself. Have one, Hoyt? You, Paterson?"

Cruel, thin, casual talk clicking against the teeth in nervous haste; the commercial talk of men bartering their lives against each tick of the clock; men caught like rats in a trap, wtih no escape but death or a lucky chance like Mallory's. Caught and yet denying the trap—laughing at it until the low roof of the mess shack rumbled with the echo; drowning it in a whisky for the night.

Afterward, Hoyt came down the passage with him to his room—Hoyt, with his face cleaned of the afternoon's oil and his eyes slightly bright with the wine he had taken.

"We're relieved to-morrow on account of casualties," he said. "I'll tick you out early and we'll go joy riding—see what we can teach each other." He smiled. " 'Night."

Paterson undressed slowly and threw back the flap of his sleeping bag. He ran his fingers softly down the muscles of his left arm. Automatically they stopped at the spot Mallory had been hit. He stretched his thumb from the arm to his heart—seven inches. He shrugged. Nice to go that way. Clean and quick. He sat upon the edge of his cot and pulled on his pyjama trousers. Oh, well, this was the place—the last place he had to go to. This was the cot he would sleep his last sleep in. If it weren't a lonely job! That chap in the mess who wouldn't be a two-seater pilot for anything. If he could only feel like that. If he could only feel Hoyt's complacency. Hoyt, with his calm smile and the two little ribbons under his wings. Military Cross and the Legion of Honour, and three months before he had been green—pucka green!

Paterson blew out the light and turned in. Hoyt was a good fellow—damned decent. Outside he could hear Phelps-Barrington's voice muffled by the snow: "Come on, snap into it! Tender for Amiens! Who's coming?" The yell died in the roar from the car's engine.

Paterson lay for a moment thinking; then suddenly he reached for his pocket flash, snapped it, and stared nervously at the empty cot across the room. There was no bedding on it, nor any kit tucked under it; only the chair beside it, and the cracked mirror.

He got up and padded over in his bare feet. Stencilled on one corner of the canvas there was a name—J. G. H. Lyons. There had been no Lyons introduced to him in the mess. Perhaps he was on leave. Perhaps he had flu with Trent and was down at the base. The spot of fear in his heart trembled slightly and he knew suddenly where J. G. H. Lyons was. He was dead! Somewhere out in the snow, miles across the line, J. G. H. Lyons slept in a shattered cockpit.

The door behind him opened softly. It was Hoyt, in pyjamas. "Got a cigarette?" he asked casually.

Paterson turned sharply and grinned. "Right-o," he said. "There on the table."

Hoyt took one and lighted it. "Can't sleep," he said. "Come in and take Mallory's cot if you want to. I've some new magazines and I can tell you something about our work here until we feel sleepy."

Hoyt was a good fellow—damned decent.

The cold wet mist lay upon the fields like a soft veil drawn across the face of an old woman who had died in the night. Mechanics, with their balaklavas pulled down across their ears, were running about briskly to keep warm—kicking chocks in front of undercarriage wheels, snapping propellers down with mighty leaps and sweeps until the cold engines barked into life and settled to deep concert roaring. Dust and pebbles, scattered by the backwash, swept into the billowing hangars in a thin choking cloud that pattered against the canvas walls. Hoyt's machine trembled and crept out of the line, with Phelps-Barrington after it. Trent, who had come back from the base the day before, taxied out next.

Paterson waved to the mechanics to pull out his own chocks. They yanked mightily on the ropes, and he blipped his motor with his thumb. Behind him and to the left came Yardley, the new man who had come up from Pool to fill Mallory's place. Then MacClintock, sitting high in his cockpit, rushed out with a roar and a swish of gravel. MacClintock was deputy leader.

Hoyt waved his hand in a quick nervous sweep, and the flight started. Through the mist they roared with their engines howling into sharp echo against the hut walls. A moment later tails whipped up and wheels bounced lightly upon the uneven ground. Then Hoyt's nose rose sharply and he zoomed into the air in a broad climbing turn, with the five others after him in tight formation.

Paterson glanced at his altimeter—five hundred feet. He looked ahead and to the left. There was Bapaume in its raggedness, half drowned in the mist. Suddenly Phelps-Barrington's machine burst into rose flame and every strut and wire trembled like molten silver—the sun. He could see the red rim just peeping up ahead of him and he was warmer for the sight of it. Below, under the rim of his cock-pit, the ground was still wrapped in its grey shroud.

They were climbing up in close formation. The altimeter gave them four thousand feet now. He glanced to the left. Yardley waved. Yardley was going through the agony of his first patrol over the line—the same agony he had gone through himself the week before. Only Yardley seemed different, somehow—surer of himself—less imaginative. He was older, too. Behind them, MacClintock, the watch-dog, was closing in on their tails and climbing above them to be ready to help if the Hun swooped from behind unexpectedly.

There were clouds above—grey blanket clouds that came together in a solid roof, with only a torn hole here and there to show the blue. Bad clouds to be under. Hoyt knew it and kept on climbing. Almost ten thousand feet now. The ground below had cleared slowly and thrown off most of its sullen shroud. Here and there, in depressions, the mist still hung in arabesque ruffles like icing in a confectioner's window or the white smoke of a railway engine.

The line was under them now, running south and east like a jagged dagger cut, in and out, in and out across the land, not stopping for towns, but cleaving straight through their grey smudgy ruins with a cold disregard and a ruthless purpose. The first day he had seen it, it had seemed a dam to him; a breakwater built there to hold something that must not flow past it; a tourniquet of barbed wire twisted and held by half the world that the blood of the other half might not flow. Some day something would break and the whole thing would give way for good or evil. Curiously, now, like Hoyt, he didn't care which. And suddenly he knew how his older brother had felt, on that last leave, and he had called him unsporting in the pride of his youthful heart!

Hoyt was still climbing. Thin wraiths of cloud vapour groped awkwardly for the six tiny Camels, like ghost fingers, trying desperately to stop them and hold them from their work. Paterson glanced again at Yardley. He had been glad when Yardley came. He was still green himself, but Yardley was greener. It helped buck him up to think about it.

The line was behind them now. Hoyt turned south to pass below the anti-aircraft batteries of Cambrai, and presently they crossed the tarnished silver ribbon of the Somme-Scheldt Canal. Mechanically, Paterson reached for his Bowden trigger and pressed it for a burst of ten shots to warm the oil in his Vickers gun against the bite of the cold air. Then he clamped the joy-stick between his knees and reached up for the Lewis gun on his top plane.

His throat closed abruptly, with a ghastly dryness, and his knees melted beneath him. The wing fabric beside his gun was ruffling into torn lace and he could see the wood of the camber ribs splintering as he watched! For a moment he was paralysed, then frantically he whipped around in his seat and swept the air above him. Nothing. There was the torn fabric and the staring rib and nothing else. MacClintock was gone. Yardley was still there, lagging, with the smoke coming in puffs and streaks from his engine. Then Hoyt turned in a wild climb to the left. Phelps-Barrington dipped his nose suddenly and dived with his engine full on, and at once, where there had been only six Camels, the sky was full of grey machines with blunt noses and black crosses.

Blindly he pressed his Bowden trigger and fired into the empty air, blindly he dived after Phelps-Barrington. Somewhere to the left he saw a plume of black smoke with something yellow twisting in the sunlight on its lower end. A blunt nose crossed his propeller—into his stream of bullets. He screamed and banked wildly, still firing. He saw Hoyt above him. He forgot the machine in front and reached for his Lewis to help Hoyt. He tried to wait—something about the outer ring of the rear sight —but his fingers got the better of him and he fired point-blank.

As quickly as it had begun it ended. There was Hoyt circling back, and two other Camels to the left and below him—four of them. They closed in on Hoyt and he wondered where the two others were. He looked for them—probably chasing after the Huns. He could see dots to the southward—too far away to make out the markings. Hoyt had signalled the washout and they were headed back across the line. Funny those two others didn't come. He wondered who they were. Probably Phelps-Barrington and MacClintock, hanging on to the fight until the last. They worked together that way. He had heard them talk in the mess about it. They'd be at it again to-night, and to-night he could join them for the first time. He'd been in a dog fight! Shot and been shot at! The spot of fear shrank to a pin-point.

The brown smudge of the aerodrome slid over the horizon. He blipped his motor and glided in carefully. No use straining that top wing —no telling what other parts had been hit. No use taking chances.

Hoyt was standing beside his machine with his glove off, staring at his finger-nails. Phelps-Barrington was climbing out. Paterson taxied in between them. The man in the fourth machine just sat and stared over the rim of his cockpit. Phelps-Barrington walked slowly across to Hoyt and laid a hand on his shoulder. Hoyt shrugged and stuffed his bare hand into his coat pocket. Paterson sat with his goggles still on and his throat quite dry. The man in the fourth machine vaulted out suddenly, ripped off his helmet and goggles and hurled them to the ground. It was Trent.

He climbed out of his own machine and walked over toward Hoyt. Phelps-Barrington, who had a wild word for all occasions—Phelps-Barrington, who led the night trips to Amiens—was silent. When Paterson came up he shrugged and scowled ferociously.

"Is it you, Pat?" said Hoyt. "Thought it was Yardley."

"'Struth!" said Phelps-Barrington. "Let's go and have a drink."

Paterson thrilled as the man slipped an arm through his. For one awful moment he had thought——

"Well," Hoyt said, "those things will happen." And he shrugged again.

"I saw dots to the southward," said Paterson. "Maybe they'll be in later."

"No, little Rollo," said Phelps-Barrington. "They won't be in later or ever. I saw it with my own eyes—both in flames. I thought it was you, and until Trent landed I thought he might be Mac. But I was wrong. Let's shut up and have a drink!"

Then suddenly he knew, and his mind froze with the ghastliness of the thought. If he'd been quicker—if he'd turned and climbed above Yardley when he saw him lagging, with the smoke squirting from his hit motor—he could have saved him. If he had kept his eyes open behind instead of dreaming he might have saved MacClintock, too. In a daze, he stumbled after Phelps-Barrington. That's why Trent had hurled his helmet to the ground and walked off. That's why Hoyt had shrugged and said: "Those things will happen." It was his fault—his—Paterson's. He'd bolted and lost his head and fired blindly into the empty air. He hadn't stuck to his man. He had let Yardley drop back alone to be murdered.

"Look here, P.-B.," he muttered, "I'm not drinking." He wanted to be alone—to think. So quick it had all been.

Phelps-Barrington grabbed his arm and pushed him stumbling into the mess shack. Trent was slumped down at the table with his glass before him, thumbing over a newspaper. He raised his head as they came in. "Two more of the same, steward—double."

They sat down beside him, and Phelps-Barrington reached for a section of the paper.

"It says here," said Trent, "that Eva Fay didn't commit suicide. Died of an overdose of hashish she took at a party in Maida Vale the night before."

The steward brought the glasses. Trent raised his and looked at Paterson. "Good work, son."

Paterson stared at him in amazement. Trent sipped his whisky and went on reading as if he had never stopped. Some time later, Paterson left them and went down to the flight office to find Hoyt. The thought of the morning still bothered him, in spite of Trent's words, and he wanted to clear it up. Hoyt smiled as he came in. "Washed the taste out in Falernian?" he asked.

"Some. Look here, skipper—this morning—what about it?"

"What about it?"

"My part—I was fast asleep. I saw Yardley lagging, and I had a moment to cross above him, but I lost my head, I'm afraid, and went wild."

The smile faded and Hoyt laid down his pencil. "Do you really think you could have saved him?"

"He was behind me already when I saw him lagging, just as you climbed and P.-B. dived."

"Then you couldn't have helped him, because Mac was done for when I saw him and climbed, and half a tick after I climbed, P.-B. saw Yardley burst into flames. There you are."

"But if I'd kept my eyes back instead of trusting to Mac?"

"Look here," said Hoyt, "no man can keep his eyes on everything. Something always happens in the place he isn't looking. Bear that in mind and forget this morning. You've seen a dog fight from the inside and lived. Take it easy. You're not here to do everything. You're here to stick to us. You might have run away. Remember that and be afraid of it. Remember if you get away by leaving a pal—he may live to come back. Then you'll have to face him, and engine trouble is a poor excuse.

"Trouble with you youngsters is that you've been fed up on poobah. And the myth of the fearless air fighter. Put it out of your mind. There's no such thing. Some are less afraid than others. Some are drunker—take your choice. Class dismissed." Hoyt grinned. "Go get cleaned up. We'll jog into Amiens for tiffin. Tender in half an hour. Tell Trent and P.-B."

They spent most of the afternoon at Charlie's Bar with some of the men from the artillery observation squadron. For dinner they went to the Du Rhin and the glasses flowed red. Afterward, in another place, there was a fight, as usual, and chairs crashed like match sticks, until whistles sounded outside and the A.P.M.'s car, siren screaming, raced up the street. They poured out into the alleyway and ran, leaving the waiter praying in high, shrieking French.

Trent had a bottle with him. They rode all the way home singing and shouting to high heaven, forgetting that there were two empty chairs in the mess and that there might be more to-morrow.

> Take the cylinders out of my kidneys,
> Take the scutcheon pins out of my brain,
> Take the cam box from under my backbone
> And assemble the engine again!

They were good fellows—Billy Hoyt, P.-B., Pat, and Ray Trent. Have 'nother li'l' drink.

They roared along like a Juggernaut, with the exhaust splitting the night air. Sometimes they were on the road and sometimes they were off. No one cared so long as they kept hurtling into the darkness.

Phelps-Barrington was fast asleep. Pat woke him up at the aerodrome and tumbled him into the hut.

They stumbled over a kit-bag in the dorway. P.-B. straightened up suddenly. "Good-bye, Mac, old lad, sleep tight."

Trent kicked the bag out of the way. "Damned Adjutant! Take P.-B. in with you, Pat. I'm bunking with the skipper. Might have the decency to take Mac's kit over to squadron office and not leave it lying around the passage. 'Night."

Paterson was quite sober. He tumbled P.-B. into bed and stood for a moment at the open window, staring out across the ground mist that billowed knee high in the faint night breeze. He rested his elbows on the sill and hid his face in his trembling hands. If he could only be like the others—casual—calloused. If he had less imagination—more sand— stamina—something. MacClintock had planned this night himself, at breakfast. Yardley had left a letter addressed and stamped on his window sill.

Paterson's mind jumped miles to the eastward. He saw the two blackened engines lying somewhere in the bleak fields beyond, ploughed into the ground, with their mats of twisted wires coiled around them in a hideous trap.

Their families would get word to-morrow. "Missing," it would read. And then later: "Previously reported missing, now reported killed in action." And to-morrow—perhaps his own family. Why can't it be quick?

There was a noise behind him. Someone fumbling at the door latch—Hoyt. "Had this bit left. Bottoms up! Quick!" He took the glass and drained it. The liquor bit into his veins and burned him. Hoyt set his own glass down on the washstand with a sharp click. "Get into bed now, you idiot. Good-night."

Spiked drink. Hoyt was a good fellow—damned decent. Do anything for Hoyt. Never let Hoyt go. Like my brother—before the War. Good old Hoyt. And he sank suddenly into a dreamless fuddle of sleep.

The weeks crawled on slowly. Paterson felt like a man climbing a steep ladder. Each day was a rung behind him. Each new rung showed an infinite number still ahead, waiting for him to go on, luring him with their apparent safety, waiting for him to reach the one rotten rung that would do him in. Some day he would reach it, and it would crack under him, or his fingers would slip and hurtle him into the abyss under his charred engine.

Offensive patrols and escort for the artillery observation squadron filled their time, with sometimes a road strafe to vary the monotony. These he liked best, for some quaint reason—perhaps because there was less space to fall through. Sometimes there would be a battalion on those roads—a battalion to scatter and knock down like tin soldiers on a nursery floor. Quite impersonal. They were never men to Paterson. Like dolls they ran and like dolls they sprawled awkwardly where they fell.

P.-B. and Trent and Hoyt carried him through somehow. Mallory was back again, but Mallory never counted much with him. P.-B. and Trent and Hoyt were a bulwark. They meant safety. It was good to wake up at night and hear P.-B. snoring on the other cot, to know that Hoyt and Trent were asleep in the next cubicle. It was good to see them stamping to keep warm before the patrol took off in the half light of early morning. So different from one another and yet so alike underneath. Hoyt was nearer his kind than the two others. Tall and spindly like his brother, with a straight, thin nose that quivered slightly at the nostril when he was annoyed. Hoyt, who smiled and sanctioned the childish depravity of little P.-B., but never quite met it with his own, although always seeming to, on the night trips to Amiens. Trent, glowering and quiet, with a keen hatred for everything political that he learned in the offices of the London and South-Western before the War, when the Army to him had meant young wastrels swanking the Guards' livery in the boxes of theatres— wastrels who had died on the Charleroi Road three years before.

Suddenly, from one of his mother's letters, he found that he had been in France almost three months. He stiffened with the thought and remembered what Hoyt had told him that day he had come: "I've been here three months. When I came, I came just as you did to-day—pucka green." He knew then that all his hopes were false. He was the same to-day as he had been that first day. He would always be the same. The spot of fear would always be with him. Some day it would swell and choke him and his hands would function without his frozen brain. He should never have tried to fly. He should have gone into the infantry as his brother had. Too much imagination—too little something. In three months he had learned the ropes, that was all; how to fire and when to fire, where the Archie batteries were near Cambrai, how to ride a cloud and crawl into it—nothing more.

The weeks went on, creeping closer and closer to the twenty-first of March—the twenty-first of March—and with them the feeling crept into Paterson's heart—a feeling that something frightful was to happen. Things had been quiet so long and casualties had been few. C Flight hadn't been touched in weeks. He brooded over the thought and slept badly. He went to Amiens with P.-B. more frequently. If it was to be any of the three, he knew he wouldn't be able to stand it. His bulwark would crumble and break and he would break with it. On the dawn patrols, those few minutes before they climbed into the cockpits and took off were agony: "This will be the day. It must be to-day. We can't go on this way. Our luck will break."

One day when they were escorting 119, four dots dived on them from behind and he knew suddenly what he would do. Stark, logically, the thing stood before him and beckoned through the wires of his centre section. If a shot hit his plane, he would go down. They were far over the lines, taking 110 on a bombing show. He would wabble down slowly, pushing his joy-stick from side to side in a slow ellipse as if he were out of control. Then he would land and run his nose into the ground and be taken prisoner. The others would see him and swear that he'd been hit—and he wouldn't do it until his machine had been hit. That for his own conscience's sake and for the years he would have to live afterwards.

But A Flight, behind and far above, saw the dots and scattered them, and the chance was gone.

Then day by day he waited for another. He knew now that he would do it at the first opportunity. He slept better with the thought, and the minutes seemed shorter now while he waited at dawn for his bus to be run out. All the details were worked out in his mind. If any one of the three were close to him, he'd throw up his hands wildly before he started down. They'd see that and report it. Then when he landed he'd pull out the flare quick and burn his machine so that they would think he had crashed and caught fire. It was so easy!

He spent less time with P.-B. now. Somehow the old freedom was gone. Somehow Hoyt wasn't the same to him either. He was working with three strangers he had never really known—three casual strangers he would leave shortly and never see again.

On the morning of the fourteenth of March the caller turned C Flight out suddenly, without warning, about an hour after P.-B. and Trent had returned from Amiens. A special signal had come in from wing headquarters. B Flight had the regular morning patrol, but there was to be an additional offensive patrol besides. A Flight had morning escort and the dusk patrol. That meant C for the special. Paterson could hear Hoyt swearing about it next door. P.-B., across the room, uttered a mighty curse and rolled over. Paterson got him a bucket of cold water and doused his feverish head in it. Trent and Hoyt were still cursing pettishly in the next cubicle.

Sleep-stupid, the four of them stumbled into the mess for hard-boiled eggs and coffee. Mallory and the new man, Crowe, were already eating, white-faced and unshaven. They slumped down beside them in silence.

In silence, they trooped across the dark aerodrome, buttoning their coats and fastening helmet straps against the cold wretchedness of the March wind. The machines were waiting for them in a ghostly line like staring wasps that had eaten the food of the gods and grown to gigantic size.

They climbed in and taxied out mechanically. B Flight had already left on the regular dawn patrol. They blipped their motors and roared away, leaving their echo and the sharp smell of castor oil behind on the empty 'drome.

Hoyt led them south to the crumpled ruins of Péronne and out to the line, climbing high to get the warmth of the sunlight that began to tint the clouds above them. They were going over to Le Cateau and beyond. Intelligence wanted pictures to confirm certain reports of new Hun shell dumps and battery concentration. The photographic planes were to go out and get them under escort as soon as there was enough light. As additional precaution, offensive patrols were to be kept up far over the enemy's lines to insure the success of the pictures. They passed the sullen black stain that was Le Câtelet and turned to the eastward. The ground was already light and the camera busses would be starting.

Hoyt took the roof at eighteen thousand feet and skirted the cloud wisps, watching below for customers. Paterson watched P.-B. anxiously. He had been roaring drunk an hour before. Groggy and drunk still, probably. He closed in a trifle and climbed above him, but P.-B. waved him down and wiggled his fingers from the end of his nose.

He looked ahead and down at Trent. Trent had been drunk, too, but he was steady now, sawing wood above and slightly behind Hoyt.

Then, suddenly, beyond Trent and far below, he saw a Hun two-seater alone. The old stunt. Hoyt shifted and pulled up his nose to climb above it and wait. Trent followed him up. Somewhere above that two-seater, and a half-mile behind, there would be a flight of Hun scouts skulking under the clouds, waiting to pounce on whoever dived for the two-seater. Hoyt knew it for a decoy. Paterson knew it. They would climb above the cloud edge, circle back, and catch the Hun scouts as they passed underneath.

Paterson trembled slightly. This was his chance at last. There'd be a long dive and a sure fight from behind, and in the mix-up he'd wabble down and out of the War via Lazaret VI in Cologne. He glanced around to see if Mallory was above him, and suddenly, out of the corner of his eye, he saw P.-B. shove his nose full down and throw himself into a straight dive for the decoy bus.

He gazed and shouted "No!" into the roar of his engine, P.-B., in a nasty temper and half fuddled, didn't smell the trick. There was one awful second, while Crowe closed up into P.-B.'s place and Hoyt banked to wait above for the Hun scouts to pounce down on the Camel.

P.-B. fired, pulled up, and dived again, far below them. The Hun two-seater banked sharply and came up and over in an Immelmann turn to get away. P.-B. caught it halfway over and a trickle of smoke swept out from its engine. Then in an instant Hoyt dived, with the rest of C Flight after him.

The next thing Paterson knew there were two Huns on his tail and a stream of tracer bullets pecking at his left wing. He pulled back on his stick and zoomed headlong up under Mallory. So close he was for a second that he could see the wheels turning slowly on Mallory's undercarriage and almost count the spokes glinting in the sunlight where the inside canvas sheathing had been taken off.

Mallory pulled away from him in a quick climbing turn and the Huns passed underneath, banking right and left. Paterson picked the left-hand one, thundered down on him in a short dive, and let go a burst of ten shots into the pilot's back. He saw the pilot's head snap sideways and his gloved hands fly up from the controls. Then Mallory dived over him after the other one. He turned in a wild split-air and followed Mallory.

There were more Huns below him and to the left, with two of the C Flight Camels diving and bucking between them. He raced furiously into a long dive, picked the nearest, and opened fire again in short, hammering bursts. His Hun wabbled and started down awkwardly in long sweeps. He picked another, still farther below, and pushed his stick forward until the rush of air gagged him. Wildly he fired as he ploughed down on it, and the chatter of his guns stabbed through the roar of his engine. He yelled like a madman, shot under the Hun, pulled up sharply, and fired into its grey mud-streaked belly. There was a fan of scarlet flame and a shock that tossed him to one side. He stalled and whipped out into a spin. Far below him he could see the decoy two-seater trailing a long plume of reddish smoke and flopping, wings over, toward the floor.

Then, suddenly, he saw his chance to wabble down and get away. He ruddered out of the spin and ran his stick once through the slow ellipse he had planned. But somehow he had to force himself to do it. There wasn't the relief he had expected. He looked back. Three C Flight machines were still above him, fighting madly—P.-B., Trent, and Hoyt. No—not this time. He pulled his stick back and climbed up. There were five Huns circling the Camels. It was a long shot, but he fired at the nearest and came up under the tail just as one of the Camels hurtled into a nose dive, twisted over, and snapped off both wings. He saw the pilot's arms raised wildly in the cockpit and no more.

Blood streamed into his mouth. He had torn his lips with his teeth in the excitement. The warm salty tang mounted to his brain. His goggles were sweat-fogged. His fingers ached with their pressure on the joy-stick, and his arm was numb to the elbow. In a spasm of blind hatred, he fired. Tracers raced across his top plane and struck with little smoke puffs that ripped the fabric into ribbons. His own bullets clawed at the Hun above him and fanged home.

He threw himself up and over in an Immelmann turn and came under the next, still firing. He let go his stick and jerked his Lewis gun down its sliding mount on his top plane. It fired twice and jammed. He yanked madly at the cocking lug, but it stuck halfway. He hurtled down again in another spin. The ground swept around in a quick arc that ended in clouds and more Hun busses. He caught his thrashing joy-stick. Again the ground flashed through his centre section struts in a brown smudge, with the blaze of the sun hanging to one end of it. Then there was a Camel above him and a Camel below him. He closed in on the one below and squinted at the markings. Hoyt. He looked up at the other Camel, but the numerals on the side of its fuselage were hidden with a torn flap of fabric. Together, the three turned westward and started back.

Presently, near the line, the bus above him wabbled and dipped its nose. He stared at it. It went into a long, even glide that grew slowly steeper as he watched. He looked down for Huns. There were none. The glide became a dive, the dive twisted into a aimless spin, like the flopping of a lazy swimmer turning over in shallow water. The spin flattened and the Camel whipped out upside down, stalled, snapped out again, and again spun downward in that ghastly slow way. Over and over, only to whip out, stall and spin again. It was miles below him now. Nothing to do. Fascinated, he watched it as he followed Hoyt's tail. It was a mere dot now, flashing once or twice in the sun as it flopped over and over. Close to the ground now—closer. Then, suddenly, a tiny sheet of pink flame leaped up like the flash of a far beacon. That was all.

Hoyt was side-slipping below him, and he saw his own aerodrome under the leading edge of his bottom wing. He followed Hoyt down. They landed together and taxied slowly in toward the hangars. They stopped side by side and climbed out stiff-legged. Paterson looked down and saw that his right flying boot was torn and flayed into shreds across the outer side. There was a jagged fringe on the skirt of his coat where the leather had been ripped into ruffles. Dumbly, he looked back into his cockpit. The floor boards were splintered and the wicker arm of his seat was eaten away. He shrugged and walked over toward Hoyt. There was blood on the rabbit fur of Hoyt's goggles, blood that oozed slowly down and dripped from his chin piece in bright drops.

"Cigarette?"

Paterson gave him one. They walked into the flight office and slumped into chairs. Hoyt ripped off his helmet and dabbed at the scratch on his cheek. "I'm glad you got out, Pat," he said absently.

Then the fear spot broke and spattered into the four corners of Paterson's soul. He sprang up trembling, with his fists beating the air.

"The dirty lice!" he screamed. "They've killed P.-B.! They've killed Trent! D'y' hear me, Hoyt?—they've killed 'em! They're gone! They'll never come back! They've——"

Hoyt's voice came evenly, calmly, through his screaming. "Steady, boy! Steady! You can't help it. No one can. Steady, now!"

A mat of white oil-splotched faces stared at them from the open doorway that led into the hangar. The boy turned wildly. "Clear out!" he shrieked. They vanished, open-mouthed. Hoyt drew him down into a chair. "No, Hoyt, no! Can't you see? P.-B. and you and Trent have meant everything to me. I can't go on. I've fought this thing till I'm crazy." Hoyt reached quickly and slammed the door. "I've fought it night and day!" He threw up his arms hopelessly and covered his face with his shaking hands.

Hoyt put his hand on his trembling shoulders and patted them. "Steady, now! Steady! None of that!" he said awkwardly.

Paterson's head whipped down across his sprawled arms on the desk top and the sobs tore at his throat in great gusts that choked him. "Oh, God!" he sobbed. "What's it all about, Hoyt? What's the use of it?"

"Steady, son! I don't know. Nobody knows. It just happened, as everything happens. It's much too late to talk causes. We're here and we know what we have to do. That's enough for us. It's all we have anyway, so it must be enough." He took his blood-soaked cigarette from his mouth and hurled it into a corner. It landed with a soft spat.

Someone knocked at the door. "Come in." It was the runner from squadron office. He saluted. "Yes?" said Hoyt.

The man glanced at Paterson's face and snapped his eyes quickly back to the Captain's.

"Beg pardon, sir," he said. "Squadron's just been signalled through wing. One of the C Flight machines came down near B Battery, the 212th."

"Who was it?" asked Hoyt.

"Lieutenant Mallard, they reported it, sir. That'll be Lieutenant Mallory, sir, won't it?"

"Yes." Hoyt's voice was quite flat. "Thank you."

The man saluted again and shut the door. Hoyt dabbed at his cheek and reached into his desk drawer for another cigarette. Paterson stood up suddenly and grabbed his arm. "Listen, skipper!" Hoyt's eyes met his calmly. "I'm going to tell you something. I'll feel better if I do. I've been a weak sister in this flight. I've planned for days to go down and let myself be taken prisoner—to get out of it all. I've been sick of it—sick of it, d'y' hear, until I couldn't think straight. I wanted to get out alive. I wanted to get away in any way I could. This morning I broke. I let go and started down——"

Hoyt smiled. "Your trouble, Pat, is that you think you're the only person in this jolly old war."

Paterson stared at him. "But I did! I started down, out of it, this morning!"

"How'd you get here?" asked Hoyt.

"But if I hadn't broken for that moment this morning——"

"That's a lie!" snapped Hoyt. "You're talking poobah! I know how those things happen. If P.-B. hadn't gone down after the two-seater they'd all be here now; and by the same reasoning, if my aunt wore trousers she'd be my uncle. The important thing is that it's you and me now and nothing else matters. We'll have four brand-new men to whip into shape to-morrow, and whatever you think of yourself, you've got to do it. I can't do much, for I'll be ahead, leading. You'll be behind them and you'll have to do it all. They'll be frightened and nervous and green, but the job's to be done. Understand? You've got to goad them on and get them out of trouble and watch them every minute, so that in time they'll be as good as P.-B. and Trent—so that when their turn comes they can do for other green men what P.-B. and Trent did for you. Do you see now what this morning has done for you?" He paused for a moment, and then, in a lower tone: "Afraid? Who isn't afraid? But it doesn't do any good to brood over it."

C Flight did no duty the next day, nor the day following. Hoyt went up to the 212th and identified Mallory for burial, while Paterson flew back to the Pool for the replacement pilots and a new Camel for Hoyt.

In Amiens he heard the first whispered rumours of what was going to happen. Intelligence was ranting for information. Everybody had the story and nobody was right. The hospitals were evacuating as fast as possible. Fresh battalions were being hustled up. It wasn't a push. Anyone could tell that with half an eye. Something the Hun was doing. The spring offensive a month earlier this year. G.H.Q. was plugging the gaps frantically, replacing and reinforcing and wondering where the hammer would fall and what it would carry with it. Hence the pictures that had cost the lives of P.-B. and Trent. The air itself trembled with uncertainty, and rumours flew fast and thick.

Paterson flew back with the four new pilots and brought the rumours with him. Hoyt had more to barter in exchange. The talk ran riot at dinner.

"It's a Hun push, all right, but where, nobody knows. We'll have word in a day or so, but it'll be wrong whatever it is, mark what I say!"

And then on the evening of the twentieth things started. A signal came for the Major just as they sat down to mess. He went out and presently called out the three flight commanders. When they came back they took their places thoughtfully. Silence trembled in the room like the hush that precedes the first blasting stroke of a great bell in a cathedral tower. The Major swept his eyes down the board.

"You will remain at the aerodrome to-night, gentlemen, and remain sober. Officers' luggage is to be packed and placed on lorries which Mr. Harbord is providing for that purpose." He paused for a moment. "This is a precautionary move, gentlemen. We are to be ready to retire at a moment's notice. Flight commanders have the map squares of the new aerodrome. You can take that up later among yourselves." He leaned back in his chair and beckoned to the mess sergeant. "Take every officer's order, sergeant, and bring me the chit."

The talk broke in a wild flood that roared and crackled down the length of the table. The tin walls trembled with the surge of it and the echoes broke in hot discord among the rough pine rafters. Offensive patrols for all three flights, to start at five minutes to 4 a.m. Air domination must be maintained. Wing's instructions were to stop everything at all costs. Go out and fight and shut up. Somebody presented the Adjutant with the sugar bowl and asked him if he had his umbrella for the trip back. The Adjutant had spent eighteen days without soles to his boots in 1914. He and the medical officer stood drinks for the squadron.

About ten o'clock, Hoyt called the five men of C Flight into his hut. "To-morrow, something is going to happen, I'm afraid, and you've got to meet it without much experience. What I want you to understand is simply this: You've got Pat and you've got me. Follow us and do what we do. We won't let you down so far as it is humanly possible. If the flight gets split up in a dog fight, then fight your way out two and two— and go back to the new 'drome two and two. Don't go separately. Further"—he paused—"if anything happens to me"—Paterson looked up at him quickly and something tugged sharply at his heart; Hoyt went on quietly—"take your lead from Mr. Paterson. You'll be Number 5, Darlington. You'll climb up as deputy leader. And if anything happens to Pat, then it's up to you to bring the rest home." He smiled. "There is a bottle of Dewar's in this drawer. Take a snifter now, if you want it, and one in the morning. It's for C Flight only. Oh yes, one more thing: The fact that we're moving back to a new aerodrome seems to indicate that staff thinks nothing can stop the Hun from breaking through. The fact that nothing can stop the Hun seems to indicate that, for the nonce, we are losing our part of the War. If the thought will help you—it's yours without cost."

The caller rapped sharply and threw back the door. Paterson leaped to his feet half asleep and pushed back the window curtains. The clouds were down to about four hundred feet, lowering in a grey mass over the mist on the aerodrome. He went into the next cubicle and turned Hoyt out. Hoyt sat up on the cot edge and ran his hand across his forehead.

"Stop the caller," he said. "Let's see what's what before we turn everybody out." They shrugged into their flying coats and groped down the passage to the Major's cubicle in the next hut block.

"Let 'em sleep," said the Major. "Can't do anything in this muck. Turn out one officer in each flight to watch for the break and to warn the rest. Send Harbord to me if you see him wandering about."

They woke up the skippers of A and B Flights and told them the news. Paterson took the watch for C. He turned up his coat collar and went out. It was cold and miserable in the open, and the chill crept into his bones. The smoke from his cigarette hung low about him in the still air.

Presently to the eastward there came a low roar. He looked at his wrist watch. The hands pointed to six minutes to four o'clock. The ground trembled slightly to the sound of the distant guns and the air stirred in faint gusts that pulled at blue wraiths of his cigarette smoke. The push had started. His muscles stiffened at the knees as he listened. The first shock of the guns was raw and sharp in the quiet air; then it settled into a lower, full-throated rumble like the heavy notes of an organ growling in an underground basilica. Now it rose again in its greater volume—rose steadily, slowly, as if it were a colossal express train hammering down the switch points at unthinkable speed. Presently it soared to its highest pitch and held the blasting monotony of its tone. The minutes ticked off, but the guns never faltered in their symphony of blood. At 4.35 one pipe of the organ to the south-eastward cut out suddenly and almost immediately began again, closer than before. Again it broke as he listened, and crept nearer still.

He walked down the line of huts, thrashing his arms and blowing on his cold hands. An impersonal thing to him, yet he shivered slightly and stared upward at the low clouds. Men out there to the eastward were in it. The suspense was over for them. And suddenly he found himself annoyed at the delay, annoyed at the fog and clouds above, that kept him on the ground. He wanted to see what was going on—to know. He turned impatiently and went into the mess. The sergeant brought him coffee, and presently Muirhead of A Flight came in with Church of B.

"It's on," Church said absently. "I suppose this fog means hell up the line."

They drank their coffee and smoked in silence. The sound of the guns crept nearer and nearer, and one by one the rest of the squadron drifted in for breakfast.

Hoyt sat down next to Paterson. "I don't like it," he said. "Something is giving way up there." He went to the window and looked out. "Clouds are higher," he said, "and the fog's lifted a bit. What do you think, Major?"

They crowded out of the mess doorway and stood in an anxious knot, staring upward. It was well after six o'clock.

"All right"—the Major turned around—"get ready to stand by."

C Flight collected in a little knot in front of Hoyt's Camel, smoking and talking nervously. Paterson kept his eyes on Hoyt and stamped his feet to get the circulation up. A strange elation crept into his veins and warmed him. In a moment now—in a moment. Awkward waiting here. Awkward standing around listening to Darlington curse softly and pound his hands together.

Somewhere behind him on the road, a motor-bike roared through the mist, and then to the southward a shell crashed not a thousand yards from the 'drome, and the echo of it thumped off across the fields. Darlington jumped and stared at the mushroom of greasy black smoke. A moment more—a moment now. Paterson reached over and tapped Darlington's sleeve. "Keep your guns warm, old boy." Darlington nodded fiercely.

The Major climbed into his cockpit and a mechanic leaped to the propeller. The engine coughed once and the propeller snapped back. The mechanic leaped at it again. It spun down and melted into a circle of pale light. Everyone was climbing in. Hoyt flicked his cigarette away sharply and put a leg up into his stirrup.

They were taxi-ing out into the open ground, with the mechanics running after them. Presently they could see the road. Paterson stared at it in amazement. It was brown and crawling with lorries and troops. Something had happened! A Flight, with the Major, sang off across the ground and took the air together in a climbing turn. B Flight waited a brief second and followed. Out of the corner of his eye Paterson could see the mess sergeant climbing up on the lorry seat beside Harbord, the equipment officer. Then Hoyt waved his hand. Mechanics yanked at the chock ropes and waved them off. They blipped their motors and raced out after Hoyt.

At five hundred feet they took the roof in the lacy fringe of the low clouds. Bad, very bad, Paterson thought. He ran his thumb across the glass face of his altimeter and his globe became wet with the beaded moisture. He could hardly see Darlington's tail. Ahead of them the clouds were a trifle higher. Hoyt led them up and turned northward. Murder to cross the line at that height, with the barrage on. Darlington was lagging a bit. Afraid of the clouds. He dived on Darlington's tail and closed him up on Number 3. Darlington glanced back at him and ducked his head.

Hoyt was circling back now in a broad sweep. Over there somewhere was Cambrai. He looked up for an instant just in time to see the underside of a huge plane sweep over him. He ducked at the sight of the black crosses, but the plane was gone before he could whip his Lewis gun into action. Almost immediately one corner of his windshield ripped away and the triplex glass blurred with a quick frosting of a thousand cracks. He cursed into the roar of his motor and kept on.

They were higher now, but the visibility was frightful—like flying in a glass ball that had been streaked with thick, dripping soapsuds. Here a glimpse and a rift that closed up as soon as you looked; there a blank wall, tapering into tantalising shreds that you couldn't quite see beyond. He fidgeted in his cockpit and turned his head from Hoyt, below him, to the grey emptiness behind. Nothing.

Presently Hoyt banked around, and following him, the compass needle on Paterson's instrument board turned through a half circle. They were going back toward the south again and climbing still higher. An even thousand feet now—just under the rising, ragged clouds. He felt a drop of rain strike his cheek where his chin piece ended. It bit his skin like a thorn and stung for seconds afterward. His goggles were fogging. He ran a finger up under them and swept the lenses.

Then, in a breath, it happened. A grey flash swept down out of the clouds in front of the formation. Hoyt zoomed to avoid it. The Hun zoomed, and they came together and melted into each other in a welter of torn, rumpled wings and flying splinters. Something black and kicking rose out and disappeared. The cords stood out in Paterson's neck and his throat closed. Somewhere his stomach leaped and kicked inside of him, trying to get out, and he saw coffee dripping from the dials of his instruments.

In a second he had thrown his stick forward and gone down into Hoyt's place. He didn't dare look—he couldn't look. He was screaming curses at the top of his voice and the screams caught in his throat in great sobs. His goggles were hopelessly fogged. He ripped them off. Behind him the four new men closed in tightly, with Darlington above them as deputy leader.

There was blood again on his lips. He pulled back his stick and climbed. There, somewhere in the clouds, were the men who had done it! All right! All right! His eyes stung and wept with the force of the wind, and his cheeks quivered under the lash of the raindrops. With his free hand, fist clenched, he pounded his knee in stunned anguish until his muscles ached. Hoyt! Hoyt! Then he saw what he wanted, and dived down furiously at the shape in the mist. Bullets tore at his top plane and raked across the cowling behind him. He closed on the Hun and sent it spinning. There was another—three—five—nothing but Huns. He dived in between them. Fine! He was screaming again and firing. He forgot he was flying. The joy-stick thrashed crazily between his knees, and the ground and the clouds were a muddy grey scarf that swept from side to side across his eyes. Guns were the thing. Once, in a quick flash, he saw tiny men running upside down through the ring sight of his Lewis gun—the gun on his top plane—funny.

His wrists ached and his fingers were quite dead against the Bowden trigger. No, not that; that's a Camel—Darlington. He grabbed at his joy-stick and pulled it back. Funny how hard it was to pull it. Another Camel swept in beside him, and another, with startling suddenness. It had been a long time now—a long time. Somebody had been afraid once and there had been a man named Hoyt. No, Hoyt was dead. Hoyt had been killed days before. Must have been P.-B. P.-B. was probably in Amiens by now. He'd left in the tender at six o'clock. And always his guns chattered above the roar of his engine.

Abruptly, the cross wires of his centre section raced up to him from a great distance and stopped just before his eyes. He wondered where they had been all this time. He stared past them into the light disc of his propeller, and again the rain lashed into his face and stung him. He caught at the kicking joy-stick and held on to it with both hands—but one hand fell away from it and wouldn't come back. With an effort he pulled back his stick to climb up under the clouds again. Must be up under the clouds. Must wait and get more Huns. Funny things, Huns. Clumsy, stupid grey things you shot at and sent down. Go home soon, rest a bit, and get some more. He laughed softly to himself. Joke. Funniest thing in the world.

The centre section wires clouded up before his eyes and started to race away from him. Here! That's bad! Can't fly without centre section wires. He chuckled a bit over that. Absurd to think of flying without centre section wires! Come back here! You come back!

Just as his eyes closed, he saw a streak of roadway flicker through the struts of his left wing. There were faces on it quite close to him—faces that were white and staring; faces with arms raised above them. Funny. He whipped back his joy-stick with a convulsive jerk, and then his head crashed forward and he threw up his arm to keep his teeth from being bashed out against the compass.

It was very dark—dark except for a dancing blue light far away. He moved slightly. Something cool touched his forehead.

"All right," he muttered; "that's all right now. You just follow me." Someone whispered. He opened his eyes and stared into the darkness. "No," he said quite plainly. "I mean it! Hoyt's dead. I saw him go down."

He felt something sharp prick his arm. "You've got the new aerodrome pin-pointed, haven't you?" he asked.

A soft voice said: "Yes. Sh-h-h!"

"No," he said, "I can't. Darlington's alone now, and I've got to go back. They're green, but they're good boys." He moved his legs to get up. "There's a bottle of Dewar's——"

"No," said the voice beside him.

"Oh yes," he said quietly. "Really, this is imperative. I know I crashed."

A stealthy languor crept across his chest and flowed down toward his legs. He thought about it for a moment. "I ought to go," he said pettishly. "But I'm so tired."

"Yes," said the voice. "Go to sleep now."

"Right-o," he said. "You call a tender and wake—me—half—an—hour." He was quiet for a moment more and then he chuckled softly. "Tell 'em it's poobah," he said sharply.

"All right," said the voice. "It's poobah."

His breathing became quiet and regular, and footsteps tiptoed softly down the ward away from his bed.

AMONG THE TRUMPETS

by LEONARD NASON

"He paweth in the valley, and rejoiceth in his strength: he goeth on to meet the armed men. He mocketh at fear. . . . He saith among the trumpets, Ha, Ha; and he smelleth the battle afar off, the thunder of the captains, and the shouting. The glory of his nostrils is terrible."—JOB xxxix.

THE MORNING was well advanced; that is to say, it was some time after nine o'clock. Westward the high-banked clouds that were the remnants of those that had deluged the countryside with rain the night before were still black and menacing, but eastward the sky was blue, and the sun already gave promise of unpleasant heat later on.

From the black woods on the right, gloomy and sinister beneath the clouds, to the rolling hills of the horizon stretched a wavy band of newly ploughed earth. It was wide, it was irregular, it ran up and down hill and squirmed along the side of crests as if the man that had furrowed it had been either drunk or blind. That wavy band of earth, though made with steel, had not been ploughed. It marked the German front line in front of Richecourt; it showed where the defence system that the French had crowned with such names as the Trench of the Goths, Trench of the Vandals, and Trench of the Barbarians had once frowned on Seich-prey and Jury Wood. The system was no more. Parapet and parados had been flattened into one uneven heap of mangled earth; the wire had been plucked up by shells, tossed about, rolled up, and flattened again by the passage of tanks. Dug-outs and strong-points that had defied assault for four years had gone as the snows of yesteryear.

The American attack that had begun at dawn had crossed this band of ploughed ground in one jump, found no resistance, and had gone on across the fields to the north, where they were already out of range.

The American artillery, most of its guns outranged, and the others unable to direct the barrage at such a distance from the target, had ceased firing. The Germans, their guns abandoned or in retreat, had done likewise. Deep silence had fallen where so short a time before thunderbolts had crashed, and the ground had trembled with the recoil of a thousand guns. Where all had been smoke and shouts and frantic rockets were now only peaceful fields and quiet, shady woods, except for that long, waving, sinister gash that was like a wound that had killed this countryside.

Reprinted by permission of Houghton Mifflin Company.

From a hollow suddenly appeared a group of horsemen. They drew rein before their silhouettes cut the skyline and hurriedly examined the ground to the right flank with their field-glasses. The fields, through a field-glass, were not at all deserted.

The leader of the horsemen, a Captain of United States cavalry, could see men stringing telephone wire, prisoners in groups of three and four coming back, ambulances being loaded with wounded, and, far away northward, white puffs of smoke that came from bursting grenades, and that showed where the American advance was bombing its way toward an objective it had not hoped to reach until the morrow.

"We're through the first line," said the Captain decisively; "the road will be about there." He pointed to his left front, then looked curiously at Mont Sec, a sugar-loaf hill that rose abruptly a thousand feet from the surrounding plain. Its summit was crowned with smoke, from which came the continuous flash of bursting shells. "I doubt if any Boche up there can see us," said the Captain. "We'll assume not. Can you make out the road, Lieutenant? We'd better locate it before we start across."

The officer addressed wore the blue of the French Army. He had a round, bullet head and moustaches that were much too long. He polished his field-glasses with a white handkerchief, breathing upon them, wiping them carefully, and holding them to the light to see if they were clean.

The Captain tightened his lips impatiently. Behind him he heard the stamping of a horse, and, turning about, saw a sergeant who had just ridden up.

"Where the hell have you been?" barked the Captain.

"Sir, I had to come in from the extreme left, and this horse ain't much of a horse."

The sergeant panted slightly. It was apparent from his flushed countenance that he had been having difficulties with his mount.

"Well, if you can't ride him, turn him in," snapped the Captain, and turned back to the French officer.

An enlisted man, his legs seemingly lost behind the high pommel of his packed saddle, under-slicker, gun boot, sabre, saddle-pockets, blanket roll, and two days' grain ration, moved his horse over next to the sergeant's.

"Hey, goldbrick!" he whispered. "Where yuh been?"

The sergeant turned. "Hey, Mac!" he cried. He suddenly paused. He noted that the other wore a trumpet slung across his shoulders, and on the sleeve of his blouse, plainly discernible, was the scar of recently removed chevrons.

"You been busted?" went on the sergeant. "Huh? Drunk? A.W.O. loose? A guy with your service! Yuh oughta know better!"

"Naw, naw," grinned the trumpeter, "I got caught with a pair o' leather putts on. 'N' by the corps commander, too, no less. Don't worry; I got a better job blowin' horn. Why dinyuh join up with us at Mandrees? Where yuh been, anyway, the last three months?"

"At Besançon, learnin' machine-rifle. I'm commandin' the machine-gun troop. How come else I got invited to a council of war? Whaddyuh think, kid? See any other sergeants around?"

The trumpeter grinned a slow grin, then ejected tobacco juice. "Machine-gun troop, huh? You an' them two machine-rifles! Well, if you get from here to them woods with 'em I'll buy yuh a drink."

"You think that's the entrance then?"

The Captain's voice came clearly in the silence that followed.

"Very well; I think I'll move them across there in echelon of double columns. I don't think we'll meet any resistance yet. The infantry would never have got by the woods if there were any squareheads in a fighting mood there.

"Troop commanders! You will cross the open space by troops, in echelon of platoons in double column. You will regulate the gait according to the nature of the ground and the circumstances, without attempting to maintain the regularity of the squadron formation. On arriving at the woods we'll again resume column formation. I will be with 'H' troop's first platoon. Understand? Posts!"

"Boy," whispered the trumpeter, "if any o' them take up the gallop he won't have a man left in the saddle."

"How come?" demanded the sergeant. "What yuh been doin' all summer?"

"Diggin' a sewer for the Q.M. corps at Gievres," grinned the trumpeter. "Ninety per cent. o' this here 'raggedy pants cadet' outfit ain't never been on a horse before in their lives."

"No kiddin'?"

"No kiddin'. If we meet up with any Boche that's on the peck any, there'll be a hot time in the old town, now, what I mean."

"Sergeant Lee!"

"Sir!"

"Where are your machine-rifles?"

"In rear of 'H' troop, sir."

"Good. Ride with me so that I can give you orders for their employment. Off we go!"

The troop commanders—there were but two, and one of them a Lieutenant—rejoined their troops, there was an arm signal, a few moaning whistle blasts, then the squadron, in a formation very similar to that which old-timers used to style "column of bunches," topped the skyline, and, hurriedly descending into the hollow beyond, proceeded at a fast trot toward the distant woods. A fast trot. Too fast, for the slower horses began to canter, whereat the faster ones, hearing tremendous clatter and thumping of hoofs, wanted to canter too; and here and there a bolter began to go from rear to front of a platoon column, to the accompaniment of squeals and kicks from the other horses, and untrammelled language from the riders, who had received a blow from a rifle butt on the thigh, a cinch ring on the knee, or who had been nearly torn from the saddle by the impetuous rush of the bolting horse.

"They'll get over that," observed the trumpeter sagely. "They been fillin' 'em with oats. They won't prance very long under them full packs."

"They didn't waste any oats on mine," panted the sergeant. He had, by dint of voice, heel, and a club he carried, urged his horse into a shambling trot.

"Nor on that Frog Looey's either."

The French officer's horse was one of those who are averse to travelling alone, and who will not leave ranks or picket line for any persuasion. This steed was proceeding at a sort of drifting gait, going sideways like a yacht with no centre-board, and making always toward 'H' troop's second platoon. The French officer kept the horse's head firmly toward the woods, so that the steed could not see his companions; but he knew they were there, and kept ever an ear turned in their direction. Spur and whip prevailed for a time, but the moment the Lieutenant stopped to draw breath or rest his tired leg the drifting began again, accompanied by head tossing and lightning-like thrusts of the neck, which attempts had the effect each time of nearly unseating the French officer.

"That's a nice horse for an officer to ride," observed the sergeant. "You'd think he'd know better than to bring a goat like that with him."

"We give it to him. It's an 'H' troop horse. 'Sidewinder,' they call him. He's like Coke Gillis. He ain't gone straight since he was born."

"We give it to him!" protested the sergeant. "That's a great way to treat an officer and an ally. Give him a star-gazin' goat like that!"

"Huh!" grunted the trumpeter, helping himself to another chew. "The French give him to us in the first place. Let 'em see now how they like their own horses."

They arrived, finally, at the edge of the woods. No sign of life. Not a shot fired. There was a narrow field there, along the edge of which ran a rough track, an old cart path, but now beaten flat by many feet. Beyond, across the field, were more woods, into which this cart path led. There was a trench along the edge of the woods, but empty, and the hurdle that barred the road where it went through the wire had been so hastily put in place that the advance guard had been able to unwire it and drag it clear before the main body had come up.

Across the field went the squadron, skirting a communication trench, then the advance guard was seen to halt, troopers galloped out to left and right, and some indecision was manifested.

"What's the matter?" demanded the Captain, riding up.

"There's four roads here," replied one of the troopers of the advance guard.

"Which road, Lieutenant?"

The French officer pulled up his horse and dragged forward his map-case.

"You're not going to look at a map, are you?" demanded the Captain. "I can look at a map myself. I thought you knew this country. Do you realise that I've got a squadron of horse standing here in a field that runs from Apremont halfway to Metz? Do you suppose the Boche are going to sit down and wait for us to cut them off? They're running so fast now we won't catch up with them before night."

"The other end of this field is held by French troops," replied the French Lieutenant. "They won't fire because they have been warned not to. There will be plenty of Boche very soon, don't worry." He bent over his map.

"Very well," snapped the Captain. "I'll make my own decision."

"If you do," replied the other, lifting his long moustache in a sneer, "you are liable to come into an area that is under our own artillery perparation, in which case the responsibility will be yours."

The Captain flushed, but said nothing. After all, this French officer had been sent for just that purpose, to keep his squadron out of areas that the French were pounding. It would not advance the situation to have the squadron destroyed by friendly artillery fire.

The French officer put away his map, took out a cigarette-case, extracted one, and lighted it.

"The road to the right," said he.

The trumpeter tossed his chin meaningly in the direction of the French officer.

"Ah, don't worry about him," replied Sergeant Lee. "The French are probably just as proud of him as we are of some of the mail order wonders we got. Boy, they got 'em in all armies, like coots."

Thick trees but no underbrush, huts, scattered grey overcoats, then, suddenly, long lines of waggons and empty picket lines. Loose horses, many of them wounded, could be seen among the trees, some trotting and whinnying at the sight of the advancing troops, others bounding away, and one or two limping in their direction, as if to ask for help from others of their kind.

Suddenly, at an alley that crossed the main track, the Americans saw men. The Captain, the trumpeter, an orderly, and Sergeant Lee saw them almost simultaneously. There was a group of ten or fifteen that had probably heard the advance guard thud by and had come out of their holes to see what it was all about.

The Captain swung his horse, whipped out his pistol, and charged. "H" troop's leading platoon followed him. Pistols barked, and Sergeant Lee's horse, that up to that time had given but the faintest signs of life, bolted, and, having gotten a firm grip of the bit before the sergeant had recovered himself, was well away into the trees.

It was impossible to circle the runaway in the trees, but the sergeant saw before him an opening in the woods, into which the horse presently tore. Here was the place to reach out, seize the head-stall, and by main strength drag the horse's head around so that he must run in a circle and eventually stop.

Bark!

"Cut out shooting, you damned fool!" shouted the sergeant. "Can't you see this horse——"

Bark! Bark!

There was another man there, on a black horse. Flame spat from his hand. It was a German. Lee whipped out his sabre, and, instantly stopped all attempts to control his horse, let him go headlong for the black. The black, however, did not wait for the attack, but leaped aside, and its rider shot at Lee, as he tore by, at point-blank range.

But Lee had pinked him with the sabre. Not badly, he knew, but he had felt resistance as he had lunged out. If only now he could pull this goat down!—but they had crossed the glade and were again amidst the trees.

Bark! Again! The man on the black was pursuing him! Swiftly through the sergeant's mind passed the realisation that he was very probably drawing his last breath. The German was behind, hence Lee would have to either sheathe his sabre—impossible at that gait—let it hang by the sabre-knot while he drew his pistol—impossible, because he had not put his hand through the wrist-loop when he had drawn it—throw it away, and then engage in a pistol combat with the German—impossible, because if he turned around the horse would undoubtedly dash headlong into the first tree—or just lay on the horse's neck, say a prayer, and pour the hooks into him.

How many shots? The German's gun must be nearly empty now. Ah, no, the German pistol held ten. Before him suddenly loomed wire—a parapet. Would the horse jump it? He was done now, anyway.

The horse bucked to a halt. Lee dropped his sabre, tore out his pistol, and, swinging around in the saddle, had one wild shot with it, anyway. He shouted and fired again, more shouts, crashing, then the black horse tore by, saddle empty, and came to a rearing halt at the belt of wire, like a horse that has thrown his rider before the barrier in a riding hall.

There were Americans there—the trumpeter, pistol in hand, two privates of the advance guard.

"Hey, Lee!" cried the trumpeter. "We come down the road! I got that guy on the black!"

He and the two privates rode back to look at the German. He was on his face, but when one had dismounted and turned him over, they saw that he was dead. He was a private, with the black medal that indicates one wound and the light blue and yellow shoulder-straps of a Jaeger zu Pferde, or mounted rifleman.

"Striker, probably," decided the trumpeter, "because this here horse looks like an officer's."

"I'll say," agreed Sergeant Lee. He had ridden over and taken the black's bridle, and then led him back to the others.

"Well, let's go," said the others hurriedly. "This ain't no place to match pennies. These woods are full o' Boche."

"Right!" agreed Lee. "Where's the rest of 'em?"

"On the road. Wachuh dismountin' for?"

"I'm goin' to mount up on this black horse."

"You are?" cried the trumpeter. "Why, if anyone mounts him, I do! I knocked the guy off his back with a .45."

"How do you know?" demanded the sergeant, picking up the sabre he had dropped. "I had two or three shots at him myself."

"No, it was the trumpeter got him," said one of the privates, looking nervously about him. "We better be gettin' back. I see the Captain out there. No, the trumpeter got that kraut. I seen it."

"Well, this horse is mine," said Sergeant Lee, mounting, "because I'm rankest man. What's the good of having three stripes if you can't rank somebody out of a bunk or a horse or something?"

"What are you men doing in there? See anything?" called a voice from behind the trees.

All wheeled their horses and went out. The alley down which they had charged curved, and the Captain with the rest of the platoon had halted there.

"The trumpeter shot a German, sir," said Sergeant Lee. "He was chasing me. I've captured his horse."

"Nice horse that," remarked the Captain. "Better change saddles the first chance you get. We'll be able to use all the extra horses we can get before we're through. Trumpeter, ride back and tell Lieutenant Bennett to push a patrol forward on the road. I'm going to prospect around in here a little to see what we've run on to, to see if there is any sign of a force here, if this is just a bunch of waggoners and stable orderlies that we've run into. See that that French officer knows what's going on.

"Corporal Petersen, take your squad and see if there are any Germans left in those huts. Write down any regimental numbers you see on the waggons.

"Sergeant Lee, take a set of fours and follow along that trench to see what you find. When you hear three blasts of the whistle, rejoin."

He blew a short blast on his whistle. "Foragers, ho-o-oh!" The platoon, in line of foragers, at "raise pistol" moved off among the trees.

Sergeant Lee, riding the black and leading his own horse, led his four men along the line of the trench that had stopped the runaway rush of his horse. The trench was shallow, and had been newly dug. They found shortly after a small house, a sort of shelter for foresters or shepherds, very strongly built of stone. The trench was evidently part of an attempt to make a strong point out of this house, to prevent, perhaps, the flanking of positions farther back in the woods by attack from the road. The house, however, seemed to be abandoned, for its door hung open.

Sergeant Lee, his pistol ready, rode up, but there was nothing in the interior but scattered bed-clothing and the disorder of boots, belts, and equipment that told of hasty flight.

"Number One," said the sergeant, "take this horse. Don't turn him loose, whatever happens, because he's got everything I own on him. I'm going to ride on a little. Listen for the three whistles and repeat them if you hear them."

He turned over his own horse, and being now free could enjoy the feel of riding the black. The horse was a thoroughbred. Lee had never been on one like him before. It was like sitting on a dynamo. He could feel beneath him the nervous energy and the power of those steel muscles running up and down. A touch of the spur, a flexion of the wrist, and the black was cantering. A turn of the shouter, a shift of the left leg, and the black had changed leads. What a horse! Schooled, intelligent, powerful. Lee, without pressure on the reins, closed his legs and leaned slightly back. The horse slowed his gait. He leaned farther back. The black halted.

"Ah, boy! That's a horse!" breathed the sergeant to himself. What couldn't a man do with a mount like that? He saw himself leading a charge, outstripping Lieutenants, Captain, everyone, hurling himself upon the enemy, capturing their commander, their flags, raging about among them on that black horse——

"Hey, sergeant! Three whistles!"

There was, alas! a war on. The sergeant, taking one last look about him, moved his hand ever so slightly to the left, and the black, coming around beautifully, cantered back to the others. The sun, higher, began to glitter through the trees. No sign of the enemy, no crash of shell, no crackle of machine-guns.

"Come on with that set of fours!" called someone faintly. "Rejoin! Rally! Ralle-e-e!"

Lee gathered his four men and, trotting through the underbrush, rejoined the platoon, which the Captain was leading back in the direction of the road they had left. They came out, in a minute or two, into the sunlight, and found there the head of the column, the trumpeter, and the French Lieutenant.

"What did you see, sergeant—anything?" demanded the Captain.

"No, sir, only blankets and stuff lying around. That trench hadn't even been finished."

"We're losing time," said the Captain quickly. "There was no force in there. We'll probably be seeing stragglers and orderlies and first-aid men and all sorts of goldbricks running loose in these woods, but that's not what we're here for. Now then, we'll push forward vigorously. Pass the word back that if any isolated enemy are seen to shoot at them, but not to delay the advance to try to capture them. Leave that for the doughboys. That agree with your thoughts, Lieutenant?"

The French officer nodded. "Quite right, Captain," said he. He did not turn his face, however, in the Captain's direction. His eye was upon the black horse that Sergeant Lee rode. "Captain," he went on, "I think I shall have to ask you to give me that horse that man is riding."

"Huh? Give you that horse? That's a German horse. He captured it."

"I see that by the equipment, but it is a much better horse than mine. I want it."

"Perhaps you do," said the Captain, gathering his reins, "but we don't take horses away from non-commissioned officers in this man's army."

"Do you mean to say, sir," cried the French officer, "that you will not give an officer of an Allied army a captured horse simply because some soldier found it first? Which is the most important for the success of our mission—that he should be well mounted, or that I, who am the guide and the officer of liaison and the interpreter, should have the best horse? I think that Higher Authority would not take very long to decide the question."

It was in the Captain's mind to make no reply but to order the advance to be resumed. But then this French officer would make a report of it when he returned, which report would come drifting down from corps headquarters, gathering indorsements and bitterness like a descending snow-ball, until it came into the hands of the squadron commander's immediate superiors. He would get Hades. And he would get no more details to command provisional squadrons.

"Give him the horse, sergeant," ordered the Captain.

The sergeant's face hardened, and for just a second his blazing eyes met the Captain's, whereat that officer's jaw muscles stood out like cords.

"DISMOUNT!" he barked.

The sergeant obeyed, as well as some half-dozen troopers, who thought that the Captain had meant them, too. In the slight confusion attendant on these men being cursed back into their saddles by their respective corporals, Sergeant Lee was able to turn over the black, go to Number One and get his own horse, and mount. The column moved forward again, at a rapid trot.

Sergeant Lee and the trumpeter were once more side by side, Lee muttering under his breath his opinion of some nameless person. His language was picturesque, for he decorated it with idioms learned in bar-room, barrack, and camp, from Jolo in the days of the Sultan of Sulu to the Camp de Valdahon at the present moment.

"You talkin' about that French Looey?" inquired the trumpeter.

"Well, who the hell else would you think?" demanded Lee.

The trumpeter spat expertly between his horse's ears. "Well, I dunno. You ain't got any kick against him. He was just rankest man. What's the use o' bein' rankest man if you can't rank someone out of a bunk or a horse or somethin'?"

The sergeant's reply was horrible, whereat the trumpeter grinned so widely that he lost his chew.

There were signs now of distress from the squadron. The gait of the head of the column was too fast for that of the rear, so that the last third was at a slow gallop. The smothered admonitions of platoon leader, sergeant, and corporal to "Keep that horse back!" or "Four feet from head to croup, you—you know what that means?" or "Tully! you ridin' that horse or is he ridin' you? Git him into ranks!" were becoming louder and more frequent.

The pack of a man in the second set of fours had come undone, so that the shelter half trailed behind him like an old-fashioned caparison, and his blankets he was carrying over his free arm in a most unsoldierly manner. Finally, a poorly cinched saddle turned, the rider was thrown, and the horse, the saddle under its belly, went the length of the column, kicking and squealing, until it caught one foot in the trailing stirrup, fell, and had two men hurl themselves from their saddles and sit on its head. The column perforce halted, for one of the men was the acting troop commander of "H" troop and the other Sergeant Lee.

"And the rest of the dash blanked Johns sitting in their saddles looking at us!" exclaimed Lee.

"Get the saddle off him!" ordered the squadron commander. "Whose horse is it? Take his name, sergeant. Give him a month in the kitchen and all the spare horses to saddle up. Maybe he'll learn to cinch properly. Have 'H' troop dismount and look over their equipment. When they've finished, have 'I' troop do the same. This will be your last chance. I'm not going to stop again until I run into the enemy. Time flies. They'll all be in Berlin if we don't show more progress than this."

Sergeant Lee took the opportunity to have a look at his machine-rifles, riding in rear of "H" troop. He met, on his way there, the French Lieutenant, prancing along on the black horse. Lee ground his teeth. He had not ridden a McClellan saddle for a long time, and stirrup-buckle and gun-boot were beginning to rub sores on his unaccustomed shins.

How much more pleasure he would have had riding the beautiful officer's saddle on that black! Saddle! That wasn't the half of it! He would have ridden that horse bareback! It grinds a man to have his horse taken away from him. The mildest man will fly into a murderous rage. Lee thought of a man he had known with a clear record during three enlistments that had deserted because his horse had been taken for the polo team. Well, that bird had the right idea. When the march was resumed Lee still thought of him. He, Lee, would go "over the hill." He would find an outfit where a guy was appreciated.

"Forget it," said the trumpeter finally, wearied of Lee's silence. "Don't worry about it no more. The Frog's gone an' good riddance."

"He's not gone," replied Lee, spurring his horse savagely. "He's riding with 'I' troop."

"What for?"

"How the hell should I know?"

"Well, cheer up, anyway. Maybe we'll run into somebody that'll rank that horse away from *him*."

They continued the march through the silent woods. They passed collections of huts, then a rustic village built about a tiny lake that was obviously a recreation centre, a narrow-gauge railway yard, more waggons, more loose horses, and one or two isolated wandering men that took to their heels, pursued by random pistol bullets, as soon as they had identified the nationality of the horsemen.

The column crossed hurriedly a surfaced road that cut through the forest from east to west. At one end, in the hazy distance, they could see the roofs and steeple of a town, and to the west, against the foot of the forest-covered hills, another. But in between all was deserted. Across this road they found fewer huts, then, after a while, nothing. The brush grew thicker on both sides.

The Captain suddenly reined up his horse. Lee, startled out of his black thoughts, raised his head. The advance guard had halted where the road came to the edge of the woods. It was only a grove, because Lee could see the trees where the road entered the forest again farther on. But two of the advance guard had dismounted, and one was wildly pumping his rifle up and down above his head in the old army signal that means "Enemy in large number."

"Hold the squadron in readiness!" ordered the Captain hurriedly. "Trumpeter, Sergeant Lee, follow me!"

The three of them went down to the advance guard as swiftly as their horses could carry them. They did not need to have the enemy pointed out to them.

There was a wide circular cut in the woods here, made by an open field, across which the road they were on took its way to enter the forest once more. This field sloped sharply down on the right, and at the bottom of the slope was another road, wide and surfaced, with a narrow gauge track running along.

On this road was a column of infantry, perhaps a battalion, marching steadily along, in good order, and with their rifles slung, German fashion, across their breasts. In front were two mounted officers. Behind the infantry, rapidly approaching, was a truck column, eight, ten, perhaps more—they could not see the end of them. There were eight hundred Germans there at least, and they were not to be charged with one-quarter that number.

"Bring up the auto-rifles, trumpeter," whispered the Captain, "and fast. Everyone dismount. Put the led horses in the brush. Now, sergeant, where shall we put the guns?"

"They've got to be fired prone," said the sergeant hurriedly. "The grass —now that will be all right." He threw himself on the ground. "You can't see over the slope here," he decided. "They'll have to be moved downhill —maybe along the edge of the woods. I'll have a look."

"Don't let any of those square-heads spot you. Don't waste too much time, now."

The German infantry continued to advance, unsuspecting. They had no advance guard out, no flankers. The Captain's heart swelled. The classic rôle of the cavalryman was to be his, to drive far behind the enemy's lines and fall upon unsuspecting troops. That truck column should be his, too, and the smoke of its burning would spread terror and alarm! On the heels of this panic the squadron would be on to Vigneulles, destroy the railway-station there, and cut off the retreat of all the mass of troops along the heights of the Meuse. But first, destroy this infantry.

"Hold the rifles here," ordered the Captain, as the gunners with their ammunition bearers appeared. "There's no rush. We'll site them together, let the column pass, and then each gun take half with traversing fire. Now damn those trucks! They'll get here at just the wrong time."

The trucks, however, did not pass the infantry, but halted. Perhaps the road was too narrow, perhaps those trucks contained the battalion's baggage. The Germans came on, while the Americans watched with beating hearts, holding their breath so that the enemy could not hear them. The Germans would pass at less than a hundred yards!

"When I give the signal," hissed the Captain, "rush out, flop, set up the guns, and turn loose."

The column drew near, and the dismounted Americans flattened themselves in the brush. The enemy marched by, boots slumping, bayonets rattling, the harsh coughing of the men coming clearly to the ears of the watchers. Waggons creaked past, one of the drivers idly cracking his whip. Then, the second company.

There was a thud of hoofs from behind the Americans. The Captain swung around. Who was this that had left the squadron without permission? It was the French officer, on the shining black, galloping up from "I" troop to see what the halt was about.

"Get off that horse!" husked the Captain. "Get him back out of sight!"

The black halted. He was alone. Far behind him the squadron waited impatiently. The black tossed his head. He smelled the concealed horses of the advance guard and the machine-rifle men in the brush, or did he see an old stable fellow down there on the road? Did he smell his countrymen? He tossed his head again, then neighed shrilly. The horses in the brush and another in the squadron answered them.

White faces from the marching troops looked up the hill, curious at the sound. Not many, but enough. The Captain, wordless, but thinking many things, rose out of the bush and leaped for the black's head. The black, like all thoroughbreds, was nervous. The sudden rush of the officer from the bushes frightened him. He reared and bolted, and in two jumps was in the meadow. His rider flung himself clear, but too late. The Germans below, open-mouthed, had first heard horses neigh in those woods, and had then seen, clearly against the dark background, a figure in the horizon-blue uniform of the French Army hurl itself from the saddle and run back into the woods again.

"Out with the guns!" shouted the Captain. "Action front. At enemy in road! Fire at will!"

The guns spat, but the road was already half empty. Two seconds more, and the whole column had taken refuge in the ditch on the other side. Waggons, mounted officers, all disappeared.

But the blast of firing that had begun could not have come from the machine-rifles alone! The air crackled, the ear drums rang with the sudden pound of heavy firing. Astonished, the Captain turned about. From the alley in the woods came a thunder of hoofs. Horses reared, others were down and kicking. Dismounted men ran about. There was smoke and the flash of pistols, but the noise was so great that the Captain could not hear the bark of the .45's.

He looked behind him at the road below. The machine-rifles roared, but the road was empty. There were packs there and bundles that the marching troops had dropped in their haste to get to cover, but the Captain could see no bodies.

The German infantry were now in position behind the road. The only thing for two troops of cavalry in front of a battalion of entrenched infantry is to withdraw. The squadron seemed to have already made up its mind to this.

In just the three seconds that the Captain had spent in looking at the road his men had stampeded. They were going, tails high, saddle-bags flying, hell for leather down the road. Even as he watched, dark figures in bucket-shaped helmets appeared from the woods, shot down a dismounted trooper, and began to plunder the saddle-pockets of the dead horses.

There still remained to him, however, the auto-rifles. He leaped back, threw himself down beside the gunners, and shouted in their ears: "Cease firing!"

The gunners heard and complied. With the roar of the auto-rifles stilled, a sudden hush seemed to fall.

"You! Number One gun! Action rear. Searching, in those woods, two clips! Commence firing! Number Two gun—" He stopped.

Below and to the left, in the centre of that white road, head high, tail outstretched like a plume, stood the black horse. Rifles cracked, men shouted, machine-guns roared, but the horse paid no attention. He pawed the ground, and the Captain could have sworn that he neighed again the shrill, proud shriek that had alerted the Germans and ruined the squadron. That was the horse that had been frightened by the Captain's rising from the brush! Never! He had bolted purposely! He was a German horse; he had known!

"Number Two gun!" ordered the captain. "Get me that horse on the road, damn his black soul!"

He was not himself, for he had seen his men butchered from ambush, his squadron destroyed, and he knew that the span of his own life could be measured in minutes.

The muzzle of the gun shifted ever so slightly, and the gunner's body thumped the ground as he wiggled himself into his new position. The gun roared. The horse tossed his head quickly, for he must have heard bullets crack by. A German dashed from the shelter of the ditch to seize the trailing bridle, but he seemed to slip in the mud and then fall, a flat, shapeless, motionless heap.

"The horse!" cried the Captain. "Never mind the men; get the horse."

Another burst. Tchk! Silence. "Gimme another clip," panted the gunner.

"Hey, for crysake, bring up that other gun!" shouted Sergeant Lee. "We got an opening here."

"Take up your rifle!" ordered the Captain. "Fall back and report to Sergeant Lee!"

Then the Captain, drawing his pistol, dropped on one knee, and, supporting his right hand on his left arm, took aim at the black horse.

"Hey, Captain!"

The shout in his ear disturbed the officer's aim, and the bullet went skyward.

"What the hell is the matter with you?" he snarled. But it was Sergeant Lee.

"They had machine-guns in the brush," panted the sergeant. "We put one of 'em down. They don't seem to be firin' now. If we're ever gonna get out of here we better go."

From the road below came a deep shout, "Hoch!"

On the heels of it a thin line of the enemy leaped up and, crossing the road, took shelter in the grass at the lower edge of the field.

The Captain emptied his pistol at them, then rose and reloaded. The Germans saw him, for fire crackled along their line.

"Let's get the hell out of here!" said the Captain.

The black horse had turned and, trotting down the road, now faced the German infantry, as though he carried on his back an officer who urged his men on. The Captain would have taken one more shot at him, but bullets whispered about his ears, or cracked overhead like whips. At the edge of the woods the men had already mounted. The Captain, stifling a curse, rejoined them.

Poorly fed horses in full pack, even when stampeded, will not run far, and the Captain, riding off down the woods with his chin on his breast, like Napoleon retreating from Moscow, found the squadron at the cross roads, from whence they had been able to see the two towns.

It had been a rear or flank guard that had ambushed them, and there had been no pursuit. Non-commissioned officers were already displaying their vocabularies, saddles were being transferred from wounded horses to well ones, men were binding up each other's wounds or refilling empty pistol clips.

Into the scene arrived the Captain like an avenging angel. He was a man of few words, but those to whom he addressed himself would remember his remarks to their dying day.

Sergeant Lee, having the care of his auto-rifles first in mind, withdrew them to one side, questioned the gunners, overhauled the ammunition supply, and inspected the horses. His own mount was nearly foundered. Seeing at a little distance a man holding three horses, he went in his direction, thinking he might make an exchange. The other man was the trumpeter, ruefully examining his trumpet that had been punctured by a bullet.

"It'll blow," said the trumpeter, as Lee approached, "but I have to keep my finger over the hole. It don't look military to blow a trumpet that way."

"How's chances on one o' those horses?" demanded Lee. "Mine's about outta breath."

"Naw. One's mine, one's the skipper's, and one's for the Frog Lootenant. He's goin' back."

"Goin' back?"

"Yuh. The Old Man says to him: 'What was the grand idea to gallop out in front where all the Boche would see you? Want them to admire your horsemanship or something?' And the Looey says: 'We rode into an ambush. We went too far without reconnaissance. We haven't lost any ground because this here is the Heudicourt-Nonsard road that we're on now, and we weren't supposed to be here for half an hour yet.' 'Awright,' says the skipper; 'you know the country so well, you go back and report our progress and where we run into the enemy.' 'But I'm your guide!' says the Looey. 'Well, we'll try to struggle along without you!' bites the Old Man. So then—psst!"

The French officer, his bullet-shaped face like a thundercloud, strode toward the two men. They paid not the slightest attention as he took his old horse, mounted, and rode off.

"You mighta held his stirrup for him, at least," observed the trumpeter.

"Who was his dog-robber last year? Anyway, I'm a sergeant. I don't hold nobody's stirrup."

The trumpeter hitched his pistol-belt higher and tilted his helmet just a little farther over his left eye.

"John Lee," said he, "did it ever occur to you you owe that Looey a whole lot? Suppos'n he hadn't ranked you off that black horse? Wouldn't he nickered just the same and give us away to the Boche?"

"Hey?" gasped the sergeant.

Wouldn't the horse have nickered with him? Oh, man! Yes, he would have. And then what would the skipper have done to Lee? He was not an officer but a buck sergeant. He choked at the thought. If it had been his horse that had nickered—well, the least they would have done would have been to hang him. His name would have been a mock and a disgrace throughout the mounted arm of the United States Army from that day forth. Gone would be his stripes! Gone his pistol and sabre! He would wield nothing but a dish-rag for the rest of his military career!

"Naw," said he to the trumpeter, "that black wouldn't have done it with me. I'd ha' *ridden* him."

"Uh-huh!" remarked the trumpeter. "Well, if you're lookin' for a horse, try Corporal Scully's. Scully's hit. That's a good horse for a sergeant."

"No," said the sergeant, "I guess I'll stick to the one I got. He ain't much on looks, but he's no nickerer."

AN ARGONNE RAID

by CLARK VENABLE

I

IN LATE AUGUST the regiment again went into a quiet sector of the Vosges for another tour of duty, practically reliving their first trench experience, save that they were now content to conserve their strength for more important fronts. Their position was the inferior one, occupying a salient which might easily be pinched off should the enemy become so minded.

Wingate still patrolled No Man's Land, encountering little opposition, for the enemy, knowing now that the Americans were at last in France in considerable force, were well satisfied to rest and save themselves for the great struggle to come.

For a week armed amity held sway and then a regiment of artillery was set down behind the infantry for its first taste of warfare. On the very first night the colonel of artillery changed a peaceful front to audacious warfare. All night his shells whined over, with a liberal sprinkling of gassers thrown in for good measure.

The following evening the enemy replied in kind, and for the remainder of that tour the infantry troops lived in their gas masks, cursing the ambitious artillery and praying for relief.

Relief came at last but no rest followed. In camions and on foot the men were rushed up to more open country. More troops were seen. Trucks roared back and forth and artillery rumbled over the roads all night long, halting in the woods during the day and again taking up their advance with the coming of darkness.

"There's going to be a war somewhere up here," Captain Steele said to Wingate one night as they marched along a road filled with trucks, guns, and staff cars filled with hurried, profane officers.

From: *Aw Hell!* Copyright 1927. The Reilly & Lee Co.

"It looks it. All this concentration means something. What's the big idea, Captain?"

"It's a secret yet. Companee—halt! What the devil! We can't march a city block without being tied up. Another cross road, I guess."

Again and again during the march they had moved to one side to let artillery go by. Gruff voices swore in the dark. Sweating, steaming horses tugged and strained at bogged down fieldpieces. At every cross road chaos reigned and officers rode back and forth, trying to straighten out a tangled, jumbled army.

"Oh, Lord! It's starting to rain again," Wingate complained as they again got in motion. "Look at the light in the sky over there, Captain. There's some real shooting going on up here. How much further do we go?"

"According to my map we should reach Neuvilly in the next half hour. That's the last town back of the lines. We are going in back of a hill called Vaquois."

"Hill country again?"

"No, rolling. Vaquois commands all the country round about. I understand the top is held by the enemy, but the French hold one side of it. I think they are going to give us a chance to take it. That's what the colonel hinted."

"They're moving in enough of us to take most anything. What sort of man is this new K. O.?"

"Young, and sensible enough to know he doesn't know everything. Pretty decent. He was in the Philippines for a number of years. Been jumped from a captaincy almost over night, but it hasn't hurt his head any. Hello! Here's the beginning of what's left of a town. Neuvilly, I make it."

"Check. Where do we go from here?"

"On up. We've got to be in the woods back of the line and covered up before daylight. Damn the rain! I'd give a hundred dollars for ten minutes of dry feet and warm clothing."

Wingate laughed. "Sherman was right, Captain. Do you know when we attack?"

"Don't know that we do, but you can use your eyes and make a fair guess. It's the famous Hindenburg line, too."

"So much the better. I'm fed up with hearing about the Marines and the First Division. To hear those birds tell it you wouldn't think there were any Guard outfits in the war."

"Time enough, John. The war isn't over yet and won't be for two or three more years."

"You really think that?"

"I do."

"Good Lord!"

"Cold feet, John?"

"No. Wet. Just think of two more years of this. I hope you're right about this being an attack on the Hindenburg line. I'm mad enough to break through all by myself. What's the sector called?"

"Argonne forest, I believe."

"Heavy woods?"

"Don't know. You've pumped me dry. Go back along the line and see how the kitchens are coming. I don't want them to get lost in this jam. Better check up on House, too. He's back picking up the stragglers."

"There won't be many now, Captain. I found one of my men starting out to-night with a fever high enough to fry an egg. But do you think he was going to quit? No, sir! He smelled powder. They all seem to feel that a big show is on. Look me up, when we get into our position, Captain. I've got two dry blankets stored in the rolling kitchen and a nip of something good for a cold."

"Good! That makes four blankets and two nips all in the same kitchen. Who's watching yours?"

"Brice. Gawd Almighty! Just look at that gun, Captain!"

On a spur railway line a great naval rifle poked its long barrel out from under its camouflage. Looming against the sky it took on colossal proportions.

Exclamations ran up and down the line of marching men. "Oh, boy! That's artillery what is artillery!"

"You tell 'em! Wouldn't you like to see that big baby go off?"

"Yeah. Some G. I. can she sends over. And just listen to those guns up ahead. This is goin' to be a real show, big boy, I mean to tell ya."

An hour later the regiment came into the woods directly behind Vaquois Hill. Guns were everywhere, hub to hub and still coming in.

Captain Steele, by some miracle, found cover for most of his men, but many of the companies were forced to camp under the dripping trees and find what comfort they could.

At sun-up a runner came to Captain Steele.

"The colonel wants to see you at headquarters, sir," he said. "And he directs you to bring all your officers along."

"Where is headquarters?" Steele asked.

"Right down this little narrow gauge, sir. About a kilometer."

"You'd better wait and show us the way."

"Sorry, sir, but I'm trying to locate the three majors. Do you know where they are, sir?"

"No. I don't even know where *I* am. Oh, Lieutenant!" he called, catching sight of Wingate moving along under the trees. "Find Gordon, House and Gregory."

"That's easy, Captain. Do you know where those black-hearted devils are?"

"No. Where?"

"They put it over us. We slept out in the rain and right under us those conscienceless scoundrels were curled up in a nice dry dugout. We slept right on top of it."

"Damn! *C'est la guerre*. Get 'em out! The old man wants to see us, *pronto*."

Colonel Howard was almost warm in his greetings as the staff officers came in by twos and threes.

"I believe we are all here now," he said at last.

"Major Gregory has not arrived," Major Cushing prompted.

"I regret to inform you, gentlemen, that Major Gregory has been relieved. Just last night. He is on his way to division now."

They were thunderstruck, but they held their tongues, not yet sure of this new commander and made doubly suspicious by this alarming news.

"The commanding general decided that he was too near the age limit at such a time as this," the colonel hastened to explain. "As you doubtless know, or suspect, we are about to begin a great drive and the general feared the hardships would be too great for the major. I understand he has a fine record behind him, and doubtless the general will find a place for him with division staff where he will be of value."

Lieutenant Gregory flushed and looked at the floor, conscious that the eyes of every officer were upon him. But he sensed that their sympathies, like his own, were all with his father.

"I want you to know, gentlemen," the colonel went on, "that I come to you with no preconceived ideas of your efficiency. So far as I am concerned there will be no last minute shifting around."

The staff breathed easier.

"It is perhaps unfortunate," he continued, "that I have been sent to you almost on the eve of battle. Because of this, I have asked all my specialists to attend this meeting. Particularly do I want to confer with those lieutenants commanding the scout, signal, Stokes and one pounder platoons. You gentlemen are supposed to know your jobs. I dare say you do. I know the uses of these arms only in a general way, and I shall look to you for efficient and hearty cooperation."

The officers cast amazed glances at each other. What manner of colonel was this? He admitted he did not know all things and put them at ease by promising no shake-ups; even expressing willingness to let efficiency speak for itself.

"Now, gentlemen, we will get down to business. As you doubtless know, we have at last been given a purely American sector. It is a tough one. A general advance is about to begin all along the Western front. We are to break through here. Much depends on our success—perhaps every-thing. I have heard that General Pershing has said, 'Hell, Heaven or Ho-boken by Christmas.' I doubt if he ever uttered it, but it is a straw show-ing the determination back of this drive.

"Gentlemen, I have just received the order for the attack. We go over on the morning of the twenty-fifth—day after to-morrow. Every hour we stay here increases the peril of our position and the danger of the enemy learning of the concentration in this sector. This regiment has been chosen to start the advance on our front."

"*Mon dieu!*" exclaimed the French attaché, a captain of infantry with four years of service behind him. "A regiment! Why, *mon Colonel,* we have been trying for three years with a corps. Now they give the task to a regiment. *Mais non!* It is a madness."

"Perhaps," answered Colonel Howard, not greatly impressed with the hazard. "But I am no nut specialist. I am only a colonel of infantry. I am ordered to advance as far as Cheppy by the evening of the twenty-fifth, and by the gods! I propose to do it."

"To Cheppy? *Ce n'est pas possible!* It is——"

"Not impossible!" the colonel completed. "You forget, Captain, that we are fresh."

"Ah, yes, and so foolish—so brave. I weep." The stout-hearted captain wagged his head sadly and showed every sign of being in deep sorrow.

"Now, gentlemen," the colonel went on, placing some maps and orders on the table. "I want you to realize that this is our first major sector, en-tirely under our own command. The English will be watching. The French will be watching, and what is more, the people back home will be watching. Now let us go over the order, remembering that the entire mat-ter is of a highly confidential nature."

The staff gathered around the table, grim-faced, silent. Real action had come at last. The eyes of the world were upon them.

II

At dusk that evening Captain Steele and his platoon leaders gathered in the dugout which Gordon and House had appropriated the night before.

"I'm going back to headquarters now," Captain Steele began, "and I want to report that you are all ready for to-morrow night. What about you, Gordon?"

Gordon laughed. "Sure, I'm ready. Only about um-teen more miles of wire to spool, a trip back to division headquarters to talk the chief signal officer out of some more equipment and a few little things like that which shouldn't take more than a week. Sure, I'm ready."

"You can do what you have to do," Steele answered. "What about you, Gregory? Ready?"

Lieutenant Gregory merely nodded, dourly. All knew that he was broken-hearted over the order which had relieved his father from command of his old battalion.

"You, House? Ready?"

"Like hell! Not a nickel's worth of ammunition. I'll be dragging those damned one pounders clear to Berlin with nothing to shoot. I can't find anyone who seems to know anything about ammunition."

"Get it!"

"Get it? How am I to get it? This is a helluva army!"

"It's no better than its officers, certainly. You can't expect some one else to look out for your detail work. Get that ammunition—if you have to make it. What about you, Wingate? Your men will have to serve as guides when we go up to-morrow night, you know."

"Sure, I know. I'm ready. I've had my men out all day getting acquainted with the sector and they're out again to-night. They'll know this sector like a book by jumping off time. Brice has been over to the division on our right and reports that they're running around like chickens with their heads chopped off."

"It's a green outfit," Captain Steele replied, frowning. "I don't like it. They have never been under fire before and there is going to be some hot stuff up here before we get through. If they should falter, fail to keep up, we'll come in for some enfilading fire from those hills to our right."

"Who's on our left?" House asked.

"Old troops—Pennsylvania outfit. They'll carry through. Wingate, I want you to send back word at once, if you should notice that the division on our right is faltering. It is the job of the liaison officer, but you make it your job, too."

"Sure. Any little added burden like that is gratefully received. A scout officer has so little to look out for. Captain, do you know where I'll be by nine o'clock day after to-morrow morning?"

"You may be playing a harp."

"Not me. I'm not musical. Look!" He bent over a large map on the table and stabbed his finger down on a dark spot indicating a town. "See there? That's Cheppy. While the rest of you are trying to get across this little creek here, I'll be over in Cheppy forcing a square-head to fry me a dozen eggs. There must be plenty of eggs over there. I've looked for them in vain in every other town in France."

"See here, Lieutenant, I want you to take this thing seriously," Steele said, frowning.

"I am. I have to go ahead, don't I, and find out what's doing? Well, when I locate eggs I don't intend to pass 'em up. I'll be there a half hour ahead of you."

"You're old enough to quit acting crazy," Steele said guffly. "Your job as a scout officer doesn't call for you to try to win the war alone. You can't win it with those old smoke wagons you carry."

"No, but I can distribute myself freely."

"Or be distributed. We need you alive, not dead. You start poking your nose in unexpected, uninvited places on this drive and somebody is going to send you off to meet your reward."

"Not if I see him first. But I'll be careful, Captain. I'm old, as you say, and a bit creaky. Can't afford to get reckless, especially in my job. My job, of course, calls for drawing maps of dugouts—from the inside."

Steele laughed. "All right, John. You're ready, and that means a lot. Now gentlemen, I am going to report that we are all set. Whatever you have left to do, do it!"

Lieutenant Gregory handed him a letter.

"What's that?" Steele asked.

"A letter—to my mother. Wish you'd post it back at headquarters. I've a hunch it is my—my last one."

"Nonsense! Buck up! You are depressed on account of what happened to your father. Probably the best thing. He's sixty-two, you know."

"Yes, I know, but he has lived for this hour. Then to think they would take him away and put him in some dinky little job back at division. It's a rotten shame. You won't forget the letter, sir?"

"No."

House and Gordon both stepped forward and handed him letters. Captain Steele smiled bravely.

"You fellows act like we were already in the casualty report," he said, laughing. "Where's your letter, John? Aren't you going West too?"

"Maybe, but no one will be interested much, and my address is so damned uncertain."

III

Soon after dark on the evening of the twenty-fourth the troops began moving up through the communicating trenches to their positions. Wingate's platoon, aided by the French, was given the job of guiding them in, and by eleven o'clock all save a few units were in their places.

The night was hot and sticky. The rain had ceased, and a heavy white fog was rising from the warm, wet earth. It was impossible to see more than a few feet ahead and anyone, not familiar with the sector, would soon have been hopelessly lost.

Near midnight Jep was making his last trip up with a few men. Wingate was with him, and at one place they decided to leave the muddy trench and cut across the open face of the hill and thus shorten their journey.

"Shells drop in here once in a while," Wingate told the men, "but it's shorter and the guns are quiet now. We can beat it across in a jiffy. Let's go."

As they hurried across the open hillside, seeing nothing and keeping close together in order not to become lost, Wingate ran headfirst into some one coming from the other direction. Both men went down.

"Who the devil are you?" an angry voice grunted.

It sounded like rank, but Wingate was taking no chances. On such a night it would be easy enough for a spy to slip through the lines.

"Who the devil are you?" Wingate challenged, regaining his feet and bending over the man.

"I am Captain Obadiah Brundage, liaison officer of the division on the right of this hill. I got lost in those damned woods down there and I can't see my hand in front of me. Do you know where I am?"

Wingate controlled his laughter. "Oh yes, sir, I can tell you exactly where you are. I suppose you want to find your way back to your headquarters?"

"I do."

"Oh, Jep!"

"Here, sir," Jep spoke, almost at Wingate's elbow.

"Oh, I couldn't see you. Here, you men, beat it on across to the trench and wait there for me. It's straight ahead, not more than fifty yards. Jep, do you know how to get this captain over to the outfit on our right?"

"Yes, sir."

"Sure?"

"Shore. I bin over there two-three times."

"Good. Show him the way and rejoin me at our new headquarters, up on the hill."

Jep set a killing pace across the open hillside. He crossed several trenches, and found a lateral trench that lead his way, but he scorned them all.

☆   ☆   ☆   ☆

IV

Returning along the trench traversing the near brow of the hill, Jep found Wingate standing outside the dugout which now housed headquarters. He was looking down into the valley and casting frequent glances at his luminous wrist watch. The woods below were blanketed in a white sea of mist, and the hill upon which they stood rose out of the fog like Ararat lifting its head above the turbid flood.

"They'll open up in another minute or two," Wingate said. "Stick around and see the fireworks."

Hot, wet with sweat, his throat throbbing, Jep eased out of his pack and leaned back against the side of the dugout. A moment later the colonel stepped out, followed by his entire staff. All took up positions of vantage and stood waiting. It was a hushed moment.

Somewhere back in the woods a battery, over-anxious, sent over a salvo of shells.

"A minute early," the colonel said quietly.

Calm again. Back at the railhead in Neuvilly one of the great naval rifles poked her nose to the sky and voiced the signal for the barrage. The great shell screamed over, wailing like a lost banshee, its high screech growing fainter and fainter as it traveled far back into enemy territory.

"Listen to that freight train! Some G. I. can! How'd you like——"

The sentence was lost in cataclysmic sound. An unseen hand rolled back a great door leading to the bowels of the earth and hell itself spewed forth steel, hate, fire and smoke. The valley and woods below blazed with light from flashing guns. Hub to hub, and in echelon after echelon, they flashed and recoiled, flashed and recoiled in a vain effort to add their voice to unincreasable tumult. Shells streamed over in mass, no sound above the other, but constant and strong in volume—like an organist thundering through a prelude of monotonous overtones.

After watching for a little while, the colonel turned back into the dugout, motioning the others to follow.

"Well, gentlemen, the show is on," he said. "Five hours of this and we shouldn't be able to find a mouse alive."

"You will," Wingate commented. "And a lot of rats, too. If the Colonel has nothing further to take up with me I'd like to turn in for an hour or two. I won't get any sleep after to-night."

"Sleep? Lord, man! Can you sleep in this?"

"Yes, sir. An exemplary life and a clear conscience. Great assets, sir."

"Then go along. I have told you what I expect of you to-morrow."

☆   ☆   ☆   ☆

v

At five o'clock Jep awoke Wingate and together they moved along the line, checking up the men and seeing that they were with the right companies. Wingate laughed and joked with various groups, making light of what they knew was to be Armageddon.

At last the sun, a dim red ball of fire, rose over the woods to the rear. The fog, mixing with the smoke from the thundering guns, screened out all colors save the red, and the great crimson disc gave little light and no heat.

"It's goin' to be mighty hard to keep any kind of a line in this fog, Lieutenant," Landsberger said as he came up shaking his head. "Once we get down below you won't be able to see your hand in front of your face."

"It's tough. Hard to fight when you can't see what you're fighting. Two more minutes and we're off. Ready, Jep?"

"Yes, sir."

Machine guns along the top of the trenches halted their clamour long enough to lift their fire.

"Let's go!" an unseen speaker shouted through the fog.

Men began pouring over. For a moment only were they visible as they walked down the hill, then the fog swallowed them. A man ten feet away was as dim and indistinct as objects in a steam-filled room. Forms suddenly loomed out of the fog and as suddenly disappeared. It was white magic.

On they went, flanking the hill. Not a sound from the enemy, no show of opposition.

"I don't like this," an infantry captain in the first wave said to Wingate. "I can't see ten feet. I only hope we are keeping up some sort of a front."

Down into the valley at last and still no opposition.

"What the hell kind of a war is this?" the infantry captain complained. "It's getting on my nerves. I want some action."

Action came that moment. Rat-tat-tat-tat! Bullets whispered through the tall grass. The burst was low.

Down went the few men in sight as the bullets continued to spray the ground three yards ahead. A ricochet whined and some one behind let out a groan.

"Straight ahead, wasn't it, Lieutenant?" the captain asked.

"Yes, sir. Keep your men down here a minute. We know how to get those birds. Sergeant," he turned to Landsberger, "you go to the left. Jep, come with me."

On hands and knees they crept off into the fog. Minutes passed. The gun lifted its fire and bullets went cracking over. The infantrymen plastered themselves close to the cool, wet grass.

From ahead sounded two sharp explosions, almost simultaneous. Three revolver shots followed in quick succession. Later Wingate came running out of the fog.

"All right, Captain Reese. Those two lads of mine are whales with hand grenades. We can go on now."

"What were the pistol shots?" the captain asked.

"Well, I wanted to make it appear I was in on it," Wingate replied as he reloaded.

They passed the gun a moment later, located in a shell hole. A limp, headless German was hanging over the gun base and four other forms sprawled over the lip of the crater.

Further on they were again held up by fire, which this time took its toll. Again Wingate, Brice and Landsberger disappeared into the fog while the men found cover.

A long wait. At last Wingate came crawling back into the shell hole occupied by Captain Reese.

"They're at the ridge across the little creek in front of Cheppy, Captain," he said. "Three guns at least. I've sent Brice back for Gregory. He'll put up a Stokes here and polish 'em off."

"How in the name of God do you expect him to find Gregory in this fog?" asked Reese, his voice indicating his doubt.

"He'll find him. That boy was born in the middle of the woods on a dark night."

Ten minutes later a man came crawling into the shell hole dragging a heavy metal plate. He was followed by Jep and several other men carrying the mortar and ammunition.

"What'd I tell you?" Wingate said to the captain. "Where's Gregory?" he asked the grim-faced sergeant who was already busy setting up the mortar.

"He got it just back yonder, sir, on the way up here."

"What?"

"Yes sir. Right in the head. Gawd! It was awful. But just you wait."

The piece was up, its short ugly snout poking above the top of the crater. More ammunition carriers came forward, bringing cylinders that resembled potato mashers.

"Just where is that bridge, sir?" the gunnery sergeant asked.

Wingate gave him the direction and the approximate range.

The sergeant made a change in the elevation and dropped back. The gunner began dropping the black cylinders into the barrel. Explosion followed explosion. The fog was earth bound and above it the watchers saw the shells floating like aimless swallows before they began their descent. Detonation followed detonation until at last silence came from the bridge.

Wingate and Brice crept out straight ahead while Landsberger moved to the left. They knew their business.

Brice came back a little later. "All right, Cap'n. You can move ahead now."

"Where's Wingate?" Reese asked.

"Gone on ahead, him and Landsberger. Said he wasn't goin' to run any more chances havin' yore company wiped out. Cheppy ain't fur, now. We'll keep you posted," and turning he ran back into the fog.

The fighting had begun on the outskirts of Cheppy. One infantry company, encountering no opposition, had swept in from the extreme right flank. They were too soon. The artillery was still storming the town and the infantry withdrew with heavy losses.

Jep found Wingate lying behind a stone wall at the edge of an orchard bordering the town.

"Hurt, Lieutenant?"

"Get down, you fool! We're caught here. How'd you get up here?"

"Like you did. I jes' come."

"Suppose you could get back to the colonel?"

"I reckon so."

"Try it. Let's see—eight o'clock. He's supposed to have a P. C. along the road leading back from the bridge. Find him and tell him we can't hope to take this place without some tanks. And tell him we're scattered to hellangone. We've got to have mortars, one pounders and tanks if we ever take this town. It's red hot. Hurry along, now."

"Where'll you be, Lieutenant?"

"Up here, somewhere."

Jep crawled back along the wall, reached the protecting bank of the little creek, slid down the steep cut and waded up the shallow stream toward the blasted stone bridge.

With startling suddenness a machine gun began clattering above his head. Jep plunged over against the bank and looked up. The pill box was somewhere just back of the steep cut bank. Here was a situation made to order.

With a trench knife he hacked footholds in the hard clay directly under the gun, lifting himself up a step at a time. Nearing the top, he turned to look around. Nothing to be seen but an all enveloping blanket of fog. Not a man in sight, no one to witness his fall should that gun plant a bullet in his head when he peeped over.

A clump of grass, clinging to the top of the sheer bank, offered a slight screen and, turning his head to one side, he brought an eye level with the top.

Thirty feet away a crew of gunners moved uncertainly in the fog. Twenty feet! It was dead easy.

Gripping the top of the bank with one hand, Jep brought a grenade to his mouth and pulled the pin with his teeth. He must not throw too soon, else they might be able to cast it away before it exploded. He released the lever. Nine seconds before it would explode. He began counting. One-two-three-four. He could feel the thing swelling in his hand. The gun was still chattering. His arm flew up and back over the bank. He heard a surprised, warning shout, followed instantly by a terrific concussion.

The gun was silent now. Smiling, Jep released his hold and slid back into the creek. Knee deep in cold water he made his way up to the bridge and out onto the road.

Hurrying along, wondering how he was ever to locate the regimental P. C., he noticed that it was growing lighter. The sound of sharp action came from behind. He looked back and was surprised to note that he could now see the orchard and the little stone wall. They would make it hot for Wingate now.

The fog was lifting everywhere. Soldiers were coming down the road toward him and over in a field a tank was lumbering along. Something caused him to look down at his feet. Little dust dervishes were jumping and a thousand unseen feet were treading the gravel in the road, scraping, scraping. He glanced at the men. They were down like grass before a scythe and one poor devil was trying to drag himself from the road.

Headlong, Jep dived into the nearest shell hole. A gunner, angered at missing his mark, sprayed the edge of the hole. Jep lay back and looked up at the skies, now growing bluer and bluer. High above a white cloud floated lazily away.

"Humph!" he mused. "I shore didn't know where my bread was buttered when I horned in on this. Those doctors had it about right. This is a tough job fer a feller with a weak heart."

A half hour later he found the colonel lying in a shell hole nursing a badly wounded leg. Captain Steele lay on his side, white and tight lipped.

"You hurt, Cap'n?" Jep asked, forgetting his mission.

"Through the arm. It's nothing. Don't mind me."

"Where are you from?" the colonel demanded.

"From Cheppy, sir. Lieutenant Wingate sent me back before the fog lifted to tell you they couldn't ever take that town without some tanks."

"Tell me what you know about the way things are going up there."

"Well, sir, it went too easy at first. It was mighty hard to tell jes' where we was at. We didn't seem to have much—what do you call it?"

"Liaison?"

"Yes, sir. That's the word. It was sorta like squirrel huntin'. We didn't know where anybody was, 'ceptin' the enemy, so we jes' went on an' did the best we could."

A metallic clattering caused him to lift his head above the edge of the hole.

"Hot dog! Yonder comes the tanks!" he announced, jumping up and down. "They'll clean out these hornets quicker'n scat."

The colonel tried to get up but fell back, swearing and groaning. Captain Steele wormed his way up to the edge of the hole.

"He's right," he said to the colonel. "They're coming. And by the gods of mercy! There's old Record Joe with 'em!"

"It shore is!" Jep enthused.

"You mean Major Gregory?" the colonel asked.

Captain Steele nodded.

"Nonsense!" the colonel scoffed. "He is at headquarters."

"No, he ain't," Jep contradicted, forgetful of rank. "He's right out there comin' along with the tanks and the soldiers."

"Go tell him to report here at once," the colonel commanded.

"Me?" Jep asked.

"Yes, you."

A tank loomed up near the edge of the shell hole, veered suddenly and went clattering and clanking away, spewing lead from its turret. A moment later Jep brought Major Gregory to the P. C.

The Major was a picturesque, wrathful figure. His helmet was gone and a leonine shock of gray hair tumbled down over his brow. Coatless, one sleeve of his O. D. shirt torn off at the armhole and the other rolled above his elbow, he was a worker going to his work.

"What are you doing here, Major?" the wounded colonel demanded.

"What I was trained to do, sir. Fight."

"But—but you have no troops."

"You are mistaken, sir. I have picked up over two hundred men who were lost from their outfits and roaming around aimlessly. We have attached ourselves to the tanks."

"But your orders, Major. You are——"

"Damn the orders! My boy has been killed. I am going to do his work. Do you think I will sit back at headquarters and let some one else wipe out that debt?"

"Do you know that your son——"

"Yes. A runner brought word."

"Then go ahead. And God be—and good luck!"

As the old major turned away, Jep kicked viciously at a powder seared clod. Another man trying to collect for a priceless thing. Well, he too would find out . . .

"Can I go back now, too, sir?" Jep asked the colonel.

"No. You're the only runner that has been able to find me and I want you to locate brigade headquarters for me. They are supposed to be at the foot of Vaquois. Find the general and tell him the signal officers might as well be dead and in hell for all the good they're doing. Tell him my entire staff was caught in enfilade fire and shot to pieces. Ask him why they don't get some wire up here."

"Is that all, sir?"

"Yes."

"Shall I tell him you're hit?"

"No. I'll stick it out until we get reorganized."

Less than five minutes elapsed before Jep reentered the shell hole.

"What's the matter? Too hot?" the colonel asked, his mouth drawn by pain or a sneer.

"No, sir. I found the general not more'n a hundred yards away."

"What? Up here?"

"Yes, sir."

"What did he say?"

"Well, I ast him where brigade headquarters was and he said, 'Where the general is, you fool.' Then I delivered your message and he said——" Jep hesitated.

"Yes, yes. What did he say?"

"Well, sir, he said to tell you that he hadn't had word from you or anybody else and that he knew less than you did, if that was possible. He said he'd be over here in a little bit. I'd like to go back now, sir. My lieutenant will be lookin' fer me."

"All right. Go ahead."

"Can I help you any, Cap'n?" Jep turned solicitously to Captain Steele.

"No, thanks. Was Wingate all right when you left him?"

"Yes, sir. He was in Cheppy."

Steele smiled. "Eating eggs, I suppose."

"No, sir. Eatin' dirt."

VI

All day long the battle waged uncertainly, but when night came the troops held Cheppy and a good strip of land beyond. With the coming of darkness they began their reorganization, straightening out their line and digging in.

The enemy was too busy with reorganization to trouble much with fire, and by midnight, when rain began to fall, the entire line was consolidated and liaison established between units.

Losses had been heavy. Colonel Howard and Captain Steele had been evacuated. Three infantry captains were dead, Major Cushing was wounded, and as the reports continued to come in to the lieutenant-colonel now in command, he wondered what would be left after another such day.

Wingate, Landsberger and Jep lay in a shell hole outpost, well forward of the front line. Other scouts were similarly located all along the front. It was their business to see that no counter-attack was started without warning being given. They were nothing more than sacrifices on the altar of safety.

About three o'clock the rain changed to a light mist and again fog began to rise from the ground.

"Another morning like the one we just had," Wingate groaned. "I wish it had kept on raining. You can at least see through the rain."

"Maybe it was a good thing we couldn't see yesterday," Landsberger said.

"Why?"

"The way I figger it, if we had been able to see how bad we were licked we might not be here now. Believe me, if ever there was an army licked, it was us, about nine o'clock this morning. Only two people that didn't know it—us and the Germans."

Wingate laughed. "I guess you're about right. But we're 'way ahead of the game. I'm going to try something different in the morning, if it's still foggy. My platoon will act as a sort of preliminary first wave. We'll draw fire, perhaps, but it will smoke out the enemy and reduce the total losses."

"Is that the order, Lieutenant?"

"Not exactly, but there's a little section in the old I. D. R. that says a mouthful. It says, 'To be surprised by an enemy at short range is an unpardonable offense.' We are actually here for reconnaissance. Combat reconnaissance if necessary. Scout platoon! Hell! A new word for old work."

"Suicide squad would be better," Landsberger corrected.

"Right. It's a tough job. I don't know what we'll get out of this war—gold crosses or wooden—but I do know we are not going to be blamed for failing to be far enough ahead to smoke out the enemy. When we get to Berlin I want to be far enough in advance to order the first beer."

Landsberger laughed.

A long silence ensued. A few shells were coming over now, indicating that the enemy had taken up new positions for hurriedly withdrawn guns.

"War develops some odd situations," Wingate said at last, voicing the thing that was running through Landsberger's head. "Here we are, like three wise men in a bowl. Any minute a shell may flop down on us and then it will be, 'if the bowl had been stronger my tale had been longer.' Yet here we are. I knew you had a German name, but I never suspected your parents were born in Berlin. I know but little more about Brice. And you—neither of you—know anything about me. In the army we take a man at his face value and he's always up to standard until he discounts the rating we give him. But we never get really acquainted, do we?"

"Sometimes we do. On nights like this—out beyond the wire. Hey, Jep, how about opening that can of Willie you pinched off that dead machine gunner?"

No answer.

"He's asleep," said Wingate. "Let him be. He ran his ankles off to-day carrying messages. And just to think—he doesn't even belong!"

VII

At four-thirty darkness began to give way to a feeble, misty half light, but dawn never came.

Wingate awoke Jep. "Wake up and hear the early birds sing," he said, shaking Jep into consciousness. "The old bullet birds will be looking for a worm pretty soon and I want my breakfast in peace. Where's that can of horse meat you've been boasting about?"

Yawning, Jep opened the can, placed the solid cube of cold meat on the edge of his poncho and, using his trench knife, carved it into thirds.

"This is what I hate about war," Landsberger growled as he wolfed down his portion. "They send you out to get killed before breakfast. There should be a little more consideration."

"You're dead right," Wingate agreed in mock seriousness. "It is inconvenient, not to say discouraging, to get shot before breakfast. I'm never myself until I've had my coffee."

"How long 'fore the general attack?" Landsberger asked.

Wingate looked at his watch. "Barrage is about due now. Thirty minutes preparation before the general advance. You and Brice wait here. I'm going over to the right to check up on some outposts. Be back in a little."

The barrage began a few minutes after he left, and Jep and Landsberger sat crouching in the crater, listening to the shells.

Wingate returned in a few minutes.

"Let's go," he said. "The advance starts soon and we'd better go out and have a look-see."

"Fat chance we've got to see anything," Landsberger replied. "We'll be right on top of a pill box before we see it."

Like grey ghosts they slipped out of the hole and began a cautious advance. Sharp explosions, from enemy shells, came out of the curtain of mist. A machine gun barked three or four times and as one man the three scouts hit the dirt.

"Where was that?" Wingate asked.

Both men shook their heads.

"Can't see a thing," Landsberger whispered. "And this damned fog makes the sound seem to come from ever' place. Straight ahead, I think."

"How far?"

"Don't know. Close."

Again they began creeping forward. A hundred yards, and suddenly a gun directly ahead sprayed the ground at their feet. Headlong they dived into the nearest hole.

"Whew!" Landsberger exclaimed. "That boy is close! Did you see him, Lieutenant?"

"No. So much the better."

"He must see us," Jep commented, nodding to the rear of the hole where steel jacketed bullets were kicking up dirt.

Wingate nodded and looked at his watch.

"We've got to put him out," he said gravely. "The infantry starts forward in a few minutes and he can do a lot of damage."

Landsberger looked surprised. "But there are a dozen others all along——"

"One at a time is all we can do," Wingate interrupted. "Never mind about the others. All we have to do is get the ones in front of us. Get your grenades ready. I'll go first—to the right. You go left, Sergeant. Jep, you wait until we draw some fire and then try to slip up close enough to bust him with a grenade. We're pretty close now, but not close enough to see him. The sergeant and I can get beyond the range of his traverse pretty quick. You come in from the front while we flank him. Ready?"

"No," Landsberger answered vehemently. "The first man out of this hole is going to catch a plenty. You're needed, Lieutenant. I'll go first."

Landsberger started out of the hole but Wingate caught his foot and dragged him back.

"You'll do as you're told, Sergeant," he said, his voice severe but his eyes betraying his true emotions.

"To hell with what I'm told!" Landsberger retorted, and wrenching himself free jumped over the top. The machine gun rattled furiously and at its signal Wingate jumped out and started running to the left.

Jep heard the machine gun barking jerkily. It could not be more than twenty yards away, but he could not throw until he could locate the gun.

Pulling the pin from the grenade, he sprang forward. Landsberger lay just outside the hole, motionless, his legs twisted grotesquely and his head bent under his body.

Jep glanced to the left. Wingate was down, but he was getting up now and running again. Just then Jep caught sight of the gun. He was almost upon it, could see its jumping, smoking barrel trained away from him. He released the lever on the grenade and glanced toward Wingate just in time to see him sink to earth under a hail of bullets.

The gun stopped firing abruptly and Jep saw a man working over it in feverish haste. A jam, eh? Then a form rose up out of the hole, pointing toward him with a pistol. He felt a stinging, burning sensation in his side, and as his legs began to give way he hurled the grenade as one would throw a baseball, squarely in the face of the man working over the gun.

Something hot tore at his side, spinning him around. Subconsciously he noted that Wingate was still down and motionless. Then thunder sounded. The grenade. . . . Crazy stars went shooting across a black curtain and then swiftly the curtain blotted out all light.

The show was over for three men of iron.

THE BASE AT BORDEAUX

by HUGH WYLIE

> "Phœbe wuz a feeble baby bee,
> Phœbe maybe sting you
> Like she done stung me."

AN EMERGENCY CALL for more tracks in the St. Sulpice terminals resulted in a sudden demand for the brunet track-building experts of the Fust Service Battalion. The Wildcat and his associates were presently back in their old camp and glad to be free of the arduous loafing business in the cellars of ships at the Bassens Docks.

"How come you niggers can't keep step past de office when Cap'n

Reprinted from: *Wildcat* by Hugh Wylie, by permission of and special arrangement with Alfred A. Knopf, Inc.

looks out de do'?" The Wildcat preached at his gang on the way to work in the railroad yards.

"When I columns you lef', you heads fo' de work an' not to'a'ds de kitchen. Column—lef'! Lef', I says! Lef'! Head dat squad roun', co'p'al! Follow dat mascot!"

The Wildcat's platoon scattered to the four winds of France. "Rally roun' Lily—rally roun' dat mascot goat!"

After five minutes' work the Wildcat accumulated his platoon and headed them towards the scene of the day's work. "Wuz sweat worth a nickel a quart, today you niggers makes fo' bits apiece. Ah neveh seed such a slew-foot triflin' outfit. Follow dat mascot—dat's all I tells you!"

"Sergeant, I'se lame. Kin I route step some?"

"Lemme see yo' laig—is you lyin' Ah'll lame you!"

"Kaint see is I—iodine whut de doctor paints me wif don't show. I tells yo' I'se same as a cripple."

" 'Ceptin' in de appetite. Ah seed you at brekfus'—wuz po'k chops swellin' you couldn't git into a box car."

The marching platoon passed a detail of German prisoners carrying railroad ties. "Rustle dem ties white boys!" the Wildcat called. "How is us gwine to win dis wah if you-all don't he'p us?"

> "Phœbe wuz a fliah,
> Come f'm Ten-o-see.
> Phœbe lit a fiah
> Where she lit on me."

"Wisht I wuz in Ten-o-see 'stid of in dis wah! Wisht I wuz in heaven."

"Only way you'll git to heaven is wuz heaven a jail an' some white man knowed you like I does."

"Neveh seed such a lastin' job—wondeh when de end of the wah'll be, Wildcat?"

"Front end done been—hind end'll come when ol' Republicans starts winnin'."

"Some Democrats is all right—Cap'n's a Democrat."

"How come you-all knows so much 'bout Cap'n?"

"I knows. I seed him walk home f'm de banquet 'thout no he'p—rest o' de officers had to be carried. Lootenant's a Republican—had to watch him an' bed him down like a mule. Cap'n sho' is Democrat—he's out-drunk ev'y officeh what showed up so fah."

"Cap'n sho' kin ca'y his gin ration—sho' kin ca'y a load."

"I'll say he kin—he may be old but he's got kid gloves."

"Detail . . . 'tenshun! Detail . . . halt! Scatteh out an' see kin yo' earn yo' rations. Tie dat mascot in the vineyard an' leave him eat grapevines."

"Betteh tie him to de track an' see kin a train kill him. He et two pairs of shoes an' de linin' out of a ovehcoat yistiddy. Neveh seed such a goat f'r raiment lunch. Wuz he attached to ol' supply sahgent f'r rations he'd figgeh he'd landed in heaven!"

The platoon strung out along the track and languidly began the day's work.

The Wildcat figgered a little rest would help him some. He called to a waterboy. "Roust me out afteh I'se laid a couple hours." He coiled himself up in the shade of a pile of lumber and was asleep before his head hit the ground.

No sooner was the Wildcat asleep than several members of his crew gravitated about a push car which stood beside the track. In the group were Cube and the Backslid Baptis', DeWitt Massey, The Lizard, Moon Eye, and half a dozen more domino gallopers.

"Shoots a franc," the Backslid one announced.

"Lemme see de dice—I knows you, Baptis'."

"Seven . . . li'l lady love . . . Whoof!"

The Wildcat moved uneasily in his sleep.

"Ace an' a dooce—loses nuthin' but yo' money, Moon Eye. Roll 'em!"

The Wildcat sat straight up. In four seconds he had elbowed himself into action. "Gimme dem dice! Gimme dem dice! Shoots ten francs . . . Whuf! Five an' fo' is nine . . . an' a six-tray. Lay dead. Shoots twenty . . . fade me is you reckless . . . Mawnin' seven—I lets it lay. Shoots forty . . . Lady Luck, I aims to run yo' ragged. Fade me field han's, fade me! Money, rally roun'! Wham! . . . two top sides says 'leven!"

" 'Ten-shun!"

The Captain, fifty feet away, gazed calmly at the group.

"Wildcat, come here!"

"Cap'n, yessuh! Me an' dese boys wuz jes' waitin' fo'——"

"You won't have long to wait for what's coming to you. Come back to camp with me. Rest of you boys get to work."

The Captain's voice was singin' low like a boiler just before she busts. The Wildcat began to worry about himself. "Cap'n, suh, whut is it whut's comin' to me—I'se——"

"Shut up before I knock you loose from your ears!"

"Cap'n, yessuh!"

Black clouds obscured the four quadrants of the Wildcat's horizon. "Cap'n's foamin' agin. Lady Luck, whah at is you hid?"

Followed by the drooping Wildcat, the Captain entered the battalion office and made his way to a smaller room partitioned off in one corner of it.

"Come in here!"

"Cap'n, yessuh."

Five minutes later the Wildcat dragged his remains to his quarters and put himself to bed. "Wuz they one stick o' stovewood wif my name wrote on it, Cap'n sho' foun' it."

Cinnamon, the Captain's striker, a brunet New Orleans boy, drifted in with his guitar. "Wilecat, you likes music—nex' time Cap'n gits th'oo 'ith you I'll play at yo' funeral."

"Boy, snatch me Memphis Blues. Ol' Cap'n ain't hurt me—'ceptin' I bust my voice yellin' so's he'd think so."

Having accomplished the first success in a series of battles with the triflin' Wildcat, the Captain proceeded to frame an elaborate series of charges which his clerk incorporated in a court-martial. "What date do you wish to have him up?" the clerk asked.

"Right now—this minute—as soon as I can sign my name. I'll break that nigger of shootin' craps in public or kill him. Send an orderly after him and we'll have his trial now."

Cinnamon, who had drifted to the office, was dispatched after the Wildcat. "Cap'n says burn yo' shoe. He's waitin' fo' you in his office."

"Hope he ain't foun' no more stovewood—neveh seed such a heavy club."

Cinnamon laughed derisively. "I bet we gits a holiday to-morr'—an' a band an' marchin' an'——"

"How come?"

"Funeral p'cession, Wildcat—us marches slow an' you leads."

"Boy, you makes me sick." The Wildcat started for his doom.

"Fo' long you gits some flowehs readin' 'Rest from now on.'"

The court-martial was fast business. "Guardhouse for three months, forfeits three months' pay, reduced from grade of sergeant to private, effective to-day."

The Wildcat dragged himself over to report to the Sergeant of the Guard. "Cap'n sho' learned to speak his piece by heart."

The Wildcat, languishing in the guardhouse, rapidly established himself in the mixed company therein. Before he had been within its walls an hour he had become the financial center of his little world. Prisoners are not supposed to have money with them but under the surface discipline the army is an informal aggregate of fractured rules and busted regulations, known and overlooked by the governmentalities who wear the stars and varnished boots of rank.

Pretty soon the Wildcat became a medium good languisher. The guardhouse was humid and warm and except for three or four hours' work around camp each day the prisoners had nothing to do but eat and sleep and gamble. Cinnamon, observing this, came to envy his associate.

"Cap'n has me draggin' roun' f'm sun-up to when de owls hoot," he complained. "Wisht I could git me th'ee months in jail whah at ol' Wilecat is."

He analyzed the process by means of which the Wildcat had accomplished his nominal punishment. "Me—I'se neveh knowed Lady Luck to fail me," he announced blandly one evening after supper. "Gimme dem dice. C'm out heah whah I kin roll 'em wild." He selected an area of high visibility in front of the barracks and talked loud. "Shoots five francs. . . ."

The Cap'n responded under forced draft. He suddenly appeared in front of Cinnamon. "Boy," he said to his striker, "at nine o'clock to-night maybe I'll kill you. Report over to the guardhouse under arrest."

The thankful Cinnamon picked up his five francs. "Cap'n, yessuh," he said. He walked rapidly to the sentry outside of the guardhouse. "Cap'n of us boys Fust Service Battalion ordehs me repo't heah under arrest."

"Corporal th' guard!" the sentry bawled. "Git inside, boy, before I shove this gun through you."

"How come you heah?" the Wildcat asked in greeting.

"Me—Wilecat, I has me a drag avec ol' Lady Luck, ness pa!"

"Us sho' is rollin' strong, Cin'mun! Me—I stays heah goin' on 'leven weeks mo'. Ol' wah ain't so bad dis way. Wisht I could stay heah f'm now on. Us kin——"

"Vitus Marsden!" The Wildcat heard his name called by the sergeant of the guard who stood in the doorway of the enclosure.

"Dat's me." The Wildcat stepped importantly towards the source of the summons.

"Report at once on parole for duty as personal orderly for the Captain of the First Service Battalion."

"Cinnamon, doggone you, heah you is—an' I'se persecuted with yo' job draggin' roun' mawnin' an' night fo' ol' Cap'n Jack. Lady Luck, wuz you a rabbit, I'd gallop you to death!"

☆

☆   ☆

Tʜᴇ A. E. F. was long, theoretically, on moral and physical cleanliness. On Sunday evening the Wildcat was exposed to forty minutes' preaching, under orders.

"Lootenant preacheh 'spounded 'bout a boy he called Mis' P'odigal's son," he later explained to Cinnamon. "Sho' wuz plum dead f'm his collar o'naments up. Boy et shucks an' fed all de cawn to some hawgs. Me—I'd et me a cawn pone an' could I get me a Barlow, I'd butcher me a hawg and have me some po'k chops an' side meat an' ham an' spah ribs an' gravy an' chittlin's an' mebbe some mo' ham—Wondeh what time din-neh'll be ready."

"Mebbe them hawgs wuz penned up neah a house—an' watched close. Ol' constable calls it stealin' is you ketched."

"Ain't been yit—an' I craves not to be. Hawgs don't care who owns 'em—killin' day boun' to ketch 'em anyhow, come Thanksgivin' time."

A messenger interrupted the conversation. "Wilecat, Cap'n says whah in hell is you."

The Wildcat adapted his pace to the tenor of the summons.

"Cap'n—whut wuz it, suh? I wuz hangin' yo' light unifohm on de line an'——"

"Tell Cinnamon to report to the cook for K. P. duty," the Captain said. "Give the sergeant at the guardhouse this paper."

The Wildcat carried the glad tidings. "Yo' gits fo'teen hours a day roun' de kitchen. "I'se et worse'n I has lately, but I depen's heavy on you, Cinnamon—'long as you an' me is frien's an' you is he'pin' in de kitchen. Mos' all de time I'se hungry."

"Boy, we eats heavy, ness pa?"

"Sho' do—how come you sez 'ness pa' all de time?"

"Ness pa is French fo' sayin' wuz Lady Luck a bird, us has a handful of tail feathers."

In Washington, behind an elaborate mahogany bulwark, a quarter-master colonel calculated an intricate soap problem affecting the epidermis of several million men. "Ultimate strength of three million in the Zone of Advance, Watkins—put down three million—multiplied by the number of days in two years. Say three million by seven hundred. What does that give you?"

"Twenty-one hundred million."

"Very good. Say they use an ounce of soap a day—more than that up there where the—ah—insects are thickest, means twenty-one hundred million ounces. Get out a requisition covering that at once. Liquid soap—twenty-one hundred million ounces of liquid soap to be shipped immediately to the Commander-in-Chief, A. E. F.—Hoboken to Bordeaux for distribution from the St. Sulpice Storage Depot."

"Yessir." Watkins sought his own refuge and began winding the red tape around the soap. He discovered that the liquid soap order amounted to over sixty-five thousand tons of material without considering containers.

"Ten shiploads—sure is a big war."

And on a morning when everybody from the front line to the base ports in France went hungry at breakfast time because the subs had sunk a dozen shiploads of food, the first four cargoes of liquid soap sailed from an Atlantic port bound for somewhere in France where the cooties grew wild.

An order issued from G. H. Q. covering the theory that cleanliness is next to loaning money to the sentry at the pearly gates. "Daily bath, hell!" commented the A. E. F. "If I had water enough for a bath, I'd drink it."

At St. Sulpice open storage spaces and warehouses rapidly filled with steel drums full of liquid soap. The Fust Service Battalion, detailed to unload the trains arriving from the docks near Bordeaux, sweated and heaved and grunted day after day at its endless task. "How come so much soap?" Moon Eye complained. "Neveh seed so much soap. Wuz it sorghum sweetenin', they might be some sense to it. Us needs soap 'bout like a cootie needs wings." Moon Eye scratched himself and swung onto another barrel of soap.

Over at the Captain's quarters the Wildcat was busy straightening up the site of a poker battle which had raged throughout the night.

Close in his wake followed the goat, Lily, nominally mascot of the Battalion, but in reality the personal protégé of the Wildcat. Lily, munching contentedly on the nine of clubs and a shredded face card, gave forth a plaintive bleat.

"Shut up—no wondeh your insides hurts. When you eats th'ee socks an' two cigahs an' half a deck of cyards yo' has yo' mis'ry comin'. Leggo 'at papeh!"

The Wildcat finished his work and proceeded to the Battalion office adjoining the Captain's quarters. The room was untenanted at the moment, and while the Wildcat swept the litter which lay about, into the dark corners of the room where it might accumulate unnoticed, Lily grazed here and there at will.

"Neveh seed such a ol' goat f'r eatin' cigahs. Lay off 'at long one—I aims to smoke 'at cigah myse'f afteh me an Cinnamon eats us a li'l snack." The Wildcat stowed the half smoked cigar in the left pocket of his shirt and made his way to the kitchen, leaving Lily safely confined behind closed doors. "Stay theh an' walk yo' post whilst I 'cumulates some rations."

Lily walked a staggering post for a few minutes until a neatly culti-vated garden of Service records attracted her attention. In the midst of the alphabet she found a menu to her taste. She browsed lightly on the documentary evidence covering the military biography of Moon Eye and the Blackslid Baptist. Of Vitus Marsden, the Wildcat, she ate all but the two wire staples which bound his folio. She gorged on Cinnamon, Lizard and young Cube Calvin. From the Captain's desk she partook of a cellu-lose dessert consisting of the courtmartial charge sheets of the Wildcat and Cinnamon, covering the crime of being publicly discovered shootin' craps. She drank lightly of crimson wine from an inkwell and found it not pleasing to her taste. "Blaa!"

"Lily, you debbil, come off dat desk." The Wildcat, returning to the office, accumulated the mascot. "Wuz cyclones hawns and hair, you is six. Ah'll 'Blaa' you wid a chair in a minnit."

The Wildcat straightened out the remaining disordered documents and dragged Lily to an area back of the Captain's quarters. "Roam heah an' see kin you eat ground."

He tied the mascot securely and began looking over the Captain's socks. "See kin I find ol' socks big enough to fit me. Sho' need me some socks to-morr' when I gits Cap'n's unifawm in Bo'deaux f'm 'at tailor man."

An urgent demand for gasoline for the Motor Transport Corps in the Zone of Advance sang along the midnight wires.

"We have five cargoes of gasoline, but have no containers," answered the general commanding Base Section No. 2. He rang for his adjutant. "Rush this wire to G. H. Q.—no containers for gasoline."

The adjutant, an exceptional colonel who was not all bone above his collar ornaments, read the message which the general handed him.

"Why not ship some gas in those steel drums that the damned liquid soap came in?" he suggested. "The carpenter force at St. Sulpice could build a wood tank overnight big enough to hold two or three shiploads of that deleted soap—and we could ship the gasoline in the empty drums."

"Great work! Excellent idea!" the general approved. "Issue orders at once. That's what I call efficiency. Won't forget that. Rush it."

An order issued twenty minutes later over the telephone to St. Sulpice to construct a wood reservoir five hundred feet long, two hundred feet wide and ten feet deep; and to empty the drums of liquid soap into this reservoir. "Ship empty drums to gasoline reserve depot Sursol Docks. Rush."

At midnight six thousand men were at work on the huge wood tank and by nine o'clock the next day it was half filled with the liquid soap.

The spur tracks leading to the great tank near the river were filled with carloads of empty drums bound for the Gasoline Reserve Depot.

"Compliment you on the expedient," wired G. H. Q. to the general commanding Base 2. The general forgot that the idea originated with his adjutant.

Meanwhile the ponderous tank of soap grew warm in the afternoon sun and cooled in the frosts of evening.

At evening the Captain of the Fust Service Battalion came to his quarters. The Wildcat was teaching the mascot goat, Lily, not to eat shoes.

"Boy, build me a fire and build it quick." The Captain was cold.

"Cap'n, yessuh." The Wildcat began tying a complicated twist in Lily's picket rope which he hoped might endure until his return.

The Captain began opening his mail. In the first envelope was a bill from a Bordeaux tailor. In the second was a request from a brother officer in Paris for the loan of twelve hundred francs. In the third was a notification from Washington stating that the Captain had been overpaid seventy-three dollars on his last pay voucher, and that refund must be made at once.

All this finance bounced back and hit the Wildcat. "Are you going to build that fire before I kill you or afterwards?" The Captain moved easily toward the Wildcat.

Lily and the confining knot were suddenly abandoned. "Cap'n, they ain't no chunk wood heah—nothin' 'ceptin' kin'lins—I'se gwine fo' some right now."

The Wildcat trotted out of the door, one eye open for firewood, and the other looking into the dismal future that promised to be his unless the Cap'n's mood changed mighty sudden. Under a carwheel, over the spur track leading to the tank of liquid soap, the Wildcat saw a nice piece of two by four. "Dry wood—sho' burn noble." He kicked the two by four from where it was wedged under the carwheel. A car length ahead he saw another similar block which he retrieved. "Three is plenty fo' a start." He kicked the third block loose and started towards the office with it. He had gone only a little way when a noise behind him attracted his attention. He turned and discovered that the string of cars from under which he had removed the blocks, was in motion. "Sho' kin roll easy down hill."

He looked about him. "Mebbe dese heah blocks wuz all de brakes ol' cars had. Mebbe I'se instigated a ruckus. Hope nobody seed me an' tells Cap'n."

The Wildcat's second mebbe suffered a rapid transition into reality. Hornet railroaders began pouring towards the racing train. Each man ran a little way and then stood gazing breathlessly at the rattling tornado headed for the soap tank a mile down hill. . . .

The chill rain of evening began to fall as the Wildcat lighted the Captain's fire. In the Captain's fifth envelope was an invitation from the artillery gang at Souge to sit in the following night at a five card enterprise where a gentleman bets that something he doesn't hold outranks the hand some other gentleman is inflicted with.

"Soon as you get that fire built, head for Bordeaux on the six-twenty and get my new uniform from Mesuret's tailor shop on the Rue Intendence. Here's your pass."

"Cap'n, yessuh." The Wildcat breathed heavy. Here, delivered into his hands, was a quick evasion of the heavy swinging club with which Lady Luck was about to caress him.

From the distance there came the echo of a terrific crash. For five seconds there followed a heavy sustained roar. The Captain suddenly abandoned his correspondence. "What the hell broke loose?"

"Speck ol' sergeant's blowed up some stumps mebbe. Cap'n, suh— mebbe ol' thundeh sto'm bust—mebbe——"

The Captain had joined in the race towards the side of the soap tank where twelve heavy freight cars had plowed through a fabric of splintering timber. When he arrived near the scene the sloping terrain from the tank to the river was ten feet deep in a dancing foam created by the impact of a myraid raindrops mingling with the liquid soap. On the choppy surface of the Gironde there presently foamed enough soapsuds to last a million Mondays.

☆

☆   ☆

Aᴛ ᴇᴠᴇɴɪɴɢ the Wildcat leading the mascot goat, Lily, entered Bordeaux via the stone bridge that spans the Gironde. The smothery soap-suds blanket was rolling up the river and spreading into the city streets.

An automobile ran into a great bank of foam and died. The driver and his passenger raced on foot from out of the menace of the translucent mass of bubbles.

The Wildcat, observing the bubble phenomena, headed for the tailor shop. He paused a moment to absorb a few slugs of cognac. The goat, Lily, which he led beside him, gave a plaintive bleat. "Is you a mascot, you'd betteh begin workin' at it heavy, Lily. Us needs to ketch up now wif Lady Luck—else we'se gwine neveh to see 'at woman again."

The Wildcat noticed that the twinkling lights that lined the Intendence revealed a stream of humanity headed in one direction only—away from the river.

At the door of the tailor shop an M. P. hailed the Wildcat. "Boy, halt! What are you doing in town this time of night?"

The Wildcat's heart got up on a trapeze and tried a tail spin. Here was the hand of the Law—a heavy hand closely followed by the Law's foot clad in the new and heavy marching shoe.

"Me—nuthin'. I never knowed dat ol' railroad train'd run away 'count of a li'l stick o' wood bein'——"

The M. P. decided the Wildcat had missed his train. "Old stuff! Can th' bunk! Lemme see your pass."

The Wildcat explored his raiment and finally produced the slip of paper which spelled temporary freedom. "I'se gwine back—me and Lily, soon as I 'cumulates Cap'n's uniform f'm ol' tailor man in the sto' right heah."

"Beat it then—and lay off the coonyak." The M. P. read the pass and gave the Wildcat a little parting advice.

The Wildcat entered the tailor shop five minutes before closing time. A hare-lipped young clerk struggling with a .22 cal. English vocabulary, discovered the motive of the Wildcat's visit and returned presently with a bundle in which an officer's uniform was neatly folded.

"Eet is charged, M'sieur nagur. Voilà! 'Revoir."

The Wildcat plus the goat, Lily, entered into the night. "Tell us, 'Wallow in de riveh!' Never seed white boys sassy like dese heah French frogs is."

The Wildcat started towards the river on his journey home. And then, quite suddenly, he and Lily reversed their line of march and headed up the street. Approaching them in gentle jumps of a hundred feet was a wall of soap bubbles fifty feet high. "Neveh seed such heavy drams o' coon-yak. Us sho' is had plenty, an' then some. Lily, you mascot, see kin yo' laigs rattle a gallop. Git out o' town. Le's go!"

At the distant crescent Avenue which lay about the city the Wildcat paused long enough to take on four more slugs of cognac. The paper covering about the uniform, soggy in the rain, burst when it lay between the Wildcat's feet. He picked it up and started out of the café with it. Through the opening in the package, the brilliant scarlet of French cavalry breeches assaulted the Wildcat's heavy eyes. "Lily, us travels! I'se stahted seein' red! Sho' is a bad sign!"

In the obscurity of the great trees which fringed the boulevard the Wildcat completed his investigation of the package. "Eyes tol' me true. Ol' pants sho' is red. Dese is clo'es like French Cap'ns weahs."

From down the street there came the measured beat of the nine o'clock guard relief. "Cap'n kill me sho', does I go back. Ol' M. P. jail me does he ketch me in Bo'deaux. Me—I fades out."

The Wildcat emerged from the total eclipse of a wide spreading tree five minutes later wearing the French uniform, but instead of the bars of a Captain's rank on his sleeves there gleamed the polished stars of a general of the line. On the Wildcat's head was a cap encircled by two wreaths of golden leaves.

"Lily—you follows me. I sho' aims not to lead you—me totin' all dis rank."

In the rays of a street lamp the Wildcat strutted past his first M. P. That young soldier focused his eyes carefully on the glittering insignia and then rendered a strenuous salute.

"First nigger general I ever saw. These frogs sure beat hell."

The next M. P. which the Wildcat passed came from another part of the United States. He did the best he could to express his sentiments in profane language, neither appropriate nor available for present use. Then he swung his club savagely in the darkness at an imaginary adversary.

Meanwhile the Gironde River, the Wildcat's captain and a twin star general of the A. E. F. were each and severally foaming at the mouth.

General Bore, a party to a session of refined military poker, played his game wisely during the early part of the evening, and then fully alcoholized, played not too well. At midnight the members of the party one by one departed through the rain in their respective official conveyances. The general lingered for a final drink at the urgent invitation of his host.

Just then the general's car was laying abandoned in a bank of soap bubbles beside a residence near the river in which the general's chauffeur had discovered a practically flawless feminine pearl. "No carburetor on earth can mix soapsuds and gas so it'll explode, mon cherie. T'ell with th' old bird. Leave him walk home—or fly if his boots is too tight. Drag out another one of them vang blinks whilst I tells you about life in San Francisco."

An hour after midnight, the general sailed grandly down the street through the rain. Over the shoal places in the sidewalk he backed and filled to steerage way, came about smartly, luffed from the menace of a tree and tacked to the smooth residential cliffs that lined his channel. Softly, at times, he sang: "Shine on, you doggone silv'ry—hic! G'wan, baby. Shine some f'r the love of—hic! Never saw a blacker night. Rain on, gentle rainlets. How dry I yam—How driyam—Likell I yam. I should —hic!—worry!"

A soldier of the A. E. F. approached. The general stiffened during the second of proximity and snapped a return to the M. P.'s salute.

"Not a globe busted and the dynamo goin' a million—lit up like a dimun' palace—an' him wearin' two stars!" The M. P. did some heavy thinking as he walked his post.

Pulsing through the night toward a secret base for subs, the wireless from Berlin hissed an order to the Herr Lieutenant von Stutz. "To the Gironde approaches from America a convoy of twelve food ships, six ammunition cargoes, four with troops. Protection six subchasers. Sink the food ships first."

Eight minutes after the radio had reached the commander's hands, four undersea boats were driving through a choppy sea toward the mouth of the Gironde. At five o'clock in the morning the four submarines lay, decks awash, off the mouth of that river.

Steaming toward their certain fate, the wallowing hulls of the great convoy slushed through the phosphorescent sea.

The Wildcat, in his French general's uniform, closely convoyed by Lily, the goat, prowled through the mysterious darkness of Bordeaux.

Approaching him over a heavy rolling sea, carrying a capacity cargo, sailed the twin-star general.

The enlarging blanket of soap bubbles fifty feet deep, bulged from its inexhaustible source in gentle but incessant hundred foot leaps.

Looming out of the night the two-star general saw the Wildcat. First the red breeches became visible, then the coat with its heavy insignia. In the wake of the figure General Bore saw a ghostly goat. The Wildcat's face blended so perfectly with the shadows that he appeared to be headless.

General Bore, fearing for an instant that he was beginning to see things, was reassured by the gleaming whites of the Wildcat's eyes.

The Wildcat saw the bedraggled general and laughed. His mouth, opening in a wide crescent, gave him the look of a man whose throat had been cut considerably more than the technique of throat cutting demands.

General Bore, still doubting his own reason, saluted the French uniform. "Bon sore, mon General."

"Cap'n, so is mine," the Wildcat replied pleasantly. "Mah bones sho' is sore—dis rain likely. Mah feet is wuss."

General Bore looked puzzled. "Voo parley English?" he asked. He kicked sideways at the goat, Lily, to assure himself of the mascot's reality. His booted foot landed heavily on Lily's ribs.

"Lay off dat goat, man. Lily ain't done nuthin' to you."

Lily, however, made a sudden resolution. She backed off twenty feet and accumulated a few million slugs of momentum. She landed on General Bore south of his equatorial Sam Browne belt. General Bore landed somewhere in France.

The Wildcat grabbed the rope which trailed from the mascot's collar, and together they galloped into the gulf of night.

The general assembled himself and got to his feet, posing for a moment like an advertisement for a rheumatism cure. And then he also raced from the scene. Coming toward him was a great black wall which slithered as it moved. The wall glistened in spots like polished flint.

"Whiskey since I was twelve," he reflected, "but never another drop if I regain my reason."

The surging wall of bubbles engulfed him and his resolve. He began a wild peal of laughter which gurgled to silence in the blanket of bubbles. The general's eyes began to smart. Around him was absolute darkness. He stumbled over the curb and fell down heavily.

He had his boots on when he fell. "Never mind the guard," he muttered. "As you were! At—rest!" He fanned at the breaking bubbles once or twice like a seal wriggling its flippers, and then he fell asleep.

SOISSONS

by THOMAS BOYD

IMMENSELY IMPOSING by greatness of numbers, three divisions were gathered in ranks on the field. Presenting a huge sight of restless attention, they swayed like the waves of a mud-colored sea. Before them an officer stood on a platform, his hat in his hand, the wind blowing his hair. Not far off, on the outskirts of a ramshackle village, old Frenchmen, their wives, and their grandchildren watched. The officer lifted his hand with a gesture, commanding a silence that none could mistake. He hunched up his shoulders and frowned disapproval; he fastened his thumbs in the strap of his belt. His protuberant belly kept him from being an exact replica of an old turkey-cock. Now, tearing to shreds the phlegm in his gullet, he opened his mouth:

"Men, no doubt some of you, most of you, believe that you are here by chance. That any divisions might have been called in place of you. Men, you are not here by chance. It is because I, personally, requested our distinguished commanding officer that your divisions make up my army corps that you are here."

Here he paused. He was a major-general and he was wondering how much longer the war would last, hoping that it would continue through the year.

"I have watched you enter the lines, green and unseasoned troops, at Cantigny and Château-Thierry, and assault the enemy with such force that you threw back his most valiant troops, the Prussian Guards. You have shown your sterling mettle at Soissons and Saint Mihiel, advancing far beyond the objective given you. Jaulny and Thiaucourt and Montfaucon have fallen under your irresistible onslaught. Now you may be considered, you are considered, wherever civilization is known, as shock troops, second in valor to none."

He paused, wondering irresistibly whether his impending rise to lieutenant-general would give his wife access into the more imposing homes of Washington.

"And so you are here, good soldiers who have done your duty and are willing to do it again.

"Many of you men came over to France with the belief that the war

From: *Through the Wheat.* Copyright 1923. Charles Scribner's Sons.

would soon be over and you would return home again to indulge in your inalienable right to life, liberty, and the pursuit of happiness." ("Hooray!" shouted the men.) "You will return home soon, but not as soon as you expected. Not until we have pierced the enemy lines and brought them to our feet." ("Take him out—to hell with you—how does he get that way"—the muttered comments rose indistinctly from the sea of mud.) "It depends upon you men right here as to how long you will stay in France. You can stay until hell freezes over or you can renew your good work and be home before you know it. Our commanding general has said: 'Hell, Heaven, or Hoboken by Christmas,' and it is up to us to stand by him." ("Oh, my God—let's go home—we're hungry—chow"— ending in a dull chanting, "When do we eat?")

The general was going along famously. He felt his gift of rhetoric as he never before had felt it. His eyes dimmed and a lump rose in his throat at the frenzied cheering of the men.

"You men are assembled here to-day to be told of the great offensive in which you will soon take part. Many of you will not return from it, but that is war. Some of you will come off non-commissioned officers, and, as should be the case in a democratic army, others will have a chance to be officers, made so by an act of Congress."

("Pipe down—bunk.")

He believed that he was being cheered again. He continued his address for fifteen minutes longer than he intended. When he stepped from the platform to the ground there were tears in his eyes.

In making the estimates of the divisions before him, the major-general had only spoken aloud what the men secretly believed—that they were the "finest flower of chivalry," the epitome of all good soldierly qualities. But to hear themselves so praised sounded unethical, made them embarrassed. Had they been told that they were not shock troops, that they were not the best soldiers in the known world, they would have been indignant. Therefore they hid their gratitude and commendation under a torrent of mordant remarks. The long lines were formed into squads, demanding food, speculating upon the nearness of the attack, as they marched back to their respective towns where they were billeted.

Hicks had not recovered from his despondency. His stomach felt as if he had swallowed a stone every time reference was made to the attack. He had done about enough in this war, he thought, wondering vaguely whether there were no chance of escape. The thought of the sound of the guns depressed him, their monotonous tom-tom beating in memory on his skull like water dripping slowly on a stone. Disgusting! And no letters from home, no change of scene, no clean clothing, nothing but the hopelessness of routine, the bullying of petty officers, the prospect of the front.

He was still brooding when the platoon reached its billets in the town to which it had come from the last drive. Instead of the unsavory food steaming under a fire in the field kitchen, there was an issue of corned beef, and slabs of black bread to be eaten. The field kitchens were packed, the supply wagons were loaded. The persevering little mules that hauled the machine-gun carts stood waiting. Orders were passed for the men to pack up their equipment and be ready to fall into line on the company street in half an hour. "Shake it up, you men," the officers called, walking back and forth past the buildings. "We haven't got all night." Somebody asked where the platoon was going. "To the front," an officer answered. "Make it snappy."

☆

☆   ☆

For two days now the bombardment had continued, heaving over the live, huge shells that broke in the distance with a dull, sullen fury. Lightly it had begun, and with an exchange of salutes from the six inch rifles. Then a number of batteries in the centre of the sector started ferociously to bark. Along the left the heavy detonation of the exploding shells was taken up, later to be joined by the smaller pieces of artillery, which went off with mad, snapping sounds. The guns on the right brought the entire line into action.

Artillerymen, their blouses off, their sleeves rolled, sweated in torrents as they wrestled with shells, throwing them into the breeches of their guns. Each gun was fired, and as it recoiled from the charge another shell was waiting to be thrown into the breech. The officers of the gunners, their muscles tense, their lineaments screwed up so that their faces looked like white walnuts, made quick mathematical calculations, directing the shells unerringly to strike their targets. Orderlies hurried from gun-pit to gun-pit, carrying messages from a higher officer which, when delivered to the battery commanders and passed to the gunners, would strike or spare a hundred men, an old church, or a hospital.

Wagons and heavy motor-trucks rumbled over the roads leading to the forests where the long-range guns were hidden, bringing always more food for the black, extended throats of the guns. The batteries in the centre had been drawn up in a thick woods a few miles from the present front line. There, from the height of a steady swell in the earth, they were able better to watch the effects of their pounding.

Between the inky mass of forest which concealed the guns and the jagged front line were the crumbling ruins of a village of which not a building now stood. The ruins were at the edge of the front line, which zigzagged unendingly in either direction. Barbed wire, rusted and ragged, was strung from posts before the trench. Chevaux-de-frise, inspiring confidence in their ability to withstand penetration, were placed at intervals, wherever gaps had been blown in the barbed wire.

The space between the front line and the German listening posts was a yellowish gray. Its face was pockmarked and scabbed with tin cans, helmets, pieces of equipment. Bones, grayed in the sun and rain, were perceptible occasionally. A leather boot stuck grotesquely out of one of the unhealthy indentations in the lifeless ground. The flat chrome earth lay for several hundreds of yards and then was split by a strip of shadowy black woods.

Past the woods the barren earth continued, rising and disappearing at a distance, in a hill studded with trees.

Beyond lay mystery and a gargantuan demon who, taking whatever shape he chose, might descend with a huge funnelled bag from which he might extract any number of fascinatingly varied deaths.

The night before, out of a still, starlit sky, a sudden rain had fallen. It had drenched the trees and the grass and soaked the clothing of the troops who were lying in the woods awaiting the hour for the attack. The rain made a long, slimy, muddy snake out of the roads leading to the front line. Where the caisson tracks had bitten into the ground, hasty rivulets now ran. Water from the evenly plotted fields had drained into the ditch that ran alongside the road, overflowing.

Bandoliers of ammunition slung over their shoulders, their pockets stuffed with heavy corrugated hand-grenades, carrying shovels and picks, the platoon followed along the muddy road in rear of a machine-gun company. Rudely awakened from an irresistible sleep beneath the trees, they had been marshalled before supply wagons, had been given articles of extra equipment to use in the attack. Now, whenever the body of troops before them halted, the lids closed readily over their sleepy eyes and their bodies swayed with fatigue. The halts were frequent, for the machine-gunners carried their heavy rifles and tripods on their shoulders.

The road was slippery and the travel laborious, and after innumerable pauses whenever the advancing line became clogged, the men sat down, completely fatigued, in the mud and water. Uneasiness could be felt in the tightly packed mass that waddled along the road. It lay on the tongues of the platoon, preventing them from showing their exasperation at the long delay. Curses would rise to their lips and die unuttered. A word spoken aloud, the jangling of metal, would infuriate them. From fear and habit, the explosion of a gun near them would cause them to stop, standing without a tremor. A distance of less than two miles, the platoon crawled along like an attenuated turtle. They felt that dawn would find them still on the road, their feet struggling with the clinging mud. The night was as thick and black as coal-tar. Progress through it seemed impossible.

Behind the barely moving lines the guns continued their *boom, boom,* like the sound of distant thunder. The shells whistled overhead, the report of their explosion only faintly to be heard. There was no retaliation. The enemy seemed willing to take the brunt without a murmur. But to the platoon their silence was suspicious. Accustomed to hearing the crashing reply to a bombardment, when the men did not hear it they grew fearful. They began to wonder if they were not being led into a trap. Fed too fully upon the German-spy propaganda issued by the Allied governments, they wondered whether the general directing the attack might not be a minion of the Kaiser, leading them to their deaths. Or else the Germans were planning some great strategic coup.

The failure of the enemy guns to reply was so annoying that it became the absorbing notion in the minds of the men. Their ears were strained, waiting to hear the familiar whine of a shell fired toward them. It made their nerves feel ragged and exposed. On the road sounded the decisive beat of horses' hoofs. It was deeply perturbing. Stretching their necks, unmindful of the slippery road, the danger of sliding into the ditch, the men watched the horse and rider, believing it portentous. The horse was turned back to the woods.

Like a latrine built for a corp of monsters stretched the slippery trench. Approaching it through the narrow communication gully, the men slid and stumbled from the slatted-board bottom into the mire. They would withdraw their legs from the mud, the mud making a "pflung" as the foot rose above it.

The platoon filed into the trench, and crouched low against the firing bays, their bayonets peeping over the top. After hours on the road the trench was warm to their bodies, despite its mud and slime. Their eyes staring into the black night, the men waited.

Hard, cold, and unfriendly dawn broke over the earth like a thin coating of ice shattering in a wash-basin. In the eerie light the tangled masses of wire, the weather-beaten posts from which the wire was strung, the articles of equipment and clothing once worn by men looked unreal. The woods ahead, a grayish black, lay against the sky like a spiked wall.

Hicks, his face pressed against the muddy side of the trench, felt sick. Along the road his body had been shaken with chills. Now the muscles of his stomach were contracting, forcing him to gag. He thought of poking his soiled finger down his throat, but the thought of it was so revolting that he only gagged more violently.

Crouching there, he had no desire to leave the trench. Why should he leave it, he asked himself, and could find no reason. Possibly for an hour during his whole life he had hated the German army. Now he only dis-, liked them. And for one reason: because they marched in a goose-step. He felt that for any people to march in that manner was embarrassing to the rest of humanity. Somehow it severed them from the rest of their kind. But that was little reason, he realized, to drag his weary body over a repulsive ground. He was conscious of a sensation of numbness.

"Je's, I'm sick," he groaned to the man next to him. "I don't know whether I can go over. I'm all in."

"Why don't you go back? Tell one of the officers. He'll send you back."

"Yeh. And have every one of you birds think I'm yellow? I *will* not. I'll be all right," he added.

The roar of the guns deepened. A heavy curtain of exploding shells lay between the platoon and the German lines. The barrage lifted and started to move.

Whistles were imperatively blown along the trench, commanding the men to rise and begin the advance. As if it were their last mortal act, the men clambered out of the trench and started to walk.

Bent over, like a feeble old man, Hicks walked abreast of the first wave. His respirator hung heavily from around his neck. He clutched at his collar, loosening it more freely to breathe. His legs were made of wood, they felt light, but hesitated to bend. His nostrils were being flattened against his face by huge, unseen thumbs. "Hell, Heaven, or Hoboken by Christmas," he thought, adding "Probably hell for all of us."

The day brightened, and as he approached the trees they became separate identities. The trees stared at him menacingly. They embarrassed him by their scrutiny. He found himself making excuses for advancing toward them. It was exasperating that no bullets were fired from the trees. He wondered why it could be. And then he was at the woods, entering with the rest of the men, and the underbrush parted with a crackling sound. He drew back, frightened.

Because of the thickness of the underbrush and the irregularity of the setting of the trees, he veered off to a path that led through the woods. On it other men had made their way and were stealthily tramping through, their eyes darting from one side to the other.

At a place where another path crossed, an ammunition wagon stood. The bodies of four horses lay dead on the ground, their hides mutilated, pierced by pieces of flying shell. The dead horses were a squeamish sight, lying there with large reproachful eyes and slender necks that seemed to have been broken. Their stomachs were inflated as if they had eaten too much fresh clover. Hicks grew more depressed, his own stomach wanted to describe a parabola inside of him. Hicks gagged, engaged in a spasm of retching. The woods were covered with saffron, their trunks were gaunt, and yellow splotches stuck out from the branches. The grass wore a bilious complexion. He looked down at his shoes; they, too, were yellow, unfamiliar, indefinable from the color of his puttees or his mustard uniform.

He tramped on through the woods, hoping that his sickness would overpower him, cast him to the ground where he could rest.

"If only I'd get so sick I couldn't walk," he thought, "how nice it would be."

He walked on, thinking of the spot in which he would like to lie, judging with a discerning eye the softness and safety of various spots of ground. The sight of a small hollow, with breastworks of fallen trees thrown up on the dangerous side, was attractive to him. He was about to succumb, but decided against it, thinking of the awkwardness of his position in case some one should pass. And they were sure to pass, some snooping lieutenant or orderly.

But he was supposed to be in an attack. Pugh and the rest were facing the enemy at this very moment. And here he was lagging behind! Choking with fright, he hurried out of the woods. The rest of the line had just broken through the trees and now he joined them as they marched steadily ahead.

The field over which they were advancing stretched like a gridiron for perhaps a mile, then it was lost in the thickly wooded hill that rose majestically and invincibly. "God," Hicks thought, "do we have to take that hill?" It was inconceivable that it could be done, yet inconceivable that it would not be done. There it rose—a Gethsemane—towering in the air, austere and forbidding.

Below, four waves of men with their bayoneted rifles held at high port, advanced along the flat field toward the hill. Hicks felt weak, as if he wanted to crumple up. Machine bullets clicked like keys on the typewriter of the devil's stenographer. Rifled bullets announced their swift, fatal flights by little "pings" that sounded like air escaping from a rubber tire. They seemed to follow each other closely enough to make a solid sheet of metal.

Slowly the men marched, trying to maintain an even line under the rapid firing. Silently and unexpectedly a whistle blew and the long lines dropped to the ground. For the distance they had advanced their losses were too great.

To lie down in the face of the firing was more unendurable than moving toward it. The bodies of the men felt to them more conspicuous than when they were on their feet. They tried to hug the ground, to expose as little of themselves as they could.

"What the hell are we going to do? Go to sleep here?"

"No, they're lookin' for the Angel of Mons to tell us when to advance."

"This is an awful way to win a war. Are they tryin' to get us all killed?"

"Oh, one of these German spies is in command, that's all."

So ran the comment of the men, interspersed with cries for assistance from the wounded. At last the whistles blew again and the men rose to their feet, chafing, half-frightened, half-angry, under the restraint of the regulated advance. One man started ahead of the line and an officer, raising his voice above the frightful racket, yelled:

"Come back here, you damned fool. Do you want to get killed by your own barrage?"

The barrage was falling short of its mark. Shells struck the fringe of the woods toward which the men already had closely advanced.

An avion sailed over the field, a serene, self-satisfied dove of peace. The pilot fired a rocket when he was directly above the front line, and wheeled back. The barrage lengthened, the shells crashing into the trees. But if the barrage had delayed their progress on the field, it had hastened it in the woods. The coils of barbed wire which had been strung before the German front-line trench were blown to bits. Great gaps in the wire appeared all along the line. The men rushed through, fell into the trench, and scrambled out the other side. The German trench had been abandoned. The main body of their troops was withdrawn and the hill had been protected only by a heavy rear-guard.

Through the woods men were running like mad, beating small, inoffensive bushes with the butts of their rifles, and calling: "Come out of there, you damned Boche." Wherever they saw a dugout they hurled a pocketful of hand-grenades down the entrance, following them with threatening exclamations. They were the new men who had joined the platoon at the last village at which it had been billeted.

It was a night for love, a night for beautifully mantillaed women to rest their elbows on the window casement of picturesque houses and lend their ears to the serenade of their troubadours—a night to wander listlessly through unreal woods and offer words of love beneath the benediction of a round moon.

Through a long, tortuous trench which, now and again, had been partially obliterated by the explosion of a large shell, Hicks tramped. He had been sent out by the platoon commander to find the French army, whose left flank was supposed, according to orders issued before the attack, to adjoin the right of the platoon. Picking his way through the barbed wire over the rough ground, he swung along with large strides. Importantly he adjusted the strap of his helmet more tightly about his chin. He girded his pistol belt tighter, until his waist was wasp-like. To his leg he buckled his holster until it interfered with the circulation of his blood. He liked the feel of the pistol against his thigh. It made him feel equal to any danger. He was a Buffalo Bill, a Kit Carson, a D'Artagnan.

Progress, walking in the trench, was too dreary for his mood. He climbed out and commenced to stride along the field, his chest inflated, his chin high. He thought of the men lying along the trench, huddled together, three men under one blanket, and he felt motherly toward them. He thought of the Allied armies waiting for the war to be over, so that they might return to their homes and children, and he felt protective toward them. He thought of President Wilson, bearing the burden of the saving of civilization on his thin, scholarly shoulders, and he felt paternal toward him. Hicks it was who had been ordered to find the French army, to link it up with the American army so that there might be no gaps in the ranks when the attack began on the morrow. He walked on and on and somehow in the dim light he lost the direction of the trench.

The blasted French army was not going to be as easy to find as he had imagined. He had now walked much farther than he had been told to walk, and still there was no sight or sound of them. A little farther on his attention became divided between the French army and the trench. If he lost the direction of the trench, how could he find the army, he thought.

Out of the stillness of the night a Maxim sputtered. Hicks started, then ran as swiftly as he could. He fell into the trench, quite breathless. Feeling forlorn, he crept along the trench, with all his native cunning. After he had been walking he knew not how long, a form was vaguely seen to move ahead. Hicks halted. "Français soldat?" he questioned. "Who the devil is that?" a voice answered. He had returned unwittingly to his own platoon. The platoon commander, hearing the voices, came up.

"Is that Hicks?"

"Yes, sir."

"Well, where have you been? I told you to come back if the Frogs weren't near here. They probably haven't arrived yet."

Hicks sought out Pugh and lay down beside him underneath his blanket. Their heads covered, they talked in whispers.

"Gimme a cigarette," Hicks commanded.

The cigarette, badly crumpled, was produced from one of Pugh's pockets.

"Now give me a match."

After waiting a while Pugh produced a box of matches. Then with a sigh: "Ah doan mind givin' you cigarettes, Hicksy, but I hate like hell to carry 'em around for you."

Silence.

"Where ya been?"

"Oh, out tryin' to find some damned Frogs."

"When do we go over again?"

"In the morning, I guess."

Hicks, having been in touch with the commanding officer to the extent of carrying out an order of the lieutenant's, was expected to know these things.

The obverse bank of the large ridge was barren of foliage. No trees reared their protecting heads, shielding the men who slipped quietly down the side. Nor did there seem to be any need of shelter. In the half light of the gray dawn men moved without the usual accompaniment of firing from the enemy. To the silently advancing men it seemed as if there were no enemy in front of them, nothing to hinder their progress into the town that rested in delicate contours on the near bank of the hill ahead. Warily they proceeded near to the lines of jagged barbed wire that ran like a gantlet, one near the low point of the ridge, the other several hundreds of yards away, where the hill rose to the town. The ground, with the deep green of long, untrampled grass, was springy under the feet of the men. Their mouths tasted as if they had eaten mud. Breathless, the blunt air lay against them. From the sombre purple trees on the hill, the unnatural stillness of the village, there was a portent of evil.

Carefully, as if they were dressed for inspection, the men avoided the barbs of the wire that reached out to grasp and tear their clothing. There was no hurry. Every movement was made calmly and a trifle ponderously. Under the silence the platoon had acquired a fictitious dignity.

The last man through the tangled wire, the platoon formed in line again, moving forward. And then, in the dim light, the trees shot sparks of fire. Bullets sizzled hotly into the pen. They struck with an ugly hiss. In consternation the platoon stood for a moment, then fell to the ground. Their hearts flopped—and stood still. Inside their heads wings of mammoth windmills were revolving. Bullets spattered on, demanding, screeching for, death. The whole sound was reminiscent of ivory dice being frantically shaken in a metal box.

Hicks, by sheer straining, tried to force his body into the ground. He felt that his helmet was a magnet for the flying pieces of steel. His shoulders felt bare, the flesh undulating over his body. A bullet struck at the right of him, throwing up a puff of dust in his face. Cautiously, counting every move, he unfastened his respirator from his neck and wriggled it in front of him. He dropped his chin, letting his helmet fall from his head upon the respirator box. A group of bullets struck near his elbow. It hastened his piling his bandoliers of ammunition in front of him. Then he regretted his action. Supposing a bullet should strike the bandoliers and set off the cartridges! How many? Two hundred and twenty. And what would be left of him? He threw the bandoliers to the side. The bullets hailed, beating fiercely like an early spring storm. He crossed his arms in front of him, hiding his head and shutting his eyes. But the desire to see, to witness, was strongest, and he guardedly twisted his neck.

Around him men were whining for stretcher bearers. Plaintive and despondent, their cries reached his ears. He did not care. A dead man was a dead man. He grew sulky, restive, at their repeated cries for assistance.

"Why can't they let a fellow alone?" he thought. The enemy continued with their torrent of fire.

God, this was ticklish business, lying here like a bump on a log! Could nothing be done about it?

He crooked his neck, looking to the right, where the platoon commander lay. The platoon commander was so still that for a moment Hicks thought he was dead. Then something in his tense position informed him that he was alive.

"Why doesn't he do something? What the devil is he good for?" Hicks wondered.

Pugh was lying in a spot thoroughly without shelter. Around him the bullets spat viciously, covering him with fine dirt. Ahead of him a small hump of ground enticed him. It was small, not much bigger than the crown of a hat, but to Pugh it looked mountainous. He had watched it now seemingly for hours, afraid to move, believing that if he lay quite still the enemy would think he was dead and not fire at him. But ever the bullets came closer. He wriggled a few inches on his belly, and stopped. He tried it again. If only the machine-guns would let up for a moment he was sure that he could make it. He twisted a few more inches, working his body snakelike. Now he could almost touch the mound of dirt. He reached out his hand and grasped at the hump. The fingers of his hand had been stretched out. Now they slowly crumpled, making a weak, ineffectual fist. His arm remained outstretched. His head flattened against the earth, his body relaxing. From the left side of his head blood dripped, forming a little pool that was quickly absorbed by the dirt. Slowly his body stiffened out.

Hicks had watched him, fascinated, wanting to cry out warning, yet fearing that his effort to help would be a hindrance. He felt himself, with Pugh, striving to attain shelter behind the absurd little mound. It was his hand that reached out to touch it!

"Pugh!" he called. "Oh, Pugh!" He was excited. "Can't you make it, Pugh?" In his consciousness the thought pounded that Pugh was dead, but he combated it. "Why, Jack can't be dead," he argued with himself. "Why, he just gave me a cigarette last night!" There was total unbelief of the possibility of connecting death with Pugh in his tone. "Jack Pugh dead? Damn foolishness." But he was dead, and Hicks knew it. It made him sick to think of it. "That's right. It's something you can't fool yourself about."

He rose straight as any of the posts from which was strung the fatal barbed wire. He stooped over and picked up his bandolier of ammunition. He looked around at the men lying there on the ground and a sneer came over his face. Methodically, as if he were walking home, he started toward the end of the barbed-wire pen. A bullet neatly severed the fastening of his puttee. He was unmindful of the fact that it unrolled the folds of the cloth falling about his feet.

Now, along the line, other men had got to their feet. They were all in a daze, not knowing what was happening. They sensed an enemy in front of them, but they were not fully aware of his presence.

Whizzing past, the machine-gun bullets were annoying little insects. Hicks struck at his face, trying to shoo the bothering little creatures away. How damned persistent they were! He reached the strands of barbed wire which lay between him and the enemy and calmly picked out a place where the wire had been broken, and walked through. Now he had entered the fringe of the forest. Dimly he recognized a face before him to be that of a German. There was the oddly shaped helmet covering the head, the utilitarian gray of the German uniform. The face did not at all appear barbaric. It was quite youthful, the chin covered with a white down. He veered the muzzle of his rifle toward the face, and, without raising his rifle to his shoulder, pulled the trigger. The face disappeared.

Gray uniforms, with helmets like distorted flower-pots, fled through the woods, in front of the mass of men that now surged forward. Hicks followed after them, not particularly desirous of stopping them, but wanting to overtake them before they reached the crest of the hill.

Men poured into the woods, making a firm wall studded with bristling bayonets. On their faces was a crystallized emotion, presumably hate. Lying out on the ground but a short time ago they had been frozen with fear. They were hounds on a leash being tortured. The leash had snapped and the fear was vanishing in the emotion of a greater fear—the maddened fight for self-preservation. And so they scoured the woods, charging the Germans with a white fury, recklessly throwing hand-grenades in front of them.

Their cowardice made them brave men, heroes. Pushing on, they swung to the right toward the town. Through the open field they ran in little spurts, falling on their faces, rising and rushing on. From the windows of the houses and beside the walls bullets zinged past, stopping men and sending them headlong upon the ground. A small number of them rushed into the town.

Bullets flew in every direction. Men toppled down from the windows of houses. Others raced up the steps of the dwellings. Men ran through the streets, wild and tumultuous. They returned to the pavement, guarding their captives. Men poured the hate of their beings upon the town. They wept and cursed like lost souls in limbo. All of their fear, all of their anxiety, all of the restraint which had been forced on them during the morning when they lay like animals in a slaughter-house and their brains numbed with apprehension, came out in an ugly fury.

Once the Germans found that the town was invaded, that the men had broken through the woods and barbed wire, they offered a weak and empty resistance. They would readily have given themselves up to be marched in an orderly procession back to a prison camp. There was only a section holding the town. But the men did not know this. All of the stories of German frightfulness, of German courage, of the ruthlessness of the German foot troops, made them battle on in fear.

At last two squads of worn, frightened Germans were assembled in the town square and, threats following after them, were marched back to the rear. It was pitiful to see the Germans reaching in their breast pockets and bringing forth cigars which they cherished, and offering them to their captors as an act of amelioration. Some had bars of chocolate which they readily gave and which the men readily accepted. Some of the Germans tried even to smile, their efforts proving pathetic because of their fear.

The afternoon sun threw wan rays on the distorted bodies which fear and surprise had drawn out of shape. As had been the case with life, death had not fashioned their features identically. Some wore expressions of peace, as if they were about to enjoy a long and much-needed rest; others sprawled with sagging chins, from which a stream of saliva had flowed; one face grinned like an idiot's. The shadows lengthened, blanketing the unresisting bodies. The men marched out of the town, leaving it to the dead and the night.

The ground over which they were advancing looked stunted, blighted by the incessant bursting of shells, the yellow layers of gas that, now and again, had covered it. The grass was short and wiry, with bare spots of earth showing. A desultory firing was being kept up by the artillery; every now and then machine-guns would cut loose, spattering their lead through the air. But the front was comparatively quiet. In an hour at most the advancing line would have to halt. The sun already had made its retiring bow in a final burst of glory, and now dusk curtained the movements of the men.

Orderlies hurried wearily through the rough field, carrying messages which would affect the activities of the troops in the morning. Officers, indistinguishable from enlisted men, moved along, their air of command forgotten in the effort to keep spirit and flesh together. Their lineaments expressed a dumb horror, through which appeared an appreciation of the grim, comic imbecility of the whole affair. When spoken to, the men grinned awkwardly, trying to mask the horror of war with a joke.

Some of the more energetic among them attacked the hard ground with their shovels; the older and wiser men sought out shell holes large enough to protect their bodies in case of a counter-attack.

The front was still, save for a nervous tremor running through the opposing line and manifesting itself in the jerky firing of flare pistols.

Through the dull purple dusk three airplanes circled overhead, snowy angry geese. From their present altitude it was not discernible which were engaged in the assault, which the attacked. The motors, which distinguished to the experienced ear whether the airplane was German or Allied, were not to be heard. Red streaks traced a brilliant course through the sky, forming a network of crimson between the fluttering planes. The airplanes drew near each other, then darted away. They revolved in circles, each trying to rise higher, directly over the other, and pour from that point of vantage volleys of lead.

Detached, the men lying on the ground watched the spectacle, enjoying it as they would have enjoyed a Fourth of July celebration.

Without warning, the airplane that circled beneath the other two rose straight in the air. Above, it volleyed streams of bullets into the backs of the others. The pilot of one of the planes beneath seemed to lose control. Wing over wing, it fell like a piece of paper in a tempered wind. The two remaining planes raced each other out of sight.

THE SQUAD IN ACTION
by JAMES B. WHARTON

A COMPANY RUNNER fumbles down along the line of abandoned, Boche dugouts, covered over with slabs of corrugated sheet-iron, sticks, stones and earth.

"Where th' hell's Lieutenant Osgood?" he mutters into the mouths of various holes.

"Five down," some one answers out of the earth. "What's on? Jesus, we ain't goin' up, are we?"

"Goin' somewhere, fer it's full pack," the runner replies.

Opposite the fifth hole down, he repeats his message formally: "Lootenant, orders are roll full packs an' be ready to move out in ten minutes."

"All right," the Lieutenant mumbles out of his hole. Then louder: "Jackson, hey, Jackson, wake up. Goin' to move. J-a-c-k-s-o-n, come to. . . .

From: *Squad*. Copyright, 1928, by Coward-McCann, Inc.

You awake? All right. Notify the corporals to get the men up, roll full an' be ready to clear out in ten minutes."

Jackson's bulk moves about in the darkness.

"Hey, you squad leaders, bust out—rouse 'em up—we're gonna move out!"

Gray comes awake with the sensation that he's just fallen off to sleep. He lights a cigarette and looks at his watch by its ember. Eleven o'clock. He turned in at nine. He crawls out of his hole, fully dressed and shod, rubs his eyes and shivers in the cool night air. He goes down along the line of his Squad, thrusts his arm through the mouths of the holes and pokes whatever portion of a body presents itself.

"Full packs an' be ready to move in ten minutes," he says.

He sets to work on his pack, while his Squad mates crawl out of holes, dragging blankets and equipment behind them. They grumble, but roll packs quickly. Bodies bend obediently to months of discipline, while minds stay virtually asleep. They put on slickers for the sake of warmth, grunt into packs, lean dejectedly, sleepily, on rifles and shiver with chill. The Lieutenant comes along:

"Follow me," and the Platoon straggles behind him through the woods and out onto a road.

Again the soldiers stand and shiver, until the Captain comes by:

"Osgood, fall in at the tail of the Third Platoon—double column o' files—one on each side of the road."

The soldiers sling rifles over shoulders. They are heavy and quiet with sleep, and hunched forward under the hump of their packs. Silently, they shuffle forward until the units drag out into two long thin columns. The road goes on ahead, a straight, white band which cuts across flat, open country that stretches away desolately into the darkness. The quiet is broken by the Lieutenant's voice:

"Don't bunch up—keep that five-pace distance!"

"It's hell how they always bunch up at night," he says to the Captain. The two officers walk together in the middle of the road, between the two single columns.

"At the start they bunch and at the end they straggle—poor devils!" the Captain says, and the two officers join in the silence of the columns.

It is quiet and still. No trucks lumber up past the infantry to-night. No traffic moves along the road. No sounds, no sights.

The road dips into a wooded hollow and mounts abruptly.

"Hell . . ." Some one begins to speak and breaks off.

A flare goes up and bursts like a skyrocket. It drifts slowly downward and casts a pale, flickering light across the tree tops. A machine-gun, far away, goes rat-tat-tat-tat-tat. . . .

"God! There it is! There's the Front!"

Tensely, they watch for another flare, another burst of machine-gun fire. Again, a star-shell mounts, bursts and flickers down. Again a machine-gun rivets out sightless death in the dark. Again it is quiet.

"God, ain't that queer!" says Waglith. "Just that, and nothink else."

"That's what that corporal from the 101st told us!" Gray exclaims excitedly. "Remember, that fellow we met on the road yesterday, who'd lost his squad? That's just how he described it. Quiet—nothing moving about. Remember, he said a fellow who'd once been up claimed he could 'smell' the Front!"

"Dam' if I ain't glad," says Marzulak. "I'd rudder get killed dan live to hike ferever, only I'm gonna get one first."

"Awright, Jim, you'll git one before sunset—er one'll git you," says O'Connors. "Either way, seems like, you'll be satisfied. Wit' me, that don't go. It's only gonna work one way."

"Must I always hafta remind you about your size, Mike?" Waglith speaks up. "Don't forget you're twice as big as me. Twice as many bullets can hit you. You hafn't gotta chance."

"Shut up, you Yiddish bum, you must wanta see me under th' sod!"

The tail of the Squad is silent. Novelli walks easily, steadily, with the butt of a dead cigarette between his lips. He never speaks. No one speaks to him or expects him to talk. Whittaker straggles double his distance in rear. He, too, is silent.

Ahead appears a glare, which grows steadily brighter. As the columns round a bend in the road, a huge fire comes into view among the trees.

"What's that?" asks O'Connors.

"Ammunition dumps," Waglith answers. "An' we gotta go right by it!"

The wooden boxes and burning powder sputter like firecrackers. As the columns go by they swerve away from the heat towards the bushes on the far edge of the road. While the soldiers are silhouetted against the light, overhead sounds of pss-pss-pass, a whit-whit-whit, like the whistle of wild ducks before dawn, while the birds are still invisible in the air. A light, featherish sound. From far away comes the rat-tat-tat of a machine-gun.

Marzulak cocks an eye into the darkness overhead.

"Get dat, Mike?" he asks.

"Sure I git it, you think I'm deaf," and O'Connors' voice ends in a growl.

"Say, is that the noise bullets make!" exclaims Waglith. "That gentle sound? War ain't what it's said to be. I'm gettink more convinced of that every day I live."

"Jesus, those things don't sound like they could hurt you," Whittaker calls up from his position at the rear of the Squad.

Beyond, the columns pass a company of machine-gunners with their Hotchkiss guns tripoded in an irregular, camouflaged line up the side of a hill.

"Go to it, doughboys," calls a voice out of the dark. "We'll give you a hell of a good barrage."

"Barrage, hell, listen to th' heavy artillery soundin' off! Why don't you guys join th' infantry an' see th' war?" O'Connors answers.

"They can talk," says Gray. "They're dug in for the night an' I'll bet their chow carts are handy. Hell, we move every night an' we've just about given up eating. I'd like to know when we're gonna stop?"

"At Berlin," says Waglith.

"Mose, you'll be lucky if you git five miles closer to Berlin than you are right now," O'Connors says, and a tense, alarmed cry puts a period to his sentence.

"GAS!"

The alarm leap-frogs along the road. Each man spits out the curt word before he throws his mask over his face. Hooded, the columns go on. The eye-pieces cloud with the humidity inside the masks, so that the soldiers stumble blindly through a glazed darkness.

"Why, whata yuh doughboys dressin' up fo'? Theah ain't any gas 'round heah," drawls a voice out of the night.

"All cleah!" it shouts loudly. Then tauntingly, as the infantry takes off masks:

"Yeah, join th' infantry an' see th' wa'. Ain't thet what yuh-all said when yuh passed me back on th' road a way? When th' infantry don't know th' diff'ence between gas an' a dead hoss. You guys must be just outa trainin' camp, puttin' on masks eve'y time th' wind blows."

"How th' hell can we know when some dam' fool up ahead shouts gas?" O'Connors demands.

"Wise up. Wait'll you smell it. You talk tough enough to stand a whiff o' two."

The columns go on, towards the flares and the tapping machine-guns. A shell whines overhead and bursts far beyond the road.

"Uh-huh," says O'Connors. "What's that mean?"

Another shell shrieks at the columns and crashes close. Instinctively, without command, the columns flatten into the ditches. The soldiers hit the ground hard, with a jangle of equipment, as they dive for whatever cover offers. Steadily now, shells scream and burst. They seem to fall in an even line, up and down, in a field thirty yards beyond the road.

Wh-o-o-o-m pa-oww—wh-o-o-m pa-oww—wh-o-o-o-m pa-oww

Jagged pieces of metal casing sing through the air.

The soldiers lie belly down, unutterably grateful now for the thickness of the pack and equipment on backs. They hump themselves under the packs. They adjust helmets to cover the nape of the neck. They lie taut, faces ground into the grit of the ground. Tensely, they listen for the coming screech. They jam bodies against the earth as the awful howl ends with a crash. A moment of relaxation, but only until they pick up the commencement of another wail. It grows into a roaring scream almost too fast for senses to follow its increase in volume. Nerves tighten. They grind themselves into the earth. A colossal crash and the let-up . . . and all over again, again and again and again, for a mental eternity of fifteen minutes of actual time.

Ended, and the columns are up and on.

"God, th' Heinies must be like cats—able to see in th' dark. That wuz accurate fire."

"No, but they know there's a road here. They've got the range of it an' they know dam' well, where there's a road, there'll be infantry on the move at night."

"If they'd cut their range down fifty yards we wouldn't all be going on now."

The columns come to a rough, timbered bridge across a shallow stream.

"Form single column," comes the Lieutenant's voice. "Column on the left of the road fall in behind that on the right."

The hobs and steel-rimmed heels of shoes strike the timbers with a ring. Out of holes, cut into the road-bank close by, voices curse:

"More goddam infantry! Fer Jesus' sake, can't you walk without makin' such a hell of a racket? You'll draw more shell-fire sure. That's awright for you guys. You're goin' on, but we gotta stay here."

The voice comes from a gang of engineers detailed to maintain the bridge. Every time it is blown away, they have to quit their holes, come out in the open and carpenter under shell-fire.

"Th' hell wit' yer bridge. We don't need it. We kin walk through yer two-by-four crick."

"Yeah, you doughboys can—but how about th' artillery an' th' ambulances? Ther' ain't nothin' up where you're goin' but Dutchmen. An' maybe some o' you babies's gonna git hurt up there an' wanta go to th' rear, lying purty in a ambulance. An' what then? Then you'll want this goddam bridge, huh?"

The column reaches the outskirts of a town, passes a few scattered houses and enters on a cobbled street. The tread of feet gives out a hollow, dead sound. Paneless, black windows gape out of empty, stone houses. The town is silent, vacant, lifeless. From one end of it, a glare goes up into the sky and casts the shadow of the column against the house-fronts.

Midway down the main street, the column halts and the Fourth Platoon files through an archway into a courtyard.

"Down that cellar," says the Lieutenant, pointing. He speaks in a hoarse whisper, yet his voice sounds loud in the enclosed quiet.

"An', Sergeant Jackson," he adds, "have one man stand to out here."

"All right, Sir." Jackson looks towards the Platoon. He catches Marzulak's eye.

"Yeah, Sarge, lemme stay out?"

"All right. Wake Guilford, out of the sixth squad, in two hours."

The Platoon disappears down the cellar hatch. It leaves the courtyard bare and quiet. The Serb weaves around in the dark, then goes through the archway out to the street. He looks down it, where it is dark, and up, towards the glare. All ways, it is quiet. He holds his rifle at the ready.

"Aw, where are dey, anyhow?" he mutters to himself. "Dey c'n come on anytime."

He turns away with a shrug of his shoulders, and meanders back into the courtyard. He pauses, then goes through a door near the cellar hatch and reappears with a chair. He tips it against the wall of the house and sits down, rifle balanced across his knees. He takes out of one of his blouse pockets a cake of chocolate—a handout of a few days ago from a "Y" man along a road—unwraps it and slowly munches it. He finishes each bit before he takes another, licking the remnants off his teeth and gums, clearing his mouth of the taste after each nibble.

"What a quiet," he says to himself. "Might be a million miles from de Front!"—he looks towards the black hole that descends into the cellar —"or comin' off the graveyard shift back at de mines . . . Dose guys back dere, hell, dey're gettin' more a week now dan I'm makin' in a mont'— an' not walkin' near so far fer it . . . An', hell, dey call dis war!"

He reaches for a cigarette, but changes his mind as he listens to the quiet, and draws a plug of tobacco out of his blouse pocket. He bites off a chew and looks about. Near by, forming a dark spot on the flagstones, lies a jagged piece of shell casing. From now on, regularly, sounds the splash of spit striking the metal.

Gradually, the reflection of the fire at the other end of the town fades. A streak of light appears across the house-tops. Stretching away from the courtyard, Marzulak sees a pleasant, green lawn, interlaced with gravel walks bordered with pieces of statuary. In the center, just discernible in the weak light, is a playing fountain.

"Gee, it's funny. A whole dam' town dat no one owns. Everyting here's mine fer de taken'."

As daylight mounts, a sudden, quick whip sounds against the tile of a house-roof.

"If dat ain't a bullet, I don't know my name!"

He's up, rifle at the ready, peering about.

"Hmmm," excitedly. "Dey ain't so far off at dat. Dawn's bringin' 'em to!"

II

Even the thick, vaulted roof of the cellar fails to muffle the din outside —the strident screams and bursts of shells, the impact of stone against stone and the reverberating rumble of falling masonry.

"They're hittin' back awright . . . sounds like some one wuz usin' a maul on th' town."

A rustle comes out of the dark, the flare of a match and O'Connors shows up, kneeling beside a chair as he lights the stub of a candle.

"Say, Corp, it's a good thing we got underground when th' gittin' wuz good."

He melts the candle stub on the arm of the chair and rises:

"Wonder if ther' c'd be any grub 'round here?" He fumbles about the dark corners of the cellar.

Gray goes over to the doorway and shouts up the stairs:

"Oh, Guilford, you all right up there?"

"Yeah," the reply comes back indistinctly. "I'm in th' shelter of the doorway. But it's somethin' terrible outside."

"Oh, boy, look at that!" O'Connors exclaims gleefully, as he pulls a bottle of wine out from under a pile of cast-off German clothes heaped on a board shelf.

Marzulak, prone on a mattress on the floor, rises up halfway and blinks: "What's dat?"

"Vin, buckoo vin. Come on, Squad, let's hit it!"

He pours several long swallows down his own throat, passes the bottle on to Marzulak and he to Novelli, who squats on the floor, a cigarette between his lips, the butt of his rifle resting in the triangle formed by his crossed legs. Its fixed bayonet leans over his shoulder.

"Come on, Mose, what th' hell're you doin' over there?"

"I ain't got time to drink. I'm puttink a gas curtain over this door so you won't be disturbed at your pleasures." Waglith drapes his blanket across the entrance to the cellar.

"Yer a dam' fool, Mose. . . . Say, it's a good thing ther' ain't a case o' this stuff here er th' war'd be over fer me to-day."

A crash falls overhead. It snuffs the candle. The cellar trembles. Mortar falls out from between the bricks and smoke seeps through the cracks.

"Great God, that must 'a' bin a direct hit on th' house!"

"What th' . . . ?" exclaims Waglith, as some one clatters down the stairway and catapults himself through the gas curtain into the middle of the chamber.

"Orders are to take up position to meet a counter-attack!" a voice shouts out in the dark, breathlessly, fearfully.

Gray strikes a match, relights the candle and calls into the adjoining cellar:

"Lieutenant, here's a runner with orders!"

The Company Runner's helmet is awry. His eyes glisten in the candle-light. Steadier now, he takes off his helmet and wipes the sweat off his face with his sleeve.

"Holy, jumpin' Jesus, but it's awful out there. Better stick to th' rear o' th' houses. I'd never got here if I'd stepped out on th' street. Ther' shells an' bullets all over. My God, it's awful!"

The Lieutenant comes into the dugout through a communicating passageway. The rest of the Platoon is at his heels.

"Sir, orders are to take up position to meet a counter-attack!" says the Company Runner.

"Load and lock pieces—fix bayonets!" the Lieutenant turns towards the soldiers, jammed into the one chamber and with equipment already on backs. "An' follow me!"

At the head of the stairway, daylight is shut out suddenly by a figure that jumps through the cellar hatch simultaneously with the burst of a shell in the courtyard outside.

"Who's that?" asks the Lieutenant tensely.

"It's Holloway. That you, Osgood? Listen, quick! Message's just come from Battalion sayin' th' Boche're oozin' into town across th' river—under cover o' this hellish barrage—we're goin' to meet the attack along th' line o' these houses—you're on th' extreme left flank o' th' Company sector—take up position on that corner where we came in to-day—at th' junction o' th' two streets—but for Christ's sake don't go out on th' main street—it's enfiladed—death out there—go through the rear of th' houses— along here! For Christ's sake, hold—you've got th' pivotal position . . . that's all—good luck—send a runner back when you're in position—I'll be here . . . now—get off!"

Out in the open, the town disintegrates. No longer does anything remain fixed. Explosions tear off corners of dwellings, open up roofs, burst out through the faces, tear away rafters and joists which crash entire houses. Everywhere are jets of black smoke, geysers of stone, plaster and white dust. The bursts come so close together they sound like one massive, uninterrupted roar. The volume of the detonations is so great that it obliterates the screams of shells passing through the air.

Across the courtyard and over a low, stone wall, over the roofs of out-houses, through disheveled kitchens and out through another courtyard, the soldiers stream. At the base of walls and other obstructions, they bunch. Across open spaces, they spread out. Sometimes they flatten themselves against the ground, dart under cover of a wall, dive into a ditch or around the door of a house. Stones, chunks of shell cases and bits of plaster fall about them. They go without thought, madly, in the Lieutenant's wake.

"Gray, take that gate!" he shouts and points. "An' barricade it! Williams and Ives—take your squads through that house and stand by th' front door an' windows! Jones and Catman, in th' barn there! McGuiness and Dennowitz, take cover in th' barn an' stand by to reënforce when I tell you! Jackson,—take th' two squads in th' house! Bamberger—th' squads in th' barn! I'll command here at th' gate!"

The Last Squad fills up the open gateway.

"Anything you can find!" shouts Gray.

They drag beds, mattresses, tables, chairs, bureaus, out of the adjoining houses; pile up boxes, timbers, stones and rubble. The mass of barricade grows quickly, until it reaches about the level of the eye. Loopholes are poked through, low down for the two automatic rifles, while the ordinary riflemen rest their pieces overtop.

"It's good now!" shouts Gray. "We've got enfilading fire both ways along the main street and down that cross street towards the ridge! Eyes everywhere!"

"Look sharp everywhere!" cries the Lieutenant. "Th' minute th' shellin' lets up, they'll come! Look for 'em close behind th' barrage!"

The din is so great Gray has to go to each man and shout the Lieutenant's warning into every ear.

The roar goes on. Fountains of black smoke and particles of earth geyser into the air behind the tense line of soldiers. Across the street, white dust bursts out of the houses, with bits of plaster, timbers and tiles. At the barricade, the soldiers duck their helmets against the rubble that strikes about them. The white dust settles over their uniforms and packs.

Suddenly, the curtain of shell-fire lifts and numbed ears ring in the apparent silence. Gradually, that silence ceases as another sound impinges on ears, another uninterrupted score:

pss-pss-pss-pss-pss

dzing-dzing-dzing-dzing-dzing

That comes from close overhead, while from farther away sounds the incessant rat-tat-tat-tat-tat of innumerable machine-guns.

"Stand to, everywhere!" shouts the Lieutenant. "They'll be comin' now!"

Far overhead, airplanes circle against a clear sky, like vultures drawn to and poised above a place of death.

Artillery in rear of the infantry opens fire. The shells pass overhead with a siren of sound and burst in a broad line that climbs the face of a hill, across the bridge and river, a kilometer distant. The neat line of bursts rakes the hill, down and up, up and down.

"Ain't that purty! Now they're gettin' theirs!"

The supporting machine-guns tap into the orchestration of fire. The bullets drone overhead, indistinguishable from the enemy lead.

The Last Squad leans against its barricade. Whittaker, with a rifle, presses himself into the angle between the barricade and the house on its right. Below him, Marzulak lies on the ground, staring fixedly along the barrel of his Chauchat, trained down the cross street towards the bridge. Novelli crouches beside him, with extra pans of ammunition piled between him and the automatic rifle. O'Connors lies a yard to the left, another Chauchat pressed against his shoulder, and Waglith hugs his side with ammunition. Gray, rifleman, stands at the extreme left of the barricade.

The Lieutenant weaves restlessly behind the Squad. He bends low, opens and closes his hands nervously. He looks like a quarter-back behind a football line-up.

"Where are they? Where are they? Aren't they goin' to come?" he mutters aloud.

"Light me a cigarette, Mose," says O'Connors.

"That's right," Gray puts in quickly, glad of the distraction.

He reaches in his blouse pocket with his right hand and extracts a single, bent cigarette. He ask Waglith to light it for him. He never takes his eyes away from along his rifle barrel. With a deep inhalation, he draws the smoke down into his lungs.

"Maybe that'll be th' last smoke." His lips form the syllables, but he doesn't actually speak.

They seem surrounded, hemmed in by the riveting machine-guns. The bullets whisk overhead ceaselessly. Out forward, as far as they can see, there is no life. The main street, to the right and left, is bare. So is the cross street, down which they can see as far as the bridge, a hundred yards distant. Across the street, and stretching down towards the bridge, the broken houses seem vacant. Occasionally a rafter or a stone gives way and rubble slides.

"How're they likely to come?" asks Waglith.

"Don't know," replies Gray. "Up that cross street, I guess . . . but keep your eyes to the left, too, down the main street. They'll come fast, I guess, and in a bunch."

"Look sharp! Look sharp!" the Lieutenant keeps saying.

"I'm doin' that, awright," Marzulak growls, without taking his eyes off his Chauchat barrel.

No one has seen anything, when suddenly a Potato Masher flips through the air and explodes just in front of the barricade. Down the cross street a gray arm withdraws into the window of one of the houses.

"Open fire—you Chauchats—into the windows of those houses!" screams the Lieutenant. "They're seeping through . . ."

His words are lost in the clack of Chauchats and the snap of rifles. Lead pours down the cross street and splashes against the house-fronts.

A momentary pause, while the Chauchat feeders slip fresh pans under the automatics and the riflemen open the bolts of their pieces and jam full clips into the breeches.

No sign of life appears out forward. Then, from the corner of the roof of a house diagonally across the street, another gray arm waves upward against the sky. Another clumsy Potato Masher hurtles, end over end, towards the barricade . . . over the barricade . . . at Gray.

He ducks, then straightens up as if he realizes a mistake. He swings his rifle at the object and catches it full, as one would a baseball. It hurls the grenade to one side of the barricade, where it explodes harmlessly in the air.

"Good . . ." shouts the Lieutenant, but again his words are lost in the clatter of the Chauchats. He pulls a hand grenade off his belt, jerks the pin and lobs it up over the corner of the roof. It bursts full over the top, shedding its unseen bits of metal against the tiles and through the holes. A gray arm is flung out, over the edge of the roof. It jerks a bit, and then lies still.

While Novelli clips a fresh pan under the automatic, Marzulak twists 'round and winks at the Lieutenant.

Other gray arms are flung out of the windows, and the tiny, black bores of Maxims are poked out of the corners. Now there is a crisscross of fire between the houses along the one edge of the cross street and that particular corner of the town occupied by the Fourth Platoon.

The smoke soon renders everything blind fire. The windows are blotted out. But lower down, where the smoke has lifted, a German jumps through a doorway out into the street. He goes down immediately, pitching forward headlong and throwing his arms out wide before his body. For a few moments he twists about over the cobbles, then lies quiet.

"Come on, you reserve squads, man the barricade!" shouts the Lieutenant. "They're tryin' to rush it!"

Bent over, the two extra squads rush onto the barricade and double the fire that goes out from it.

The Lieutenant lies on the ground, behind the base of the barricade. From time to time he tosses bandoliers of cartridges and musette bags full of loaded Chauchat pans to the squads. Once he raises himself too high, as he chucks a heavy musette, and a burst of machine-gun fire catches him in the shoulder. The impact swings him around in a semicircle.

"They've got me, Gray!" he yells. "You take command!"

He crawls into the shelter of the barn and lies there quietly, gritting his teeth, while blood soaks through the shoulder of his blouse. He extracts his First Aid kit from his belt, but can't open the tin with only one hand. He tries to tear it open with his teeth, but can't. He lies there and swears.

"Lieutenant's got it!" shouts Gray. "We've gotta hold now!"

"What's dat? Lootenant hit?" Marzulak asks Novelli, who nods his head. "De basdards!"

He draws the Chauchat out of its loophole and rises to his feet.

"Where you goin', for Christ's sake?" asks Gray.

"Too slow dat way," the Serb answers.

He puts the stock of the automatic against his shoulder, leans up over the edge of the barricade and sprays fire down the street, swinging the gun from side to side. His helmet topples off, bumps across the barricade and rolls over the cobbles. His black hair is tumbled over his head. His dark eyes blaze.

"Oh, you basdards—basdards—basdards!" he grits out. "I'll pay you fer it all—de hikin'—de night work an' de empty bellies."

He climbs onto the barricade and calls to Novelli for another pan of ammunition. He twists himself from side to side . . . until, all at once, he collapses. His body crumples, falls onto the parapet and somersaults out forward. The Chauchat clatters against the barricade, against the cobbles of the street.

It is suddenly quieter. The smoke commences to lift. No more gray arms are flung out of the windows. The tiny bores of the Maxims disappear inside the bullet-pocked faces of the houses.

"They're givin'! Keep up the fire!" Gray shouts. "By God, Jim did it! They must 'a' thought we were comin' over with th' bay'nit!"

Novelli, who no longer has an automatic to serve, straddles the barricade, leans down and takes Marzulak's body under the shoulders. He drags him over the parapet and lays him on the ground, at the base of the barricade. There is a small hole in the center of his forehead. Out of it, bluish bubbles ooze and burst. His eyes are closed. He is silent, although his lips move, open and close, for a few moments.

"Gone—nothin' do," says Novelli, helplessly.

"All right, Novelli, then look to the Lieutenant, by the barn," says Gray.

Novelli disappears through the smoke.

"Stand to, everywhere! They may come on again!"

The smoke clears and all fire ceases. Out forward, there is no sign of life. The German who stepped out of the doorway lies across the pavement, his head in the gutter. Another leans out of a ground floor window, buckled over the sill. Up over the corner of the roof, that arm hangs. The blood from it has made a stain on the white face of the house, and another on the pavement below. Alertly, the Last Squad stands at its post.

"God, it's all over," says Gray.

Novelli comes up.

"I took Lieutenant to Captain—he says Sergeant Jackson command Platoon."

Jackson appears at the kitchen door of the adjoining house. He rests there, with his hands clutching the jambs on either side.

"Where's th' Lieutenant?" he asks.

"Wounded," Gray answers. "An' the Skipper says you're in charge of the Platoon."

"All right, what're the orders?" He turns 'round and shouts into the house: "Watkins, go back to Company Headquarters and ask Captain Holloway for the orders." He turns to Gray:

"Any casualties?"

"Marzulak's knocked off," and he points to the body, beside the barricade.

"Tough. I had two wounded, but no one killed. Wonder how the other squads made out? Purty hot there for a while, huh?"

"God, yes!" fervently.

Captain Holloway, face streaked with sweat and filth, comes along.

"You did good. We held all along the line." He looks appreciatively at the squads at the barricade.

"Many casualties?"

Gray points to Marzulak.

"No one else?"

"Don't know about Sergeant Bamberger, on the left," Jackson answers. "I'll send for him."

"Can't wait. We've got to go forward. The only way we can hold against another attack like that is to occupy the town up to the river. Take the platoon forward and occupy all houses down that street as far as the bridge. Listen for my whistle. Don't go forward until you hear it. An' be careful. Don't let yourself get enfiladed on any of these streets."

He goes off as he came. Bamberger appears.

"How'd you make out, Bamby?" asks Jackson.

"Not so good." He shakes his head. "Two killed an' three wounded— all by one shell before we ever saw a German. Hear th' Lieutenant got it in th' shoulder?"

"Yeah, I'm in charge. Th' Skipper's just been here an' says we've gotta go forward as far as th' bridge down there—when his whistle blows. Send your wounded back to Company Headquarters. Leave th' dead where they lie—I guess."

The airplanes are gone out of the sky. No more shells scream through the air and burst. No more bullets whisk overhead, and the riveting of the machine-guns is gone. Quietness everywhere. The Platoon assembles at the barricade and tensely awaits the whistle.

It blows.

"All right," says Jackson. "Take it slow now. Take advantage of all th' cover you can get. Two at a time. Bamby, you lead off."

Cautiously, in the half-light, they go forward. They hold rifles at the ready, so that the bayonets stick out like feelers. Two at a time, with a long distance between each couple, they file along the edge of the houses, and wind in and out of the doorways.

Twilight and darkness. Marzulak, the Serb—the Serbian son-of-a-bitch the others sometimes called him—lies alone beside the barricade. The bluish blood has clotted over his broad, low forehead.

THE END